Universitext

Universitext

Universitext is a series of textbooks that presents material from a wide variety of mathematical disciplines at master's level and beyond. The books, often well class-tested by their author, may have an informal, personal, even experimental approach to their subject matter. Some of the most successful and established books in the series have evolved through several editions, always following the evolution of teaching curricula, into very polished texts.

Thus as research topics trickle down into graduate-level teaching, first textbooks written for new, cutting-edge courses may make their way into *Universitext*.

For further volumes:
www.springer.com/series/223

Michèle Audin · Mihai Damian

Morse Theory
and Floer Homology

Translated by Reinie Erné

 Springer

Michèle Audin
IRMA
Université Louis Pasteur
Strasbourg Cedex, France

Mihai Damian
IRMA
Université Louis Pasteur
Strasbourg Cedex, France

Translation from the French language edition:
Théorie de Morse et homologie de Floer
by Michèle Audin and Mihai Damian
EDP Sciences ISBN 978-2-7598-0704-8
Copyright © 2010 EDP Sciences, CNRS Editions, France.
http://www.edpsciences.org/
http://www.cnrseditions.fr/
All rights reserved

ISSN 0172-5939   e-ISSN 2191-6675
Universitext
ISBN 978-1-4471-5495-2   e-ISBN 978-1-4471-5496-9
DOI 10.1007/978-1-4471-5496-9
Springer London Heidelberg New York Dordrecht

Library of Congress Control Number: 2013955874

Mathematics Subject Classification: 53Dxx, 57R17, 53D40, 57R58

Printed on acid-free paper

Springer is part of Springer Science+Business Media (www.springer.com)

For him:
to him, poet with a discrete sensibility,
with an intimate caloric sharpness and
foremost with a profound understanding of
the Romanian spirituality that has created
this native state. A tribute to the great
patriot who joins the voivodes.

For her:
to her, whose sense of justice, sensibility
and human authority creates the frame
that is also needed by soccer, like any
attempt to gather people, their energies
and their passions, the deep tribute to her
who makes an effort in sport, coming up
against all obstacles in order to
understand the truth.

Preface

Floer homology is today an essential technique in symplectic topology. Inspired by ideas of Witten and Gromov in the 1980s, it has made possible the resolution of many difficult problems, and continues to do so.

This book is devoted to the solution of one of these problems, a famous conjecture due to Arnold, which proposes to give a lower bound for the number of periodic trajectories of a Hamiltonian system using an invariant that depends only on the topology of the symplectic manifold on which this system evolves. This lower bound greatly resembles the famous Morse inequalities, which give a lower bound for the number of critical points of a function. The similarity is not accidental: Floer homology is an (infinite-dimensional) analogue of the homology of the manifold as computed by the Morse complex "à la Witten": in both cases the main role is played by the moduli spaces of trajectories connecting the critical points (of a function for the Morse homology, of a functional for the Floer homology).

In 2004–2005, we gave a course, or rather two courses, on these notions for first- and second-year graduate students. We of course began with Morse theory. We like Milnor's book very much, in which we had both learned about the existence, the abundance and especially the usefulness of Morse functions, so we started writing notes for the students, it was quite easy...

And then it became more difficult—there was no book giving the more modern point of view on Morse homology, with the construction and the invariance properties of the Morse complex defined using spaces of trajectories, which would allow us to move on to the construction of the Floer complex. We could no longer copy; we now needed to use a bit of imagination.

Having completed the first part of the course to the satisfaction of the students, we tackled Floer homology. The objects and techniques of Morse homology that we, topologists and geometers, use every day, were transformed into objects and techniques of Floer homology. The charm, or one of

the charms, and the strength, of this theory, lie in the fact that in addition
to geometry and topology, it uses much analysis, Fredholm operators and
Sobolev spaces. Explaining this to genuine students is not an easy task. This
is why we decided to continue writing lecture notes.

Even though many works of research have used and still use these techniques, and many students need them at present, no reasonably self-contained
book existed on this subject.

Five years have passed, in which we have honed, corrected, lengthened,
made more precise, added upper bounds, lower bounds, equalities, compar-
isons, stated and proved seventy-three theorems, one hundred and twenty-one
propositions and one hundred and three lemmas, drawn ninety-eight figures[1]
(and set out a certain number of exercises that, contrary to custom, do not
contain the proof of any important result "left as an exercise for the readers")...

Five years have passed, in which other students have read these notes and
have made remarks that convinced us that our notes satisfied a need and that
it would be stupid not to improve them even further in order to turn them
into a book.

Here is the book, devoted to the power and glory of homological methods
"à la" Morse–Floer.

What You Need to Know...

It was difficult pretending to write a self-contained book. Nevertheless, it
results from a course given to genuine graduate students—for whom we first
needed to "recall" what a manifold is. Keeping them and their fellow students
in mind, we therefore gathered at the end of the book, in three appendices,
"what you need to know": the basic results of differential geometry, algebraic
topology and analysis that we use. Sometimes we include complete definitions
and/or proofs, other times we only give indications. The index should help
readers find their way.

Thanks

To all students who have undergone this course, in particular to Emily Burgunder, Olivier Dodane, Shanna Li, Alexandre Mouton, Emmanuel Rey, Nel-
son Souza.

To Agnès Gadbled who carefully read many preliminary versions of this
text. To Clémence Labrousse and Vincent Humilière for their questions and

---

[1] See footnote 2.

suggestions. To André Carneiro for the corrections he suggested. To Emmanuel Opshtein for the answers he helped us find.

To François Laudenbach, Dusa McDuff. To Jean-Claude Sikorav for his close and enthusiastic reading, the many pages of comments he wrote, the stimulating discussions we had with him.

To Claude Sabbah, for his technical advice, for having welcomed this book into his collection and especially for having patiently waited for it.

Preface to the English Edition

The first edition (in French) appeared in 2010. For this new version:

- Following the advice of the Springer referees, we added a few pages on the relation Morse/cellular homology (this is Section 4.9).
- Following the advice of some of our first readers, we corrected hundreds (and there is no exaggeration here) of misprints and mistakes (among which, we must confess, quite a few mathematical errors).[2]

We are very grateful to all these people and we thank them.

We are especially grateful to Felix Schlenk for his friendly suggestions and questions. A warm thank you again to Dusa McDuff for her kind advice and remarks.

We have also updated the list of references (see footnote 3 page 451), adding especially recent books and papers of some of the leading experts in the field, the very clear paper on the definition of the Conley–Zehnder index [43], as well as the new results obtained by one of the authors [23, 24] and a few words on the history of the Arnold conjecture by the other [6].

Note that the symbol □ means either the end of the proof or the absence of proof.   □

Last, but not least, we thank Reinie Erné, who managed to make, very kindly and patiently, a great translation work of a quite technical text.

Michèle Audin
Mihai Damian

---

[2] This led us to add a few items to those mentioned above, so that this edition contains seventy-four theorems, one hundred and twenty-four propositions, one hundred and eleven lemmas and one hundred and two figures.

Contents

    8.5   The Transversality.. 242

    8.6   The Solutions of the Floer Equation Are "Somewhere
          Injective"... 255

    8.7   The Fredholm Property 269

    8.8   Computing the Index of L 285

    8.9   The Exponential Decay 296

9   Spaces of Trajectories 305

    9.1   The Spaces of Trajectories 305

    9.2   Broken Trajectories, Gluing: Statements 311

    9.3   Pre-gluing 313

    9.4   Construction of ψ 315

    9.5   Properties of $\widehat{\psi}$: $\widehat{\psi}$ Is an Immersion 333

    9.6   Properties of $\widehat{\psi}$: Uniqueness of the Gluing 334

10 From Floer to Morse 359

    10.1 The Results.. 359

    10.2 The Linearization of the Flow of a Pseudo-Gradient Field,
         Proof of Theorem 10.1.3...................................... 362

    10.3 Proof of Theorem 10.1.2 (Regularity) 371

    10.4 The Morse and Floer Trajectories Coincide 376

11 Floer Homology: Invariance............................... 383

    11.1 The Morphism Φ^{Γ} 384

    11.2 Proof of Theorem 11.1.16...................................... 397

    11.3 Invariance of Φ^{Γ}: Proof of Proposition 11.2.8.............. 413

    11.4 Proof of Theorem 11.3.14...................................... 426

    11.5 Conclusion of the Proof of the Invariance of the Floer
         Homology: Proof of Proposition 11.2.9 437

    11.6 Conclusion 451

12 The Elliptic Regularity of the Floer Operator............ 453

    12.1 Elliptic Regularity: Why and How? 453

    12.2 Proof of Lemma 8.7.2 459

    12.3 Proof of Theorem 12.1.2...................................... 461

    12.4 (Nonlinear) Elliptic Regularity of the Floer Operator,
         Proofs 465

**13 The Lemmas on the Second Derivative of the Floer
    Operator and Other Technicalities** 477

    13.1 Versions of the Floer Operator 477

    13.2 The Two Lemmas on dF 478

    13.3 The Operator $\widetilde{\mathcal{F}}_{\rho}$ 480

    13.4 Proof of the Two Lemmas: The First One 484

    13.5 Proof of the Two Lemmas: The Second One 491

    13.6 Another Technical Lemma................................. 497

Appendices: What You Need to Know to Read This Book

Part I
Morse Theory

Introduction to Part I

This first part is devoted to Morse theory, with as its main objective the complex defined by the critical points of a Morse function and the trajectories of a gradient field.

It is a theory whose very first building block is the remark that studying a (well-chosen) function can give rather precise information on the topology of a manifold. The most classic example—these are often also the most instructive ones—is that of the "height" function $\mathbf{R}^3 \to \mathbf{R}$ and its restriction to the different submanifolds represented in Figures 1 to 3. In the three cases we consider, the function f is the restriction of $(x, y, z) \mapsto z$.

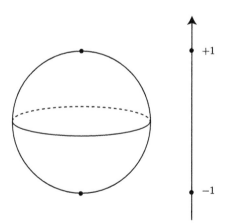

Fig. 1 The round sphere

The first figure (Figure 1) represents the "round" sphere, that is, the unit sphere

$$S^2 = \left\{ (x, y, z) \in \mathbf{R}^3 \mid x^2 + y^2 + z^2 = 1 \right\}.$$

The level sets $f^{-1}(a)$ are

$$
\begin{cases}
\varnothing & \text{if } a < -1 \\
\text{a point} & \text{if } a = -1 \\
\text{a circle} & \text{if } -1 < a < 1 \\
\text{a point} & \text{if } a = 1 \\
\varnothing & \text{if } a > 1.
\end{cases}
$$

Moving upward along the values of the function, we note that the level sets all have the same topology until we meet an accident where the topology changes and subsequently remains the same until the next accident.

The same holds for the "sublevel sets", that is, what lies below a given level. These are first empty, then (briefly) one point, then a disk, and finally the whole sphere.

The accidents are the critical values of the function, which correspond to the critical points, those where the differential of f is zero, where the tangent plane is horizontal, the north and south poles of the sphere. Of course, the south pole is the minimum of the function and the north pole is its maximum.

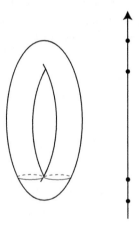

Fig. 2 The torus

The situation is analogous for the torus in the next figure (Figure 2), except that there are now critical points that are not extrema of the function, namely the two "saddle" points. The corresponding level sets are curves in the form of an eight (one is traced in the figure), and are therefore not submanifolds. The regular, noncritical level sets must all be submanifolds because of the submersion theorem.

One of the first results of this theory is a theorem due to Reeb (at least for Morse functions). We will prove it in this context. It asserts that a compact manifold on which there exists a function with only two critical points is homeomorphic to a sphere. Of course, there are also functions on the sphere with more critical points.

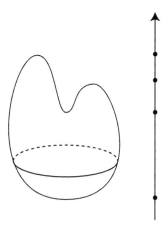

Fig. 3 A different sphere

The third figure (Figure 3) is included to illustrate this. Since it is easy to visualize, we have kept the "same" height function and "made a dent" in the sphere. Consequently, the submanifold is obviously still diffeomorphic to a sphere, but the function now has two local maxima and a saddle point. Note that the parity of the number of critical points of the new function is the same as that of the original one. If we assume that they are nondegenerate (an important property that will be defined later (and that is satisfied by the critical points in our figures)), then modulo 2 the number of critical points equals the Euler characteristic of the manifold, an invariant that does not depend on the function but only on the manifold.

The concept of Witten spaces of trajectories allows us to present a finer invariant. It is clear that the torus and sphere are very different manifolds even if the two admit a function with four nondegenerate critical points. This invariant is what is nowadays called the Morse homology $HM_k(V)$ of the manifold. It is the homology of a complex, the Morse complex, constructed from the critical points of a Morse function by "counting" its trajectories along a vector field that connects them... These trajectories are those of the gradient of the function (with respect to some metric). In the case of the height function (and the Euclidean metric) one could think of the trajectories of water drops flowing on the surface from one critical point to another. Ultimately, this homology depends only on the (diffeomorphism type of the) manifold. The remarks we just made concerning the number of critical points on such and such manifold can be expressed in the famous "Morse inequalities": the number c_k of critical points of index k of a Morse function on a manifold satisfies

$$c_k \geq \dim HM_k(V).$$

It is therefore natural for these objects to be the subject of the first part of this book.

Chapter 1
Morse Functions

All manifolds and functions we consider here are of class $\mathcal{C}^\infty$, even if, in general, $\mathcal{C}^1$ regularity suffices!

1.1 Definition of Morse Functions

1.1.a Critical Points, Nondegeneracy

Let V be a manifold and let $f : V \to \mathbf{R}$ be a function. A *critical point* of f is a point x such that $(df)_x = 0$.

Remark 1.1.1. We know that at least if V is compact, f always has critical points, since it has at least a minimum and a maximum.

At a critical point of f we can define the *Hessian* or second-order derivative.

Remark 1.1.2. Recall that a function on a manifold does not have a second-order derivative: we can always compute a second-order derivative in a chart, but the result depends on the choice of the chart. The second-order derivative is well defined on the kernel of the first-order derivative... We will content ourselves with defining it at the critical points. See Exercise 1 on p. 18.

Rather than using a chart and showing that the result does not depend on it, let us invoke a more intrinsic argument (as in [54, p. 4]). If x is a critical point of f and if X and Y are vectors tangent to V at x, then we set

$$(d^2 f)_x(X, Y) = X \cdot (\widetilde{Y} \cdot f)(x),$$

where $\widetilde{Y}$ denotes a vector field extending Y locally. Since

$$X \cdot (\widetilde{Y} \cdot f)(x) - Y \cdot (\widetilde{X} \cdot f)(x) = [\widetilde{X}, \widetilde{Y}]_x \cdot f = (df)_x([\widetilde{X}, \widetilde{Y}]_x) = 0,$$

M. Audin, M. Damian, *Morse Theory and Floer Homology*,
Universitext, DOI 10.1007/978-1-4471-5496-9_1,
© Springer-Verlag London 2014

the expression is a symmetric bilinear form in X and Y. The same computation also shows that this form is well defined, that is, the result does not depend on the chosen extension $\widetilde{Y}$.

We will say that a critical point is *nondegenerate* if this bilinear form is nondegenerate. Moreover, we will say that a function is a *Morse* function if all its critical points are nondegenerate.

1.1.b Examples and Counterexamples

The critical points of the height function on the sphere are nondegenerate. Indeed, in the neighborhood of the point $(0, 0, \varepsilon) \in S^2$, we can take (x, y) as local coordinates. Then

$$f(x, y) = z = \varepsilon\sqrt{1 - x^2 - y^2}$$

is a function whose second-order derivative is the quadratic form

$$(d^2 f)_{(0,0,\varepsilon)}(x, y) = -\varepsilon(x^2 + y^2),$$

which is indeed nondegenerate.

Constructing functions with degenerate critical points is very easy, for example by taking a degenerate quadratic form, which will be its own second-order derivative at 0, or worse, by taking a polynomial of higher degree, such as the function $x \mapsto x^3$ from $\mathbf{R}$ to $\mathbf{R}$, which has a degenerate critical point at 0.

For other examples, see [54] and this chapter's exercises (see also Remark 4.4.5).

1.2 Existence and Abundance of Morse Functions

Showing that there exist Morse functions on all manifolds is less easy, but it is true. In this section (which paraphrases [54]), we show that on a compact manifold there exist many (in a precise sense) Morse functions (in fact, we will show this for any manifold that embeds as a submanifold into $\mathbf{R}^n$ for some n).

1.2.a Existence of Morse Functions

Let us use the embedding theorem (Theorem A.1.2) and show the existence of Morse functions on the submanifolds of $\mathbf{R}^n$.

Proposition 1.2.1. *Let $V \subset \mathbf{R}^n$ be a submanifold. For almost every point p of $\mathbf{R}^n$, the function*

$$f_p : V \longrightarrow \mathbf{R}$$
$$x \longmapsto \|x - p\|^2$$

is a Morse function.

Proof. The differential of f_p is

$$T_x f_p(\xi) = 2(x - p) \cdot \xi,$$

so that x is a critical point if and only if $(x - p)$ is orthogonal to $T_x V$. We choose a local parametrization of V (as authorized by the submanifold theorem, that is, Theorem A.1.1) by

$$(u_1, \ldots, u_d) \longmapsto x(u_1, \ldots, u_d).$$

In these coordinates, we have

$$\frac{\partial f_p}{\partial u_i} = 2(x - p) \cdot \frac{\partial x}{\partial u_i}$$

and

$$\frac{\partial^2 f_p}{\partial u_i \partial u_j} = 2\left(\frac{\partial x}{\partial u_j} \cdot \frac{\partial x}{\partial u_i} + (x - p) \cdot \frac{\partial^2 x}{\partial u_i \partial u_j} \right).$$

The point x is therefore a nondegenerate critical point if and only if the vector $x - p$ is orthogonal to $T_x V$ and the matrix above has rank d. To show that f_p is a Morse function for almost all p, it therefore suffices to show that the p that do not satisfy this condition are the critical values of a $\mathcal{C}^\infty$ map and to apply Sard's theorem (Theorem A.2.1). We therefore consider the "normal fiber bundle" of V in $\mathbf{R}^n$, that is, the space

$$N = \{(x, v) \in V \times \mathbf{R}^n \mid v \perp T_x V\} \subset V \times \mathbf{R}^n,$$

and the map

$$E : N \longrightarrow \mathbf{R}^n$$
$$(x, v) \longmapsto x + v.$$

The proposition is then a consequence of the following lemma.

Lemma 1.2.2. *The normal vector bundle N is a submanifold of $V \times \mathbf{R}^n$.*
The point $p = x + v \in \mathbf{R}^n$ is a critical value of E if and only if the matrix

$$\frac{\partial^2 f}{\partial u_i \partial u_j} = 2 \left(\frac{\partial x}{\partial u_j} \cdot \frac{\partial x}{\partial u_i} - v \cdot \frac{\partial^2 x}{\partial u_i \partial u_j} \right)$$

is not invertible.

Proof. Since V is a submanifold of $\mathbf{R}^n$, there is a (local) chart that sends $\mathbf{R}^n$
onto an open subset of $\mathbf{R}^n$, and $\mathbf{R}^d$ onto an open subset of V. The tangent
map of the chart sends the canonical basis of $\mathbf{R}^n$ onto a basis of vectors
tangent to V followed by vectors generating a complement. It then suffices
to make this basis orthonormal in order to obtain $n - d$ vectors $v_1, \ldots, v_{n-d}$
that at every point of V form an orthonormal basis of $(T_x V)^\perp$. The map

$$(u_1, \ldots, u_d, t_1, \ldots, t_{n-d}) \longmapsto \left(x(u_1, \ldots, u_d), \sum_{i=1}^{n-d} t_i v_i (u_1, \ldots, u_{n-d}) \right)$$

is then a local parametrization of N, which is therefore a submanifold of
$V \times \mathbf{R}^n$. In these coordinates, the partial derivatives of E are

$$\begin{cases} \dfrac{\partial E}{\partial u_i} = \dfrac{\partial x}{\partial u_i} + \sum_{k=1}^{n-d} t_k \dfrac{\partial v_k}{\partial u_i} \\ \dfrac{\partial E}{\partial t_j} = v_j. \end{cases}$$

Computing the inner products of these n vectors with the n independent
vectors

$$\frac{\partial x}{\partial u_1}, \ldots, \frac{\partial x}{\partial u_d}, v_1, \ldots, v_{n-d}$$

gives a matrix that has the same rank as the Jacobian of E and that is of
the form

$$\begin{pmatrix} \left(\dfrac{\partial x}{\partial u_i} \cdot \dfrac{\partial x}{\partial u_j} + \sum_k t_k \dfrac{\partial v_k}{\partial u_i} \cdot \dfrac{\partial x}{\partial u_j} \right) & \left(\sum_k \dfrac{\partial v_k}{\partial u_i} \cdot v_\ell \right) \\ 0 & \mathrm{Id} \end{pmatrix}.$$

Now v_k is orthogonal to $\partial x / \partial u_j$, so

$$\frac{\partial}{\partial u_i} \left(v_k \cdot \frac{\partial x}{\partial u_j} \right) = \frac{\partial v_k}{\partial u_i} \cdot \frac{\partial x}{\partial u_j} + v_k \cdot \frac{\partial^2 x}{\partial u_i \partial u_j} = 0.$$

This completes the proof of the lemma. . .   □

and therefore that of the proposition.   □

We will come back to the points p for which f_p is not a Morse function in Remark 1.4.1.

Remark 1.2.3. Note that this proof uses a nontrivial part of Sard's theorem (though not the most difficult one, which would be the case where the dimension of the source is greater than that of the target: here the two manifolds N and $\mathbf{R}^n$ have the same dimension).

1.2.b Genericness of Morse Functions

Proposition 1.2.1 shows that there exist many Morse functions on any submanifold of $\mathbf{R}^n$. Using the same tools and still following [54], we will now show that every $\mathcal{C}^\infty$ function can be approximated by a Morse function.

Proposition 1.2.4. *Let V be a manifold that can be embedded as a submanifold into a Euclidean space and let $f : V \to \mathbf{R}$ be a $\mathcal{C}^\infty$ function. Let k be an integer. Then f and all its derivatives of order $\leq k$ can be uniformly approximated by Morse functions on every compact subset.*

Proof. We fix a real number c (whose aim is to be sufficiently large). We then choose an embedding of V in $\mathbf{R}^n$ for n sufficiently large, where the first coordinate is the function f (it suffices to add this coordinate to an embedding into a space of dimension $n - 1$):

$$h(x) = (f(x), h_2(x), \dots, h_n(x)).$$

By Proposition 1.2.1, for almost every point

$$p = (-c + \varepsilon_1, \varepsilon_2, \dots, \varepsilon_n)$$

near $(-c, 0, \dots, 0)$, the function f_p is a Morse function. Consequently,

$$g(x) = \frac{f_p(x) - c^2}{2c}$$

is obviously also a Morse function. Moreover,

$$g(x) = \frac{1}{2c} \left((f(x) + c - \varepsilon_1)^2 + (h_2(x) - \varepsilon_2)^2 + \cdots + (h_n(x) - \varepsilon_n)^2 - c^2 \right)$$

$$= f(x) + \frac{f(x)^2 + \sum h_i(x)^2}{2c} - \frac{\varepsilon_1 f(x) + \sum \varepsilon_i h_i(x)}{c} + \sum \varepsilon_i^2 - \varepsilon_1,$$

which shows (for c sufficiently large and the ε_i sufficiently small) that g is a uniform approximation of f on any compact subset, as announced. $\qquad\square$

Without embedding the manifold V and by using transversality, the following result can be proved.

Theorem 1.2.5. *Let V be a compact manifold. The set of Morse functions on V is a dense open subset of $\mathcal{C}^\infty(V; \mathbf{R})$.*

The proof can be found in Exercise 9 on p. 20 (using "transversality with constraints") and, if necessary, the definition of $\mathcal{C}^\infty(V; \mathbf{R})$ can be found in Subsection A.3.b.

1.3 The Morse Lemma, the Index of a Critical Point

Let us now describe what happens near a critical point of a Morse function.

1.3.a The Morse Lemma

In the neighborhood of a critical point, a function is closely approximated by (half of) its second-order derivative. The Morse lemma gives a much better result: after changing the chart, if necessary, the two are equal.

Theorem 1.3.1 (Morse lemma). *Let c be a nondegenerate critical point of the function $f : V \to \mathbf{R}$. There exist a neighborhood U of c and a diffeomorphism $\varphi : (U, c) \to (\mathbf{R}^n, 0)$ such that*

$$f \circ \varphi^{-1}(x_1, \dots, x_n) = f(c) - \sum_{j=1}^{i} x_j^2 + \sum_{j=i+1}^{n} x_j^2.$$

Proof. This result can be proved by using Hadamard's lemma, as Milnor does in [54]. The proof we choose here is a direct application of the implicit function theorem and can be found in [47].[1]

By using a chart, since the result is local, we may, and do, assume that $V = \mathbf{R}^n$ and that the critical point c is 0. By taking the composition with an isomorphism of vector spaces, we moreover may, and do, assume that the quadratic form $(d^2 f)_0$ is diagonal.

---

[1] The main advantage of this proof is that it gives a slightly more general result than the Morse lemma: near a critical point, a function can be written as the sum of a constant, a quadratic form of rank $k \leq n$ and a function in the remaining $n - k$ variables whose partial derivatives of orders 1 and 2 are all zero at the point in question.

We will prove the result by induction on the dimension. We begin with the case $n = 1$, where

$$f(x) = f(0) + \frac{1}{2}f''(0)x^2 + \varepsilon(x)x^2$$
$$= f(0) \pm ax^2(1 + \varepsilon(x))$$

for a positive real number a and a C^∞ function ε, namely

$$\varepsilon(x) = \frac{1}{2}\int_0^x f^{(3)}(t)(x - t)^2 \, dt.$$

We set

$$x_1 = \varphi(x) = x\sqrt{a(1 + \varepsilon(x))}.$$

It is clear that φ is a local diffeomorphism (since $\varphi'(0) = \sqrt{a} \neq 0$), which allows us to apply the local inversion theorem, so that in the neighborhood of 0, we have

$$f \circ \varphi^{-1}(x_1) = f(x) = f(0) \pm x_1^2.$$

This is the theorem for $n = 1$.

Next, we write $\mathbf{R}^n = \mathbf{R} \times \mathbf{R}^{n-1}$, with points denoted by (x, y). We write $f(x, y) = f_y(x)$, considering the functions f_y in one real variable as the parameter y varies in $\mathbf{R}^{n-1}$. The second-order Taylor polynomial of f is

$$f(x, y) = f_y(0) + f_y'(0)x + \frac{1}{2}f_y''(0)x^2 + x^2\varepsilon(x, y).$$

If the term $f_y'(0)$ is zero, then we proceed as in the case $n = 1$, since $f_y''(0) \neq 0$ (otherwise there would be a zero column in the matrix of second-order derivatives of f), which allows us to write

$$f(x, y) = f_y(0) \pm a(y)x^2(1 + \varepsilon(x, y)) \quad \text{with } a(y) > 0.$$

The map

$$\varphi : (x, y) \longmapsto (x_1 = x\sqrt{a(y)(1 + \varepsilon(x, y))}, y_1 = y)$$

is a local diffeomorphism as in the case $n = 1$ and, again as in that case, gives

$$f \circ \varphi^{-1}(x_1, y_1) = \pm x_1^2 + f(0, y_1),$$

allowing us to conclude by induction.

Let us therefore show that it is possible to reduce to the case where $f_y'(0) = 0$. Let us seek the critical points of f_y, that is, the solutions of the equation

$$\frac{\partial f}{\partial x}(x, y) = 0.$$

Under our hypotheses on $(d^2 f)_0$, we know that

$$\frac{\partial^2 f}{\partial x^2}(0, 0) \neq 0,$$

so that the implicit function theorem asserts that, in the neighborhood of $(0, 0)$, our solutions are the points of the graph $x = \varphi(y)$ of a function φ defined and of class $\mathcal{C}^\infty$ in the neighborhood of $0 \in \mathbf{R}^{n-1}$. Since we have supposed that the second-order derivative is diagonal, the derivative of $\partial f / \partial x$ with respect to the variable y is zero at $(0, 0)$. Consequently, $(d\varphi)_0 = 0$.

We now use the local (in the neighborhood of 0) diffeomorphism $\Phi(x, y) = (x + \varphi(y), y)$, whose differential at 0 is the identity. The function $f \circ \Phi$ satisfies

$$\begin{cases} \dfrac{\partial}{\partial x}(f \circ \Phi)(0, y) = 0 \\ d^2(f \circ \Phi)_{(0,0)} = (d^2 f)_{(0,0)}. \end{cases}$$

By integrating the local diffeomorphism Φ into the notation, that is, by using the notation f for the function $f \circ \Phi$, we reduce to the case of a function with the desired property. This concludes the proof of the Morse lemma. $\qquad \square$

A chart in whose open set the coordinates given by the Morse lemma are defined is called a *Morse chart*.

An immediate corollary of the Morse lemma is the following (see also Exercise 2 on p. 18).

Corollary 1.3.2. *The nondegenerate critical points of a function are isolated.* $\qquad \square$

In particular, a Morse function on a compact manifold has finitely many critical points.

The integer i that appears in the statement of the Morse lemma is the *index* of the critical point (it depends only on the critical point, $(n - i, i)$ is the signature of the second-order derivative quadratic form).

Remark 1.3.3. A critical point of index i of f is a critical point of index $n - i$ of $-f$.

1.3.b Examples of Critical Points

Extrema.

A local minimum of a Morse function is a critical point of index 0. The figures below represent a minimum of the height function (on the manifold) and a few level sets of the function near a minimum in a Morse chart.

Fig. 1.1 A minimum   **Fig. 1.2** Critical point of index 0

A local maximum is a critical point of index n (the dimension of the manifold). Figure 1.2 can also represent the level sets of a function in the neighborhood of a maximum.

Index 1.

The critical points of index 1 of a function in two variables are those that we saw appear on the torus. These points are called "saddle" points or "passes". Figure 1.3 explains the word "saddle". The term "pass" also fits well: this figure can also evoke a mountain pass, "the highest point between two summits", as "defined"[2] by geography manuals. Likewise, Figure 1.4 evokes level curves in the neighborhood of a pass on a topographic map.

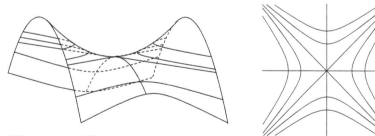

Fig. 1.3 A saddle point

Fig. 1.4 Critical point of index 1

---

[2] The definitions "narrow passage between two mountains" or "depression forming a passage between two mountain summits" found in dictionaries are not much more precise.

1.4 Examples of Morse Functions

The classic examples of Morse functions we present here will be used in this book.

1.4.a The Function (Square of the) Distance to a Point

As said in Subsection 1.2.a, the functions $f_p = \|x - p\|^2$ are, in general, Morse functions. Figure 1.5 shows the two critical points of such a function on a torus and the unit sphere in $\mathbf{R}^3$.

Remark 1.4.1. The only point for which f_p is not a Morse function on the sphere is the center of the sphere. More generally, we call the points p of $\mathbf{R}^n$ for which f_p is not a Morse function "focal points" of V. This terminology is justified by the fact that at such a point (for a hypersurface) infinitesimally close normal vectors meet. If we imagine the hypersurface to be a light source and the normal vectors to be the light rays that it emits, then the light intensity builds up at these points, whence the name "foci" or "focal points".

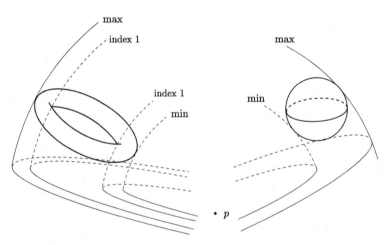

Fig. 1.5 The function "distance to p" on a torus and on a sphere

In general, a point of a submanifold is critical for the distance function if the submanifold is tangent (nontransversal) to the sphere with center p passing through this point.

1.4.b Height Functions

The three height functions presented in the introduction are Morse functions:

- On the sphere S^2, with two critical points of indices 0 (the minimum, south pole) and 2 (the maximum, north pole)
- On the torus T^2, with four critical points: the minimum, the maximum and two intermediate critical points of index 1
- Again on the sphere S^2, with four critical points: the minimum, a critical point of index 1 and two local maxima.

Remark 1.4.2. We can also see the height as the distance to a point at infinity in the direction of the z-axis.

1.4.c On the Torus T^2

There are many other Morse functions on the torus! Consider, for example, the function

$$f : \mathbf{R}^2 \longrightarrow \mathbf{R}$$
$$(x, y) \longmapsto \cos(2\pi x) + \cos(2\pi y)$$

and the function that it defines on the torus $T^2 = \mathbf{R}^2/\mathbf{Z}^2$, which we also denote by f. This is a product function. It has four critical points:

- A minimum, the point $(\frac{1}{2}, \frac{1}{2})$
- Two critical points of index 1, the points $(\frac{1}{2}, 0)$ and $(0, \frac{1}{2})$
- A maximum, the point $(0, 0)$.

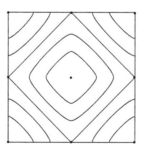

Fig. 1.6 A Morse function on the torus

We invite the readers to verify these assertions (the verifications are straightforward). Figure 1.6 shows a few level sets of the function f on the torus. Note that the minimum is at level -2, the two critical points of index 1 are at the same level 0 and the maximum is at level 2.

Exercises

Exercise 1. Let U be an open subset of $\mathbf{R}^n$ and let $f : U \to \mathbf{R}$ be a $\mathcal{C}^\infty$ function. Let V be an open subset of $\mathbf{R}^n$ and let $\varphi : V \to U$ be a diffeomorphism. Compute $(d^2(f \circ \varphi))_y$ (for $y \in V$).

Let M be a manifold and let $g : M \to \mathbf{R}$ be a function. Show that the bilinear form $(d^2 g)_x$ is well defined on the vector subspace

$$\mathrm{Ker}(dg)_x \subset T_x M.$$

Exercise 2. The cotangent vector bundle $T^\star V$ of the manifold V is endowed with its natural manifold structure (recalled in Appendix A). Verify that we can see the differential df of a function $f : V \to \mathbf{R}$ as a section

$$df : V \longrightarrow T^\star V$$

of the cotangent vector bundle (which is an embedding of V in $T^\star V$).

What are the critical points of f in this terminology? Show that the point a is a nondegenerate critical point of f if and only if the submanifold $df(V)$ is transverse to the zero section at the point in question.

Prove that a nondegenerate critical point of a function is isolated (without using the Morse lemma!).

Exercise 3 (Monkey Saddle). We consider the function

$$f : \mathbf{R}^2 \longrightarrow \mathbf{R}$$
$$(x, y) \longmapsto x^3 - 3xy^2.$$

Study the critical point $(0,0)$. Is it nondegenerate? Draw a few regular level sets of the function f as well as its graph.

Exercise 4. If $f : V \to \mathbf{R}$ and $g : W \to \mathbf{R}$ are Morse functions, then $f + g : V \times W \to \mathbf{R}$ is also a Morse function whose critical points are the pairs of critical points of f and g.

Exercise 5 (On the Complex Projective Space). By passing to the quotient, the function on $\mathbf{C}^{n+1} - \{0\}$ defined by

$$f(z_0, \ldots, z_n) = \frac{\sum_{j=0}^n j \, |z_j|^2}{\sum_{j=0}^n |z_j|^2}$$

induces a function on the complex projective space $\mathbf{P}^n(\mathbf{C})$, which we still denote by f.

Verify that this is a Morse function whose critical points are the points $[1, 0, \ldots, 0]$ (of index 0), $[0, 1, 0, \ldots, 0]$ (of index 2) and so on up to $[0, \ldots, 0, 1]$ (of index $2n$).

Readers eager to know where this function may well have come from (from [54], of course, but before that?) can turn to Remark 2.1.12.

Exercise 6 (On the sphere and on the real projective plane). With essentially the same formula, let us now consider the function

$$f : S^2 \longrightarrow \mathbf{R}$$
$$(x, y, z) \longmapsto y^2 + 2z^2$$

and the resulting function $g : \mathbf{P}^2(\mathbf{R}) \to \mathbf{R}$ on the real projective plane that follows from it by passing to the quotient. Verify that f (and therefore g) is a Morse function and show that it has six critical points (and therefore that g has three):

- Two points of index 0, the points $(\pm 1, 0, 0)$, at level 0
- Two points of index 1, the points $(0, \pm 1, 0)$, at level 1
- Two points of index 2, the points $(0, 0, \pm 1)$, at level 2.

Figure 1.7 shows a few level sets of this function on the sphere. The critical level set containing the two points of index 1 consists of the two circles defined by intersecting the sphere with the planes $z = \pm x$.

Exercise 7. In a square, draw the level sets of the height function on the "inner tube" torus (the answer is somewhere in this book).

Exercise 8 (A projective quadric). We consider the "quadric" Q in $\mathbf{P}^3(\mathbf{C})$ defined by the equation

$$z_0^2 + z_1^2 + z_2^2 + z_3^2 = 0.$$

Show that Q is a compact submanifold of the manifold $\mathbf{P}^3(\mathbf{C})$ of (real) dimension 4.

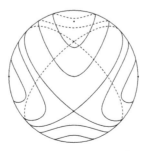

Fig. 1.7 A Morse function on the real projective plane

Let us write $z_j = x_j + iy_j$ (for $0 \leq j \leq 3$) and $z = x + iy$ for $z \in \mathbf{C}^4$, with $x, y \in \mathbf{R}^4$. We fix two real numbers λ and μ and, for $z \in \mathbf{C}^4$, we set

$$\widetilde{f}(z) = \lambda(x_0 y_1 - x_1 y_0) + \mu(x_2 y_3 - x_3 y_2).$$

Verify that for $|u| = 1$, we have

$$\widetilde{f}(uz) = \widetilde{f}(z)$$

and deduce from it that $\widetilde{f}$ defines a function

$$f : \mathbf{P}^3(\mathbf{C}) \longrightarrow \mathbf{R}.$$

Suppose that the real numbers λ and μ occurring in the definition of f satisfy $0 < \lambda < \mu$. Let g be the restriction of f to Q. Show that g is a Morse function that has a local minimum, a local maximum and two critical points of index 2.

Exercise 9. In this exercise, we propose a different proof of the existence of numerous Morse functions on a manifold, and more precisely of Theorem 1.2.5:

(1) Using, for example, Exercise 2, show that the set of Morse functions on the compact manifold V is open for the $\mathcal{C}^2$ topology, and therefore also for the $\mathcal{C}^\infty$ topology.

(2) Let $a \in V$ and let U be the open set of a chart centered at a. We let $\mathcal{F}$ denote the space of differentials of the functions defined on U (or of exact 1-forms), seen as a subset of $\mathcal{C}^\infty(U; (\mathbf{R}^n)^\star)$ (for every $x \in U$, $(df)_x$ is a linear functional on $\mathbf{R}^n$). Note that $\mathcal{F}$ is not an open subset. Let α be a plateau function with support in U and value 1 on a compact neighborhood K of a. For $\varphi = df \in \mathcal{F}$, we let

$$F : U \times (\mathbf{R}^n)^\star \longrightarrow \mathbf{R}$$
$$(x, A) \longmapsto f(x) + \alpha(x) A \cdot x.$$

Compute[3] $(D_1 F)_{(x,A)}$ for $x \in K$ and show that F is a submersion

$$K \times (\mathbf{R}^n)^\star \longrightarrow (\mathbf{R}^n)^\star.$$

Show that $\mathcal{F}$ is locally transversal to $\{0\}$ (in the sense of Subsection A.3.c).

---

[3] If f is a function of two arguments $(u, v) \in U \times V \subset E \times F$, then we let $(D_1 f)_{(u,v)}$ denote the linear map

$$(D_1 f)_{(u,v)} : E \longrightarrow \mathbf{R}$$

that is the partial differential of f with respect to the first variable. The analogue holds for $(D_2 f)_{(u,v)}$.

(3) Show that every point a of V admits a compact neighborhood K such that the set of functions $f : V \to \mathbf{R}$ whose critical points in K are nondegenerate is dense in $\mathcal{C}^\infty(V; \mathbf{R})$.

(4) Deduce a proof of Theorem 1.2.5 from this.

Chapter 2
Pseudo-Gradients

In this chapter, we define, construct and study pseudo-gradient fields, whose trajectories connect the critical points of a Morse function. These vector fields allow us to define the stable and unstable manifolds of the critical points, which will play an important role. We call attention to the "Smale property" because of which, for example, there are only finitely many trajectories connecting two critical points with consecutive indices and we prove the existence of pseudo-gradient fields satisfying this property.

2.1 Gradients, Pseudo-Gradients and Morse Charts

2.1.a Gradients and Pseudo-Gradients

If f is a function defined on $\mathbf{R}^n$, then we are familiar with its *gradient*, the vector field grad f, whose coordinates in the canonical basis of $\mathbf{R}^n$ are

$$\operatorname{grad}_x f = \left(\frac{\partial f}{\partial x_1}, \dots, \frac{\partial f}{\partial x_n} \right).$$

More succinctly, it is (also) the vector field defined by

$$\langle \operatorname{grad}_x f, Y \rangle = (df)_x(Y)$$

for every vector $Y \in \mathbf{R}^n$ (where, of course, the angle brackets $\langle \ , \ \rangle$ denote the usual Euclidean inner product in $\mathbf{R}^n$). The most important properties of this vector field are due to the fact that this inner product is a *positive definite* symmetric bilinear form:

(1) It vanishes exactly at the critical points of the function f.

M. Audin, M. Damian, *Morse Theory and Floer Homology*,
Universitext, DOI 10.1007/978-1-4471-5496-9_2,
© Springer-Verlag London 2014

(2) The function f is decreasing along the flow lines of the field $-\mathrm{grad}\, f$:

$$\frac{d}{ds}\left(f(\varphi^s(x))\right) = -\|\mathrm{grad}_{\varphi^s(x)} f\|^2 < 0.$$

Remark 2.1.1. More generally, if the manifold V is endowed with a Riemannian metric (see Section A.5), then a function on V has a gradient defined by the same formula,

$$\langle \mathrm{grad}_x f, Y \rangle = (df)_x(Y)$$

for every $Y \in T_x V$.

Remark 2.1.2. There is no doubt that the conjunction of the terms "flow" and "height" is at the source (if we dare say so) of the (recent) tradition to use the negative gradient: the flow moves downward. We have conformed to this convention, as do [66] and [49], but not [46].

Let $f : V \to \mathbf{R}$ be a Morse function on a manifold V. A *pseudo-gradient field* or *pseudo-gradient* adapted to f is a vector field X on V such that:

(1) We have $(df)_x(X_x) \leq 0$, where equality holds if and only if x is a critical point.
(2) In a Morse chart in the neighborhood of a critical point, X coincides with the negative gradient for the canonical metric on $\mathbf{R}^n$.

Remark 2.1.3. A pseudo-gradient is a rather particular vector field. See Exercise 10 on p. 51 for vector fields that are not pseudo-gradients.

2.1.b Morse Charts

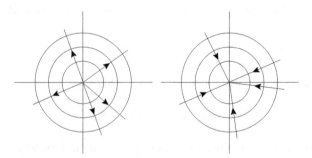

Fig. 2.1 Maximum and minimum

This notion allows us to make the Morse charts more precise by specifying the trajectories of a pseudo-gradient field X. For example, Figure 2.1 finally shows the difference between a maximum (on the left) and a minimum (on the right).

Figure 2.2 shows a Morse chart for a critical point of index i. The chart or, strictly speaking, the model in $\mathbf{R}^n$, appears on the left. On the right we can see its image in the manifold (the function is the height). Let us fix some notation. In $\mathbf{R}^n$, the quadratic form Q is negative definite on V_-, a subspace of dimension i, and positive definite on V_+. We set

$$U(\varepsilon, \eta) = \left\{ x \in \mathbf{R}^n \mid -\varepsilon < Q(x) < \varepsilon \text{ and } \|x_-\|^2 \|x_+\|^2 \le \eta(\varepsilon + \eta) \right\}.$$

Since we are in $\mathbf{R}^n$, the function Q has a gradient, namely

$$-\mathrm{grad}_{(x_-, x_+)} Q = 2(x_-, -x_+).$$

The boundary of $U(\varepsilon, \eta)$ is made up of three parts:

- Two subsets of the sublevel sets of Q:

$$\partial_\pm U = \left\{ x \in U \mid Q(x) = \pm\varepsilon \text{ and } \|x_\mp\|^2 \le \eta \right\}$$

- A set of pieces of trajectories of the gradient $\mathrm{grad}\, Q$:

$$\partial_0 U = \left\{ x \in \partial U \mid \|x_-\|^2 \|x_+\|^2 = \eta(\varepsilon + \eta) \right\}.$$

See Figure 2.2. The notation we use here is that of [46].

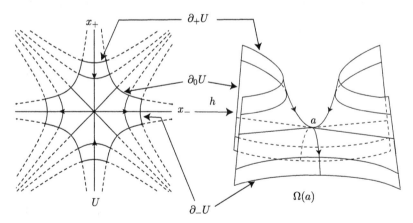

Fig. 2.2 A Morse chart

Remark 2.1.4. By the definition of the gradient in $\mathbf{R}^n$, the trajectories of the gradient are orthogonal to the level sets of the function (the tangent space to a level set is the kernel of the differential of the function). It is therefore not a coincidence that on the model shown in Figure 2.2, they show up as equilateral hyperbolas from two orthogonal families.

Taking a closer look at the two parts of the figure proves to be useful. In both parts, we have indicated the critical level set (let us say that it is level 0), two positive regular level sets and two negative regular level sets and trajectories of the gradient that delimit the chart, as well as trajectories of the negative gradient that end or begin at the critical point.

If a is a critical point of the function f, then a neighborhood of a is described by the Morse lemma as the image of some $U(\varepsilon, \eta)$ under a diffeomorphism h. We will denote such a neighborhood by $\Omega(a)$. We will also write

$$\partial_{\pm} \Omega(a) = h(\partial_{\pm} U), \quad \partial_0 \Omega = h(\partial_0 U),$$

etc. We will try to use the following notation consistently, as in Figure 2.2:

- Ω for the images of charts (Ω is a subset of the manifold)
- U for the chart domains, the models (U is a subset of $\mathbf{R}^n$).

2.1.c Existence of Pseudo-Gradient Fields

Pseudo-gradient fields exist for all Morse functions on all manifolds. This is, for example, a consequence of the existence of Riemannian metrics and, more exactly, of the existence of Riemannian metrics with a prescribed form on a given subset of the manifold (a neighborhood of the critical points). In any case, it is a simple consequence of the existence of partitions of unity, as we will show now.

Proof of the Existence of Pseudo-Gradients. Let $c_1, \ldots, c_r$ be the critical points of f on the manifold V (there are finitely many because V is compact and the critical points of a Morse function are isolated) and let $(U_1, h_1), \ldots, (U_r, h_r)$ be Morse charts in the neighborhoods of these points. The open images Ω_j are, of course, assumed to be disjoint. We add more sets and obtain a finite open cover $(\Omega_j)_{1 \le j \le N}$ of V by images of open sets of charts (U_j, h_j). We may, and do, assume that in this cover, the critical point c_i is contained only in the open set Ω_i.

For a function g defined on an open subset of $\mathbf{R}^n$, we let $\operatorname{grad} g$ be its gradient for the standard Euclidean metric on $\mathbf{R}^n$. For every index j, we define a vector field X_j on the open set Ω_j by pulling back the gradient of $f \circ h_j$ to V, that is, by the formula

$$X_j(x) = -(T_{h_j^{-1}(x)} h_j)(\operatorname{grad}_{h_j^{-1}(x)}(f \circ h_j))$$

(the formula may seem complicated, but the object itself is very simple: we have taken the gradient of the function $f \circ h_j$, a vector field on U_j, and have transformed it in a natural manner into a vector field on Ω_j). By the very definition, $X_j \cdot f \leq 0$ on Ω_j (this is one of the properties of the negative gradient). Moreover, X_j vanishes only at the critical point of f on U_j (for $j \leq r$).

Next, we use a partition of unity $(\varphi_j)_j$ associated with the cover $(\Omega_j)_j$ to extend the local vector fields X_j to vector fields $\widetilde{X}_j$ defined on all of V, setting

$$\widetilde{X}_j(x) = \begin{cases} \varphi_j(x) X_j(x) & \text{if } x \in \Omega_j \\ 0 & \text{otherwise.} \end{cases}$$

The last step is to set

$$X = \sum_{j=1}^{N} \widetilde{X}_j.$$

As expected, the resulting vector field X is a pseudo-gradient adapted to f, since we indeed have

$$(df)_x(X_x) = \sum_{j=1}^{N} (df)_x((\widetilde{X}_j)_x) \leq 0.$$

If this inequality is an equality, then $\varphi_j(x) X_j(x) = 0$ for every j, so that either x is a critical point, or $\varphi_j(x) = 0$ for every j (which is absurd).

Let c_i be one of the critical points of f. By construction, X coincides with the image of the Euclidean gradient on the complement in U_i of the union of the other open sets U_j, a complement that is a neighborhood of c_i that contains a small Morse chart in the neighborhood of c_i.   □

2.1.d Stable and Unstable Submanifolds

Let a be a critical point of f. Denote by φ^s the flow of a pseudo-gradient. We define its stable manifold to be

$$W^s(a) = \left\{ x \in V \mid \lim_{s \to +\infty} \varphi^s(x) = a \right\}$$

and its unstable manifold to be

$$W^u(a) = \left\{ x \in V \mid \lim_{s \to -\infty} \varphi^s(x) = a \right\}.$$

In an open subset $U = U(\varepsilon, \eta)$ of $\mathbf{R}^n$ as in Section 2.1.b, we have

$$W^s(0) = U \cap V_+ \quad \text{and} \quad W^u(0) = U \cap V_-.$$

In the notation of Subsection 2.1.b, the stable manifold of a is obtained from the union of $h(U \cap V_+) = h(W^s(0))$ and

$$h(\partial_+ U \cap V_+) \times \mathbf{R}$$

by identifying (x, s), for x on the boundary and $s \geq 0$, with $\varphi^s(x)$. See Figure 2.3. If k is the index of the critical point a, then $h(\partial_+ U \cap V_+)$ is a sphere of dimension $n - k - 1$; it is the image under the diffeomorphism h of the sphere $\|x_+\|^2 = \varepsilon$ in V_+ (vector space of dimension $n - k$).

Hence the stable manifolds and, likewise, the unstable manifolds, are submanifolds: outside of the critical point, the stable manifold is the image of the embedding $(x, s) \mapsto \varphi^s(x)$ and in the neighborhood of the critical point, it is the image of V_+. This argument also shows that $W^s(a)$ is diffeomorphic to the disk of dimension $n - k$ (and likewise that $W^u(a)$ is diffeomorphic to the disk of dimension k): $W^s(a)$ can be obtained by compactifying $S^{n-k-1} \times \mathbf{R}$ by adding the unique "point at infinity" a. It is also the quotient of $S^{n-k-1} \times \left] -\infty, +\infty \right]$ by the equivalence relation that identifies the sphere $S^{n-k-1} \times \{+\infty\}$ with a unique point.

We have proved the following result.

Proposition 2.1.5. *The stable and unstable manifolds of the critical point a are submanifolds of V that are diffeomorphic to open disks. Moreover, we have*

$$\dim W^u(a) = \operatorname{codim} W^s(a) = \operatorname{Ind}(a). \qquad \square$$

Here, $\operatorname{Ind}(a)$ denotes the index of the point a as a critical point of f.

Trajectories of the Pseudo-Gradient Field.

Let φ^s_X or φ^s denote the flow of the pseudo-gradient X. The most important property of the flow lines or trajectories of the vector field X is that they all connect critical points of the function f: all trajectories come from a critical point and go toward another critical point.

Proposition 2.1.6. *We suppose that the manifold V is compact. Let $\gamma : \mathbf{R} \to V$ be a trajectory of the pseudo-gradient field X. Then there exist critical points c and d of f such that*

$$\lim_{s \to -\infty} \gamma(s) = c \quad and \quad \lim_{s \to +\infty} \gamma(s) = d.$$

Proof. Let us show that $\gamma(t)$ has a limit when t tends to $+\infty$ (for example) and that this limit is a critical point. We must prove that $\gamma(t)$ reaches $S_+(d) = \partial_+ \Omega(d) \cap W^s(d)$ for some critical point d of f. We suppose that this is not

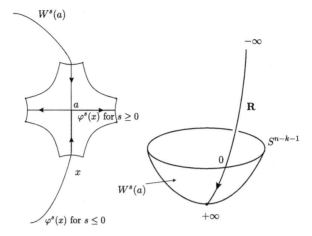

Fig. 2.3 Stable manifolds

true. Then every time that the trajectory γ enters a Morse neighborhood, it must also leave it without ever being able to return to it since f is decreasing along γ. Let s_0 be the time at which γ leaves the (finite) union of the Morse charts of the critical points, that is,

$$\Omega = \bigcup_{c \in \mathrm{Crit}(f)} \Omega(c)$$

(of course, $\mathrm{Crit}(f)$ denotes the set of critical points of the function f) for the last time. There exists an $\varepsilon_0 > 0$ such that

$$\forall x \in V - \Omega, \quad (df)_x(X_x) \le -\varepsilon_0.$$

Consequently, for every $s \ge s_0$, we have

$$f(\gamma(s)) - f(\gamma(s_0)) = \int_{s_0}^{s} \frac{d(f \circ \gamma)}{du} \, du$$
$$= \int_{s_0}^{s} (df)_{\gamma(u)}(X_{\gamma(u)}) \, du$$
$$\le -\varepsilon_0(s - s_0),$$

so that

$$\lim_{s \to +\infty} f(\gamma(s)) = -\infty,$$

which is absurd. □

2.1.e Topology of the Sublevel Sets: When We Do Not Cross a Critical Value

The topology of the level sets does not change as long as we do not cross a critical value. The same holds for that of the sublevel sets. Let

$$V^a = f^{-1}(]-\infty, a])$$

denote the sublevel set of f for a. In Subsection A.2.c, we said that if a is a regular value, then V^a is a manifold with boundary.

Theorem 2.1.7. *Let a and b be two real numbers such that f does not have any critical value in the interval $[a, b]$. We suppose that $f^{-1}([a, b])$ is compact. Then V^b is diffeomorphic to V^a.*

Proof. We use the flow of a pseudo-gradient X to retract V^b onto V^a. We fix a function $\rho : V \to \mathbf{R}$ with values

$$
\begin{cases}
-\dfrac{1}{(df)_x(X)} & \text{on } f^{-1}([a, b]) \\
0 & \text{outside of a compact neighborhood of this subset.}
\end{cases}
$$

The vector field $Y = \rho X$ is zero outside of a compact set, so that its flow ψ^s is defined for every $s \in \mathbf{R}$. For a fixed point $x \in V$, we consider the function $s \mapsto f \circ \psi^s(x)$ in one real variable. If $\psi^s(x) \in f^{-1}([a, b])$, then we have

$$\frac{d}{ds} f \circ \psi^s(x) = (df)_{\psi^s(x)} \left(\frac{d}{ds} \psi^s(x) \right)$$
$$= (df)_{\psi^s(x)} \left(Y_{\psi^s(x)} \right)$$
$$= -1.$$

Hence, for $\psi^s(x) \in f^{-1}([a, b])$, we have

$$f \circ \psi^s(x) = -s + f(x).$$

It follows that the diffeomorphism ψ^{b-a} of V sends V^b onto V^a.   □

Remark 2.1.8. The map

$$r : V^b \times [0, 1] \longrightarrow V^b$$

$$
(x, s) \longmapsto
\begin{cases}
x & \text{if } f(x) \leq a \\
\psi^{s(f(x)-a)}(x) & \text{if } a \leq f(x) \leq b
\end{cases}
$$

is a deformation retraction of V^b onto V^a, that is, $r_0 = \mathrm{Id}$, r_t equals the inclusion on V^a for all t and r_1 has image V^a. Consequently V^a is a deformation retract of V^b.

Corollary 2.1.9 (Reeb's theorem). *Let V be a compact manifold. Suppose that there exists a Morse function on V that has only two critical points. Then V is homeomorphic to a sphere.*

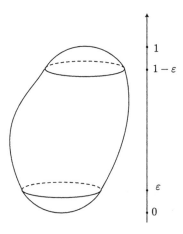

Fig. 2.4 Reeb's theorem

Proof. The two critical points must be the minimum and the maximum. We may, and do, assume that $f(V) = [0, 1]$. Then for $\varepsilon > 0$ sufficiently small, the Morse lemma asserts that $f^{-1}([0, \varepsilon])$ and $f^{-1}([1 - \varepsilon, 1])$ are disks D^n. By Theorem 2.1.7, the sublevel sets V^ε and $V^{1-\varepsilon}$ are diffeomorphic. Hence $V^{1-\varepsilon}$ is also a disk D^n and V is the union of two disks glued along their boundaries. It is a classic result that V is then homeomorphic to a sphere: we can construct an explicit map

$$h : D_1^n \cup_{\mathrm{Id}} D_2^n \longrightarrow D_1^n \cup_\varphi D_2^n$$

by setting

$$h(x) = \begin{cases} x & \text{if } x \in D_1^n \\ \|x\| \, \varphi(x/\|x\|) & \text{if } x \in D_2^n - \{0\} \\ 0 & \text{if } x = 0 \in D_2^n. \end{cases}$$

This is a homeomorphism from the standard sphere (where the two disks are glued via the identity map on S^{n-1}) onto our manifold (where the two disks are glued via the diffeomorphism φ). $\qquad\square$

Remarks 2.1.10. First, the theorem remains true if the two critical points are not assumed to be nondegenerate. Second, it is not true that the manifold V is *diffeomorphic* to a sphere; this is even an important argument in the construction of manifolds that are homeomorphic to the sphere without being diffeomorphic to it. For these two results, see the references in the book [54, p. 25].

2.1.f Topology of the Sublevel Sets: When We Cross a Critical Value

Both the topology of the level set and that of the sublevel set will change. The following theorem expresses how.

Theorem 2.1.11. *Let $f : V \to \mathbf{R}$ be a function. Let a be a nondegenerate critical point of index k of f and let $\alpha = f(a)$. We suppose that for some sufficiently small $\varepsilon > 0$, the set $f^{-1}([\alpha - \varepsilon, \alpha + \varepsilon])$ is compact and does not contain any critical point of f other than a. Then for every sufficiently small $\varepsilon > 0$, the homotopy type of the space $V^{\alpha+\varepsilon}$ is that of $V^{\alpha-\varepsilon}$ with a cell of dimension k attached (the unstable manifold of a).*

Remark 2.1.12. This theorem allows us to justify the appearance, or rather the parachuting in, of the Morse function on $\mathbf{P}^n(\mathbf{C})$ that was discussed in Exercise 5 on p. 18.

We begin with a very natural description of the (say, complex) projective space. It is, as all geometers know, the union of an affine space and a hyperplane "at infinity". By considering things the other way around, we can say that the complex projective space $\mathbf{P}^n(\mathbf{C})$ is obtained from $\mathbf{P}^{n-1}(\mathbf{C})$ by adding a $\mathbf{C}^n$, or disk D^{2n}. Step by step, this defines a "cellular decomposition" of $\mathbf{P}^n(\mathbf{C})$: we begin with a point (this is $\mathbf{P}^0$, the point $[1, 0, \ldots, 0]$), we attach a disk of (real) dimension 2 (we now have $\mathbf{P}^1(\mathbf{C})$, the cell of points $[a, b, 0, \ldots, 0]$), and so on.

The Morse function in Exercise 5 enables this reconstruction, as is explained in Theorem 2.1.11. We begin with the minimum (this is precisely our point $[1, 0, \ldots, 0]$), where the function has value 0. The first critical value is then 1. This corresponds to the critical point $[0, 1, 0, \ldots, 0]$, which has index 2... and enables us to attach a cell of dimension 2, and so on. In this sense, this function is "perfect".[1]

Proof of Theorem 2.1.11. Let us begin by presenting the ideas of the proof while contemplating Figure 2.5. The cell D^k is the piece of the unstable

---

[1] There is also a precise mathematical definition of the expression "perfect Morse function", of which the one considered here is the prototype.

manifold of a shown in this figure. We proceed as follows:

(1) By modifying f, we construct a function F that coincides with f outside of a neighborhood of a where $F < f$, so that $F^{-1}(]-\infty, \alpha - \varepsilon])$ will be the union of $V^{\alpha - \varepsilon}$ and a small neighborhood of a (the part with horizontal hatching in Figure 2.5).
(2) Now, Theorem 2.1.7 and Remark 2.1.8 applied to the function F give the hatched part $F^{-1}(]-\infty, \alpha + \varepsilon])$ as a retract of $V^{\alpha + \varepsilon}$ (which is also the sublevel set of the modified function F for $\alpha + \varepsilon$).
(3) We can then position ourselves in a Morse chart to show that the subset of V consisting of the piece of the unstable manifold together with $V^{\alpha - \varepsilon}$ is a deformation retract of $F^{-1}(]-\infty, \alpha + \varepsilon])$.

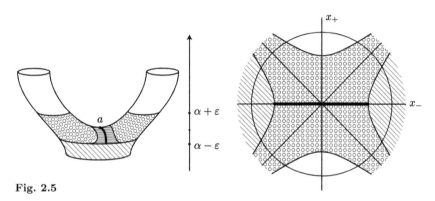

Fig. 2.5

Fig. 2.6

Construction of F.

We choose a Morse chart (U, h) in the neighborhood of a and an $\varepsilon > 0$ that is sufficiently small that $f^{-1}([\alpha - \varepsilon, \alpha + \varepsilon])$ is compact and that U contains the ball of radius $\sqrt{2\varepsilon}$ with center 0. The disk D^k is the subset of U consisting of the (x_-, x_+) such that $\|x_-\|^2 < \varepsilon$ and $x_+ = 0$. In Figure 2.5, as in Figure 2.6, the sublevel set $V^{\alpha - \varepsilon}$ is indicated with oblique hatching while $f^{-1}([\alpha - \varepsilon, \alpha + \varepsilon])$ is dotted. The cell, the disk D^k, is a thick line segment.

We construct the function F by using a $\mathcal{C}^\infty$ function $\mu : [0, +\infty[\to [0, +\infty[$ with the following properties:

- $\mu(0) > \varepsilon$
- $\mu(s) = 0$ for $s \geq 2\varepsilon$
- $-1 < \mu'(s) \leq 0$ for every s

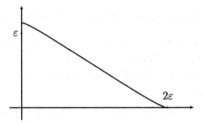

Fig. 2.7 The function μ

We define F by setting

$$F(x) = \begin{cases} f(x) & \text{if } x \notin \Omega(a) \\ \alpha - \|x_-\|^2 + \|x_+\|^2 \mu \left(\|x_-\|^2 + 2\|x_+\|^2 \right) & \text{if } x = h(x_-, x_+). \end{cases}$$

Note that the sublevel set of F for $\alpha + \varepsilon$ is exactly the sublevel set $V^{\alpha+\varepsilon}$ of f. Indeed:

- Outside of $\|x_-\|^2 + 2\|x_+\|^2 \leq 2\varepsilon$, we have $F = f$.
- In the interior of the ellipsoid in question, we have

$$F(x) \leq f(x) = \alpha - \|x_-\|^2 + \|x_+\|^2 \leq \alpha + \frac{1}{2}\|x_-\|^2 + \|x_+\|^2 \leq \alpha + \varepsilon.$$

Moreover, the critical points of F are the same as those of f, since

$$dF = \underbrace{\left(-1 - \mu'(\|x_-\|^2 + 2\|x_+\|^2)\right)}_{<0} 2x_- \cdot dx_-$$

$$+ \underbrace{\left(1 - 2\mu'(\|x_-\|^2 + 2\|x_+\|^2)\right)}_{\geq 1} 2x_+ \cdot dx_+$$

vanishes only for $x_- = x_+ = 0$, that is, at a.

We now know that

$$F^{-1}([\alpha - \varepsilon, \alpha + \varepsilon]) \subset f^{-1}([\alpha - \varepsilon, \alpha + \varepsilon]);$$

in particular, this region is compact. Moreover, it does not contain any critical points of F: the only possible candidate would be a, but

$$F(a) = \alpha - \mu(0) < \alpha - \varepsilon.$$

It follows that $F^{-1}(]-\infty, \alpha + \varepsilon])$ is a deformation retract of $V^{\alpha+\varepsilon}$. Let H be the horizontally hatched part in Figure 2.5 (it is clear in Figure 2.8), that is, the closure of $F^{-1}(]-\infty, \alpha + \varepsilon]) - V^{\alpha-\varepsilon}$. We have, in particular,

$$F^{-1}(]-\infty, \alpha + \varepsilon]) = V^{\alpha-\varepsilon} \cup H.$$

The Retraction.

We define the retraction by following the arrows indicated in Figure 2.9. Explicitly, r_t is the identity outside of $\Omega(a)$ and we define r_t on U (rather

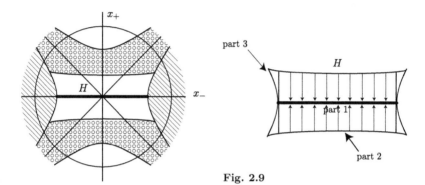

Fig. 2.9

Fig. 2.8

than on $\Omega(a)$, to simplify the notation) as follows:

- On region 1 (Figure 2.9), that is, on $\|x_-\|^2 \leq \varepsilon$,

$$r_t(x_-, x_+) = (x_-, tx_+).$$

- On region 2, defined by $\varepsilon \leq \|x_-\|^2 \leq \varepsilon\|x_+\|^2$, we set

$$r_t(x_-, x_+) = (x_-, s_t x_+),$$

where

$$s_t = t + (1-t)\frac{\sqrt{\|x_-\|^2 - \varepsilon}}{\|x_+\|}$$

is the appropriate number to make the formulas continuous.

- On region 3, which corresponds to $V^{\alpha-\varepsilon}$ and where $\|x_+\|^2 + \varepsilon \leq \|x_-\|^2$, we simply take $r_t = \text{Id}$. □

2.2 The Smale Condition

Let us return to the stable and unstable manifolds of the critical points.

2.2.a Examples of Stable and Unstable Manifolds

Here are the stable and unstable manifolds of the critical points of the examples considered earlier.

The Height on the Round Sphere.

Let a be the minimum and let b be the maximum. We have

$$W^s(a) = S^2 - \{b\}, \quad W^u(a) = \{a\}$$

and likewise

$$W^s(b) = \{b\}, \quad W^u(b) = S^2 - \{a\}$$

(for every pseudo-gradient field).

The Torus.

We begin with the height function on the inner tube torus. Let a, b, c, d be the critical points ordered according to the values that the function takes in them (Figure 2.10). The pseudo-gradient field used here is simply the gradient for

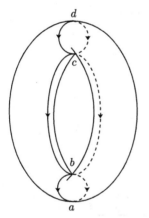

Fig. 2.10 The height on the torus

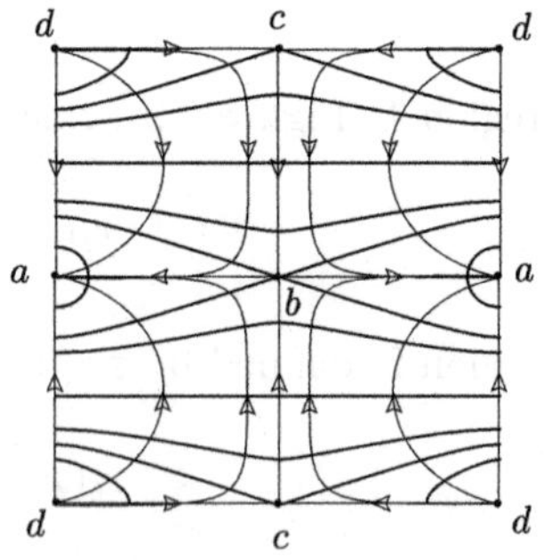

Fig. 2.11 Another point of view on the same thing

the metric induced by that on $\mathbf{R}^3$. The stable manifold of a consists of all points that descend to a, that is, the complement of the trajectories in the figure that end at b or at c. Hence $W^s(a)$ is homeomorphic to an open disk. The stable manifold of b consists of the two trajectories starting at c and ending at b. Hence $W^s(b)$ is diffeomorphic to an open interval. The same holds for the stable manifold of c, which consists of the two trajectories starting at d that we see in the figure. We should note that in this example (which was chosen for this reason), the unstable manifold of c and the stable manifold of b have two open intervals in common. Figure 2.11 shows a few level sets of the same function in a square, which solves an exercise suggested in the previous chapter. It also shows a few trajectories of the gradient.

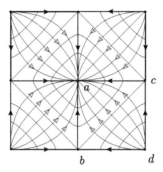

Fig. 2.12 The torus, again

The situation is somewhat different in the case of the other Morse function that we encountered on the torus T^2, namely

$$f(x, y) = \cos(2\pi x) + \cos(2\pi y).$$

Let us again denote the extrema by a and d and the critical points of index 1 by b and c. Figure 2.12 shows the gradient lines that connect the two critical points (here we use the gradient for the "flat" metric on the torus, that is, for the usual metric on $\mathbf{R}^2$; as we can see, the lines in question form true right angles with the level sets). We can clearly see that $W^s(a)$ is the open square (that is, an open disk), that $W^s(b)$ is an open interval (the horizontal side of the square in the figure), as are $W^u(b)$ (vertical segment), $W^s(c)$ (vertical side) and $W^u(c)$ (horizontal segment), while $W^s(d)$ is reduced to d. Note that $W^u(b)$ and $W^s(c)$ do not meet.

The Height on the "Other" Sphere.

From Figure 2.13, the readers will be able to determine the stable and unstable manifolds of the four critical points of the height function (for the gradient of the metric induced by that on $\mathbf{R}^3$).

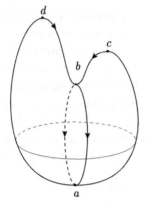

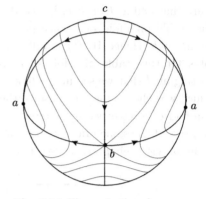

Fig. 2.13 The other sphere

Fig. 2.14 The projective plane

The Morse Function on $\mathbf{P}^2(\mathbf{R})$.

Figure 2.14, in turn, shows the stable and unstable manifolds of the three critical points a (minimum), b (index 1) and c (maximum) for the function considered before (in Exercise 6 on p. 19) on the real projective plane $\mathbf{P}^2(\mathbf{R})$.

2.2.b The Smale Condition

We say that a pseudo-gradient field adapted to the Morse function f satisfies the *Smale condition* if all stable and unstable manifolds of its critical points meet transversally, that is, if

$$\text{for all critical points } a, b \text{ of } f, \quad W^u(a) \pitchfork W^s(b).$$

Remark 2.2.1. Certain stable and unstable manifolds always meet transversally. For example, we always have:

- $W^u(a) \pitchfork W^s(a)$ (for the same critical point), which is what we see in a Morse chart around a.
- $W^u(a) \cap W^s(b) = \varnothing$ if a and b are distinct and $f(a) \leq f(b)$ (in particular, these stable and unstable manifolds are transversal).

If the vector field satisfies the Smale condition, then for all critical points a and b, we have

$$\text{codim}(W^u(a) \cap W^s(b)) = \text{codim}\, W^u(a) + \text{codim}\, W^s(b),$$

that is,

$$\dim(W^u(a) \cap W^s(b)) = \text{Ind}(a) - \text{Ind}(b).$$

Under our condition, this intersection is a submanifold of V, which we will denote by $\mathcal{M}(a, b)$. It consists of all points on the trajectories connecting a to b:

$$\mathcal{M}(a, b) = \left\{ x \in V \mid \lim_{s \to -\infty} \varphi^s(x) = a \text{ and } \lim_{s \to +\infty} \varphi^s(x) = b \right\}.$$

Proposition 2.2.2. *The group* $\mathbf{R}$ *of translations in time acts on* $\mathcal{M}(a, b)$ *by* $s \cdot x = \varphi^s(x)$. *This action is free if* $a \neq b$.

Proof. The fact that this is a group operation is clear. If $a \neq b$, then there is no critical point in $\mathcal{M}(a, b)$. Let $x \in \mathcal{M}(a, b)$. Since x is not a critical point, we know that $f(\varphi^s(x))$ is a decreasing function of s, so that if $\varphi^s(x) = \varphi^{s'}(x)$, we necessarily have $s = s'$. Hence the action is free. $\square$

The quotient is therefore a manifold, which we will call $\mathcal{L}(a, b)$. Its dimension is

$$\dim \mathcal{L}(a, b) = \operatorname{Ind}(a) - \operatorname{Ind}(b) - 1.$$

Remark 2.2.3. It is clear that the quotient is a separated space. In fact, the most convenient way to consider this quotient is the following. If α is a value of f lying between $f(a)$ and $f(b)$, then $\mathcal{M}(a, b)$ is transversal to the level set $f^{-1}(\alpha)$: this level set has codimension 1 and the vector field X is transversal to it (by definition, it is not tangent to the level set, or we would have $df(X) = 0$ at a noncritical point). All trajectories starting at a meet this intermediate level set at exactly one point, so that $\mathcal{L}(a, b)$ can be identified with $\mathcal{M}(a, b) \cap f^{-1}(\alpha)$.

Hence, if a and b are two (distinct) critical points and if the gradient that is used satisfies the Smale condition, then for $\mathcal{M}(a, b)$ or $\mathcal{L}(a, b)$ to be nonempty, we must have

$$\operatorname{Ind}(a) > \operatorname{Ind}(b).$$

In other words, the index decreases along the gradient lines.

We will come back to these spaces at length in the next chapter.

Examples 2.2.4. All examples presented above satisfy the Smale condition,[2] except for that of the height function on the torus. Indeed, the manifolds $W^s(b)$ and $W^u(c)$ are not transversal, as we have already noted without knowing the example in Subsection 2.2.a and Figure 2.10. Moreover, we have trajectories connecting two critical points of index 1, which, as we just saw, is forbidden. This "bad" vector field is the gradient for the Riemannian metric on the torus induced by the surrounding Euclidean metric.

---

[2] In the cases of the "other sphere" and of the projective plane, this holds, for example, by virtue of Exercise 11 (p. 51).

The Smale condition forbids the existence of flow lines such as those shown in Figure 2.15. Figure 2.16 shows the trajectories of a neighboring field satisfying the Smale condition (obtained by the general method explained in the following subsection).

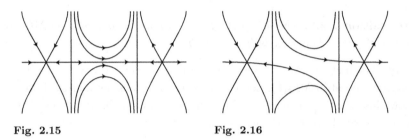

Fig. 2.15   Fig. 2.16

2.2.c Existence

Following [72], let us now show the existence and genericness of pseudo-gradient fields satisfying the Smale condition.

We first note that after replacing f by another function that is arbitrarily close in the $\mathcal{C}^1$ sense, if necessary, we may, and do, assume that f takes on distinct values at all of its critical points. Indeed, outside of Ω, we have (by compactness) $df(X) < -\varepsilon_0$ for some $\varepsilon_0 > 0$. We then choose a function h that is constant on each Morse chart Ω_i, satisfies $|dh| < \frac{1}{2}\varepsilon_0$ and for which

$$f(c_i) + h(c_i) \neq f(c_j) + h(c_j) \quad \text{for } i \neq j.$$

The function $f+h$ is still a Morse function, with the same critical points as f, and the vector field X is still an adapted pseudo-gradient, but the critical values are now distinct.

Theorem 2.2.5 (Smale Theorem [72]). *Let V be a manifold with boundary and let f be a Morse function on V with distinct critical values. We fix Morse charts in the neighborhood of each critical point of f. Let Ω be the union of these charts and let X be a pseudo-gradient field on V that is transversal to the boundary. Then there exists a pseudo-gradient field X' that is close to X (in the $\mathcal{C}^1$ sense), equals X on Ω and for which we have*

$$W_{X'}^s(a) \pitchfork W_{X'}^u(b)$$

for all critical points a, b of f.

Let us clarify the notion of $\mathcal{C}^1$ *proximity* used here: the statement asserts that for every $\varepsilon > 0$, for every cover of V by charts $\varphi_i(U_i)$ and for every compact subset $K_i \subset U_i$, there exists a vector field X' such that

$$\|T\varphi_i^{-1}(X') - T\varphi_i^{-1}(X)\| < \varepsilon$$

for the $\mathcal{C}^1$ norm on K_i, as well as the stated properties.

Remark 2.2.6. A vector field X' sufficiently close to the pseudo-gradient field X in the $\mathcal{C}^1$ sense and equal to X on Ω is itself a pseudo-gradient field. For the sake of simplicity, we will call such an X' a "good approximation" of X.

Remark 2.2.7. This theorem is sometimes called the "Kupka–Smale" theorem because Kupka also gave a proof. The one we imitate here is Smale's proof.

Proof of Theorem 2.2.5. Since the critical values of f are distinct, let us arrange them in order:

$$\mathrm{Crit}(f) = \{c_1, \ldots, c_q\} \quad \text{with } f(c_1) > f(c_2) > \cdots > f(c_q),$$

and let $\alpha_i = f(c_i)$. The proof of the theorem will use an induction based on the following lemma.

Lemma 2.2.8. *Let $j \in \{1, \ldots, q\}$ and let $\varepsilon > 0$. There exists a good approximation X' (in the $\mathcal{C}^1$ sense) of X such that:*

(1) *The vector field X' coincides with X on the complement of $f^{-1}([\alpha_j + \varepsilon, \alpha_j + 2\varepsilon])$ in V.*
(2) *The stable manifold of c_j (for X') is transversal to the unstable manifolds of all critical points, that is,*

$$W_{X'}^s(c_j) \pitchfork W_{X'}^u(c_i).$$

Let us (for the time being) admit the lemma and prove the theorem. We let $\mathcal{P}(r)$ denote the following property: there exists a good approximation X_r' of X such that for every $p \leq r$ and every i, we have

$$W_{X_r'}^s(c_p) \pitchfork W_{X_r'}^u(c_i).$$

Note that:

- Property $\mathcal{P}(q)$ is exactly the theorem.

- Property $\mathcal{P}(1)$ is true for a trivial reason: the critical point c_1 is the maximum of f and its stable manifold is reduced to itself, so that it does not meet any unstable manifold of any critical point lying below c_1.
- And Property $\mathcal{P}(2)$ follows from the lemma with $j = 2$.

Let us therefore assume that $\mathcal{P}(r-1)$ is true and show that $\mathcal{P}(r)$ is then also true. We have a vector field X'_{r-1} such that the stable manifold of c_{r-1} is transversal to all the unstable manifolds. We apply the lemma to the vector field X'_{r-1} and $j = r$. This gives a vector field X'_r that, in particular (this is the first property given by the lemma), coincides with X'_{r-1} outside of the narrow strip where $\alpha_r + \varepsilon \leq f \leq \alpha_r + 2\varepsilon$. Moreover, since for every $p \leq r-1$, the stable manifold of c_p for X'_{r-1} lies above this strip, the stable manifold is the same for X'_{r-1} as it is for X'_r (see Figure 2.17). We therefore have

$$W^s_{X'_{r-1}}(c_p) \cap W^u_{X'_{r-1}}(c_i) = W^s_{X'_r}(c_p) \cap W^u_{X'_r}(c_i)$$

for $p \leq r-1$ and for every i, so that

$$W^s_{X'_r}(c_p) \pitchfork W^u_{X'_r}(c_i).$$

For $p = r$, the lemma implies (this is the second property) that

$$W^s_{X'_r}(c_r) \pitchfork W^u_{X'_r}(c_i). \qquad \qquad \square$$

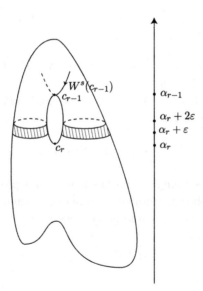

Fig. 2.17

Proof of Lemma 2.2.8. It can be useful to consider a Morse chart in the neighborhood of c_j. Figure 2.18 shows one (twice). We choose an ε sufficiently

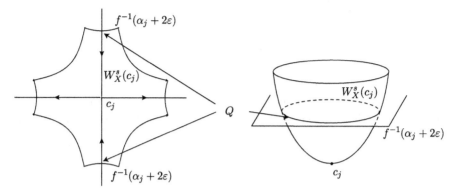

Fig. 2.18 In a Morse chart

small so that

$$\alpha_j + 2\varepsilon < \alpha_{j-1}.$$

Let k denote the index of c_j, and let $Q = W^s(c_j) \cap f^{-1}(\alpha_j + 2\varepsilon)$. Then Q is a sphere of dimension $n - k - 1$. We consider a tubular neighborhood of this sphere Q in $f^{-1}(\alpha_j + 2\varepsilon)$, of the form $Q \times D^k$, which we see in a Morse chart in Figure 2.18, and in Figure 2.19.

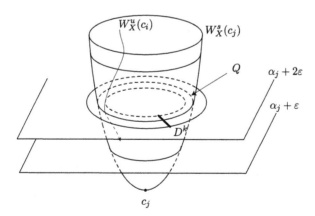

Fig. 2.19 In the manifold

Then there exists an embedding

$$\Psi : D^k \times Q \times [0, m] \longrightarrow f^{-1}(]\alpha_j + \varepsilon, \alpha_j + 2\varepsilon[)$$

such that:

- Ψ restricted to $\{0\} \times Q \times \{0\}$ is the embedding of Q in $f^{-1}(\alpha_j + \varepsilon)$.
- Ψ restricted to $\{0\} \times Q \times \{m\}$ is the embedding of Q in $f^{-1}(\alpha_j + 2\varepsilon)$.
- If z is the coordinate in $[0, m] \subset \mathbf{R}$, then

$$\Psi_\star \left(-\frac{\partial}{\partial z} \right) = X.$$

The unstable manifolds are transversal to the level sets. In particular, they meet $D^k \times Q$ along a manifold P' (that is not connected in general). If $W_X^s(c_j) \pitchfork P'$, then there is nothing to prove. The proof will therefore consist in modifying X into X' on $f^{-1}(]\alpha_j + \varepsilon, \alpha_j + 2\varepsilon[)$ in such a way that

$$W_{X'}^s(c_j) \pitchfork P'.$$

The modification will take place inside the image of Ψ. Let us therefore position ourselves in $D^k \times Q \times [0, m]$ with $X = -\partial/\partial z$. Figure 2.19 shows what happens in the manifold, while Figure 2.20 shows the model.

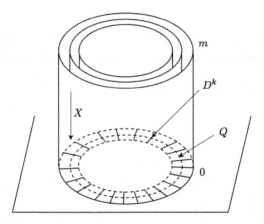

Fig. 2.20 The model

Let P be the submanifold $\Psi^{-1}(P') \subset D^k \times Q \times [0, m]$. As seen in the model, the desired transversality condition $W_{X'}^s(c_j) \pitchfork P'$ can be written as

$$W_{X'}^s \pitchfork P \quad \text{with } W_{X'}^s = \left\{ \phi_{X'}^{-s}(0, q, 0) \mid s > 0, \ q \in Q \right\}.$$

In the initial situation, $X' = X = -\partial/\partial z$, so that

$$P \cap W_X^s = P \cap \{(0, q, s) \mid s > 0, \ q \in Q\} = P \cap \{(0, q, 0) \mid q \in Q\} = g^{-1}(0),$$

where $g : P \to D^k$ is the projection $(x, q, z) \mapsto x$.

The proof will consist in making 0 a regular value of g. By Sard's theorem, there is a vector w in D^k, as close to 0 as we want (say $\|w\| = \delta$), such that w is a regular value of g. We are going to construct a perturbation X' of the vector field X such that

$$W^s_{X'} \cap \{z = m\} = \phi^{-m}_{X'}(0, q, 0) = (w, q, m).$$

We will then have $W^s_{X'} \cap P = g^{-1}(w)$, which implies that $W^s_{X'} \cap P$ is a submanifold of codimension k in P. The equality

$$\operatorname{codim}_P W^s_{X'} \cap P = \operatorname{codim}_V W^s_{X'}$$

implies the transversality of the two submanifolds $W^s_{X'}$ and P.

The lemma "in the manifold" now results from the following lemma "in the model".

Lemma 2.2.9. *There exists a vector field X' close to $-\partial/\partial z$ (in the $\mathcal{C}^1$ sense) such that:*

(1) $X' = -\partial/\partial z$ *near* $\partial(D^k \times Q \times [0, m])$.
(2) $\varphi^{-m}_{X'}(0, q, 0) = (w, q, m)$.

Proof. Let $(v_1, \ldots, v_k)$ be the coordinates of $w \in D^k$. We set

$$X' = -\frac{\partial}{\partial z} - \sum_{i=1}^{k} \beta_i(z)\gamma(x)\frac{\partial}{\partial x_i},$$

where:

- The function β_i is zero outside of $[0, m]$ and satisfies $|\beta_i(s)| < \eta$, $|\beta'_i(s)| < \eta$ and $\int_0^m \beta_i(t)\, dt = v_i$ (where η is a small fixed positive number corresponding to the desired precision of the approximation).
- The function γ is, in turn, defined on D^k, has values in $[0, 1]$, is identically zero near ∂D^k and satisfies $\gamma \equiv 1$ on $\|x\| \leq 1/3$ and $|\partial\gamma/\partial x_i| \leq 2$.

See Figures 2.21 and 2.22.

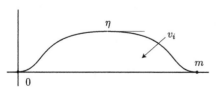

Fig. 2.21 The function β_i

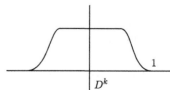

Fig. 2.22 The function γ

It is clear that the vector field X' satisfies the first stated property. To prove that it also satisfies the second one, we first consider the vector field

$$X'' = -\frac{\partial}{\partial z} - \sum_{i=1}^{k} \beta_i(z) \frac{\partial}{\partial x_i}$$

(we have left out $\gamma(x)$). To determine $\varphi_{X''}^{-m}(0, q, 0)$, we must solve the differential system

$$\begin{cases} \dfrac{\partial x_i}{\partial s} = -\beta_i(z(s)), & x(0) = 0 \\[2mm] \dfrac{\partial q}{\partial s} = 0, & q(0) = q \\[2mm] \dfrac{\partial z}{\partial s} = -1, & z(0) = 0 \end{cases}$$

whose solution is

$$\begin{cases} x_i(s) = \displaystyle\int_0^s -\beta_i(-t)\, dt = \int_0^{-s} \beta_i(-t)\, dt \\[2mm] q(s) = q \\[2mm] z(s) = -s. \end{cases}$$

We therefore have

$$\varphi_{X''}^{-m}(0, q, 0) = (w, q, m)$$

and, since for $s \in [-m, 0]$, the norm satisfies $\|x(s)\| \leq 1/3$ (for sufficiently small β_i, that is, for sufficiently small w), we remain in the part of the disk where $\gamma \equiv 1$, so that the formula indeed gives the flow of X'.   □

This completes the proof of Lemma 2.2.8.   □

2.2.d An Illustration, the Height Function on the Torus

Let us return to the example of the height function on the torus of dimension 2, with gradient field X that does not satisfy the Smale property, as noted in Examples 2.2.4. We first copy Figures 2.10 and 2.11, indicating the two level sets for $\alpha + \varepsilon$ and $\alpha + 2\varepsilon$ above the critical point b between which we need to modify the vector field.

A Morse neighborhood of the critical point b is clearly visible in the middle of Figure 2.24. We extract it from this figure (Figure 2.25) and modify the vector field in the useful part of the model (Figure 2.26). This last figure shows the same model as Figure 2.20, namely a $Q \times D^k \times [0, m]$, but Q is now a sphere of dimension $n - k - 1 = 0$ and D^k is a disk of dimension $k = 1$.

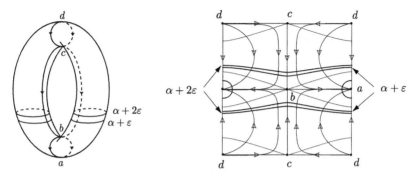

Fig. 2.23

Fig. 2.24

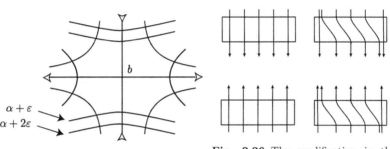

Fig. 2.25 Extract of the model

Fig. 2.26 The modification in the model

Put back into the surface, the modification gives a vector field with the expected property (Figure 2.27).

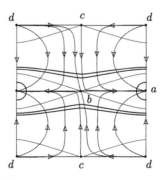

Fig. 2.27 The modified field

2.3 Appendix: Classification of the Compact Manifolds of Dimension 1

2.3.a Morse Functions and Adapted Vector Fields on a Manifold with Boundary

Let us now consider a manifold with boundary V. We fix a vector field X defined in a neighborhood of ∂V in V, which we assume to be *incoming*, that is, such that for every chart $\varphi : U \to V$ (where U is an open subset of the half-space $x_n \leq 0$ in $\mathbf{R}^n$) and every $x \in \partial V \cap \varphi(U)$, we have

$$T_{\varphi^{-1}(x)}\varphi^{-1}(X_x) = \sum_{i=1}^{n} a_i \frac{\partial}{\partial x_i} \quad \text{with } a_n(\varphi^{-1}(x)) < 0.$$

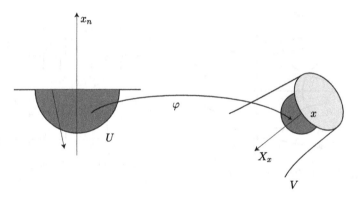

Fig. 2.28 Incoming vector field

Constructing such a vector field is easy, for example by starting out with the vector field $-\partial/\partial x_n$ on $\mathbf{R}^n$ and using a partition of unity.

We can also construct a Morse function f on V such that

$$df(X) < 0 \quad \text{in the neighborhood of } \partial V$$

by first defining it in the neighborhood of the boundary, setting

$$f(\varphi_X^{-s}(x)) = s \quad \text{for } s \in [0, \delta[\text{ if } x \in \partial V,$$

then extending it arbitrarily to V and finally taking a perturbation, if necessary, in order to have a Morse function.

Next, we extend X, which up to now has only been defined in the neighborhood of the boundary, to a pseudo-gradient field adapted to f that we will still call X.

Remark 2.3.1. It is not true that every Morse function on a manifold with boundary admits a pseudo-gradient field transversal to the boundary (think of the projection of the unit disk onto a straight line). That is why in this construction we have chosen to start out with the vector field.

2.3.b The Classification Theorem

Theorem 2.3.2. *Let V be a compact connected manifold of dimension 1. Then V is diffeomorphic to S^1 if $\partial V = \varnothing$ and diffeomorphic to $[0,1]$ otherwise.*

Proof. Let X be a vector field that is incoming along the boundary, let f be a Morse function for which X is an adapted pseudo-gradient field (we can construct such a vector field and such a function as indicated above). The critical points of f are local minima and maxima. The proof is based on the fact that all trajectories that are not stationary at a maximum end up at a minimum. Let $c_1, \ldots, c_k$ be the minima of f. The stable manifold $W^s(c_i)$ is diffeomorphic to an (open) interval; it consists of the two trajectories ending at c_i and the point c_i itself. In the closure A_i of this stable manifold there are (moreover) the starting points of these two trajectories. These starting points:

- either are both maxima (in which case they can either coincide or not)
- or at least one of them is a boundary point of V (in which case they are distinct).

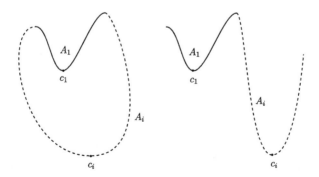

Fig. 2.29

It is also clear that, as the closure of a connected space, A_i is connected. Clearly, if A_i consists of $W^s(c_i)$ and a unique point, then the latter is a maximum and A_i is diffeomorphic to a circle. Likewise, if A_i consists of the stable manifold and two added points, then A_i is diffeomorphic to a closed interval.

Note that the union of the A_i is all of V: if $x \in V$, then its trajectory tends to a minimum and lies in one of the stable manifolds, unless x is a maximum, but then it lies in the closure of a stable manifold.

If $k = 1$, then the theorem has now been proved. Otherwise, since V is connected, there exists an $i \geq 2$ such that $A_1 \cap A_i \neq \varnothing$. This intersection contains only local maxima, since these are the only points from which we can descend to two different minima. In particular, $\partial V \cap (A_1 \cap A_i) = \varnothing$. In $A_1 \cap A_i$, there are at most two points. We have two possibilities:

- If this intersection contains two points, then the two are maxima, $A_1 \cup A_i$ is diffeomorphic to S^1 and we are done.
- If, on the contrary, it contains only one point, then $A_1 \cup A_i$ is diffeomorphic to $[0, 1]$. If $A_1 \cup A_i = V$, then we are done.

And if this is not the case, then we continue adding A_i's until they run out.   □

There exist other ways to prove this theorem, which may be simpler (see [55]). This proof using Morse theory has the advantage of preparing other, analogous, proofs, such as that of Proposition 4.5.1.

2.3.c An Application, the Brouwer Fixed Point Theorem

We will now use Sard's theorem and our knowledge of manifolds of dimension 1 to prove Brouwer's famous theorem (this proof comes from Milnor's book [55]).

Theorem 2.3.3. *Let* $\varphi : D^n \to D^n$ *be a continuous map; then it has a fixed point.*

Proof. The first part of the proof consists in reducing to the case where φ is a $\mathcal{C}^\infty$ map. We will not give the details here (see [45]). Next, starting from φ, which is assumed to be $\mathcal{C}^\infty$ and without fixed points, we construct a retraction

$$r : D^n \longrightarrow S^{n-1}$$

by sending $x \in D^n$ to the intersection point of the sphere S^{n-1} and the ray starting at $\varphi(x)$ and going through x. This way, if x is a point of the sphere, it stays in place. We thus have a $\mathcal{C}^\infty$ map r that restricts to the identity on the boundary. Sard's theorem asserts that this map has regular values. Let

$a \in S^{n-1}$ be one of them; then $r^{-1}(a)$ is a submanifold of dimension 1 of D^n, with boundary

$$\partial r^{-1}(a) = r^{-1}(a) \cap \partial D^n = \{a\}.$$

But a manifold of dimension 1 with boundary is diffeomorphic to a union of circles and closed intervals, so that its boundary consists of an even number of points. This gives a contradiction, and therefore the existence of a fixed point.   □

Exercises

Exercise 10. Show that the vector fields whose flows are drawn in Figure 2.30 are not pseudo-gradient fields.

Fig. 2.30

Exercise 11. Let V be a manifold of dimension 2 endowed with a Morse function with a unique critical point of index 1. Show that every pseudo-gradient field adapted to this function satisfies the Smale condition.

Exercise 12. We fix an integer $m \geq 2$. Find all critical points of the function $f : \mathbf{P}^1(\mathbf{C}) \to \mathbf{R}$ defined by

$$f([z_0, z_1]) = \frac{|z_0^m + z_1^m|^2}{(|z_0|^2 + |z_1|^2)^m} = \frac{|z^m + 1|^2}{(|z|^2 + 1)^m}$$

(in homogeneous coordinates or in the affine chart $z_1 \neq 0$). Verify that for $m = 2$, the function f is not a Morse function.[3]

We suppose that $m \geq 3$. Show that f is a Morse function and has two local maxima: the points 0 and ∞; m local minima: the m-th roots of -1; and m critical points of index 1: the m-th roots of 1.

---

[3] It is a Mores–Bott function (see [14]): its critical points form submanifolds (here $\mathbf{P}^1(\mathbf{R})$ for the maximum) and the second-order derivative is transversally nondegenerate.

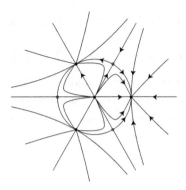

Fig. 2.31

Hint: We can determine the critical points using the derivatives with respect to z and $\overline{z}$, and then use a second-order Taylor expansion of $f(u)$ with respect to u in the neighborhood of 0 (to study the critical points at 0 and ∞) or the analogous expansion of $f(\zeta(1 + u))$ (to study the critical points at ζ with $\zeta^m = \pm 1$).

Show that there exists a pseudo-gradient field such as that shown (in an affine chart) in Figure 2.31 (for $m = 3$). More generally, see the article [9] in which an analogous function (defined on $\mathbf{P}^n(\mathbf{C})$) plays an important role.

Chapter 3
The Morse Complex

In this chapter, we consider a compact manifold V endowed with a Morse function f and a generic (that is, satisfying the Smale condition) pseudo-gradient field X. For every integer k, we let $C_k(f)$ be the vector space over $\mathbf{Z}/2$ generated by the critical points of index k of f. We will simply denote this by C_k when there is no risk of confusion. Using the connections between critical points established by the trajectories of X, we define maps

$$\partial_X : C_k \longrightarrow C_{k-1}.$$

We also show that

$$\partial_X \circ \partial_X : C_{k+1} \longrightarrow C_{k-1}$$

is the zero map, so that $(C_\star(f), \partial_X)$ is a complex of vector spaces over $\mathbf{Z}/2$, whose homology is

$$H_k(C_\star(f), \partial_X) = \mathrm{Ker}\, \partial_X / \mathrm{Im}\, \partial_X = H_k(f, X).$$

Finally, we show that even though the complex itself depends on the choices of f and X, its homology does not (for those who know what this is, it is in fact the modulo 2 homology of V).

See Section B.1 for the definitions and basic properties of the objects used here.

3.1 Definition of the Complex

We define the vector space

$$C_k(f) = \left\{ \sum_{c \in \mathrm{Crit}_k(f)} a_c c \mid a_c \in \mathbf{Z}/2 \right\},$$

where $\mathrm{Crit}_k(f)$ of course denotes the set of critical points of index k of f.

M. Audin, M. Damian, *Morse Theory and Floer Homology*,
Universitext, DOI 10.1007/978-1-4471-5496-9_3,
© Springer-Verlag London 2014

3.1.a The Differential

In order to define ∂_X on $C_k(f)$, it suffices to know how to define $\partial_X(a)$ for a critical point a of index k. This must be a linear combination of the critical points of index $k - 1$:

$$\partial_X(a) = \sum_{b \in \mathrm{Crit}_{k-1}} n_X(a, b)b, \quad \text{with } n_X(a, b) \in \mathbf{Z}/2.$$

The idea is to define $n_X(a, b)$ as the number (modulo 2) of trajectories of X going from a to b, that is, as the cardinal of $\mathcal{L}(a, b)$. We will show in Section 3.2 that this number is indeed finite.

3.1.b It Is a Complex

A complex[1] is a family $(C_\star)_{\star=1,\ldots,n}$ of vector spaces[2] connected by linear maps

$$\partial^k : C_k \longrightarrow C_{k-1}$$

satisfying $\partial^k \circ \partial^{k+1} = 0$. Consequently, the image of ∂^{k+1} is contained in the kernel of ∂^k and the quotient

$$H_k = \mathrm{Ker}\, \partial^k / \mathrm{Im}\, \partial^{k+1},$$

which measures the nonexactness of the complex, is a vector space called the *homology of the complex* (in degree k).

To prove that we are indeed dealing with a complex, we must verify that $\partial_X \circ \partial_X = 0$. Since

$$\partial_X \circ \partial_X(a) = \sum_{b \in \mathrm{Crit}_{k-1}} \left(\sum_{c \in \mathrm{Crit}_k} n_X(a, c) n_X(c, b) \right) b$$

(for $a \in \mathrm{Crit}_{k+1}$), it suffices to prove that given two critical points, a of index $k + 1$ and b of index $k - 1$, the sum

$$\sum_{c \in \mathrm{Crit}_k} n_X(a, c) n_X(c, b)$$

is zero. This number equals the cardinal of the disjoint union

$$\coprod_{c \in \mathrm{Crit}_k(f)} \mathcal{L}(a, c) \times \mathcal{L}(c, b).$$

---

[1] For this algebraic formalism, see Section B.1 and the references given there.
[2] Here we use vector spaces over $\mathbf{Z}/2$; the correct general notion uses modules over a commutative ring, which includes the case of abelian groups. See Section 3.3.

This idea is therefore to prove that this set of points (which we will have shown to be finite) is the boundary of a manifold of dimension 1.

Figure 3.1 gives a heuristic argument making this result seem plausible. It shows the unstable manifold of a, which consists of the trajectories connecting a to b (this figure is one fourth of Figure 2.12). The set of these trajectories must be a manifold of dimension 1 (represented on the right in the figure), a union of open intervals that can be compactified by adding "broken" trajectories through the points c_1, c_2 with intermediate indices, giving closed intervals or circles. The property results from the fact that the manifolds of dimension 1 with boundary have a boundary consisting of an even number of points, as we saw in Theorem 2.3.2 (and we are computing modulo 2).

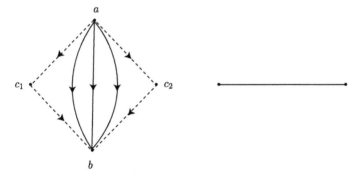

Fig. 3.1

To make this rigorous, we will need a compactness result (established in Section 3.2.b) and a precise description of the boundary, namely the fact that the set of connections from c to e can indeed by compactified by adding the broken trajectories (see Section 3.2.c).

3.1.c Examples

Let us return to the examples of Morse functions with generic pseudo-gradients given in Section 2.2.a (with the notation of that section).

The Height on the Round Sphere.

In this case, $C_0 = \mathbf{Z}/2$, with generator a, $C_1 = 0$ and $C_2 = \mathbf{Z}/2$, with generator b. The homology is

$$H_\star = \begin{cases} 0 & \text{if } \star \neq 0, 2 \\ \mathbf{Z}/2 & \text{for } \star = 0, 2. \end{cases}$$

The same computation with the height function on the unit sphere S^n in $\mathbf{R}^{n+1}$, which, again, has only a minimum and a maximum, gives

$$H_\star = \begin{cases} 0 & \text{if } \star \neq 0, n \\ \mathbf{Z}/2 & \text{for } \star = 0, n. \end{cases}$$

The Height on the Other Sphere.

This time, $C_0 = \mathbf{Z}/2$, with generator a, $C_1 = \mathbf{Z}/2$, with generator b and $C_2 = \mathbf{Z}/2 \oplus \mathbf{Z}/2$, with generators c and d. By counting the trajectories connecting the critical points naively, we find

$$\partial c = b, \quad \partial d = b, \quad \partial b = 2a = 0,$$

so that

$$\begin{cases} H_0 = \mathbf{Z}/2 \\ H_1 = 0 \\ H_2 = \mathbf{Z}/2. \end{cases}$$

Even though the complex is quite different, its homology is the same.

The Torus.

Let us now consider the function $\cos(2\pi x) + \cos(2\pi y)$ on the torus. We have $C_0 = \mathbf{Z}/2$, with generator a, $C_1 = \mathbf{Z}/2 \oplus \mathbf{Z}/2$, with generators b and c and $C_2 = \mathbf{Z}/2$, with generator d. The differentials are

$$\partial d = 2b + 2c = 0, \quad \partial b = \partial c = 2a = 0.$$

Hence the homology modulo 2 is

$$\begin{cases} H_0 = \mathbf{Z}/2 \\ H_1 = \mathbf{Z}/2 \oplus \mathbf{Z}/2 \\ H_2 = \mathbf{Z}/2 \end{cases}$$

(which is indeed the homology of the torus T^2). The readers should prove that the complex associated with the height function and the vector field described by Figure 2.27 has the same homology.

The Complex Projective Space.

This time, there are only critical points with even index, one in each dimension. The C_k are $\mathbf{Z}/2$ if k is even and at most $2n$ and 0 otherwise. All the differentials are zero and the homology of the complex is

$$H_\star = \begin{cases} \mathbf{Z}/2 & \text{if } \star = 2k \text{ with } k \le n, \\ 0 & \text{otherwise.} \end{cases}$$

The Real Projective Plane.

Now $C_0 = \mathbf{Z}/2$, with generator a, $C_1 = \mathbf{Z}/2$, with generator b and $C_2 = \mathbf{Z}/2$, with generator c. We have $\partial c = 0$ and $\partial b = 0$, so that

$$H_\star = \begin{cases} \mathbf{Z}/2 & \text{if } 0 \le \star \le 2 \\ 0 & \text{otherwise.} \end{cases}$$

We will show (this is Remark 4.1.2) that the homology of the complex only depends on the diffeomorphism type of the manifold. In particular, from the examples given above we deduce the following corollaries.

Corollary 3.1.1. *The complex projective space of (complex) dimension $n \ge 2$ is not diffeomorphic to the sphere S^{2n}.*

Corollary 3.1.2. *The sphere S^2, the torus T^2 and the real projective plane $\mathbf{P}^2(\mathbf{R})$ have distinct diffeomorphism types.*

3.2 The Space of Connections Between Two Critical Points, or of "Broken Trajectories"

3.2.a The Space of Broken Trajectories

If a and b are two critical points of f, then we let $\mathcal{L}(a,b)$ denote the set of trajectories of the vector field X that go from a to b. We define the set of broken trajectories from a to b as follows:

$$\overline{\mathcal{L}}(a,b) = \bigcup_{c_i \in \mathrm{Crit}(f)} \mathcal{L}(a,c_1) \times \cdots \times \mathcal{L}(c_{q-1},b).$$

Let us recall that the index is decreasing along the trajectories of X; hence only the $\mathcal{L}(c_i, c_{i+1})$ with $\mathrm{Ind}(c_i) > \mathrm{Ind}(c_{i+1})$ contribute.

As is suggested by the notation, this space is meant to be a compactification of $\mathcal{L}(a,b)$. The first thing to do is to endow it with a topology. This will of course need to induce the product topology on each term of the union. In the example described by Figure 3.1, $\mathcal{L}(a,b)$ is an open interval and $\mathcal{L}(a,c_1)$

and $\mathcal{L}(c_1, b)$ are points, as are $\mathcal{L}(a, c_2)$ and $\mathcal{L}(c_2, b)$. We of course hope to endow the space $\overline{\mathcal{L}}(a, b)$ with a topology that makes it a closed interval. See Figure 3.2.

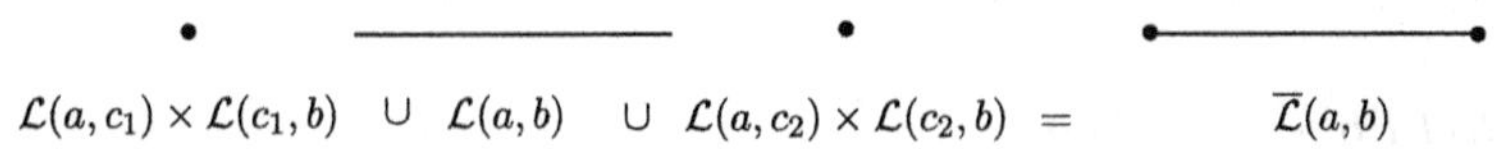

$$\mathcal{L}(a, c_1) \times \mathcal{L}(c_1, b) \quad \cup \quad \mathcal{L}(a, b) \quad \cup \quad \mathcal{L}(a, c_2) \times \mathcal{L}(c_2, b) \quad = \qquad \overline{\mathcal{L}}(a, b)$$

Fig. 3.2

Therefore let $\lambda = (\lambda_1, \ldots, \lambda_q)$ be a broken trajectory. It connects a certain number of critical points. Each of these admits a Morse neighborhood that we denote by $\Omega(c_i)$. The trajectory λ_i exits $\Omega(c_{i-1})$ to enter $\Omega(c_i)$. Let U_{i-1}^- be a neighborhood of the exit point of Ω_{i-1} contained in its level set and likewise, let U_i^+ be a neighborhood of the entry point in Ω_i contained in its level set. See Figure 3.3.

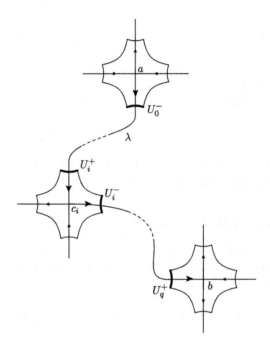

Fig. 3.3

We let $\mathbf{U}^-$ (or $\mathbf{U}^+$) denote the collection of U_i^- (or of U_i^+) respectively, and we say that $\mu = (\mu_1, \ldots, \mu_k) \in \mathcal{W}(\lambda, \mathbf{U}^-, \mathbf{U}^+)$ if there exist integers

$$0 < i_0 < \cdots < i_{k-1} < i_k = q$$

such that:

- $\mu_j \in \mathcal{L}(c_{i_j}, c_{i_{j+1}})$ for every $j \leq k$.
- μ_j exits the charts $\Omega(c_{i_j}), \Omega(c_{i_j+1}), \dots, \Omega(c_{i_{j+1}-1})$ through the interiors of the corresponding U^- and enters the charts $\Omega(c_{i_j+1}), \dots, \Omega(c_{i_{j+1}})$ through the interiors of the U^+.

The $\mathcal{W}(\lambda, \mathbf{U}^-, \mathbf{U}^+)$ form a fundamental system of open neighborhoods for a topology on $\overline{\mathcal{L}}(a, b)$.

Remarks 3.2.1. In this definition, $k \leq q$ (the trajectory μ does not have more components than λ). Moreover, if λ is a trajectory of X going from a to b, then a fundamental system of open neighborhoods of λ is given by the set of trajectories connecting a to b that leave Ω_0 and enter Ω_q sufficiently close to λ. It is clear that the resulting topology coincides with the topology on $\mathcal{L}(a, b)$ (defined earlier as the quotient of the set of points on the trajectories by the translations).

3.2.b Compactness

We now prove the following result.

Theorem 3.2.2. *The space $\overline{\mathcal{L}}(a, b)$ is compact.*

Remark 3.2.3. The topology on the space $\overline{\mathcal{L}}(a, b)$ is defined using the topology on V. It is therefore clear that it admits a countable fundamental system of open neighborhoods and it is justifiable to prove the compactness using sequences (it is moreover metrizable). The purists will also note that the only part of the compactness of this space that we will use is this property of the sequences.

Corollary 3.2.4. *If* $\mathrm{Ind}(a) = \mathrm{Ind}(b) + 1$, *then the space* $\mathcal{L}(a, b)$ *is a finite set of trajectories.*

Hence $n_X(a, b) \in \mathbf{Z}/2$ is well defined. This corollary is immediate: in this case $\overline{\mathcal{L}}(a, b) = \mathcal{L}(a, b)$ and the latter, which is a manifold of dimension 0, is now compact. $\qquad\qquad\square$

Proof of Theorem 3.2.2. Let (ℓ_n) be a sequence of trajectories in $\overline{\mathcal{L}}(a, b)$.

We begin by assuming that $\ell_n \in \mathcal{L}(a, b)$. The trajectory ℓ_n exits $\Omega(a)$ through a point ℓ_n^- and enters $\Omega(b)$ through a point ℓ_n^+. The point ℓ_n^- is in the intersection of the unstable manifold of a and the boundary of $\Omega(a)$, which is a sphere, and therefore compact. After extracting a subsequence, if necessary, we may, and do, therefore assume that

$$\lim \ell_n^- = a^- \quad \text{and} \quad \lim \ell_n^+ = b^+.$$

Let $\gamma(t) = \varphi_X^t(a^-)$ be the trajectory of a^- and let $c_1 = \lim_{t\to+\infty}\gamma(t)$, so that c_1 is a critical point and $\gamma \in \mathcal{L}(a, c_1)$. Let d^+ be the entry point of γ in $\Omega(c_1)$ (Figure 3.4). By the theorem on the dependence of the solutions of differential equations on the initial conditions, ℓ_n must also (at least for n sufficiently large) enter $\Omega(c_1)$, through a point d_n^+. We have $\lim d_n^+ = d^+$ by the following lemma.

Lemma 3.2.5. *Let $x \in V - \mathrm{Crit}(f)$ and let (x_n) be a sequence that tends to x. Let y_n and y be points lying on the same trajectory of X as x_n and x, respectively. We moreover suppose that $f(y_n) = f(y)$. Then*

$$\lim_{n\to+\infty} y_n = y.$$

Proof. Let U be a neighborhood of $\mathrm{Crit}(f)$ that does not contain x, y, x_n, y_n (for n sufficiently large). As in the proof of Theorem 2.1.7, we consider the vector field

$$Y = -\frac{1}{df(X)} \cdot X$$

defined on $V - U$. Let ψ_t denote its flow. The trajectories of Y are the same as those of X and, moreover,

$$f(\psi_t(z)) = f(z) - t.$$

We then have

$$y_n = \psi_{-f(y_n)+f(x_n)}(x_n) = \psi_{-f(y)+f(x_n)}(x_n)$$

and

$$y = \psi_{-f(y)+f(x)}(x),$$

so that $\lim y_n = y$. $\square$

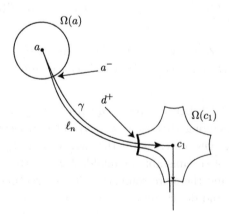

Fig. 3.4

If $c_1 = b$, then we consequently have $\lim \ell_n = \gamma$ and the sequence ℓ_n has a convergent subsequence. If this is not the case, then d_n^+ does not lie on the stable manifold of c_1, so that ℓ_n exits $\Omega(c_1)$ through a point d_n^-. We may, and do, assume that the sequence d_n^- converges to a point d^-. This point lies on the unstable manifold of c_1. If this were not the case, then d^- would be on the trajectory of a $d_\star$ with $f(d_\star) = f(d_n^+)$ that moreover is not in $W^s(c_1)$. By virtue of the previous lemma, d_n^+ tends to $d_\star$, so that $d_\star = d^+$, which is absurd since $d^+ \in W^s(c_1)$.

We are left to consider the general case of a sequence of elements of $\overline{\mathcal{L}}(a, b)$. There exist critical points $c_1, \ldots, c_{q-1}$ such that, for n sufficiently large and up to the extraction of a subsequence, we have

$$\ell_n = (\ell_n^1, \ldots, \ell_n^q) \in \mathcal{L}(a, c_1) \times \cdots \times \mathcal{L}(c_{q-1}, b).$$

We apply the previous result to ℓ_n^1, and then to $\ell_n^2, \ldots, \ell_n^q$.   □

Note that, as suggested by the notation, $\overline{\mathcal{L}}(a, b)$ is indeed a compactification of $\mathcal{L}(a, b)$, in the sense that there are elements of $\mathcal{L}(a, b)$ arbitrarily close to any element of $\overline{\mathcal{L}}(a, b)$. This is a consequence of the proposition below, which itself is a consequence of the arguments used in the proof of the compactness theorem (that is, the Cauchy–Lipschitz theorem).

Proposition 3.2.6. *Let* $\lambda = (\lambda_1, \lambda_2) \in \overline{\mathcal{L}}(a, b)$ *with* $\lambda_1 \in \mathcal{L}(a, c)$ *and* $\lambda_2 \in \mathcal{L}(c, b)$. *For every* $\mathbf{U}^-$, $\mathbf{U}^+$, *there exists an*

$$\ell \in \mathcal{L}(a, b) \cap \mathcal{W}(\lambda, \mathbf{U}^-, \mathbf{U}^+).$$ □

In the following subsection we will give more details on this proposition.

3.2.c The Structure of a Manifold with Boundary on the Space of Broken Trajectories

The following theorem implies that $\partial_X \circ \partial_X = 0$.

Theorem 3.2.7. *If* $\mathrm{Ind}(a) = \mathrm{Ind}(b) + 2$, *then* $\overline{\mathcal{L}}(a, b)$ *is a compact manifold of dimension 1 with boundary.*

We already know that $\mathcal{L}(a, b)$ is a manifold of dimension 1 (by applying the Smale condition). The theorem is therefore a consequence of the following proposition.

Proposition 3.2.8. *Let* V *be a compact manifold, let* $f : V \to \mathbf{R}$ *be a Morse function and let* X *be a pseudo-gradient for* f *satisfying the Smale property. Let* a, c *and* b *be three critical points of indices* $k + 1$, k *and* $k - 1$, *respectively. Let* $\lambda_1 \in \mathcal{L}(a,c)$ *and* $\lambda_2 \in \mathcal{L}(c,b)$. *There exists a continuous embedding* ψ *from an interval* $[0, \delta[$ *onto a neighborhood of* (λ_1, λ_2) *in* $\overline{\mathcal{L}}(a,b)$ *that is differentiable on* $]0, \delta[$ *and satisfies*

$$\begin{cases} \psi(0) = (\lambda_1, \lambda_2) \in \overline{\mathcal{L}}(a,b) \\ \psi(s) \in \mathcal{L}(a,b) \quad for \ s \neq 0. \end{cases}$$

Moreover, if (ℓ_n) *is a sequence in* $\mathcal{L}(a,b)$ *that tends to* (λ_1, λ_2), *then* ℓ_n *is contained in the image of* ψ *for* n *sufficiently large.*

Remark 3.2.9. The last assertion is essential for proving that (λ_1, λ_2) is a point on the boundary: there is only one branch arriving there.

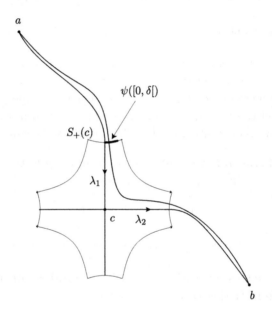

Fig. 3.5

Proof of Proposition 3.2.8. We set $f(c) = \alpha$ and we choose $\varepsilon > 0$ such that $f^{-1}(\alpha + \varepsilon)$ and $f^{-1}(\alpha - \varepsilon)$ meet the Morse chart $\Omega(c)$ along $\partial_+ \Omega(c)$ and $\partial_- \Omega(c)$, respectively. We use the notation defined before, namely

$$S_+(c) = W^s(c) \cap f^{-1}(\alpha + \varepsilon) \cong S^{n-k-1}$$
$$S_-(c) = W^u(c) \cap f^{-1}(\alpha - \varepsilon) \cong S^{k-1}.$$

Let $a_1 = S_+(c) \cap \lambda_1$. The unstable manifold $W^u(a)$ meets $f^{-1}(\alpha + \varepsilon)$ transversally along a submanifold P of dimension k. Since X satisfies the Smale property, P meets $S_+(c)$ transversally at a finite number of points including the point a_1. Let

$$D^k(\delta) = \{(x_1, \ldots, x_k) \mid \|x\| < \delta\}$$

and let $\Psi : (D^k(\delta), 0) \to (P, a_1)$ be a local parametrization of P such that

$$\mathrm{Im}\, \Psi \cap S_+(c) = \{a_1\}.$$

We may, and do, assume that $D = \mathrm{Im}\, \Psi$ is contained in $\partial_+\Omega(c)$. The disk D is shaded in Figure 3.6. By letting $D - \{a_1\}$ descend along the trajectories of X, we obtain an embedding

$$\Phi : D - \{a_1\} \longrightarrow \partial_-\Omega(c).$$

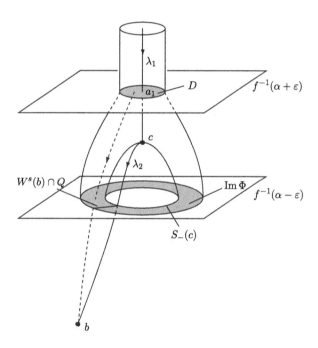

Fig. 3.6

The image of Φ is the shaded annulus shown in Figure 3.6 [3] (in this figure, $S_-(c)$ is the inner boundary of the shaded annulus). We have the following result.

Proposition 3.2.10. *After restricting the size of D, that is, after taking the restriction of Ψ to a disk with radius $\delta' < \delta$, if necessary, the union*

---

[3] This figure is the very core of the proof.

$Q = \mathrm{Im}\,\Phi \cup S_-(c)$ *is a manifold of dimension* k *with boundary, and its bound-ary is* $\partial Q = S_-(c)$.

This proposition allows us to conclude the proof of Proposition 3.2.8. The image of Φ is an open subset of the intersection of the unstable manifold of a and the level set $f^{-1}(\alpha - \varepsilon)$. Since X has the Smale property, we will therefore have

$$W^s(b) \pitchfork \mathrm{Im}\,\Phi$$

and we also have

$$W^s(b) \pitchfork S_-(c).$$

Consequently $W^s(b) \cap Q$ will be a submanifold of dimension 1 in $\partial_-\Omega(c) \subset f^{-1}(\alpha - \varepsilon)$, and its boundary is $W^s(b) \cap \partial Q = \mathcal{L}(c, b)$.

Let a_2 be the intersection point of λ_2 and $S_-(c)$ and let us define a parametrization

$$\chi : [0, \delta[\longrightarrow W^s(b) \cap Q$$

of this manifold with boundary: the point 0 is sent onto the point a_2. We also have a map

$$\Phi^{-1} \circ \chi : \,]0, \delta[\longrightarrow W^s(b) \cap (D - \{a_1\}).$$

When $s \to 0$, the values $\Phi^{-1} \circ \chi(s)$ tend to a_1 (by applying Lemma 3.2.5). We can therefore extend it to $[0, \delta[$, thus obtaining the desired ψ:

$$\psi : [0, \eta[\longrightarrow \overline{\mathcal{L}}(a, b) \quad \text{with } \psi(0) = (\lambda_1, \lambda_2).$$

Now, let (ℓ_n) be a sequence in $\mathcal{L}(a, b)$ that tends to (λ_1, λ_2). Let ℓ_n^+ and ℓ_n^- denote the entry and exit points of ℓ_n in the Morse chart of c. We have

$$\lim_{n \to +\infty} \ell_n^+ = a_1, \quad \lim_{n \to +\infty} \ell_n^- = a_2 \quad \text{and} \quad \Phi(\ell_n^+) = \ell_n^-.$$

For n sufficiently large, $\ell_n^+ \in D - \{a_1\}$, whence $\ell_n^- \in Q$, which implies that

$$\ell_n^- \in Q \cap W^s(b) = \mathrm{Im}\,\chi.$$

It follows that $\ell_n \in \mathrm{Im}\,\psi$. $\square$

We still need to prove the proposition. Let us begin by restating it in the Morse model $U \subset \mathbf{R}^k \times \mathbf{R}^{n-k}$, with

$$f(x_-, x_+) = -\|x_-\|^2 + \|x_+\|^2, \quad X = -\mathrm{grad}\,f$$

and
$$S_+ = \{(x_-, x_+) \mid x_- = 0, \|x_+\|^2 = \varepsilon\} \subset f^{-1}(\varepsilon),$$
$$S_- = \{(x_-, x_+) \mid x_+ = 0, \|x_-\|^2 = \varepsilon\} \subset f^{-1}(-\varepsilon).$$

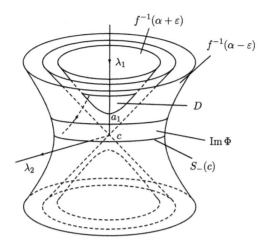

Fig. 3.7

Figure 3.7 shows exactly the same thing as Figure 3.6 but now in the Morse chart (the level sets of f are no longer represented by horizontal planes, but by quadrics).

Proposition 3.2.11. *Let $a \in S_+$ and let $D \subset \partial_+ U$ be a disk of dimension k and radius δ that meets S_+ transversally at a. Let*

$$\Phi : \partial_+ U - S_+ \longrightarrow \partial_- U - S_-$$

be the embedding defined by the flow of X. Then

$$Q = \Phi(D - \{a\}) \cup S_-$$

is a manifold with boundary, and its boundary is $\partial Q = S_-$.

To prove this proposition, we will use yet another lemma.

Lemma 3.2.12. *The embedding*

$$\Phi : \partial_+ U - S_+ \longrightarrow \partial_- U - S_-$$

defined by the flow of X is given by

$$\Phi(x_-, x_+) = \left(\frac{\|x_+\|}{\|x_-\|} x_-, \frac{\|x_-\|}{\|x_+\|} x_+ \right).$$

Proof. We simply integrate X, whose flow is

$$\varphi^s(x_-, x_+) = (e^{2s} x_-, e^{-2s} x_+).$$

If $(x_-, x_+) \in \partial_+ U$ and $x_- \neq 0$, then there exists an s such that

$$\left(\frac{\|x_+\|}{\|x_-\|} x_-, \frac{\|x_-\|}{\|x_+\|} x_+ \right) = (e^{2s} x_-, e^{-2s} x_+).$$

Since $\|x_+\| > \|x_-\|$, we have $s > 0$; moreover,

$$\left(\frac{\|x_+\|}{\|x_-\|} x_-, \frac{\|x_-\|}{\|x_+\|} x_+ \right) \in \partial_- U. \qquad \square$$

Proof of Proposition 3.2.10 *or* 3.2.11. Let D be a disk as in the statement of Proposition 3.2.11. Since S_+ consists of the x with $x_- = 0$ and since $D \pitchfork S_+$, we know that 0 is a regular value of the restriction of the projection

$$\pi : \partial_+ U \longrightarrow D^k, \quad \pi(x_-, x_+) = x_-$$

to D. Using the local inversion theorem, we may, and do, assume that

$$D = \{ (x_-, h(x_-)) \mid x_- \in D^k(\delta) \}$$

where $h : D^k(\delta) \to D^{n-k}$ satisfies

$$\|h(x_-)\|^2 = \|x_-\|^2 + \varepsilon, \quad \text{that is, } (x_-, h(x_-)) \in \partial_+ U.$$

We set $g = h / \|h\| : D^k \to S^{n-k-1}$, so that

$$D = \{ (x_-, \sqrt{\varepsilon + \|x_-\|^2} \, g(x_-)) \mid x_- \in D^k(\delta) \}.$$

By the lemma, we have

$$\Phi(D - \{a\}) = \{ (\sqrt{\varepsilon + \|x_-\|^2} \, x_- / \|x_-\|, \|x_-\| g(x_-)) \mid x_- \in D^k(\delta) - \{0\} \}.$$

Let us use "polar" coordinates $(\rho, u) \in \,]0, \delta[\times S^{k-1}$ on $D^k(\delta) - \{0\}$. Then $\Phi(D - \{a\})$ is the image of

$$H : \,]0, \delta[\times S^{k-1} \longrightarrow \partial_- U$$
$$(\rho, u) \longmapsto \left(\sqrt{\rho^2 + \varepsilon} \, u, \rho g(\rho, u) \right).$$

Since the map g is defined on the entire disk D^k, we can extend H to the product $[0, \delta[\times S^{k-1}$ by setting

$$H(0, u) = (\sqrt{\varepsilon} u, 0) \in S_-.$$

Consequently, $\Phi(D - \{a\}) \cup S_-$ is indeed a manifold with boundary, and its boundary is S_-. $\qquad \square$

Conclusion.

We have now shown, as announced at the beginning of this section, that the set of connections between two critical points can be compactified by adding broken trajectories.

3.2.d Manifolds with Boundary

The construction of $C_\star(f)$, the definition of ∂_X and the fact that $\partial_X \circ \partial_X = 0$ extend to manifolds with boundary provided that none of the critical points of f lie on the boundary and that the field X is transversal (nontangent) to this boundary, so that the connections between critical points stay far away from the boundary. See, more generally, Sections 2.3.a and 3.5.

Remark 3.2.13. We will need an analogous definition for a manifold with cornered boundary[4] $V \times [0,1]^k$. We require that near the boundary $\partial(V \times [0,1]^k)$, the pseudo-gradient is of the form

$$Y + g_1(t_1)\frac{\partial}{\partial t_1} + \cdots + g_k(t_k)\frac{\partial}{\partial t_k}$$

for a vector field Y that coincides with X near the boundary of V and for functions g_i that are nonzero at 0 and 1.

3.3 Orientation, Complex over Z

If c is a critical point of the Morse function f, then its stable manifold $W^s(c)$, which is diffeomorphic to a disk, is an orientable manifold. We now choose, for each critical point c, an orientation of the stable manifold $W^s(c)$. Note that this corresponds to choosing a co-orientation of the unstable manifold $W^u(c)$: a co-orientation of the vector space $T_c W^u(c)$ is, by definition,[5] an orientation of the complement $T_c W^s(c)$.

If a and b are two critical points, then the intersection $W^u(a) \cap W^s(b)$ (we still assume that this intersection is transversal) is therefore an oriented manifold. The same holds for its intersection with a regular level set (a regular level set is co-oriented by the transverse orientation given by the pseudo-gradient field X that is used). Hence the space of trajectories $\mathcal{L}(a,b)$ is an oriented manifold.

---

[4] We adopt this term to translate the elegant "variété à bord anguleux" introduced by François Latour [46] for "with boundary and corners".

[5] See Exercise 14 on p. 78, if necessary.

We define $C_*(f)$ to be the free abelian group ($\mathbf{Z}$-module) generated by the critical points of f. Let us repeat that we have fixed, once and for all, an orientation on each $W^s(c)$. We therefore have

$$C_k(f) = \left\{ \sum_{c \in \mathrm{Crit}_k(f)} a_c c \mid a_c \in \mathbf{Z} \right\}.$$

When $\mathrm{Ind}(a) = \mathrm{Ind}(b) + 1$, the space $\mathcal{L}(a, b)$ is an oriented compact manifold of dimension 0, that is, it is a finite number of points, each endowed with a sign. Let $N_X(a, b) \in \mathbf{Z}$ denote the sum of these signs and let us set

$$\partial_X : C_k(f) \longrightarrow C_{k-1}(f)$$
$$a \longmapsto \sum_{b \in \mathrm{Crit}_{k-1}(f)} N_X(a, b) b.$$

Note that the $n_X(a, b)$ used to define the complex modulo 2 is none other than the reduction of $N_X(a, b)$ modulo 2.

In order to guarantee that $(C_k(f), \partial_X)$ is a complex, we still need to verify that $\partial_X \circ \partial_X = 0$ in this new context. This is of course a consequence of the fact that Theorem 3.2.7 contains a statement on orientation. Clearly, the compactification of an oriented manifold of dimension 1 to a manifold with boundary gives an oriented manifold with boundary... We must still verify that the orientation induced on the boundary is indeed the one we set on the boundary. This is not very difficult, especially if we consider Figure 3.6 or [46, pp. 155–156] carefully. We therefore leave this verification to the readers.

3.4 The Homology of the Complex Depends Neither on the Function Nor on the Vector Field

In this section, we show that the homology of the Morse complex depends neither on the function nor on the pseudo-gradient field used to define it.

The following proof is inspired by [46]; it is also suggested in [49]. It is based on an original idea of Floer [31] which was, at the time, completely new, even though it was central to his work. In it, we use well-chosen deformations of one Morse function into another.

Remark 3.4.1. There exist maps $F : V \times \mathbf{R} \to \mathbf{R}$ that interpolate between f_0 and f_1 and that are Morse functions. However, in general, we cannot guarantee that each of the F_s is a Morse function: when a critical point is born or dies, we pass through a degenerate critical point. See Figure 3.8 where an intermediate function F_s has a degenerate critical point.

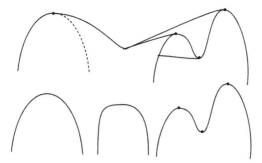

Fig. 3.8 Function F and functions F_s

Theorem 3.4.2. *Let V be a compact manifold. Let $f_0, f_1 : V \to \mathbf{R}$ be two Morse functions and let X_0, X_1 be pseudo-gradients adapted to f_0 and f_1, respectively, with the Smale property. Then there exists a morphism of complexes*

$$\Phi_\star : (C_\star(f_0), \partial_{X_0}) \longrightarrow (C_\star(f_1), \partial_{X_1})$$

that induces an isomorphism in the homology.

Proof. We will proceed in several steps. We first choose a function

$$F : V \times [0, 1] \longrightarrow \mathbf{R}$$
$$(x, s) \longmapsto F_s(x) = F(x, s)$$

such that

$$\begin{cases} F_s = f_0 & \text{for } s \in [0, \tfrac{1}{3}] \\ F_s = f_1 & \text{for } s \in [\tfrac{2}{3}, 1]. \end{cases}$$

(1) From this, we will deduce a morphism

$$\Phi^F : (C_\star(f_0), \partial_{X_0}) \longrightarrow (C_\star(f_1), \partial_{X_1}).$$

(2) We will verify that if $(f_1, X_1) = (f_0, X_0)$ and $I_s(x) = f_0(x)$ for every $x \in V$ and every $s \in [0, 1]$, then

$$\Phi^I = \mathrm{Id}.$$

(3) Finally, we will show that if $f_2 : V \to \mathbf{R}$ is a Morse function and X_2 is an adapted gradient (with the Smale property), if G is an interpolation between f_1 and f_2 that is stationary for $s \in [0, 1/3] \cup [2/3, 1]$ and if H is an interpolation between f_0 and f_2 with the same properties, then the morphisms induced in the homology by

$$\Phi^G \circ \Phi^F \quad \text{and} \quad \Phi^H : (C_\star(f_0), \partial_{X_0}) \longrightarrow (C_\star(f_2), \partial_{X_2})$$

coincide.

If these three properties are satisfied, then it is clear that Φ^F will have to induce an isomorphism in the homology. To show this, we use an interpolation G between f_1 and f_0 and the constant interpolation $H = I$ between f_0 and itself and we apply the properties, which give that Φ^F and Φ^G induce isomorphisms that are each other's inverses.

First Step.

We first extend F to $V \times [-1/3, 4/3]$ by setting

$$\begin{cases} F_s = f_0 & \text{for } s \in [-\frac{1}{3}, 0] \\ F_s = f_1 & \text{for } s \in [1, \frac{4}{3}]. \end{cases}$$

We consider a Morse function $g : \mathbf{R} \to \mathbf{R}$ whose critical points are 0 (its maximum) and 1 (its minimum), which is increasing on $]-\infty, 0[$ and on $]1, +\infty[$ and sufficiently decreasing on $]0, 1[$ that

$$\forall x \in V, \ \forall s \in {]}0, 1[, \quad \frac{\partial F}{\partial s}(x, s) + g'(s) < 0.$$

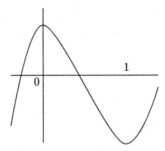

Fig. 3.9 The function g

The function $\widetilde{F} = F + g : V \times [-1/3, 4/3] \to \mathbf{R}$ is a Morse function whose critical points are

$$\mathrm{Crit}(\widetilde{F}) = \mathrm{Crit}(f_0) \times \{0\} \cup \mathrm{Crit}(f_1) \times \{1\}.$$

Moreover, for $a \in \mathrm{Crit}(f_0)$,

$$\mathrm{Ind}_{\widetilde{F}}(a, 0) = \mathrm{Ind}_{f_0}(a) + 1,$$

while for $b \in \mathrm{Crit}(f_1)$,

$$\mathrm{Ind}_{\widetilde{F}}(b, 1) = \mathrm{Ind}_{f_0}(b).$$

Using a partition of unity, we construct a pseudo-gradient field X that is adapted to $\widetilde{F}$ and coincides with

$$\begin{cases} X_0 - \operatorname{grad} g & \text{on } V \times [-\tfrac{1}{3}, \tfrac{1}{3}] \\ X_1 - \operatorname{grad} g & \text{on } V \times [\tfrac{2}{3}, \tfrac{4}{3}] \end{cases}$$

(where, of course, $\operatorname{grad} g$ denotes the Euclidean gradient of g). Thus X is transversal to the boundary of $V \times [-1/3, 4/3]$. We replace X by a small perturbation $\widetilde{X}$ that has the Smale property and that we may, and do, assume to be transversal to the sections $V \times \{s\}$ for $s \in \{-1/3, 1/3, 2/3, 4/3\}$. Note that a small perturbation of an adapted pseudo-gradient field satisfying the Smale property is an adapted pseudo-gradient field with the same property... and the same number of trajectories connecting two critical points of consecutive indices (there is a bijection between the sets of trajectories of the two fields). This is expressed in the following proposition.

Proposition 3.4.3. *Let $f : V \to \mathbf{R}$ be a Morse function and let X be a pseudo-gradient field adapted to f that has the Smale property. Every vector field $\widetilde{X}$ sufficiently close to X (in the $\mathcal{C}^1$ sense) is an adapted pseudo-gradient field that still has the Smale property. Moreover, we have*

$$(C_\star(f), \partial_X) = (C_\star(f), \partial_{\widetilde{X}}). \qquad \qquad \square$$

We can therefore choose $\widetilde{X}$ such that

$$\begin{aligned} (C_\star(\widetilde{F}|_{V \times [-1/3, 1/3]}), \partial_{\widetilde{X}}) &= (C_\star(f_0 + g|_{[-1/3, 2/3]}), \partial_{X_0 + \operatorname{grad} g}) \\ &= (C_{\star+1}(f_0), \partial_{X_0}) \end{aligned}$$

and likewise such that

$$\begin{aligned} (C_\star(\widetilde{F}|_{V \times [2/3, 4/3]}), \partial_{\widetilde{X}}) &= (C_\star(f_1 + g|_{[2/3, 4/3]}), \partial_{X_1 + \operatorname{grad} g}) \\ &= (C_\star(f_1), \partial_{X_1}). \end{aligned}$$

Let us now consider the complex associated with the Morse function $\widetilde{F}$ and field $\widetilde{X}$ on the product $V \times [-1/3, 4/3]$. The trajectories of the vector field $\widetilde{X}$ that connect two critical points of $\widetilde{F}$ can be divided into two kinds: those that remain in the section $s \in \left[-\tfrac{1}{3}, \tfrac{1}{3}\right]$ or in the section $s \in \left[\tfrac{2}{3}, \tfrac{4}{3}\right]$, which are trajectories of X_0 or of X_1, and those that go from a critical point of f_0 (in the section $s \in \left[-\tfrac{1}{3}, \tfrac{1}{3}\right]$) to a critical point of f_1 (in the section $s \in \left[\tfrac{2}{3}, \tfrac{4}{3}\right]$). We have

$$C_{k+1}(\widetilde{F}) = C_k(f_0) \oplus C_{k+1}(f_1).$$

Taking into account the above, in this decomposition,

$$\partial_{\widetilde{X}} : C_k(f_0) \oplus C_{k+1}(f_1) \longrightarrow C_{k-1}(f_0) \oplus C_k(f_1)$$

has a matrix of the form

$$\partial_{\widetilde{X}} = \begin{pmatrix} \partial_{X_0} & 0 \\ \Phi^F & \partial_{X_1} \end{pmatrix}.$$

The element

$$\Phi^F : C_k(f_0) \longrightarrow C_k(f_1)$$

is given by

$$\Phi^F(a) = \sum_{b \in \mathrm{Crit}_k(f_1)} n_{\widetilde{X}}(a,b)b,$$

where $n_{\widetilde{X}}(a,b)$ counts the trajectories of $\widetilde{X}$ connecting $a \in V \times \{0\} \cap \mathrm{Crit}(\widetilde{F})$ to $b \in V \times \{1\} \cap \mathrm{Crit}(\widetilde{F})$.

The relation $\partial_{\widetilde{X}} \circ \partial_{\widetilde{X}} = 0$ gives

$$\Phi^F \circ \partial_{X_0} + \partial_{X_1} \circ \Phi^F = 0 \quad \text{or} \quad \Phi^F \circ \partial_{X_0} = \partial_{X_1} \circ \Phi^F,$$

hence Φ^F is indeed a morphism of complexes.

Second Step.

If $f_1 = f_0$ and $X_0 = X_1$, then we begin with

$$I : V \times [0,1] \longrightarrow \mathbf{R} \quad \text{defined by } I(x,s) = f_0(x) \text{ for every } s$$

and we use a function g as above. The vector field $X = X_0 + \mathrm{grad}\, g$ is an adapted pseudo-gradient field and satisfies the Smale property. Moreover, for every critical point a of f_0, there exists a unique trajectory of X that connects $(a,0)$ to $(c,1)$ with $\mathrm{Ind}_{f_0}(a) = \mathrm{Ind}_{f_0}(c)$: the trajectory between $(a,0)$ and $(a,1)$ whose projection on V is constant. Consequently, $\Phi^I = \mathrm{Id}$.

Third Step.

We now have interpolations F, G and H from f_0 to f_1, f_1 to f_2 and f_0 to f_2, respectively. We interpolate between these functions by choosing a function

$$K : V \times \left[-\tfrac{1}{3}, \tfrac{4}{3}\right] \times \left[\tfrac{1}{3}, \tfrac{4}{3}\right] \longrightarrow \mathbf{R}, \quad K(x,s,t) = K_{s,t}(x)$$

satisfying the properties summarized by Figure 3.10:

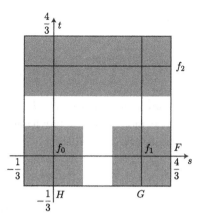

Fig. 3.10

- $K_{s,t} = H_t$ for $s \in [-1/3, 1/3]$.
- $K_{s,t} = G_t$ for $s \in [2/3, 4/3]$.
- $K_{s,t} = F_s$ for $t \in [-1/3, 1/3]$.
- $K_{s,t} = f_2$ for $t \in [2/3, 4/3]$.

We also use a Morse function $g : \mathbf{R} \to \mathbf{R}$ such as that used before (and whose graph is shown in Figure 3.9), which has as its only critical points 0 of index 1 and 1 of index 0, is increasing outside of $[0, 1]$ and satisfies

$$\frac{\partial K}{\partial s}(x, s, t) + g'(s) < 0 \quad \text{for all } (x, s, t) \in V \times \,]0, 1[\,\times\, [\tfrac{1}{3}, \tfrac{4}{3}]$$

and

$$\frac{\partial K}{\partial t}(x, s, t) + g'(t) < 0 \quad \text{for all } (x, s, t) \in V \times [\tfrac{1}{3}, \tfrac{4}{3}] \times \,]0, 1[.$$

Finally, let $\widetilde{K}$ be the function defined by

$$\widetilde{K}(x, s, t) = K_{s,t}(x) + g(s) + g(t).$$

By the choice of g, the critical points of $\widetilde{K}$ are in the shaded area in Figure 3.10, where $\widetilde{K}(x, s, t)$ can be written as $f_i(x) + g(s) + g(t)$ (for $i = 0, 1$ or 2). In particular, it is a Morse function whose critical points are

$$\text{Crit}(\widetilde{K}) = \big[\, \text{Crit}(f_0) \times \{0\} \times \{0\} \,\big] \cup \big[\, \text{Crit}(f_1) \times \{1\} \times \{0\} \,\big]$$
$$\cup \big[\, \text{Crit}(f_2) \times \{0\} \times \{1\} \,\big] \cup \big[\, \text{Crit}(f_2) \times \{1\} \times \{1\} \,\big].$$

The indices of these critical points are as follows:

- If $a \in \text{Crit}(f_0)$, then $\text{Ind}_{\widetilde{K}}((a, 0, 0)) = \text{Ind}_{f_0}(a) + 2$.

- If $b \in \mathrm{Crit}(f_1)$, then $\mathrm{Ind}_{\widetilde{K}}((b,1,0)) = \mathrm{Ind}_{f_1}(b) + 1$.
- If $c \in \mathrm{Crit}(f_2)$, then

$$\mathrm{Ind}_{\widetilde{K}}((c,0,1)) = \mathrm{Ind}_{f_2}(c) + 1 \quad \text{and} \quad \mathrm{Ind}_{\widetilde{K}}((c,1,1)) = \mathrm{Ind}_{f_2}(c).$$

Let X denote the pseudo-gradient field adapted to F constructed above and Y the one adapted to G. Once more using a partition of unity, we define a pseudo-gradient field $\mathcal{X}$ adapted to $\widetilde{K}$ such that:

- For $s \in [-1/3, 1/3]$, $\mathcal{X}(x,s,t) = Z(x,t) + \mathrm{grad}\, g(s)$, where Z is a pseudo-gradient for
$$H(x,t) + g(t) : V \times \left[-\tfrac{1}{3}, \tfrac{4}{3}\right] \longrightarrow \mathbf{R}.$$

- For $s \in [2/3, 4/3]$, $\mathcal{X}(x,s,t) = Y(x,t) + \mathrm{grad}\, g(s)$, where Y is a pseudo-gradient for G.
- For $t \in [-1/3, 1/3]$, $\mathcal{X}(x,s,t) = X(x,s) + \mathrm{grad}\, g(t)$.
- For $t \in [2/3, 4/3]$, $\mathcal{X}(x,s,t) = X_2 + \mathrm{grad}\, g(s) + \mathrm{grad}\, g(t)$.

We then take a perturbation $\widetilde{\mathcal{X}}$ of $\mathcal{X}$ in order to have the Smale property, assuming, as in the first step, that outside of $V \times [1/3, 2/3] \times [1/3, 2/3]$, the trajectories of $\widetilde{\mathcal{X}}$ connecting critical points of consecutive indices are in a one-to-one correspondence with those of $\mathcal{X}$ (Proposition 3.4.3).

Let us now consider the complex of critical points associated with $\widetilde{K}$ and $\widetilde{\mathcal{X}}$. The manifold $V \times [-\tfrac{1}{2}, \tfrac{4}{3}] \times [-\tfrac{1}{3}, \tfrac{4}{3}]$ does not have a (smooth) boundary, but the conditions of Remark 3.2.13 are satisfied. We have

$$C_{k+1}(\widetilde{K}) = C_{k-1}(f_0) \oplus C_k(f_1) \oplus C_k(f_2) \oplus C_{k+1}(f_2).$$

The diagram in Figure 3.11 shows the connections between the different morphisms we have used. In this decomposition, the differential can be written as

$$\partial_{\widetilde{\mathcal{X}}} = \begin{pmatrix} \partial_{X_0} & 0 & 0 & 0 \\ \Phi^F & \partial_{X_1} & 0 & 0 \\ \Phi^H & 0 & \partial_{X_2} & 0 \\ S & \Phi^G & \mathrm{Id} & \partial_{X_2} \end{pmatrix}.$$

The identity $\partial_{\widetilde{\mathcal{X}}} \circ \partial_{\widetilde{\mathcal{X}}} = 0$ gives

$$S \circ \partial_{X_0} + \Phi^G \circ \Phi^F + \Phi^H + \partial_{X_2} \circ S = 0$$

or

$$\Phi^G \circ \Phi^F - \Phi^H = S \circ \partial_{X_0} + \partial_{X_2} \circ S.$$

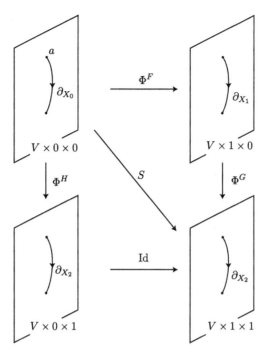

Fig. 3.11

We deduce from this that $\varPhi^G \circ \varPhi^F$ and $\varPhi^H$ induce the same morphism in the homology.   □

3.5 Cobordisms

Let us now consider cobordisms. A cobordism is a manifold with boundary V whose boundary ∂V is decomposed into

$$\partial V = \partial_- V \cup \partial_+ V$$

(the two parts $\partial_\pm V$ are unions of arbitrarily chosen components of ∂V). We generalize the construction of Section 2.3.a. We fix a vector field X (constructed, for example, using a partition of unity) on a neighborhood of ∂V in V that is:

- pointing outward along $\partial_+ V$
- pointing inward along $\partial_- V$.

We construct a Morse function f on V such that

$$df(X) < 0 \text{ in the neighborhood of } \partial V$$

as follows. We first define it in the neighborhood of the boundary, for example by setting

$$
\begin{cases}
f(\varphi_X^{-s}(x)) = s & \text{for } s \in [0, \delta[\text{ if } x \in \partial_+ V, \\
f(\varphi_X^{s}(x)) = -s & \text{for } s \in [0, \delta[\text{ if } x \in \partial_- V,
\end{cases}
$$

then we extend it arbitrarily to all of V and finally we take a slight perturbation in order to obtain a Morse function.

We can then extend X to a pseudo-gradient field adapted to f that we will still denote by X.

Let us recall (this is Remark 2.3.1) that for this construction, we need to begin with a vector field that is transversal to the boundary and that the Morse function is not completely arbitrary.

Example 3.5.1. In Figure 3.12, the manifold is a disk D^n and its boundary is a sphere S^{n-1}. The Morse function is the height and the vector field is indicated in the figure. On the left-hand side, $S^{n-1} = \partial_+ V$, on the right-hand side, $S^{n-1} = \partial_- V$.

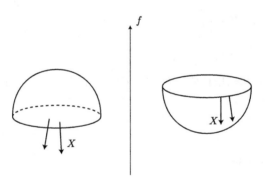

Fig. 3.12

Remark 3.5.2. The modifications that we applied to a pseudo-gradient field to give it the Smale property took place in neighborhoods of the critical points (and therefore far from the boundary in this case). We can therefore carry them out in the same manner here.

We can then also define $(C_\star(f), \partial_X)$ as in the case without boundary.

The proofs of the compactness and of the relation $\partial_X \circ \partial_X = 0$ are identical to those we gave in the case without boundary because all connections between critical points will stay far from the boundary.

Remark 3.5.3. The complex does not depend on $X|_{\partial V}$ as long as this stays transversal to the boundary, pointing outward along $\partial_+ V$ and pointing inward along $\partial_- V$ (we can modify X far from the critical points).

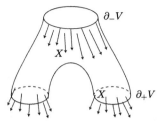

$\partial_- V$

X

$\hat{X}$ $\partial_+ V$

Fig. 3.13

Let us now show that the homology of the complex depends neither on the function nor on the vector field. Let f_0 and f_1 be two Morse functions on V, each endowed with an adapted pseudo-gradient that has the Smale property. We assume that the two vector fields X_0 and X_1 coincide in the neighborhood of the boundary. Let us choose, as before, a path f_t from f_0 to f_1 that we suppose to be stationary near the two extremities:

$$f_t = f_0 \text{ for } t \le 1/3 \quad \text{and} \quad f_t = f_1 \text{ for } t \ge 2/3.$$

We also suppose that $df_t(X) < 0$ in the neighborhood of ∂V. We extend f_t as a stationary function on $[-1/3, 0]$ and $[1, 4/3]$. We use a function g as before (Figure 3.9) such that

$$\forall t \in \left[\tfrac{1}{3}, \tfrac{2}{3}\right], \ \forall x \in V, \quad g'(t) + \frac{\partial f_t(x)}{\partial t} < 0.$$

As in the proof of the independence, we set

$$F(x,t) = f_t(x) + g(x) \quad \text{for } (x,t) \in V \times \left[-\tfrac{1}{3}, \tfrac{4}{3}\right].$$

Again as in that proof, the critical points of F are those of f_0 in the section $t = 0$ and those of f_1 in the section $t = 1$, with an index jump for those in the section $t = 0$.

Finally, we construct a pseudo-gradient $\widetilde{X}$ for F such that

$$\widetilde{X} = \begin{cases} X - \operatorname{grad} g & \text{near } \partial V \times [0,1] \\ X_0 - \operatorname{grad} g & \text{on } V \times [-1/3, 1/3] \\ X_1 - \operatorname{grad} g & \text{on } V \times [2/3, 4/3]. \end{cases}$$

We then only need to take a slight perturbation in order to obtain the Smale property. In short, we form the complex $(C_\star(F), \partial_{\widetilde{X}})$. As in the case without boundary, we have

$$(C_k(F), \partial_{\widetilde{X}}) = \left(C_{k-1}(f_0) \oplus C_k(f_1), \begin{pmatrix} \partial_{X_0} & 0 \\ \Phi_{\widetilde{X}} & \partial_{X_1} \end{pmatrix} \right),$$

which defines a morphism of complexes

$$\Phi_{\widetilde{X}} : (C_\star(f_0), \partial_{X_0}) \longrightarrow (C_\star(f_1), \partial_{X_1}),$$

which we can prove, as before, to induce an isomorphism in the homology.

To conclude, in this case, the homology of the complex depends only on V and on the partition of the boundary as $\partial V = \partial_+ V \cup \partial_- V$.

Also note that $\Phi_\star^F$ does not depend on F. To convince yourself of this, for a different "interpolation" F', take $G = \mathrm{Id}$ and $H = F'$ in step (3) of the proof of Theorem 3.4.2.

Exercises

Exercise 13. What is the homology of the complex associated with the function defined in Exercise 12 (p. 51) and the vector field suggested in the same exercise?

Exercise 14. Let E and F be two vector subspaces of a finite-dimensional real vector space. Show that an orientation of E is an equivalence class of bases of E for the equivalence relation

$$\mathcal{B} \sim \mathcal{B}' \iff \det_{\mathcal{B}} \mathcal{B}' > 0.$$

Likewise, verify that the relation

$$\mathcal{B} \sim \mathcal{B}' \iff \det_{(\mathcal{B}, \mathcal{B}_0)}(\mathcal{B}', \mathcal{B}_0) > 0$$

defines an equivalence relation on the bases of the complements of F that does not depend on the chosen basis $\mathcal{B}_0$ of F. The equivalence classes are the co-orientations of F.

Verify that if E is oriented, F is co-oriented and E and F are transversal, then $E \cap F$ is co-oriented.

Exercise 15. Determine the homology of the complex $(C_\star(f; \mathbf{Z}), \partial_X)$ for the examples of Morse functions on the manifolds $\mathbf{P}^n(\mathbf{C})$, T^2 and S^n used in this book.

Chapter 4
Morse Homology, Applications

In this chapter, we give a few computations and a few applications of Morse homology: the Künneth formula for products, the Poincaré duality, the Euler characteristic (and the Morse inequalities), the link with the connectedness and the simple connectedness of the manifold in question. We also show the functoriality of Morse homology and present a long exact sequence for a pair (W, V) (where V is a submanifold of the manifold W).

4.1 Homology

Since the homology $H_\star(f, X)$ of the Morse complex on a manifold V depends only on V, we denote it by $HM_\star(V; \mathbf{Z}/2)$ (for "Morse homology modulo 2" of V). Likewise, the homology of the complex taking into account orientations, as in Section 3.3, is denoted by $HM_\star(V; \mathbf{Z})$. In fact (for those who know what this is), it is the modulo 2 homology (and the integral homology, respectively) of the manifold V (see Section 4.9). This chapter's results are true both over $\mathbf{Z}/2$ and over $\mathbf{Z}$ (unless explicitly stated otherwise). We will mostly use the complex with integral coefficients and will denote its homology by $HM_\star(V)$.

In the case of a manifold with boundary V whose boundary ∂V is decomposed as $\partial V = \partial_- V \cup \partial_+ V$, we likewise define the relative Morse homology $HM_\star(V, \partial_+ V; \mathbf{Z}/2)$ to be the homology of the complex $(C_\star(f), \partial_X)$.

Example 4.1.1. In the case of the disk (see Figure 3.12), the figure on the left gives

$$HM_\star(D^n, S^{n-1}) = \begin{cases} 0 & \text{if } \star \neq n \\ \mathbf{Z} & \text{if } \star = n, \end{cases}$$

M. Audin, M. Damian, *Morse Theory and Floer Homology*,
Universitext, DOI 10.1007/978-1-4471-5496-9_4,
© Springer-Verlag London 2014

while the one on the right gives

$$HM_\star(D^n) = \begin{cases} 0 & \text{if } \star \neq 0 \\ \mathbf{Z} & \text{if } \star = 0. \end{cases}$$

We expect this "homology" to satisfy a certain number of properties, for example functoriality and good behavior with respect to Cartesian products.

Remark 4.1.2. Let us note a tiny step toward a type of functoriality (see, more generally, Section 4.6). If $\varphi : M \to N$ is a diffeomorphism, then φ induces an isomorphism

$$\varphi_\star : HM_\star(M) \longrightarrow HM_\star(N).$$

Indeed, if g is a Morse function on N, then $g \circ \varphi$ is one on M. If X is a pseudo-gradient field adapted to $g \circ \varphi$ on M satisfying the Smale property, then $\varphi_\star(X)$ is such a vector field for g on N. It follows that we have an isomorphism of complexes

$$(C_\star(g \circ \varphi), \partial_X) \longrightarrow (C_\star(g), \partial_{\varphi_\star X}).$$

Homology of a Disjoint Union.

Before moving on to more serious matters, let us also note that the Morse homology of a disjoint union is the direct sum of the homologies of the components. Indeed, if f and g are Morse functions on V and W, respectively, and if X and Y are *suitable* vector fields, then clearly

$$C_k(f \coprod g) = C_k(f) \oplus C_k(g) \quad \text{and} \quad \partial_{X \coprod Y} = \partial_X \oplus \partial_Y.$$

Notation.

In order to simplify both the writing of this text and its reading, we will sometimes write $C_\bullet(f, X)$ for the complex associated with a function and a vector field. We will allow ourselves to describe such a pair (f, X) as "Morse–Smale" when the first is a Morse function and the second is an adapted pseudo-gradient field satisfying the Smale condition.

4.2 The Künneth Formula

If M and N are two manifolds endowed with Morse functions f and g and pseudo-gradient fields X and Y (satisfying the Smale condition), respectively, then $f + g$ is a Morse function on $M \times N$ and (X, Y) is an adapted pseudo-gradient field satisfying the Smale condition. The critical points of $f + g$ are the points (a, a'), where a is a critical point of f and a' is a critical point of g. The index of (a, a') is the sum of the indices of a and a'. Let (a, a') be a critical point of index k of $f + g$ (with a a critical point of index i of f and a' a critical point of index j of g) and let (b, b') be a critical point of index $k - 1$ such that there exists a trajectory of (X, Y) connecting (a, a') to (b, b'). The flow of (X, Y) is

$$\varphi^t_{(X,Y)}(x, y) = (\varphi^t_X(x), \varphi^t_Y(y)).$$

In particular,

$$\mathcal{L}_{(X,Y)}((a, a'), (b, b')) \cong \mathcal{L}_X(a, b) \times \mathcal{L}_Y(a', b').$$

If $a \neq b$ and $a' \neq b'$, then for $\mathcal{L}_X(a, b) \times \mathcal{L}_{X'}(a', b')$ to be nonempty, we must have

$$\mathrm{Ind}(a) \geq \mathrm{Ind}(b) + 1 \quad \text{and} \quad \mathrm{Ind}(a') \geq \mathrm{Ind}(b') + 1,$$

that is,

$$\mathrm{Ind}(a, a') \geq \mathrm{Ind}(b, b') + 2.$$

Hence, for points (a, a') and (b, b') with consecutive indices, we have

$$\mathcal{L}_{(X,Y)}((a, a'), (b, b')) = \begin{cases} a \times \mathcal{L}_Y(a', b') & \text{if } a = b \\ \mathcal{L}_X(a, b) \times a' & \text{if } a' = b' \end{cases}$$

and consequently

$$n_{(X,Y)}((a, a'), (b, b')) = \begin{cases} n_Y(a', b') & \text{if } a = b \\ n_X(a, b) & \text{if } a' = b' \\ 0 & \text{otherwise.} \end{cases}$$

The map

$$\Phi : \bigoplus_{i+j=k} C_i(f) \otimes C_j(g) \longrightarrow C_k(f + g)$$

defined by

$$\Phi(a \otimes a') = (a, a')$$

is an isomorphism of abelian groups.

Proposition 4.2.1. *The map Φ defines an isomorphism of complexes*

$$(C_*(f) \otimes C_*(g), \partial_X \otimes 1 + 1 \otimes \partial_Y) \longrightarrow (C_*(f+g), \partial_{(X,Y)}).$$

Proof. Let a be a critical point of index i of f and let a' be a critical point of index j of g. On the one hand, we have

$$\Phi(\partial_X \otimes 1 + 1 \otimes \partial_Y)(a \otimes a') = \Phi(\partial_X(a) \otimes a' + a \otimes \partial_Y(a'))$$

$$= \Phi\left(\sum_{b \in \mathrm{Crit}_{i-1}(f)} n_X(a,b) b \otimes a' + \sum_{b' \in \mathrm{Crit}_{j-1}(g)} n_Y(a',b') a \otimes b' \right)$$

$$= \sum_{b \in \mathrm{Crit}_{i-1}(f)} n_X(a,b)(b,a') + \sum_{b' \in \mathrm{Crit}_{j-1}(g)} n_Y(a',b')(a,b'),$$

and on the other hand, we have

$$\partial_{(X,Y)}\Phi(a \otimes a') = \sum_{(b,b') \in \mathrm{Crit}_{i+j-1}(f+g)} n_{(X,Y)}((a,a'),(b,b'))(b,b')$$

$$= \sum_{b \in \mathrm{Crit}_{i-1}(f)} n_X(a,b)(b,a') + \sum_{b' \in \mathrm{Crit}_{j-1}(g)} n_Y(a',b')(a,b'),$$

by the remark made above.   □

This works well over $\mathbf{Z}$ (with orientations) and over $\mathbf{Z}/2$ (without). Taking the homology, on the other hand, it is more convenient to work over $\mathbf{Z}/2$ (the necessary homological algebra can be found in Appendix B.1.a). From this we deduce the following result.

Corollary 4.2.2. *The modulo 2 homology of $(C_*(f+g), \partial_{(X,Y)})$ on the product $M \times N$ is isomorphic to the tensor product of the modulo 2 homologies of $(C_*(f), \partial_X)$ and $(C_*(g), \partial_Y)$.*

Corollary 4.2.3 (Künneth Formula). *If M and N are two compact manifolds, then there is an isomorphism*

$$HM_k(M \times N; \mathbf{Z}/2) \longrightarrow \bigoplus_{i+j=k} HM_i(M; \mathbf{Z}/2) \otimes HM_j(N; \mathbf{Z}/2).$$

The proof is an immediate consequence of Proposition 4.2.1 and Proposition B.1.1.   □

4.3 The "Poincaré" Duality

We know that the critical points of index k of f are the critical points of index $n - k$ of $-f$ (n is the dimension of the manifold). Moreover, if X is a pseudo-gradient adapted to f, then $-X$ is a pseudo-gradient adapted to $-f$.

If $a \in \mathrm{Crit}_k(f)$, then let $a^\star$ denote the same point regarded as a critical point of the function $-f$, so that

$$\{a \mid a \in \mathrm{Crit}_k(f)\} \text{ is a basis of } C_k(f)$$

while

$$\{a^\star \mid a \in \mathrm{Crit}_k(f)\} \text{ is a basis of } C_{n-k}(-f).$$

The vector space $C_{n-k}(-f)$ is isomorphic to $C_k(f)$, but it is better to think of it as being its dual (whence the notation):

$$C_{n-k}(-f) = C_k(f)^\star.$$

Thus, by definition, the transpose

$${}^t\partial_X : C_{n-k+1}(-f) \longrightarrow C_{n-k}(-f) \text{ of } \partial_X : C_k(f) \longrightarrow C_{k-1}(f)$$

is the differential ∂_{-X} of the complex $(C_\star(-f), \partial_{-X})$. We therefore have the following result.

Proposition 4.3.1 (Poincaré Duality). *Let V be a compact manifold of dimension n. If V is without boundary, then $HM_{n-k}(V; \mathbf{Z}/2)$ is isomorphic to $HM_k(V; \mathbf{Z}/2)$. If V has a boundary $\partial V = \partial_+ V \cup \partial_- V$, then $HM_k(V, \partial_+ V; \mathbf{Z}/2)$ is isomorphic to $HM_{n-k}(V, \partial_- V; \mathbf{Z}/2)$.* □

For example (this is the case where $\partial_+ V = \varnothing$),

$$HM_k(V; \mathbf{Z}/2) \text{ is isomorphic to } HM_{n-k}(V, \partial V; \mathbf{Z}/2).$$

In order to state an analogous result for the integral homology, we must be able to associate a critical point $a^\star$ of index $n - k$ of $-f$ *with an orientation of $W^s(a^\star) = W^u(a)$ to any critical point a of index k of f with an orientation of $W^s(a)$*. To simplify the statement, let us therefore suppose that the manifold V is oriented: an orientation of $W^s(a)$ then defines an orientation (and not only a co-orientation) of $W^u(a)$. The arguments used above remain valid and we obtain an analogous result for the free part of the homology groups.

Proposition 4.3.2 (Poincaré Duality for Oriented Manifolds). *Let V be a compact oriented manifold of dimension n. If V is without boundary, then the abelian groups $HM_{n-k}(V;\mathbf{Z})$ and $HM_k(V;\mathbf{Z})$ have the same rank. If V has a boundary $\partial V = \partial_+ V \cup \partial_- V$, then the abelian groups $HM_k(V, \partial_+ V;\mathbf{Z})$ and $HM_{n-k}(V, \partial_- V;\mathbf{Z})$ have the same rank.*   □

Remark. The torsion part of HM_k and HM_{n-k} may differ as we note for $V = \mathbf{P}^3(\mathbf{R})$, where $HM_1(\mathbf{P}^3(\mathbf{R});\mathbf{Z}) = \mathbf{Z}/2$ and $H_2(\mathbf{P}^3(\mathbf{R});\mathbf{Z}) = 0$. See Exercise 25 (on p. 123) for the computation of $HM_\star(\mathbf{P}^n(\mathbf{R});\mathbf{Z})$.

4.4 Euler Characteristic, Poincaré Polynomial

Here is a direct application of the independence of the homology.

Corollary 4.4.1. *The number of critical points modulo 2 of a Morse function depends only on the manifold and not on the function.*

Proof. Let us write down the complex associated with a Morse function and a pseudo-gradient:

$$0 \xrightarrow{\partial_{n+1}} C_n \xrightarrow{\partial_n} C_{n-1} \longrightarrow \cdots \xrightarrow{\partial_1} C_0 \xrightarrow{\partial_0} 0.$$

We then have the following equalities:

$$\# \operatorname{Crit}(f) = \sum_{k=0}^{n} \dim C_k(f)$$

$$= \sum_{k=0}^{n+1} (\dim \operatorname{Ker} \partial_k + \dim \operatorname{Im} \partial_k)$$

$$= \sum_{k=0}^{n} (\dim \operatorname{Ker} \partial_k + \dim \operatorname{Im} \partial_{k+1})$$

$$\equiv \sum_{k=0}^{n} (\dim \operatorname{Ker} \partial_k - \dim \operatorname{Im} \partial_{k+1}) \quad \mathrm{mod}\ 2$$

$$= \sum_{k=0}^{n} \dim HM_k(V;\mathbf{Z}/2) \quad \mathrm{mod}\ 2. \qquad\qquad □$$

Remark 4.4.2. What we have done is just to use algebra and the definition of the homology of the complex to show that

$$\sum_k (-1)^k \dim C_k = \sum_k (-1)^k \dim HM_k.$$

However, we have used the "rank-nullity theorem", so that it is wise to work with vector spaces, that is, to work over a field. This explains why it is the homology with coefficients in $\mathbf{Z}/2$ that we use here.

This number is the Euler characteristic of the manifold V (modulo 2). By definition, the Euler characteristic is

$$
\begin{aligned}
\chi(V) &= \sum_{k=0}^{n} (-1)^k \dim HM_k(V; \mathbf{Z}/2) \\
&= \sum_{k=0}^{n} (-1)^k (\dim \operatorname{Ker} \partial_k - \dim \operatorname{Im} \partial_{k+1}) \\
&= \sum_{k=0}^{n} (-1)^k (\dim \operatorname{Ker} \partial_k + \dim \operatorname{Im} \partial_k) \\
&= \sum_{k=0}^{n} (-1)^k \dim C_k(f).
\end{aligned}
$$

So the Euler characteristic of a manifold is the alternating sum of the number of critical points of a Morse function on it.

More precisely, we have

$$
\# \operatorname{Crit}(f) \geq \sum_{k=0}^{n} (\dim \operatorname{Ker} \partial_k - \dim \operatorname{Im} \partial_{k+1}) = \sum_{k=0}^{n} \dim HM_k(V; \mathbf{Z}/2),
$$

which leads to the following result.

Proposition 4.4.3 (Morse Inequalities). *The number of critical points of a Morse function on a manifold V is greater than or equal to the sum of the dimensions of the (Morse, modulo 2) homology groups of this manifold.* □

If we define $c_k(f)$ to be the number of critical points of index k of the Morse function f and let $\beta_k = \dim HM_k(V; \mathbf{Z}/2)$ (the kth Betti number of V), then the proposition can be written as

$$
c_k(f) \geq \beta_k, \quad 0 \leq k,
$$

a series of inequalities known as the Morse inequalities.

Example 4.4.4. We saw that in the case of the torus T^2, the sum of the dimensions of the homology groups is 4. Therefore a Morse function on the torus must have at least four critical points.

Remark 4.4.5. It is possible to construct a (degenerate) function on the torus that has only three critical points (but no less, because of Reeb's theorem, Corollary 2.1.9, and Remarks 2.1.10). In Figure 4.1, the degenerate critical point is in the middle, the two other critical points are the minimum and the maximum; it is a "monkey saddle" (see Exercise 3 on p. 18).

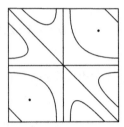

Fig. 4.1 Level sets of a function with three critical points on the torus

It is moreover possible, in a compact connected manifold of dimension n, to construct a function with $n + 1$ critical points. One strategy, developed in [76], is to first construct a Morse function on the manifold with at most $n + 1$ critical level sets, all connected (a result by Smale, see [53]), and then to modify the function in the neighborhood of each critical level set in such a way that it has only one (degenerate) critical point in this level set.

Example 4.4.6. The Euler characteristic of the sphere S^n is

$$\chi(S^n) = 1 + (-1)^n,$$

that is, 0 if n is odd and 2 if n is even. For example, the Euler characteristic of the sphere of dimension 2 is 2. This is the same Euler, the same 2 and the same alternating sum as in "Euler's polyhedral formula" on the number F of faces, E of edges and V of vertices of a connected polyhedron, $F - E + V = 2$.

Remark 4.4.7. The Euler characteristic of a compact manifold of odd dimension without boundary is zero: by the Poincaré duality, the terms in the alternating sum cancel each other out in pairs.

Using the Betti numbers, $\beta_k(V) = \dim HM_k(V; \mathbf{Z}/2)$, we define the Poincaré polynomial

$$P_V(t) = \sum_k \beta_k(V) t^k.$$

For example, $P_{S^1}(t) = 1 + t$ and more generally,

$$P_{S^n}(t) = 1 + t^n.$$

Moreover,

$$P_{\mathbf{P}^n(\mathbf{C})}(t) = 1 + t^2 + \cdots + t^{2n},$$

and

$$P_{T^2}(t) = 1 + 2t + t^2, \quad P_{\mathbf{P}^2(\mathbf{R})} = 1 + t + t^2.$$

The Künneth formula immediately gives the relation

$$P_{V_1 \times V_2}(t) = P_{V_1}(t) P_{V_2}(t).$$

Writing $T^n = S^1 \times \cdots \times S^1$ (n times), it follows that

$$\beta_k(T^n) = \binom{n}{k}.$$

In particular, by applying Remark 4.1.2, we deduce that the sphere S^n is only diffeomorphic to the torus T^n if $n = 1$. There are obviously quicker ways than Morse theory to obtain this result (for example, the sphere is simply connected and the torus is not).

It also follows (for $t = -1$) that

$$\chi(V_1 \times V_2) = \chi(V_1)\chi(V_2).$$

Example 4.4.8. We find $\chi(S^2 \times S^2) = 4$. Taking the sum of the height function on S^2 with itself gives a Morse function on $S^2 \times S^2$ that has only four critical points: a minimum, a maximum and two critical points of index 2, which is consistent with our results, since $1 + 2 + 1 = 4$.

4.5 Homology and Connectedness

4.5.a Connected Components and Homology

Proposition 4.5.1. *If V is a compact connected manifold, then*

$$HM_0(V; \mathbf{Z}/2) \cong \mathbf{Z}/2.$$

Proof. Let B be the vector subspace of dimension $r - 1$ in $C_0(f)$ generated by the $a_1 + a_i$ (for $2 \leq i \leq r$). We will show that B is exactly the image of

$$\partial_X : C_1(f) \longrightarrow C_0(f).$$

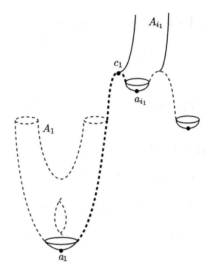

Fig. 4.2

We begin by showing that $\partial_X C_1 \subset B$, which is the easy inclusion. Let c be a critical point of index 1. Its unstable manifold is of dimension 1, there are therefore only two trajectories of X starting from c. These end up at two local minima a_i and a_j (which are not necessarily distinct). We therefore have

$$\partial_X c = a_i + a_j = (a_1 + a_i) + (a_1 + a_j) \in B.$$

Hence $\partial_X(C_1(f)) \subset B$.

Conversely, let us show that $B \subset \partial_X(C_1(f))$ (this is the central part of the proof). It suffices to show that for every i, a_i is in the same homology class as a_1. Let

$$N = V - \bigcup_{\mathrm{Ind}(x),\mathrm{Ind}(y)\geq 2} \mathcal{M}(x,y).$$

Note that with $\mathrm{Ind}(x), \mathrm{Ind}(y) \geq 2$, we have $\mathrm{codim}\, \mathcal{M}(x,y) \geq 2$, so that N is connected. For $j = 1,\ldots, r$, we set

$$A_j = \{x \in N \mid x \text{ is on a (broken) trajectory ending at } a_j\}.$$

The sets A_j are connected (all points of A_j are connected to a_j), N is the union of the A_j and A_j is the union of the stable manifold of a_j and the orbits ending at a_j and passing through a critical point of index 1. Figure 4.2 shows part of N, with the corresponding parts of A_1 and A_{i_1}.

Let us now show that the A_j are closed subsets of N. It suffices to show this for $j = 1$. Let (x_n) be a sequence in A_1 that converges to $x \in N$. We will prove that $x \in A_1$. We assume that x_n is not a critical point of f, which is sufficient for our needs. Let ℓ_n be the trajectory through x_n and let ℓ be the one through x. After taking a subsequence, if necessary, we may, and do, assume that the trajectories ℓ_n all end up at the same critical point b, which may be a_1 or another critical point of index 1, itself connected to a_1 by a trajectory.

Let c be the critical point where ℓ ends. Its index is 0 or 1 because x is in N. If $c = b$, then the proof is finished. Otherwise, let ℓ^+ be the point through which ℓ enters the Morse chart of c. By the continuity of the solutions with respect to the initial conditions, the ℓ_n also enter this chart. Let ℓ_n^+ be the entry point of ℓ_n. By Lemma 3.2.5, the sequence of the ℓ_n^+ tends to ℓ^+. Since we have assumed that $c \neq b$, the trajectories ℓ_n exit this chart through points ℓ_n^-. Still by Lemma 3.2.5, the limit of a convergent sequence extracted from the sequence (ℓ_n^-) is a $\lambda^- \in W^u(c)$ (as in the proof of Theorem 3.2.2). The trajectory λ of λ^- connects c to a critical point a that must be of index 0. Since the ℓ_n enter the Morse neighborhood of a for n sufficiently large, we necessarily have $a = a_1(= b)$ and $x \in A_1$. Hence A_1 is a closed subset of N.

Since N is connected, there exists an index $i_1 > 1$ such that $A_1 \cap A_{i_1} \neq \varnothing$. This intersection must contain a critical point of index 1, say c_1. We have

$$\partial_X c_1 = a_1 + a_{i_1},$$

so that a_{i_1} is in the same homology class as a_1. Moreover, $A_1 \cup A_{i_1}$ is connected. Therefore there exists an index i_2 such that $(A_1 \cup A_{i_1}) \cap A_{i_2} \neq \varnothing$. This intersection contains a trajectory coming from a critical point c_2 of index 1, so that we have

$$\partial_X c_2 = a_1 + a_{i_2} \quad \text{or} \quad \partial_X c_2 = a_{i_1} + a_{i_2}.$$

In both cases, the homology class of a_{i_2} is the same as that of a_1. We repeat this argument until there are no a_i left, thus showing that they are all homologous to a_1. □

Remark 4.5.2. This proof is completely analogous to the one we used in the classification of the manifolds of dimension 1 (in Section 2.3.b).

By applying the Poincaré duality, we deduce the following result from Proposition 4.5.1.

Corollary 4.5.3. *Let V be a compact connected manifold of dimension n; then $HM_n(V; \mathbf{Z}/2) \cong \mathbf{Z}/2$.* □

Remark 4.5.4. Proposition 4.5.1 is true over $\mathbf{Z}$, as can be seen by paying attention to orientations in the proof. The analogue of Corollary 4.5.3 then states that if V is a compact connected oriented manifold of dimension n, then $HM_n(V; \mathbf{Z}) \cong \mathbf{Z}$.

Corollary 4.5.5. *Let V be a compact manifold of dimension n. Then $HM_0(V; \mathbf{Z}/2)$ and $HM_n(V; \mathbf{Z}/2)$ are $\mathbf{Z}/2$-vector spaces of dimension the number of connected components of V.*

Proof. We write V as the disjoint union of its connected components:

$$V = \coprod_{i=1}^{k} V_i.$$

On each V_i, we choose a Morse function f_i and a *suitable* vector field X_i. It is clear that

$$C_\star(\coprod f_i) = \bigoplus C_\star(f_i) \quad \text{and} \quad \partial_{\coprod X_i} = \oplus \partial_{X_i},$$

giving the result.   □

Remark 4.5.6. The proof of Proposition 4.5.1 also tells us that a Morse function on a compact connected manifold that does not have a critical point of index 1 has a unique local minimum, a result that is essential in the proof of a famous theorem in symplectic geometry, the Atiyah–Guillemin–Sternberg convexity theorem (see for example [5] and the references to the original articles given there).

4.5.b Fundamental Group and Homology (Part 1)

In the same vein, and without truly using the Morse complex, let us begin comparing the fundamental group and the first homology group of the (connected) manifold V. The best possible result would be that $HM_1(V; \mathbf{Z})$ is the largest abelian quotient of the group $\pi_1(V)$. This is indeed the case. We will show later (in Section 4.8.a) a weaker result: if V is simply connected, then $HM_1(V; \mathbf{Z})$ is zero. For the moment, we content ourselves with noting the following result.

Proposition 4.5.7. *If the manifold V admits a Morse function with no critical points of index 1, then it is simply connected.*

Proof. We may, and do, assume that V is pathwise connected and choose a minimum (say a_0) of f as the base point. Let C be a loop in V. We may, and do, assume that this loop is differentiable. If b is a critical point of index k, then we know that $\dim W^s(b) = n - k$. By a general position argument, we may, and do, therefore assume that C meets none of the stable manifolds of the critical points of index greater than or equal to 2. Since we have assumed that there are no critical points of index 1, the loop C is contained in the union of the stable manifolds of the local minima, which are disjoint. Therefore C is contained in one of these stable manifolds, namely that of a_0. But this is a disk, in which we have no trouble contracting C onto the base point a_0.   □

Example 4.5.8. For example, the sphere S^n is simply connected as soon as $n \geq 2$.

4.6 Functoriality of the Morse Homology

We have seen (this is Remark 4.1.2) that a diffeomorphism between two manifolds induces an isomorphism at the Morse homology level. More generally, we would like to prove that a $\mathcal{C}^\infty$ map induces an homomorphism. Unfortunately, having a map $u : V \to W$ is not enough to construct a Morse function on V from a Morse function on W, so that we will need to be more subtle.

The manifold V that we are considering is a compact manifold, possibly with boundary, endowed with a Morse function f and a pseudo-gradient field X satisfying the Smale property, which moreover is pointing inward if $\partial V \neq \varnothing$ (with the notation used before, $\partial V = \partial_- V$).

The results we are going to prove here are the following two theorems.

Theorem 4.6.1 (Functoriality). *Let* $u : V \to W$ *be a map of class* $\mathcal{C}^\infty$. *It induces a morphism of graded abelian groups*

$$u_\star : HM_\star(V) \longrightarrow HM_\star(W).$$

Moreover, if $v : W \to Z$ *is another* $\mathcal{C}^\infty$ *map, then*

$$(v \circ u)_\star = v_\star \circ u_\star.$$

Finally, for the identity map $\mathrm{Id} : V \to V$, *we have* $\mathrm{Id}_\star = \mathrm{Id}$.

To say that $u_\star$ is a morphism of graded abelian groups is to say that this map is a collection of morphisms

$$u_k : HM_k(V) \longrightarrow HM_k(W).$$

In technical terms, this theorem states that the Morse homology is a functor from the category of differentiable manifolds and $\mathcal{C}^\infty$ maps into the category of abelian groups. It is also a "homotopy" functor.

Theorem 4.6.2 (Homotopy invariance). *Let* $u : [0,1] \times V \to W$ *be a* $\mathcal{C}^\infty$ *map. For* $u_t(x) = u(t,x)$, *we have* $(u_0)_\star = (u_1)_\star$.

The idea of the proof of Theorem 4.6.1 is to use the fact that the composition

$$V \xrightarrow{\ u\ } W = W \times \{0\} \subset W \times D^N$$

is homotopic to an embedding (for N sufficiently large) and therefore to begin by treating the case of embeddings.

Proof of Theorem 4.6.1 *for Embeddings.* Given a pair (f, X) on V with the Morse and Smale properties, the idea is to extend it to a pair $(\widetilde{f}, \widetilde{X})$ on W with the same properties. From this we will deduce a morphism of complexes

$$u_\bullet : C_\bullet(f, X) \longrightarrow C_\bullet(\widetilde{f}, \widetilde{X}).$$

We will then show that the morphism it induces on the homology does not depend on the choices of f and X.

The Case Where u Is a Diffeomorphism.

We saw in Remark 4.1.2 that the diffeomorphism u induces an isomorphism of complexes

$$C_\bullet(f, X) \longrightarrow C_\bullet(f \circ u^{-1}, du(X)).$$

Let us verify that the isomorphism induced on the homology does not depend on the choices of f and X. Therefore, let (f_0, X_0) and (f_1, X_1) be two Morse–Smale pairs on V and let (F, X) be a Morse–Smale pair on $[-1/3, 4/3] \times V$, as in Section 3.4. The pair $(F \circ (\mathrm{Id} \times u^{-1}), d(\mathrm{Id} \times u)(X))$ plays the same role for $(f_0 \circ u^{-1}, du(X_0))$ and $(f_1 \circ u^{-1}, du(X_1))$. In other words, we have the following commutative diagram.

$$
\begin{array}{ccc}
C_\bullet(f_0, X_0) & \xrightarrow{\ u_{\bullet 0}\ } & C_\bullet(f_0 \circ u^{-1}, du(X_0)) \\
\Big\downarrow{\scriptstyle \Phi^F} & & \Big\downarrow{\scriptstyle \Phi^{F \circ (\mathrm{Id} \times u^{-1})}} \\
C_\bullet(f_1, X_1) & \xrightarrow{\ u_{\bullet 1}\ } & C_\bullet(f_1 \circ u^{-1}, du(X_1))
\end{array}
$$

Obviously, for two diffeomorphisms u and v, we have $v_\bullet \circ u_\bullet = (v \circ u)_\bullet$, so that $v_\star \circ u_\star = (v \circ u)_\star$. Finally, $\mathrm{Id}_\star = \mathrm{Id}$.

The Case Where u Is the Inclusion in a Submanifold.

Let us denote it by

$$i : V \hookrightarrow W.$$

Proposition 4.6.3. *Let (f, X) be a Morse–Smale pair on V. Then there exists a Morse–Smale pair $(\widetilde{f}, \widetilde{X})$ on W that extends it and satisfies:*

(1) $\mathrm{Crit}(f) \subset \mathrm{Crit}(\widetilde{f})$ *and the index of a critical point of f is the same as its index as a critical point of $\widetilde{f}$.*

(2) *If a is a critical point of f, then $\partial_{\widetilde{X}}(a) = \partial_X(a)$.*

As a consequence of this proposition, we have an (injective) morphism of complexes

$$i_\bullet : C_\bullet(f, X) \longrightarrow C_\bullet(\widetilde{f}, \widetilde{X})$$

defined simply by sending a (seen as a critical point of f) to a (seen as a critical point of $\widetilde{f}$). Moreover, this morphism does not depend on the choice of the pair (f, X): we connect (f_0, X_0) to (f_1, X_1) as usual, using a function

$$F : [-1/3, 4/3] \times V \longrightarrow \mathbf{R}$$

and a vector field X on this product. We can make a commutative diagram

$$
\begin{array}{ccc}
C_\bullet(f_0, X_0) & \xhookrightarrow{u_\bullet 0} & C_\bullet(\widetilde{f}_0, \widetilde{X}_0) \\
\Big\downarrow{\scriptstyle\Phi^F} & & \Big\downarrow{\scriptstyle\Phi^{\widetilde{F}}} \\
C_\bullet(f_1, X_1) & \xhookrightarrow{u_\bullet 1} & C_\bullet(\widetilde{f}_1, \widetilde{X}_1)
\end{array}
$$

by extending F and X to $\widetilde{F}$ and $\widetilde{X}$ as we extended f and X, so that if a is a critical point of f_0 on V, then $\Phi^{\widetilde{F}}(a) = \Phi^F(a)$.

The Case Where $u : V \to W$ Is an Embedding.

We can view u as the composition of a diffeomorphism and the inclusion of a submanifold:

$$V \xrightarrow{u} u(V) \xhookrightarrow{i} W.$$

Starting with (f, X) on V, we construct, as above, $(\widetilde{f}, \widetilde{X})$ on W and a morphism of complexes

$$u_\bullet : C_\bullet(f, X) \longrightarrow C_\bullet(\widetilde{f}, \widetilde{X})$$

by sending a to $iu(a) = u(a)$.

We clearly have

$$v_\bullet \circ u_\bullet = (v \circ u)_\bullet \text{ and therefore also } v_\star \circ u_\star = (v \circ u)_\star. \qquad \square$$

Proof of Proposition 4.6.3. Let us consider a submanifold V of dimension n of a manifold W of dimension p.

Let c be a critical point of f on V and let U be a neighborhood of c in the (larger) manifold W. We may, and do, assume that U is of the form $U \equiv D^n \times D^{p-n}$. On such a U, it is easy to extend f by setting

$$\widetilde{f}(x, y) = f(x) + \frac{1}{2} \|y\|^2$$

and X by setting

$$\widetilde{X}(x, y) = X(x) - y$$

(that is, by adding to $X(x)$ the negative gradient of the square of the norm). We therefore choose such a neighborhood U_i of each critical point c_i of f and extend f and X by fixing this form on the U_i and extending it arbitrarily on the complement of the union of the U_i in W.

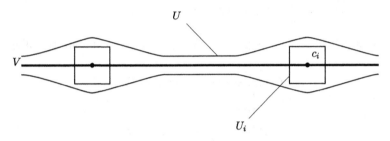

Fig. 4.3

Since all critical points of f on V are contained in the U_i and X is a pseudo-gradient, there exists an $\varepsilon_0 > 0$ such that

$$d\widetilde{f}(\widetilde{X}) < -\varepsilon_0$$

on $V - \cup(U_i \cap V)$ as well as near the boundaries of the U_i. Therefore there exists an open neighborhood U of $V \cup (\cup U_i)$ in W such that

$$d\widetilde{f}(\widetilde{X}) \leq 0$$

on U with equality exactly in the c_i.

In particular, $\widetilde{f}$ has no other critical points than the c_i on U. Since we have added a positive definite quadratic form to f, the index of c as a critical point of $\widetilde{f}$ is its index as a critical point of f.

There is no reason why the $\widetilde{f}$ that we have obtained by extending f arbitrarily should be a Morse function outside of U. We therefore take a slight perturbation that is a Morse function. We then construct a *suitable* extension of X to a pseudo-gradient $\widetilde{X}$ using a partition of unity.

Remark 4.6.4. Note that every trajectory γ of $\widetilde{X}$ with $\lim\limits_{t\to-\infty}\gamma(t)=c\in V$ is completely contained in V (we have assumed that X points inward near ∂V).

The extended field $\widetilde{X}$ does not necessarily have the Smale property. We do still have $\mathcal{L}_{\widetilde{X}}(a,b)=\mathcal{L}_X(a,b)$ for all critical points of f, so that

$$n_{\widetilde{X}}(a,b)=n_X(a,b), \text{ and therefore } \partial_{\widetilde{X}}(a)=\partial_X(a).$$

If $\widetilde{X}$ does have the Smale property, then we have the expected result. By taking a perturbation of $\widetilde{X}$, if necessary, we obtain a field that is very close and satisfies Smale. It may no longer be tangent to V but it does still satisfy $n_{\widetilde{X}}(a,b)=n_X(a,b)$. □

Remark 4.6.5. Note, in particular, that applying this proof shows that if V is a submanifold of a manifold W and if $\mathcal{V}$ is a tubular neighborhood of V in W, then $HM_\star(\mathcal{V})\cong HM_\star(V)$.

Before concluding the proof of Theorem 4.6.1 (general case of a map that is not an embedding), let us begin proving Theorem 4.6.2, which will be useful.

Proof of Theorem 4.6.2 for Embeddings. First note that since

$$HM_\star(D^N;\mathbf{Z})=\begin{cases}\mathbf{Z} & \text{if } \star=0 \\ 0 & \text{otherwise}\end{cases}$$

for every diffeomorphism $\psi:D^N\to D^N$, the map $\psi_\star$, which must be an isomorphism of $\mathbf{Z}$, can only be the identity map or its negative, that is, $\psi_\star=\pm\mathrm{Id}$. Moreover, it is the identity when ψ preserves the orientation.

Consequently, for every manifold V and every diffeomorphism ψ preserving the orientation of D^N, the map $\psi\times\mathrm{Id}:D^N\times V\to D^N\times V$ also induces the identity on the homology, since $(\psi\times\mathrm{Id})_\bullet=\psi_\bullet\otimes\mathrm{Id}_\bullet$ on the tensor product of the complexes, so that $(\psi\times\mathrm{Id})_\star=\psi_\star\otimes\mathrm{Id}_\star=\mathrm{Id}$.

Let us now consider different ways to embed V in $D^N\times V$.

Lemma 4.6.6. *For $a\in D^N$, let $i_a:V\to D^N\times V$ be the embedding defined by $i_a(x)=(a,x)$. Then:*

(1) $(i_0)_\star$ *is an isomorphism.*
(2) $(i_a)_\star=(i_0)_\star$.

Proof. We consider a Morse–Smale pair (f,X) on V identified with $\{0\}\times V\subset D^N\times V$. We extend (f,X) to $(\widetilde{f},\widetilde{X})$ as before, that is, by setting

$$\widetilde{f}(y,x)=\frac{1}{2}\|y\|^2+f(x) \quad\text{and}\quad \widetilde{X}(y,x)=-y+X(x).$$

Then $C_\bullet(f, X) = C_\bullet(\widetilde{f}, \widetilde{X})$, so that $(i_0)_\bullet = \mathrm{Id}$. This proves the first statement. For the second one, we use a diffeomorphism[1] $\psi : D^N \to D^N$ that sends 0 to a. The commutative diagram

$$
\begin{array}{ccc}
V & \xrightarrow{\;\;i_0\;\;} & D^N \times V \\
 & \searrow{\scriptstyle i_a} & \big\downarrow{\scriptstyle \psi \times \mathrm{Id}} \\
 & & D^N \times V
\end{array}
$$

gives $(i_0)_\star = (i_a)_\star$, as desired. $\square$

To prove this particular case of the homotopy invariance theorem (Theorem 4.6.2), we therefore consider a map

$$u : [0, 1] \times V \longrightarrow W$$

such that each u_t is an embedding. Then

$$
\begin{aligned}
\widetilde{u} : [0, 1] \times V &\longrightarrow [0, 1] \times W \\
(t, x) &\longmapsto (t, u_t(x))
\end{aligned}
$$

is an embedding. For the inclusions i_0 and i_1 (notation of the lemma), we have two commutative diagrams:

$$
\begin{array}{ccc}
[0, 1] \times V & \xrightarrow{\;\widetilde{u}\;} & [0, 1] \times W \\
{\scriptstyle i_0^V}\big\uparrow & & \big\uparrow{\scriptstyle i_0^W} \\
V & \xrightarrow{\;\;u_0\;\;} & W
\end{array}
\qquad\qquad
\begin{array}{ccc}
[0, 1] \times V & \xrightarrow{\;\widetilde{u}\;} & [0, 1] \times W \\
{\scriptstyle i_1^V}\big\uparrow & & \big\uparrow{\scriptstyle i_1^W} \\
V & \xrightarrow{\;\;u_1\;\;} & W
\end{array}
$$

from which we deduce

$$(u_0)_\star = (i_0^W)_\star^{-1} \circ \widetilde{u}_\star \circ (i_0^V)_\star = (i_1^W)_\star^{-1} \circ \widetilde{u}_\star \circ (i_1^V)_\star = (u_1)_\star. \qquad \square$$

Proof of Theorem 4.6.1, *General Case.* Consider a map of class $\mathcal{C}^\infty$:

$$u : V \longrightarrow W.$$

We choose a sufficiently large integer N such that there exists an embedding $\varphi : V \to D^N$. Then (φ, u) is an embedding of V in $D^N \times W$. We consider the

---

[1] The existence of such a diffeomorphism can be proved by integrating a suitable vector field on the disk D^N, an exercise whose details are left to the readers (Exercise 19 on p. 122).

diagram

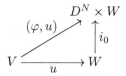

and set

$$u_\star = (i_0)_\star^{-1} \circ (\varphi, u)_\star.$$

Let us show that the resulting morphism $u_\star$ depends neither on the choice of N nor on φ (so that, in particular, if u is an embedding, then for $N = 0$ we will find what we have already constructed). We therefore consider another map $\psi : V \to D^M$ and the diagram

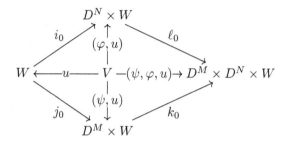

where ℓ_0 and k_0 are defined by

$$\ell_0(y, x) = (0, y, x) \quad \text{and} \quad k_0(z, x) = (z, 0, x).$$

We have $k_0 \circ j_0 = \ell_0 \circ i_0$, but the two triangles on the right of the diagram do not commute. However, the diagrams induced on the homology do commute. The homotopy "$t\psi$" connects

$$\ell_0(\varphi(x), u(x)) = (0, \varphi(x), u(x)) \quad \text{to} \quad (\psi(x), \varphi(x), u(x))$$

and likewise the homotopy "$t\varphi$" connects

$$k_0(\psi(x), u(x)) = (\psi(x), 0, u(x)) \quad \text{to} \quad (\psi(x), \varphi(x), u(x)).$$

Using the diagram and these remarks, let us now study the map $(i_0)_\star^{-1} \circ (\varphi, u)_\star$. We find

$$\begin{aligned}
(i_0)_\star^{-1} \circ (\varphi, u)_\star &= (i_0)_\star^{-1} \circ (\ell_0)_\star^{-1} \circ (\psi, \varphi, u)_\star \\
&= (j_0)_\star^{-1} \circ (k_0)_\star^{-1} \circ (\psi, \varphi, u)_\star \\
&= (j_0)_\star^{-1} \circ (\psi, u)_\star.
\end{aligned}$$

Hence our morphism $u_\star$ on the homology does not depend on the choices we made.

The verification of the functoriality follows the same course. For $u : V \to W$ and $W \to Z$, using $\varphi : V \to D^N$ and $\psi : W \to D^M$, we consider the following diagram.

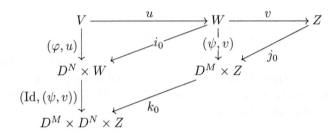

The vertical arrow $V \to D^M \times D^N \times Z$ is an embedding composed of two embeddings. We therefore already know that it satisfies the functoriality relation. Consequently, we can write

$$
\begin{aligned}
v_\star \circ u_\star &= (j_0)_\star^{-1} \circ (\psi, v)_\star \circ (i_0)_\star^{-1} \circ (\varphi, u)_\star \\
&= (j_0)_\star^{-1} \circ (k_0)_\star^{-1} \circ (\psi \circ (\mathrm{Id}, v))_\star \circ (\varphi, u)_\star \\
&= (v \circ u)_\star. \qquad\qquad\qquad\qquad\qquad\qquad\qquad \square
\end{aligned}
$$

End of the Proof of Theorem 4.6.2. It is an immediate consequence of the above. We simply regard u_t as the composition

$$
V \xrightarrow{\;i_t\;} [0,1] \times V \xrightarrow{\;u\;} W
$$

$u_t = u \circ i_t$, so that $u_\star \circ (i_t)_\star = (u_t)_\star \dots$ but we know that $(i_0)_\star = (i_1)_\star$, hence $(u_0)_\star = (u_1)_\star$. $\qquad\qquad\qquad\qquad\qquad\qquad\qquad\qquad\qquad\qquad\qquad\qquad \square$

4.7 Long Exact Sequence

Let V be a submanifold of a manifold W. We will show that there exists a long exact sequence in homology completing the map

$$
(i_0)_\star : HM_k(V) \longrightarrow HM_k(W).
$$

We will therefore use a Morse–Smale pair (f, X) on V that we will extend as in Section 4.6, this time to a tubular neighborhood $\mathcal{V}$ of V in W. This way, $\mathcal{V}$ is a manifold with boundary, as is $\overline{W - \mathcal{V}}$, both with the same boundary $\partial \mathcal{V}$.

We have at our disposition a Morse function $\widetilde{f}$ whose critical points in $\mathcal{V}$ are those of f on V and a vector field $\widetilde{X}$ satisfying the Smale condition, which points inward into $\mathcal{V}$ (and points outward from $\overline{W - \mathcal{V}}$). The inclusion $i_0 : V \subset W$ induces an injective morphism of complexes

$$(i_0)_\star : (C_\star(f), \partial_X) \longrightarrow (C_\star(\widetilde{f}), \partial_{\widetilde{X}}).$$

The first of these two complexes computes the homology of V, the second computes that of W, nothing new for the moment. We now define a (group) morphism

$$C_\star(\widetilde{f}) \longrightarrow C_\star(\widetilde{f}|_{\overline{W-\mathcal{V}}})$$

by simply sending the critical points of $\widetilde{f}$ that are in $\mathcal{V}$ to 0. Since, as we said, the critical points of $\widetilde{f}$ that are in $\mathcal{V}$ are those of f in V, we have a sequence of abelian groups,

$$C_\star(f) \longrightarrow C_\star(\widetilde{f}) \longrightarrow C_\star(\widetilde{f}|_{\overline{W-\mathcal{V}}}).$$

Our second morphism is also a morphism of complexes: a trajectory of $\widetilde{X}$ connecting two critical points of $\widetilde{f}$ that are not in $\mathcal{V}$ never enters $\mathcal{V}$. The complex $C_\star(\widetilde{f}|_{\overline{W-\mathcal{V}}}, \partial_{\widetilde{X}})$, in turn, computes the homology $HM_\star(\overline{W - \mathcal{V}}, \partial\mathcal{V})$ because the field $\widetilde{X}$ points outward from $\overline{W - \mathcal{V}}$.

As is the case for all similar sequences, this exact sequence of complexes induces a long exact sequence in homology as follows:

$$HM_k(V) \longrightarrow HM_k(W) \longrightarrow HM_k(\overline{W - \mathcal{V}}, \partial\mathcal{V})$$

$$HM_{k-1}(V) \xleftarrow{} HM_{k-1}(W)$$

∂

To simplify the notation, we set

$$HM_k(\overline{W - \mathcal{V}}, \partial\mathcal{V}) = HM_k(W, V),$$

for the relative homology.[2] The connecting homomorphism of the long exact sequence

$$HM_k(V) \longrightarrow HM_k(W) \longrightarrow HM_k(W, V)$$

$$HM_{k-1}(V) \xleftarrow{} HM_{k-1}(W)$$

∂

---

[2] For the readers who know what this is, it is indeed the relative homology obtained by excision; see for example [25].

has a simple interpretation: the map ∂ sends a class in $HM_k(\overline{W - V}, \partial V)$, represented by a critical point a of $\widetilde{f}$ in $\overline{W - V}$, to the class of the linear combination of the critical points of f connected to a by trajectories of $\widetilde{X}$,

$$\partial a = \sum_{b \in \mathrm{Crit}(f)} n_{\widetilde{X}}(a, b).$$

Let us now consider a manifold M with boundary ∂M,

$$\partial M \overset{i_0}{\lhook\joinrel\longrightarrow} M.$$

We would like to apply the above to the pair $(M, \partial M)$. It is however not completely true that ∂M is a submanifold of M. We therefore replace M by a manifold that is diffeomorphic to it and that has ∂M as a submanifold.

The boundary has a "collar" neighborhood, that is, one of the form

$$\partial M \times [-\varepsilon, 0] \overset{i}{\lhook\joinrel\longrightarrow} M \quad \text{with } i(x, 0) = i_0(x)$$

(where ε is a well-chosen positive real number and the notation is that of the previous section[3]). Note that

$$M^{-\varepsilon} = M - i(]-\varepsilon, 0])$$

is a manifold with boundary, diffeomorphic to M and with boundary $i_{-\varepsilon}(\partial M)$. We begin by adding a "mirror image" of this collar to M, by considering the obvious gluing

$$M^{+\varepsilon} = M \cup \partial M \times [0, \varepsilon]$$

(see Figure 4.4). The boundary ∂M is now a true submanifold of $M^{+\varepsilon}$. Moreover, it has a neighborhood that is diffeomorphic to $\partial M \times [-\varepsilon, \varepsilon]$.

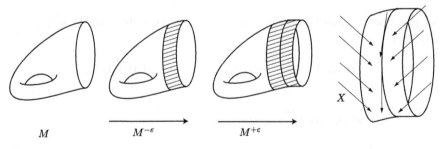

$$M \qquad\qquad M^{-\varepsilon} \qquad\qquad M^{+\varepsilon}$$

Fig. 4.4

---

[3] Recall that we can obtain such an i using the flow of a vector field that points inward.

Consider the pair (W, V) where $W = M^{+\varepsilon}$ and V is its submanifold ∂M. Since W is diffeomorphic to M, we have $HM_\star(W) = HM_\star(M)$. Moreover, $HM_\star(W, V)$, which by definition is $HM_\star(\overline{W - V}, V)$, is exactly what we defined to be $HM_\star(M, \partial M)$ in Section 3.5 on cobordisms. We therefore obtain the following long exact sequence

$$HM_k(\partial M) \longrightarrow HM_k(M) \longrightarrow HM_k(M, \partial M)$$

$$HM_{k-1}(\partial M) \xrightarrow{\quad\quad} \cdots$$

with ∂ arrow connecting.

Example 4.7.1. In the case of the disk (see Examples 3.5.1, 4.1.1 and Figure 3.12), the long exact sequence gives two isomorphisms,

$$HM_0(S^{n-1}; \mathbf{Z}/2) \xrightarrow{\ j_\star\ } HM_0(D^n; \mathbf{Z}/2)$$

and

$$HM_n(D^n, S^{n-1}; \mathbf{Z}/2) \xrightarrow{\ \partial\ } HM_{n-1}(S^{n-1}; \mathbf{Z}/2)$$

(the other groups in the exact sequence are trivial).

4.8 Applications

4.8.a Fundamental Group and Homology (Part 2)

We will now show, as announced in Section 4.5.b, that the H_1 of a simply connected manifold is zero.

Proposition 4.8.1. *If V is simply connected, then $HM_1(V; \mathbf{Z}/2) = 0$.*

Proof. We use a Morse–Smale pair (f, X) on V. We begin by describing the 1-cycles in V, that is, the elements α of $C_1(f)$ such that $\partial_X \alpha = 0$. These are linear combinations of critical points of index 1,

$$\alpha = a_1 + \cdots + a_k.$$

Moreover, $\partial_X a_1 + \cdots + \partial_X a_k = 0$. For a critical point a of index 1,

$$\partial_X a = c_1 + c_2,$$

where c_1 and c_2 are two critical points of index 0, which are not necessarily distinct (Figure 4.5): the unstable manifold of a is an open disk of dimension 1 and we continue applying Theorem 2.3.2.

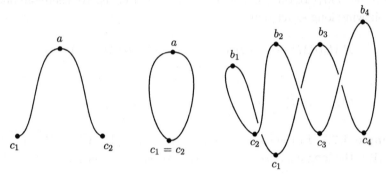

Fig. 4.5

Therefore our cycle α is the sum of cycles

$$\beta = b_1 + \cdots + b_s$$

with $\partial b_i = c_i + c_{i+1}$ for local minima $c_1, \ldots, c_s$ (with $c_{s+1} = c_1$), as in Figure 4.5.

Such a β defines an embedding u_β of the circle S^1 into V such that the function $g_\beta = f \circ u_\beta$ has the c_i as local minima and the b_i as local maxima. Each β in a basis of $\operatorname{Ker} \partial \subset C_1(f)$ defines an (injective) morphism of complexes

$$(u_\beta)_\bullet : C_\bullet(g_\beta, X_\beta) \longrightarrow C_\bullet(f, X)$$

(X_β is the vector field on S^1 whose image is the restriction of X) such that the image of

$$(u_\beta)_\star : HM_1(S^1; \mathbf{Z}/2) \longrightarrow HM_1(V; \mathbf{Z}/2)$$

is the subspace generated by the class of β.

Under the condition of simple connectedness on V, every map $v : S^1 \to V$ extends to a map $\tilde{v} : D^2 \to V$. In particular, in homology,

$$u_\beta : S^1 \lhook\joinrel\longrightarrow D^2 \xrightarrow{\ \tilde{u}_\beta\ } V$$

gives a factorization

$$(u_\beta)_\star : HM_1(S^1; \mathbf{Z}/2) \longrightarrow HM_1(D^2; \mathbf{Z}/2) \xrightarrow{\ (\tilde{u}_\beta)_\star\ } HM_1(V; \mathbf{Z}/2),$$

so that the class of β comes from $HM_1(D^2; \mathbf{Z}/2) = 0$ and is therefore zero. $\square$

4.8.b The Brouwer Fixed Point Theorem

Here is another proof of Brouwer's theorem (Theorem 2.3.3).

Proof of Theorem 2.3.3. As in the earlier proof, we begin by reducing to the case where φ is a $\mathcal{C}^\infty$ map and we assume that there is no fixed point. We then construct a retraction

$$r : D^n \longrightarrow S^{n-1}$$

by sending $x \in D^n$ to the intersection point of the sphere S^{n-1} and the ray starting at $\varphi(x)$ and going through x. This way, if x is a point on the sphere, it stays in place. The map r satisfies

$$r \circ j = \mathrm{Id} : S^{n-1} \hookrightarrow D^n \longrightarrow S^{n-1}.$$

Consequently, the composition $r_\star \circ j_\star$,

$$HM_{n-1}(S^{n-1}; \mathbf{Z}/2) \longrightarrow HM_{n-1}(D^n; \mathbf{Z}/2) \longrightarrow HM_{n-1}(S^{n-1}; \mathbf{Z}/2),$$

must also be the identity from $\mathbf{Z}/2$ to $\mathbf{Z}/2$, while $HM_{n-1}(D^n; \mathbf{Z}/2) = 0$, as we noted in Example 4.1.1. This contradiction implies the existence of a fixed point. $\square$

In a similar way, we prove that if $k < n$, then there is no retraction of the sphere S^n onto a subsphere $S^k \subset S^n$. Otherwise, in Morse homology the composition

$$S^k \xrightarrow{\ i\ } S^n \xrightarrow{\ r\ } S^k,$$

would give

$$HM_k(S^k; \mathbf{Z}/2) \xrightarrow{\ i_\star\ } HM_k(S^n; \mathbf{Z}/2) \xrightarrow{\ r_\star\ } HM_k(S^k; \mathbf{Z}/2)$$
$$\mathbf{Z}/2 \longrightarrow \qquad\quad 0 \qquad\quad \longrightarrow \mathbf{Z}/2,$$

a zero map that should be the identity.

4.8.c Modulo 2 Homology of the Projective Space

Let us consider the sphere

$$S^n = \{ x \in \mathbf{R}^{n+1} \mid \|x\|^2 = 1 \}$$

and its quotient by the equivalence relation $x \sim -x$, namely $\mathbf{P}^n(\mathbf{R})$, the real projective space of dimension n. The natural projection $S^n \to \mathbf{P}^n(\mathbf{R})$ is denoted by p.

Let f be a Morse function on $\mathbf{P}^n(\mathbf{R})$. The function $f \circ p$ is a Morse function on S^n (locally there is no difference between S^n and $\mathbf{P}^n(\mathbf{R})$). It has two critical points of index k, a and $-a$, above each critical point $p(a)$ of f.

Likewise, if X is a pseudo-gradient field adapted to f, then there exists a vector field $\widetilde{X}$ on S^n that is a pseudo-gradient field for $f \circ p$ and such that, for every x on S^n,

$$T_x(p)(\widetilde{X}_x) = X_{p(x)}.$$

So the trajectories of $\widetilde{X}$ project onto those of X. Moreover, if we suppose that X satisfies the Smale property, then the same holds for $\widetilde{X}$. In particular, for all critical points a and b of $f \circ p$ with consecutive indices, we have

$$n_{\widetilde{X}}(a,b) = n_{\widetilde{X}}(-a,-b).$$

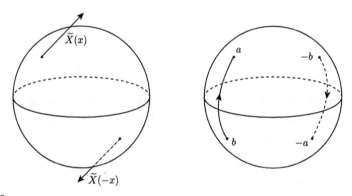

Fig. 4.6

The formula $\alpha \mapsto p(\alpha)$ defines a morphism of complexes $(C_k(\widetilde{f}), \partial_{\widetilde{X}}) \to (C_k(f), \partial_X)$ that we will denote by $p_\star$ (this is not really an abuse of notation, it is indeed the $p_\star$ defined by the differentiable map p, as can be verified using embeddings). Likewise, the formula

$$p(a) \longmapsto a + (-a)$$

defines a linear map

$$p^! : C_k(f) \longrightarrow C_k(\widetilde{f}).$$

If $\alpha = p(a) = p(-a)$ is a critical point of f, then we have

$$\partial_{\widetilde{X}}(p^! \alpha) = \partial_{\widetilde{X}}(a) + \partial_{\widetilde{X}}(-a)$$
$$= \sum_b n_{\widetilde{X}}(a,b)b + \sum_c n_{\widetilde{X}}(-a,c)c$$
$$= \sum_b n_{\widetilde{X}}(a,b)b + \sum_b n_{\widetilde{X}}(-a,-b)(-b).$$

But there exists a trajectory from a to b if and only if there exists a trajectory from $-a$ to $-b$, so that this sum equals

$$\partial_{\widetilde{X}}(p^!\alpha) = \sum_b n_{\widetilde{X}}(a,b)b + \sum_{-b} n_{\widetilde{X}}(-a,-b)(-b)$$
$$= \sum_b n_{\widetilde{X}}(a,b)(b+(-b))$$
$$= \sum_{\beta} n_X(\alpha,\beta)(b+(-b))$$
$$= \sum_{\beta} n_X(\alpha,\beta) \cdot p^!(\beta) = p^!(\partial_X \alpha).$$

Hence $p^!$ is a morphism of complexes

$$p^! : (C_k(f), \partial_X) \longrightarrow (C_k(f \circ p), \partial_{\widetilde{X}}).$$

The composition

$$(C_k, \partial_X) \xrightarrow{p^!} (C_k(f \circ p), \partial_{\widetilde{X}}) \xrightarrow{p_\star} (C_k(f), \partial_X)$$

first sends the critical point α onto $a + (-a)$ and then onto

$$p(a) + p(-a) = 2\alpha = 0.$$

More precisely, we have an exact sequence of complexes

$$0 \longrightarrow (C_k(f), \partial_X) \xrightarrow{p^!} (C_k(f \circ p), \partial_{\widetilde{X}}) \xrightarrow{p_\star} (C_k(f), \partial_X) \longrightarrow 0.$$

Indeed, a linear combination $a_1 + \cdots + a_k$ of critical points of $\widetilde{f}$, sent onto $p(a_1) + \cdots + p(a_k)$, can only be zero if each of the critical points of f in this sum appear twice, that is, if

$$a_1 + \cdots + a_k = a_{i_1} + (-a_{i_1}) + \cdots + a_{i_r} + (-a_{i_r}),$$

or in other words, if this element is in the image of $p^!$.

We therefore have an exact sequence of complexes that, as it should, defines the following long exact Morse homology sequence.

$$HM_k(\mathbf{P}^n(\mathbf{R}); \mathbf{Z}/2) \longrightarrow HM_k(S^n; \mathbf{Z}/2) \longrightarrow HM_k(\mathbf{P}^n(\mathbf{R}); \mathbf{Z}/2)$$

$$HM_{k-1}(\mathbf{P}^n(\mathbf{R}); \mathbf{Z}/2) \longrightarrow \cdots$$

It follows that the connecting homomorphism

$$\partial : HM_k(\mathbf{P}^n(\mathbf{R}); \mathbf{Z}/2) \longrightarrow HM_{k-1}(\mathbf{P}^n(\mathbf{R}); \mathbf{Z}/2)$$

is an isomorphism for $0 \leq k \leq n$. We have therefore proved the following result.

Theorem 4.8.2. *We have* $HM_k(\mathbf{P}^n(\mathbf{R}); \mathbf{Z}/2) \cong \mathbf{Z}/2$ *for* $0 \leq k \leq n$. $\square$

For the integral homology (the orientation questions must be treated with care); see Exercises 24 and 25 on p. 123.

Here is an explicit description of the connecting homomorphism of this exact sequence. To determine this, it suffices to follow its abstract definition. We begin by choosing a hemisphere of S^n, for example the southern one for a change. If α is a cycle in $(C_k(f), \partial_X)$,

$$\alpha = \alpha_1 + \cdots + \alpha_r,$$

then we choose lifts a_i of the α_i in the southern hemisphere, obtaining a sum

$$a = a_1 + \cdots + a_r$$

whose image under $p_\star$ is our cycle α. Then $\partial_{\widetilde{X}} a$ is a linear combination of critical points of index $k - 1$ of $\widetilde{f}$, which is of the form

$$\partial_{\widetilde{X}} a = \sum_{i=1}^{p}(b_i + (-b_i))$$

with b_i in the southern hemisphere. We then have

$$\partial[a] = [p(b_1) + \cdots + p(b_p)].$$

4.8.d The Borsuk–Ulam Theorem

Let us now prove the following famous theorem.

Theorem 4.8.3 (Borsuk–Ulam).   *There does not exist any continuous map*

$$\varphi : S^n \longrightarrow S^{n-1}$$

with $\varphi(-x) = -\varphi(x)$ *for every* x.

This theorem has more or less colorful, not so serious applications (for example, the fascinating fact that at every moment there exist two antipodal points on Earth with the same temperature and atmospheric pressure).

Corollary 4.8.4. *Let $\psi : S^n \to \mathbf{R}^n$ be a continuous map such that*

$$\psi(-x) = -\psi(x) \text{ for every } x.$$

Then ψ has at least one zero on S^n.

Indeed, if ψ were never zero, then it would define a map $\varphi = \psi/\|\psi\|$ with values in S^{n-1}, which is prohibited by the theorem. □

Here is the temperature–pressure theorem.

Corollary 4.8.5. *For every map $\psi : S^n \to \mathbf{R}^n$, there exists at least one point x of S^n such that $\psi(x) = \psi(-x)$.*

In particular, note that there does not exist any injection of S^n into $\mathbf{R}^n$. The corollary can be proved by considering $\varphi(x) = \psi(x) - \psi(-x)$. □

Corollary 4.8.6. *Let $F_1, F_2, \ldots, F_{n+1}$ be nonempty closed subsets of the sphere S^n whose union is the entire sphere. Then one of the F_i contains two antipodal points.*

It suffices to use the map

$$\psi(x) = (d(x, F_1), d(x, F_2), \ldots, d(x, F_n)).$$

□

Proof of Theorem 4.8.3. Of course, as in the case of Brouwer's theorem, we are going to show that there does not exist any $\mathcal{C}^\infty$ map with the desired properties (the result for continuous maps follows from it). A map φ with the stated properties would induce a map $\psi : \mathbf{P}^n(\mathbf{R}) \to \mathbf{P}^{n-1}(\mathbf{R})$ that we will show cannot exist.

So, let ψ be a $\mathcal{C}^\infty$ map from $\mathbf{P}^n(\mathbf{R})$ to $\mathbf{P}^{n-1}(\mathbf{R})$. Consider the diagram

$$
\begin{array}{ccc}
HM_k(\mathbf{P}^n(\mathbf{R}); \mathbf{Z}/2) & \xrightarrow{\psi_\star} & HM_k(\mathbf{P}^{n-1}(\mathbf{R}); \mathbf{Z}/2) \\
\Big\downarrow{\partial} & & \Big\downarrow{\partial} \\
HM_{k-1}(\mathbf{P}^n(\mathbf{R}); \mathbf{Z}/2) & \xrightarrow{\psi_\star} & HM_{k-1}(\mathbf{P}^{n-1}(\mathbf{R}); \mathbf{Z}/2)
\end{array}
$$

where the connecting homomorphism ∂ has been defined in Section 4.8.c. From this diagram we will deduce that

$$\psi_\star : HM_n(\mathbf{P}^n(\mathbf{R}); \mathbf{Z}/2) \longrightarrow HM_n(\mathbf{P}^{n-1}(\mathbf{R}); \mathbf{Z}/2)$$

is nonzero which is absurd since the latter group is zero. We prove by induction that

$$\psi_\star : HM_k(\mathbf{P}^n(\mathbf{R}); \mathbf{Z}/2) \longrightarrow HM_k(\mathbf{P}^{n-1}(\mathbf{R}); \mathbf{Z}/2)$$

is an isomorphism for $k \leq n - 1$.

For $k = 0$, this is a very general fact, which comes from the next lemma.

Lemma 4.8.7. *Let V and W be connected manifolds and let $u : V \to W$ be a $\mathcal{C}^\infty$ map. Then the induced map*

$$u_\star : HM_0(V; \mathbf{Z}/2) \longrightarrow HM_0(W; \mathbf{Z}/2)$$

is the identity map.

Proof. We use the notation of Lemma 4.6.6. By definition,

$$u_\star = (i_0^{-1})_\star \circ (u, \psi)_\star,$$

where ψ in an embedding $V \to D^N$. According to Lemma 4.6.6, $i_0 : W \to D^N \times W$ induces an isomorphism in homology. It thus suffices to prove the lemma when u is an embedding.

We showed in Proposition 4.5.1 that $HM_0(V; \mathbf{Z}/2)$ is isomorphic to $\mathbf{Z}/2$, generated by any critical point c of index 0 of a Morse function on V. On the other hand, if $u : V \to W$ is an embedding, the proof of Proposition 4.6.3 shows that $u_\star(c) = u(c)$, where $u(c)$ is a critical point of index 0 of an appropriate extension of $f \circ u^{-1}$ to W. The lemma is proved. □

Suppose now that $\psi_\star$ induces an isomorphism at HM_{k-1} level for some $k \leq n - 1$. Assume the above diagram commutes. Since the two vertical arrows are isomorphisms, by Theorem 4.8.2, $\psi_\star$ induces an isomorphism at the HM_k level.

Now consider the diagram for $k = n$. The left vertical arrow ∂ is an isomorphism (again by Theorem 4.8.2), so $\psi_\star \circ \delta$ is an isomorphism. Therefore

$$\psi_\star : HM_n(\mathbf{P}^n(\mathbf{R}); \mathbf{Z}/2) \longrightarrow HM_n(\mathbf{P}^{n-1}(\mathbf{R}); \mathbf{Z}/2)$$

is not zero, which is absurd.

It remains to prove that the diagram commutes. Let $\Gamma : \mathbf{P}^n(\mathbf{R}) \to D^N$ be an embedding. By definition, $\psi_\star = (i_0^{-1})_\star (\Gamma, \psi)_\star$, so it is sufficient to prove that the diagrams

$$
\begin{array}{ccc}
HM_k(\mathbf{P}^n(\mathbf{R}); \mathbf{Z}/2) & \xrightarrow{(\Gamma, \psi)_\star} & HM_k(D^N \times \mathbf{P}^{n-1}(\mathbf{R}); \mathbf{Z}/2) \\
\downarrow{\partial} & & \downarrow{\partial} \\
HM_{k-1}(\mathbf{P}^n(\mathbf{R}); \mathbf{Z}/2) & \xrightarrow[(\Gamma, \psi)_\star]{} & HM_{k-1}(D^N \times \mathbf{P}^{n-1}(\mathbf{R}); \mathbf{Z}/2)
\end{array}
$$

and

$$HM_k(\mathbf{P}^{n-1}(\mathbf{R}); \mathbf{Z}/2) \xrightarrow{(i_0)_\star} HM_k(D^N \times \mathbf{P}^{n-1}(\mathbf{R}); \mathbf{Z}/2)$$

$$\partial \downarrow \qquad\qquad\qquad\qquad \downarrow \partial$$

$$HM_{k-1}(\mathbf{P}^{n-1}(\mathbf{R}); \mathbf{Z}/2) \xrightarrow{(i_0)_\star} HM_{k-1}(D^N \times \mathbf{P}^{n-1}(\mathbf{R}); \mathbf{Z}/2)$$

are commutative, where

$$\partial : HM_k(D^N \times \mathbf{P}^{n-1}(\mathbf{R}); \mathbf{Z}/2) \longrightarrow HM_{k-1}(D^N \times \mathbf{P}^{n-1}(\mathbf{R}); \mathbf{Z}/2)$$

is defined by an analogous exact sequence of complexes.

The second diagram is obviously commutative: if we use the Morse function $x \mapsto \|x\|^2$ on D^N, the two exact sequences of complexes are identical and $(i_0)_\star = \mathrm{Id}$. We consider now the first one.

Recall that ψ was defined by a map

$$\varphi : S^n \longrightarrow S^{n-1} \quad \text{with} \quad \varphi(-x) = -\varphi(x).$$

This implies that

$$(\Gamma \circ p, \varphi) : S^n \longrightarrow D^N \times S^{n-1}$$

is an embedding. Now, we take a Morse–Smale pair (f, X) on $\mathbf{P}^n(\mathbf{R})$. We lift it to a Morse–Smale pair $(f \circ p, \widetilde{X})$ on S^n as before. Then we extend $(f \circ (\Gamma, \psi)^{-1}, T(\Gamma, \psi)X)$ to $(\overline{f}, \overline{X})$, a Morse–Smale pair on $D^N \times \mathbf{P}^{n-1}(\mathbf{R})$, as in the proof of Proposition 4.6.3. We lift $(\overline{f}, \overline{X})$ to $(\overline{f} \circ p, \widetilde{\overline{X}})$ on $D^N \times S^{n-1}$ (which is an extension of $(f \circ p \circ (\Gamma \circ p, \varphi)^{-1}, T(\Gamma, \varphi)\widetilde{X}))$. This yields the diagram

$$
\begin{array}{ccccccccc}
0 & \longrightarrow & C_\bullet(f, X) & \xrightarrow{p^!} & C_\bullet(f \circ p, \widetilde{X}) & \xrightarrow{p} & C_\bullet(f, X) & \longrightarrow & 0 \\
& & \downarrow{\scriptstyle(\Gamma, \psi)_\bullet} & & \downarrow{\scriptstyle(\Gamma \circ p, \varphi)_\bullet} & & \downarrow{\scriptstyle(\Gamma, \psi)_\bullet} & & \\
0 & \longrightarrow & C_\bullet(\overline{f}, \overline{X}) & \xrightarrow{p^!} & C_\bullet(\overline{f} \circ p, \widetilde{\overline{X}}) & \xrightarrow{p} & C_\bullet(\overline{f}, \overline{X}) & \longrightarrow & 0
\end{array}
$$

with horizontal exact sequences, commutative squares and vertical arrows defined by Proposition 4.6.3. Using the definition of the connecting morphism ∂, it is then easy to check that the diagram is commutative. Note that when we identified the left vertical arrows of the two diagrams, we implicitly used the fact that ∂ does not depend on the choice of the Morse–Smale pair on $D^N \times \mathbf{P}^{n-1}(\mathbf{R})$. This is because ∂ is an isomorphism and the only isomorphism of $\mathbf{Z}/2$ to itself is the identity. $\square$

4.9 Appendix: The Morse Homology is the Cellular Homology

In this appendix, we show that a Morse function and a pseudo-gradient field on a manifold allow us to define a cellular decomposition of the manifold, and that the Morse complex and the cellular complex are isomorphic.

We begin by recalling the definitions of decomposition and cellular complexes. Following Latour [46], we then describe the cellular decomposition associated with Morse–Smale pairs.[4]

4.9.a Complexes and Cellular Homology

In this section, we follow Dold's book [25]. A cellular decomposition of a space V (this can be any separated topological space; we will apply it to compact manifolds) is a family $\mathcal{E}$ of subspaces of V with the following properties:

- Every element e of $\mathcal{E}$ is homeomorphic to an open disk
- $\mathcal{E}$ is a cover of V (by disjoints subsets).

The e are called cells. The union of the cells of dimension at most k of V is called the k-skeleton of V and is denoted by $V^{(k)}$.

- For every e of dimension k in $\mathcal{E}$, there exists a continuous map

$$\Phi_e : (B^k, S^{k-1}) \longrightarrow (V^{(k-1)} \cup e, V^{(k-1)})$$

(called an attachment map) whose restriction to $B^k - S^{k-1}$ is a homeomorphism on e.

We will assume that there are only finitely many cells.

Examples 4.9.1.

(1) On the sphere of dimension n, the complement of a point (say the south pole S, to illustrate the ideas) is an open disk of dimension n. Together with the missing point, it forms a cellular decomposition of the sphere, whose skeletons of dimensions at most $n - 1$ are all the point S.

---

[4] For another point of view, we refer to Laudenbach's appendix in [12].

(2) The projective space is the union of an affine space and a hyperplane at infinity, which in turn is the union of an affine space and a hyperplane at infinity... and so on. Therefore the real (or complex) projective space admits a cellular decomposition with a cell in every dimension (or in every even dimension, respectively).

(3) The torus $T^2 = \mathbf{R}^2/\mathbf{Z}^2$, seen as a square whose sides have been identified in pairs, has a cellular decomposition with:

- one cell of dimension 2 (the open square)
- two cells of dimension 1 (one coming from the horizontal sides, the other coming from the vertical sides)
- and one cell of dimension 0 (coming from the four vertices of the square).

Remark 4.9.2. If we crush the $(k-1)$-skeleton, that is, if we take the quotient $V^{(k)}/V^{(k-1)}$, then the result is a bouquet of spheres of dimension k, each coming from a cell (a D^k) in which we have identified all points on the boundary with one point.

This bouquet can be a bouquet of zero spheres, as is the case for the sphere of dimension n with $k \leq n-1$.

In the example of the torus of dimension 2 with the decomposition given above, $V^{(1)}/V^{(0)}$ is a bouquet of two circles.

The cellular complex $K_\star$ is defined by letting K_m be the vector space over $\mathbf{Z}/2$ generated by the cells of dimension m (or the abelian group generated by the cells of dimension m if we want to define the integral homology).

The differential is defined by

$$\partial c = \sum_d N(c,d)d,$$

where the number $N(c,d)$ associated with a cell c of dimension m and a cell d of dimension $m-1$ is defined as follows:

- By definition, the cell c is the image of a map Φ_c.
- We consider the decomposition

$$\Phi_c\,|_{S^{m-1}}\colon S^{m-1} \longrightarrow V^{(m-1)} \longrightarrow V^{(m-1)}/V^{(m-2)}.$$

- The last space is a bouquet of $(m-1)$-spheres, of which one corresponds to the cell d (as noted in Remark 4.9.2); there is therefore a map

$$\Psi_d : V^{(m-1)}/V^{(m-2)} \longrightarrow S^{m-1}.$$

that crushes all the spheres except the one corresponding to d into one point.

- The number $N(c, d)$ is the degree (which we consider modulo 2) of the composed map

$$\Psi_d \circ \Phi_c : S^{m-1} \longrightarrow S^{m-1}.$$

It can be proved (see [25]) that $(K_\star, \partial)$ is a complex ($\partial \circ \partial = 0$) and that the homology of this complex does not depend on the cellular decomposition of V.

In the "Morse–Smale" context of a Morse function with a pseudo-gradient field on a manifold V, we are going to construct a cellular decomposition of V whose cells will be the unstable manifolds of the critical points of the function.

We will prove the following theorem.

Theorem 4.9.3. *Let (f, X) be a Morse–Smale pair on a manifold V. There exist a cellular decomposition of the manifold V and an isomorphism*

$$F : K_\star \longrightarrow C_\star \text{ with } \partial_X \circ F = F \circ \partial$$

from the cellular complex to the Morse complex.

Consequently, the Morse homology of the manifold V is isomorphic to its cellular homology.

If we fix an orientation on each cell and define $N(c, d) \in \mathbf{Z}$ as the degree of $\Psi_d \circ \Phi_c$, we get a complex over $\mathbf{Z}$ and Theorem 4.9.3 is still valid.

4.9.b Cellular Decomposition Associated with a Morse–Smale Pair

In this section, we follow the definitions and ideas of Latour in [46]. The compact manifold V is endowed with a Morse function f and a pseudo-gradient field X. We assume that X satisfies the Smale property.

As we said in Proposition 2.1.5, the unstable manifold of a critical point of f is an open ball of dimension the index of the critical point. We first compactify these unstable manifolds into closed balls.

Let c be a critical point. We set

$$\overline{W}^u(c) = W^u(c) \cup \left(\overline{\mathcal{L}}(c, d) \times \bigcup_d W^u(d) \right).$$

The union is taken over the critical points d such that $\overline{\mathcal{L}}(c, d)$ is nonempty, that is, over the critical points connected to c. By the Smale property, the indices of these points are less than the index of c.

We now endow $\overline{W}^u(c)$ with a topology. We of course use the topology defined on the multiconnection spaces $\overline{\mathcal{L}}(c,d)$ in Section 3.2. Let $(\lambda, x) \in \mathcal{L}(c,d_1) \times \cdots \times \mathcal{L}(d_{k-1},d) \times W^u(d)$. We can describe a fundamental system of open neighborhoods $W(\lambda, x, U^0, \mathbf{U}^-, \mathbf{U}^+)$ of (λ, x) in $\overline{W}^u(c)$ as follows:

- Obviously, U^0 is a neighborhood of x in V.
- $W(\lambda, \mathbf{U}^-, \mathbf{U}^+)$ is a neighborhood of λ in $\overline{\mathcal{L}}(c,d)$.
- If $(\mu, x') \in \overline{\mathcal{L}}(c,d_i) \times W^u(d_i)$ (for some $i \leq k$), then we say that

$$(\mu, x') \in W(x, \lambda, U^0, \mathbf{U}^-, \mathbf{U}^+)$$

if:

- $x' \in U^0$.
- The trajectory from d_i to x' passes through U_j^- for $j \geq i$ and through U_j^+ for $j > i$.
- $\mu \in W(\lambda', \mathbf{U}^{-\prime}, \mathbf{U}^{+\prime})$ (where $\lambda' = (\lambda_1, \ldots, \lambda_i)$ and the $\mathbf{U}^{\pm\prime}$ are defined as you might expect).

For example, if c is a critical point of index 0, then $W^u(c)$ equals $\{c\}$ and so does $\overline{W}^u(c)$ (this is indeed a cell of dimension 0). Here are some less trivial examples.

Examples 4.9.4.

(1) Let c be a critical point of index 1. Then $W^u(c)$ consists of points on V lying on the trajectories from c to critical points of index 0, two trajectories, whose endpoints in V would be these two (or the one) critical point(s). In $\overline{W}^u(c)$, we add a point for each of these trajectories. Whether their endpoints are the same or not, the two trajectories give distinct points: $\mathcal{L}(c,d) \times W^u(d)$ contains the two points $\{\ell_1\} \times \{d\}$ and $\{\ell_2\} \times \{d\}$. Hence $\overline{W}^u(c)$ is a closed disk of dimension 1 (Figure 4.7).

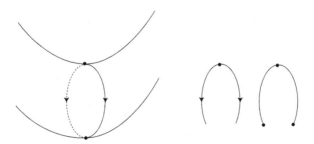

Fig. 4.7 Critical point of index 1

(2) Next, let c be a critical point of index 2. The unstable manifold is an open disk of dimension 2. Let us see what we need to add to it:

- For every critical point d of index 1 connected to c, we add the product of $\overline{\mathcal{L}}(c,d) = \mathcal{L}(c,d)$ (the trajectories from c to d, a point for each of the trajectories in question) and its unstable manifold $W^u(d)$ (an open interval, as above).
- For every critical point e of index 0 connected to c, we add the product of the set of trajectories from c to e (open segments, with their boundaries, the set of broken trajectories, which links it to the trajectories connecting c to the critical points of index 1) and its unstable manifold (the point e itself).

Figure 4.8 shows, in dimension 2, the example of a critical point c of index 2 (thick dot) connected to a unique critical point d of index 1 and a unique critical point e of index 0. The figure on the left shows three critical points of the (height) function, the figure on the right shows the closed "cell" $\overline{W}^u(c)$, with:

- The point c and its unstable manifold $W^u(c)$ (an open disk of dimension 2).
- The unique trajectory $\mathcal{L}(c,d)$ from c to d shown as the small open dot (which symbolizes the point d in the figure on the left).
- On the boundary of the disk we see the product $\mathcal{L}(c,d) \times W^u(d)$; since $\mathcal{L}(c,d)$ consists of one point, the unstable manifold of d, this product consists of an open segment (shown as a thick line segment) consisting of the two trajectories from c to d.
- The unstable manifold of the point e of index 0 is of course a single point.
- The boundary of the disk also contains $\overline{\mathcal{L}}(c,e) \times W^u(e)$, that is, the open segment $\mathcal{L}(c,e)$ of the trajectories from c to e, shown here as a cir-

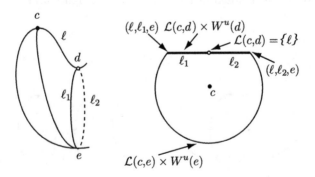

Fig. 4.8 Critical point of index 2

cular arc, as well as the two broken trajectories from c to e (through d) which are the common endpoints of the thick segment and thin circular arc.

We are going to show that the $W^u(c)$ give a cellular decomposition of the manifold V, where the attachment maps Φ_c are defined on $W^u(c)$ by the inclusion and on the "boundary" by their restriction to each "piece" as given by the projection

$$\Phi_c|_{\overline{\mathcal{L}}(c,d) \times W^u(d)} : \overline{\mathcal{L}}(c,d) \times W^u(d) \longrightarrow W^u(d) \subset V.$$

Let us begin with a few examples. We give a complete description of the different cells for the examples of Morse functions and pseudo-gradient fields used before.

Examples 4.9.5.

(1) The round sphere. For the height function on the round sphere of dimension 2, the situation is very simple. Let a be the maximum and let b be the minimum. The cell of dimension 2 around a consists of an open disk (the unstable manifold $W^u(a)$) and, at the boundary, the circle $\mathcal{L}(a,b) \times W^u(b)$. The attachment map crushes $\mathcal{L}(a,b) \times W^u(b)$ onto the point $W^u(b)$. We thus have the cellular decomposition of the sphere into a cell of dimension 0 and one of dimension 2.

(2) The example of the "other" sphere is the one shown in Figure 4.8.

(3) The torus. Figure 4.9 represents, on the left, the Morse function on the torus with the pseudo-gradient given in Section 2.2.a, and on the right, the closed cell around the critical point of index 2. To represent the cell of dimension 2, we have, as in Figure 4.8, represented the $\mathcal{L}(c,d_i)$ by small open dots, the $\mathcal{L}(c,d_i) \times W^u(d_i)$ by thick line segments and the $\mathcal{L}(c,e) \times W^u(e)$ by (round) circular arcs.

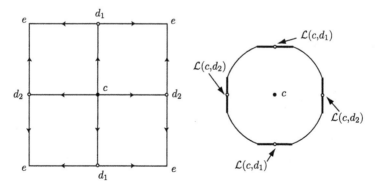

Fig. 4.9 Critical point of index 2 on the torus

4.9.c Proof of Theorem 4.9.3

We must prove two things:

(1) The $\overline{W}^u(c)$ indeed define a cellular decomposition of V.
(2) The two complexes are isomorphic.

Let us begin with the second result.

The Isomorphism of the Complexes

The complex $K_\star$ is defined in Section 4.9.a, where each cell is defined by the unstable manifold of a critical point. The map F sends this critical point to the cell. Hence F is clearly bijective.

It is an isomorphism of complexes because the number $N(c,d)$ that defines the differential of $K_\star$ is equal to the number of trajectories connecting c to d, that is, the $n(c,d)$ that defines the differential of the Morse complex.

In fact, $N(c,d)$ is the degree of the map $\Psi_d \circ \Phi_c : S^{m-1} \to S^{m-1}$ defined above, for $m = \mathrm{Ind}(c)$. The source of this map is the boundary of $\overline{W}^u(c)$, which we, for the moment, admit to be a sphere (this is one of the results proved in this subsection). The target of this map is the quotient obtained by crushing the $(m-2)$-skeleton and the spheres that do not correspond to d, that is, $\overline{D}^{m-1}/\partial\overline{D}^{m-1}$. We can also view this quotient as a compactification of D^{m-1} through the addition of a point, where the open disk D^{m-1} is identified with the unstable manifold $W^u(d) \subset V$. If $\ell \in \mathcal{L}(c,d)$, then for $m \in W^u(d)$, we have

$$\Psi_d \circ \Phi_c(\ell, m) = m$$

and the other points of the boundary of $\overline{W}^u(c)$ are sent onto the point that is the image of the boundary.

We therefore have $n(c,d)$ (the number of trajectories connecting c to d) disjoint disks on S^{m-1} that are sent onto $D^{m-1} \subset S^{m-1}$ by homeomorphisms, and the image of the complement is the remaining point. The degree $N(c,d)$ is therefore indeed the number $n(c,d)$ of trajectories.

The Cellular Decomposition

We have seen (Proposition 2.1.5) that the unstable manifold $W^u(c)$ of a critical point c is an open ball (of dimension the index of c). The restriction of Φ_c to $W^u(c)$ is a homeomorphism and its image is contained in $V^{\mathrm{Ind}(c)}$. We must show that $\overline{W}^u(c)$ is homeomorphic to a (closed) ball of the same dimension whose interior is $W^u(c)$.

To do this, consider, for every $A \in \mathbf{R}$,

$$\overline{W}^u(c, A) = \left\{ (x, \lambda) \in \overline{W}^u(c) \mid f(x) \geq A \right\}$$

and
$$W^u(c, A) = \{(x, \lambda) \in W^u(c) \mid f(x) \geq A\}.$$

For $A = f(c) - \varepsilon$ and ε sufficiently small,

$$\overline{W}^u(c, A) = W^u(c) \cap \overline{\Omega}(c),$$

where $\Omega(c)$ is the open set of the Morse chart corresponding to the parameter ε, so that $\overline{W}^u(c, A)$ is clearly homeomorphic to a closed ball.

For $A < \min(f)$, we obviously have

$$\overline{W}^u(c, A) = \overline{W}^u(c).$$

We must therefore show that the topology on $\overline{W}^u(c, A)$ does not change when A decreases from $f(c) - \varepsilon$ to very negative values. The following is a situation where this can be shown easily.

Proposition 4.9.6. *If the interval $[B, A]$ does not contain any critical value of f, then $\overline{W}^u(c, A)$ and $\overline{W}^u(c, B)$ are homeomorphic. Moreover, the homeomorphism (sends $W^u(c, A)$ onto $W^u(c, B)$ and) can also be chosen equal to the identity on $\overline{W}^u(c, A + \delta)$ for $\delta > 0$.*

Proof. Theorem 2.1.7 applied to the sublevel sets of $-f$ gives a diffeomorphism

$$\Gamma : \{f(x) \geq A\} \longrightarrow \{f(x) \geq B\}.$$

The formula

$$\chi : \overline{W}^u(c, A) \longrightarrow \overline{W}^u(c, B)$$
$$(\lambda, x) \longmapsto (\lambda, \Gamma(x))$$

defines a homeomorphism χ that has the stated properties.   □

We are left with understanding what happens to $\overline{W}^u(c, A)$ when A crosses a critical value. As in Section 2.2.c, we assume that the critical values of f are distinct. We have the following result.

Proposition 4.9.7. *Let $d \in \mathrm{Crit}(f)$, let $A = f(d)$ and let $\varepsilon > 0$ (defining a Morse chart $\Omega(d)$). Then there exists a homeomorphism*

$$\overline{W}^u(c, A + \varepsilon) \longrightarrow \overline{W}^u(c, A - \varepsilon)$$

(that sends $W^u(c, A + \varepsilon)$ onto $W^u(c, A - \varepsilon)$ and) that is the identity on $\overline{W}^u(c, A + \varepsilon + \delta)$ for $\delta > 0$.

This proposition is illustrated by Figure 4.10, which shows $\overline{W}^u(c, A)$ for $A = f(d) - \varepsilon$ (and where the shaded area represents $\overline{W}^u(c, A)$ for $A > f(d)$). In the figure, $\mathrm{Ind}(d) = \mathrm{Ind}(c) - 1$, $\mathcal{L}(c, d)$ has four elements, and there is no critical value in $]f(d), f(c)[$.

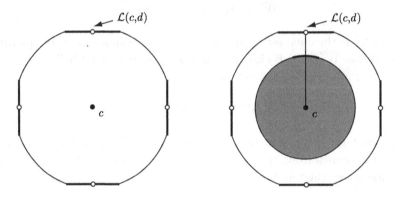

Fig. 4.10

Proof of Proposition 4.9.7. Because of the way it was defined (in the proof of Theorem 2.1.7), we know that the diffeomorphism Γ sends every point onto a point of its own trajectory. For $(\lambda, x) \in \overline{W}^u(c, A + \varepsilon)$, if the trajectory through x does not end up at d (that is, if $x \notin W^s(d)$), then we can define $\chi(\lambda, x)$ using Γ. We therefore define our homeomorphism on an open set U around

$$P = \left\{ (\lambda, x) \in \overline{W}^u(c, A + \varepsilon) \mid x \in W^s(d) \right\},$$

so that it glues well with the homeomorphism χ, which is defined on the complement of U as in Proposition 4.9.6.

We Begin With the Simple Case Where $\mathrm{Ind}(c) - \mathrm{Ind}(d) = 1$ *and* $\mathrm{Ind}(d) \neq 0$.

In this case,

$$P \subset \mathcal{M}(c, d) \subset W^u(c) \subset \overline{W}^u(c);$$

in other words, P contains only the points lying on the trajectories from c to d above the level $A + \varepsilon$. Under the condition on the difference of the indices, the set $\mathcal{L}(c, d) = \mathcal{M}(c, d)/\mathbf{R}$ of these trajectories is finite. We fix $\ell \in \mathcal{L}(c, d)$ and let $\tilde{\ell} \in \mathcal{M}(c, d)$ be the corresponding trajectory seen as the set of its points in V. Let a be the point of this trajectory at the level $A + \varepsilon$, let $a = \tilde{\ell} \cap f^{-1}(A + \varepsilon)$ and let $D \subset W^u(c) \cap f^{-1}(A + \varepsilon)$ be a small disk of dimension $\mathrm{Ind}(d)$ that intersects $S_+(d)$ transversally at a. The Smale condition plays an essential role here.

Proposition 3.2.10, which is illustrated by Figure 3.6 (the figure in the form of a bottle), tells us what happens to $D - \{a\}$ when we push it into the level set $f^{-1}(A - \varepsilon)$ along the gradient lines.

This map Φ transforms it into an annulus $C = S^{\mathrm{Ind}(d)-1} \times]0, \delta[$ that together with $S_-(d) \cong S^{\mathrm{Ind}(d)-1} \times \{0\}$ forms a manifold with boundary. We return to this figure (now Figure 4.11) to describe our homeomorphism χ in the neighborhood of $\widetilde{\ell} \cap \overline{W}^u(c, A + \varepsilon)$.

First of all, χ is the identity on $\overline{W}^u(c, A + \varepsilon + \delta)$. The neighborhood U of

$$\widetilde{\ell} \cap \left(\overline{W}^u(c, A + \varepsilon) - \overline{W}^u(c, A + \varepsilon + \delta) \right)$$

that we consider is a cylinder (the bottle's top) above D, defined by the gradient lines, as in Figure 4.11. There is a second cylinder in the figure, denoted by $\widetilde{U}$ and contained in $f^{-1}([A - \varepsilon, A + \varepsilon])$: it is the interior of the bottle. It is restricted at the top by D and at the bottom by $C \cup W^u(d, \varepsilon)$ (and its lateral part is made up of gradient lines).

We choose a homeomorphism $\Gamma : U \to \widetilde{U}$ as describe in Figure 4.11:

- Γ is the identity on the top part of U.
- Above the shaded part, it is the Γ defined by Proposition 4.9.6 (in particular, on $D - D'$ it coincides with the Φ defined and used for Proposition 3.2.10).
- Γ sends D' onto $W^u(d, \varepsilon)$.

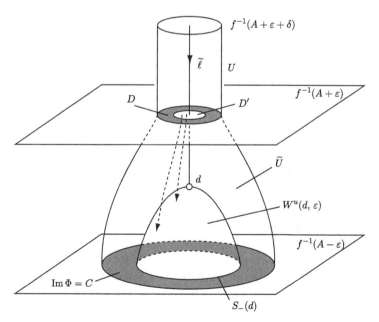

Fig. 4.11

The desired homeomorphism is defined on U by

$$\begin{cases} \chi(x) = \Gamma(x) & \text{if } x \notin D' \\ \chi(x) = (\ell, \Gamma(x)) & \text{if } x \in D'. \end{cases}$$

It glues well with the homeomorphism of Proposition 4.9.6 on the lateral part of U. Since $\mathcal{L}(c, d)$ is a finite set, we can choose neighborhoods U as above that are mutually disjoint. We obtain a finite number (namely $n(c, d)$) of cylinders $U \cup \widetilde{U}$ in V that meet only along $W^u(d, \varepsilon)$. The map χ defined above on the union of these cylinders, viewed in $\overline{W}^u(c, A + \varepsilon)$, is injective. It is also continuous, as can easily be verified. The set $\mathcal{L}(c, d) \times W^u(d, \varepsilon)$ (which is added to $\overline{W}^u(c, A)$ when A crosses the critical value $f(d)$) is indeed contained in the image, and outside of the cylinders, χ glues well with the map defined by Proposition 4.9.6.

We can verify without difficulty that it is a homeomorphism, concluding the proof in this case.

The More General Case Where $\mathrm{Ind}(c) - \mathrm{Ind}(d)$ *is Arbitrary (and* $\mathrm{Ind}(d) \neq 0$*).*

We need to define χ in the neighborhood of the points $(\lambda, x) \in \overline{W}^u(c, A + \varepsilon)$ with $x \in W^s(d)$:

(a) Let us first consider the points of P that are in $\mathcal{M}(c, d)$ as in the previous case, that is, the points $(\lambda, x) = x \in W^u(c) \cap W^s(d)$. We can see that

$$\mathcal{L}(c, d) = \mathcal{M}(c, d) \cap f^{-1}(A + \varepsilon)$$

is a submanifold of codimension $\mathrm{Ind}(d)$ of $W^u(c) \cap f^{-1}(A + \varepsilon)$.

Let D be a tubular neighborhood of $\mathcal{L}(c, d)$ in $W^u(c) \cap f^{-1}(A + \varepsilon)$. It is a disk bundle of dimension $\mathrm{Ind}(d)$ on $\mathcal{L}(c, d)$. For $\ell \in \mathcal{L}(c, d)$, the fiber D_ℓ is a disk that meets $S_+(d)$ transversally at $a_\ell = \widetilde{\ell} \cap f^{-1}(A + \varepsilon)$. For each $\ell \in \mathcal{L}(c, d)$, we therefore have a figure analogous to Figure 4.11 (D is replaced by D_ℓ) and a homeomorphism $\Gamma_\ell : U_\ell \to U_\ell \cup \widetilde{U}_\ell$ defined in an analogous way. The cylinders $\widetilde{U}_\ell$ meet each other only along $W^u(d, \varepsilon)$.

On the cylinder bundle U defined above D by the gradient lines, we then define χ by setting

$$\begin{cases} \chi(x) = \Gamma_\ell(x) & \text{if } x \notin D'_\ell \\ \chi(x) = (\ell, \Gamma_\ell(x)) & \text{if } x \in D'_\ell \end{cases}$$

(of course, D'_ℓ is the analogue of D').

(b) Let us now consider an arbitrary point P. It can be written as (λ, x), where $\lambda \in \overline{\mathcal{L}}(c, d')$ and $x \in \mathcal{M}(d', d)$. Note that for $d' \neq c$, such a point x is not in the domain U on which we have just defined χ: in fact, U is contained in $W^u(c)$. As we have just shown, we can define $\chi = \chi_{d'}$ in a neighborhood $U = U_{d'}$ of $\mathcal{M}(d', d) \cap \{f \geq A + \varepsilon\}$ (d' plays the part of c). We then define χ in the neighborhood of (λ, x) in $\overline{W}^u(c, A + \varepsilon)$ by setting

$$\chi(\lambda', y) = (\lambda', \chi_{d'}(y)).$$

We have now defined χ in an open neighborhood of P. Note that the image of χ contains $\overline{\mathcal{L}}(c, d) \times W^u(d, \varepsilon)$. We extend it to all of $\overline{W}^u(c, A + \varepsilon)$ as in Proposition 4.9.6 and verify without difficulty that it is a homeomorphism.

To Conclude the Proof, the Case Where $\mathrm{Ind}(d) = 0$.

In this case,
$$P = \left\{ (\lambda, x) \in \overline{W}^u(c, A + \varepsilon) \mid x \in W^s(d) \right\}$$
is a connected component of $\overline{W}^u(c, A + \varepsilon)$.

We define χ on P as follows:

$$\chi(\lambda, x) = \begin{cases} (\lambda, x) & \text{if } f(x) \geq A + \varepsilon + \delta \\ (\lambda, \ell, d) & \text{if } f(x) = A + \varepsilon \\ (\lambda, \Gamma(x)) & \text{if } f(x) \in \,]A + \varepsilon, A + \varepsilon + \delta[\end{cases}$$

(ℓ denotes the trajectory of x). In this formula Γ is a diffeomorphism between $W^s(d) \cap f^{-1}(]A + \varepsilon, A + \varepsilon + \delta[)$ and $W^s(d) \cap f^{-1}(]f(d), A + \varepsilon + \delta[)$ obtained by pushing along the gradient lines. Elsewhere, we define χ using Proposition 4.9.6 and verify (still without difficulty) that it is a homeomorphism.

The construction shows that χ satisfies the required properties, that is, that its restriction to $\overline{W}^u(c, A + \varepsilon + \delta)$ is the identity and that $\chi(W^u(c, A + \varepsilon)) = W^u(c, A - \varepsilon)$. This concludes the proof of Proposition 4.9.7. □

And that of Theorem 4.9.3.

Exercises

Exercise 16. Does there exist a Morse function on $S^2 \times S^2$ that has a minimum, a maximum, one critical point of index 2, and whose other critical points all have indices 1 or 3?

Exercise 17. Show that the complex projective space $\mathbf{P}^n(\mathbf{C})$ is simply connected.

Exercise 18. Is the quadric Q of Exercise 8 (p. 19) diffeomorphic to $\mathbf{P}^2(\mathbf{C})$? We send $\mathbf{P}^1(\mathbf{C}) \times \mathbf{P}^1(\mathbf{C})$ into $\mathbf{P}^3(\mathbf{C})$ using

$$([a, b], [u, v]) \longmapsto [au, bu, av, bv].$$

Show that this is an embedding whose image is described by the equation

$$z_0 z_3 - z_1 z_2 = 0.$$

Prove that Q is diffeomorphic to $S^2 \times S^2$.

Exercise 19. Figure 4.12 shows the graph of a diffeomorphism

$$\varphi : \,]-1, 1[\longrightarrow \,]-1, 1[.$$

We set $a = \varphi(0)$. Show that φ is the flow at time 1 of a vector field on $]-1, 1[$, and draw the latter. Let D be the open disk of center 0 with radius 1 in $\mathbf{R}^N$ and let $a \in D$. Construct a vector field on D whose flow satisfies $\varphi^1(0) = a$.

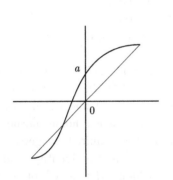

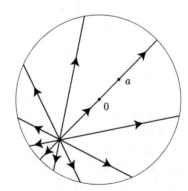

Fig. 4.12   **Fig. 4.13**

Exercise 20. If $u : V \to W$ is a $\mathcal{C}^\infty$ map and if V and W are compact connected manifolds, then

$$u_\star : HM_0(V; \mathbf{Z}/2) \longrightarrow HM_0(W; \mathbf{Z}/2)$$

is an isomorphism (it is the identity because both spaces are isomorphic to $\mathbf{Z}/2$).

Exercise 21. Let V be a compact connected manifold of dimension n without boundary and let D be a disk of dimension n embedded in V. Show that

$$HM_n(\overline{V - D}; \mathbf{Z}/2) = 0.$$

Deduce that if $u : V^n \to W^n$ is a $\mathcal{C}^\infty$ map that induces a *nonzero* map

$$u_\star : HM_n(V; \mathbf{Z}/2) \longrightarrow HM_n(W; \mathbf{Z}/2),$$

then it is surjective.

Exercise 22. Let W be a compact manifold of dimension $n+1$ with boundary and let V be its boundary, $V = \partial W$. Assume that V is connected:

(1) Prove that the inclusion $V \subset W$ induces the zero map from $HM_n(V; \mathbf{Z}/2)$ to $HM_n(W; \mathbf{Z}/2)$.
(2) Deduce that if $u : V \to Z$ is a $\mathcal{C}^\infty$ map from V to a manifold Z of the same dimension whose induced map $u_\star$ on the homology HM_n is nonzero, then u cannot be extended to a map $\tilde{u} : W \to Z$.
(3) In particular, there does not exist any map from W to its boundary that restricts to the identity on the boundary (that is, a retraction). The case $W = D^{n+1}$ is that of Brouwer's theorem.

Exercise 23. Let V be a compact manifold. Show that there does not exist any retraction of V onto a proper subset (see Section 4.8.b, if necessary).

Exercise 24. Describe the stable and unstable manifolds, with orientations and co-orientations, for the Morse function f considered in Exercise 6 and a pseudo-gradient field X on $\mathbf{P}^2(\mathbf{R})$. Compute the homology of the complex $(C_\star(f; \mathbf{Z}), \partial_X)$. Show that

$$HM_k(\mathbf{P}_2(\mathbf{R}); \mathbf{Z}) = \begin{cases} \mathbf{Z} & \text{if } k = 0, \\ \mathbf{Z}/2 & \text{if } k = 1, \\ 0 & \text{otherwise.} \end{cases}$$

Exercise 25. Consider the cellular decomposition of S^n with two cells in any dimension, one being the image of the other under the antipodal map. Determine the differential ∂ of the cellular complex induced on $\mathbf{P}^n(\mathbf{R})$ (as defined in Subsection 4.9.a). Compute $HM_k(\mathbf{P}^n(\mathbf{R}); \mathbf{Z}/2)$. Fix an orientation on each cell of $\mathbf{P}^n(\mathbf{R})$ and use the same method to compute $HM_k(\mathbf{P}^n(\mathbf{R}); \mathbf{Z})$.

Part II
The Arnold Conjecture,
Floer Homology

Introduction to Part II

The second part of this book is devoted to the construction of Floer homology, with the aim of proving the Arnold conjecture. This states that the number of periodic trajectories of period 1 of a Hamiltonian vector field on a symplectic manifold W is greater than or equal to

$$\sum_k HM_k(W; \mathbf{Z}/2).$$

As we said in the preface of this book, the juxtaposition of the Morse inequalities and the Arnold conjecture is not accidental. Indeed, the strategy of the proof, due to Floer, consists in presenting the trajectories in question as critical points—no longer of a function on a manifold, but of an "action functional"[1] on the space of loops on W (a periodic trajectory is in fact a loop on W). The next step is to construct a complex (the Floer complex) analogous to that of Morse, whose differential "counts" the solutions of the Floer equation. By construction, the homology of this complex, called the Floer homology, is linked to the number of periodic trajectories. We then need to show that this homology is isomorphic to the Morse homology of the manifold.

We give the details of this strategy on page 154, and apply it in this part of the book. Let us give both an outline of the proof of the Arnold conjecture and an overview of the contents of this part.

The first thing we need to do is to construct the "action functional" (in Section 6.3) on a space of loops on our manifold, whose critical points are the periodic solutions we are looking for. This is the analogue of the Morse function. With its critical points, we will attempt to construct a complex,

---

[1] Since Hadamard it has been the tradition to name functions defined on infinite-dimensional spaces in this way.

as in the Morse case. The grading on the $\mathbf{Z}/2$-vector space generated by the critical points is given by the Maslov index, which we will define (in Chapter 7).

To define the differential, we will use the analogue of a pseudo-gradient field, in this case the (opposite of the) gradient of the action functional with respect to some metric (see Section 6.4). We will show that its trajectories of finite energy, the solutions of the "Floer equation", connect two critical points. As in the Morse case, we will prove a compactness property for the spaces of trajectories (Theorem 6.5.4). In general, because of transversality properties, these spaces of trajectories are manifolds (Chapter 8). This enables us to count the trajectories, considered as elements of a zero-dimensional manifold, and to define the differential of the Floer complex.

To prove that the latter is indeed a complex, in other words, that $\partial \circ \partial = 0$, we will establish, as in the Morse case, a gluing property (Chapter 9). Still as in the Morse case, we will show in Chapter 11 that the homology of the resulting complex depends neither on the choice of the functional nor on that of the vector field. Before doing so, we will have shown, in Chapter 10, that in the case of a $\mathcal{C}^2$-small Hamiltonian that does not depend on time, the Floer homology coincides with the Morse homology of the manifold. This will therefore be true in general. The obvious inequality between the dimensions of the vector spaces in this complex and its homology will therefore give the expected result, in a manner completely analogous to the Morse inequalities (Proposition 4.4.3).

So the Morse complex, which was the object of the first part of this book, acts as a guide for the second part. The objects being studied are now much more complicated and require a sophisticated analysis. The Floer equation, a differential equation on the "gradient trajectories" of the action functional, is a partial differential equation, to which we are able to apply elliptic regularity techniques (given explicitly in Chapter 12). The definition of the complex requires the fact that the linearization of this equation provides Fredholm operators. The proof of the properties that allow us to assert that the Floer complex is indeed a complex is much more technical than that of the analogous statement for the Morse complex.

We have relegated to one chapter (that LaTeX has wisely chosen to number 13 and that the superstitious readers can skip) a number of technical lemmas used in particular in the proof of the gluing property.

Chapter 5
What You Need to Know About Symplectic Geometry

There are many good books on symplectic geometry, in particular [18] and [50], to which we refer for any details that may be missing here.

5.1 Symplectic Vector Spaces

These are real vector spaces endowed with *nondegenerate* alternating bilinear forms. The archetypical and, we will see, unique, example is $\mathbf{R}^n \times \mathbf{R}^n$ endowed with the form

$$\omega((p,q),(p',q')) = p \cdot q' - p' \cdot q$$

(the dot $\cdot$ of course denotes the Euclidean inner product on $\mathbf{R}^n$).

In fact, there is only one example, as stated in the following proposition.

Proposition 5.1.1. *Let ω be a nondegenerate alternating bilinear form on a finite-dimensional vector space E. There exists a basis $(e_1, \ldots, e_n, f_1, \ldots, f_n)$ (called symplectic) such that $\omega(e_i, f_j) = \delta_{i,j}$ and $\omega(e_i, e_j) = \omega(f_i, f_j) = 0$.*

Proof. Since ω is nondegenerate, it is nonzero and we can find two vectors e_1 and f_1 such that $\omega(e_1, f_1) = 1$. We can verify that ω restricts to a *nondegenerate* form on the orthogonal (for ω) of the plane $\langle e_1, f_1 \rangle$ and we conclude by induction on the dimension, after having noted that an alternating bilinear form on a space of dimension 1 is zero. □

In particular, the dimension of E is even and is the only invariant of the isomorphism type of (E, ω). In a symplectic basis, the matrix of the bilinear form ω is

$$J = \begin{pmatrix} 0 & \mathrm{Id} \\ -\mathrm{Id} & 0 \end{pmatrix}.$$

M. Audin, M. Damian, *Morse Theory and Floer Homology*,
Universitext, DOI 10.1007/978-1-4471-5496-9_5,
© Springer-Verlag London 2014

Note that this is the opposite of the matrix which corresponds to the standard complex multiplication on $\mathbf{C}^n = \mathbf{R}^{2n}$. To avoid confusions we will denote the latter

$$J_0 = \begin{pmatrix} 0 & -\mathrm{Id} \\ \mathrm{Id} & 0 \end{pmatrix};$$

see Section 5.5.

Example 5.1.2. If $(e_1, \ldots, e_n)$ is an orthonormal basis of $\mathbf{R}^n$, then we have

$$\omega((e_i, 0), (0, e_j)) = \delta_{i,j},$$

so that the basis

$$((e_1, 0), \ldots, (e_n, 0), (0, e_1), \ldots, (0, e_n))$$

is a symplectic basis of $\mathbf{R}^n \times \mathbf{R}^n$.

5.2 Symplectic Manifolds, Definition

Let us try to understand what the definition of a symplectic *manifold* might be. We will first require that every tangent space be endowed with the vector structure defined above: the manifold W will be endowed with a differential 2-form ω, that is, with an alternating bilinear form ω_x on $T_x W$ for every x. We moreover want each ω_x to be nondegenerate. If the (necessarily even) dimension of W is $2n$, then we can write this condition as

$$\omega_x^{\wedge n} = \wedge^n \omega_x \neq 0 \in \overset{2n}{\bigwedge} T_x^\star W$$

for every x. In other words, we require that the $2n$-form $\omega^{\wedge n}$ be a volume form on W. Note that, in particular, the manifold W must have a volume form and therefore be orientable.

In fact, this definition is insufficient: we also want the differential calculus that ω allows us to do on W to be locally the same as the one we already have on $\mathbf{R}^n \times \mathbf{R}^n$ using the "constant" form. Let us therefore write this form as a differential form: we denote the vectors of $\mathbf{R}^n \times \mathbf{R}^n$ by $X = (p, q)$, $X' = (p', q')$ so that we have

$$\omega(X, X') = p \cdot q' - p' \cdot q.$$

In other words,

$$\omega = \sum_{i=1}^n dp_i \wedge dq_i = d\left(\sum_{i=1}^n p_i dq_i \right).$$

In particular, ω is an *exact* form. We could require a symplectic form to be exact... unfortunately, this would preclude the use of compact manifolds. In fact, we have the following result.

Proposition 5.2.1. *On a compact manifold there do not exist any 2-forms that are both nondegenerate and exact.*

Proof. We have said that ω is nondegenerate if and only if $\omega^{\wedge n}$ is a volume form. Since W is compact, we know that the volume forms are not exact.[1] Now, if ω were exact, then we would have $\omega = d\alpha$, but then the volume form $\omega^{\wedge n}$ would be exact: $\omega^{\wedge n} = d(\alpha \wedge \omega^{\wedge(n-1)})$. $\square$

In fact, if we want to compute *locally* as in $\mathbf{R}^n \times \mathbf{R}^n$, then what we need is a condition of "local exactness"... that is, of closure. This leads us to the correct definition.

Definition 5.2.2. A *symplectic manifold* is a pair (W, ω) where W is a manifold and ω is a nondegenerate closed 2-form. Such a form ω is called *symplectic*.

A diffeomorphism φ from one symplectic manifold (W_1, ω_1) to another (W_2, ω_2) is called *symplectic* if it satisfies $\varphi^* \omega_2 = \omega_1$. We sometimes also say that φ is a *symplectomorphism*.

Of course, we will often, by abuse of notation, call W a symplectic manifold, without mentioning the form ω when there is no risk of confusion.

5.3 Examples of Symplectic Manifolds

Obviously, $\mathbf{R}^n \times \mathbf{R}^n$ with the constant form $\sum dp_i \wedge dq_i$ is a symplectic manifold.

The Cotangent Bundles

If V is a manifold, then we consider the total space of its cotangent bundle, with the projection
$$\pi : T^\star V \longrightarrow V.$$

On $T^\star V$ there is a *canonical* differential 1-form λ called the *Liouville form*, which is defined by
$$\lambda(x, \varphi)(X) = \varphi(T_{(x,\varphi)}\pi(X)),$$

where $x \in V$, $\varphi \in T_x^\star V$ and $X \in T_{(x,\varphi)}(T^\star V)$. We can easily verify that $\omega = d\lambda$ is nondegenerate (and even more easily that it is closed!). If $(q_1, \ldots, q_n)$ are

---

[1] See the basics of de Rham cohomology in, for example, [45] or Chapter VIII of Vol. I of [74].

the local coordinates on V and if $(p_1, \ldots, p_n)$ are the "dual" coordinates, then $(p_1, \ldots, p_n, q_1, \ldots, q_n)$ is a chart in which $\lambda = \sum p_i dq_i$ and $\omega = \sum dp_i \wedge dq_i$. We often say that ω is the "canonical symplectic form" on the cotangent.[2] The example of $\mathbf{R}^n \times \mathbf{R}^n$ given above can be seen as the case $V = \mathbf{R}^n$.

Surfaces

On a surface W, all differential forms of degree 2 are closed. Moreover, in dimension 2, saying that a 2-form is nondegenerate simply means that it does not vanish anywhere. On a surface, the notion of "symplectic form" coincides with that of "volume form": all orientable surfaces can be viewed as symplectic manifolds.

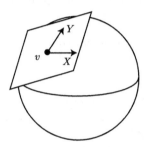

Fig. 5.1 Symplectic form on the sphere

The Sphere

We consider the unit sphere S^2 in $\mathbf{R}^3$, whose tangent space at a point v is the plane orthogonal to the unit vector v. We set

$$\omega_v(X, Y) = v \cdot (X \wedge Y)$$

(Figure 5.1). This is a nondegenerate 2-form (as can be checked directly) and therefore a symplectic form.

The Complex Projective Space

The most pleasant way to describe a symplectic form on the complex projective space is to use the quotient structure of this space. Let us therefore consider

$$\mathbf{C}^{n+1} = \{p + iq \mid p \in \mathbf{R}^{n+1},\ q \in \mathbf{R}^{n+1}\} = \mathbf{R}^{n+1} \times \mathbf{R}^{n+1},$$

---

[2] This is another example of an exact symplectic form, on a noncompact manifold, obviously.

endowed with the usual symplectic form on $\mathbf{R}^{n+1} \times \mathbf{R}^{n+1}$. The complex projective space is the quotient

$$\mathbf{C}^{n+1} - \{0\} / x \sim y \iff \exists \lambda \neq 0 \text{ such that } y = \lambda x.$$

It is often convenient to view this as the quotient of the (compact) sphere:

$$S^{2n+1} / x \sim y \iff \exists \lambda \in S^1 \text{ such that } y = \lambda x,$$

for example to show that it is a (Hausdorff and) compact space. We thus have the following diagram.

$$
\begin{array}{ccc}
S^{2n+1} & \xrightarrow{\quad j \quad} & \mathbf{C}^{n+1} - \{0\} \\
\downarrow{\scriptstyle \pi} & & \\
\mathbf{P}^n(\mathbf{C}) & &
\end{array}
$$

The 2-form $j^\star \omega$ is necessarily degenerate. Its kernel at $x \in S^{2n+1}$ is the line generated by the vector ix in the tangent space $T_x S^{2n+1} = x^\perp$ (as can be checked directly), so that $(j^\star \omega)_x$ induces a nondegenerate bilinear form on the quotient vector space $T_x S^{2n+1} / ix$ that is none other than the orthogonal of the vector x *for the Hermitian form*. On the other hand, the real line generated by ix is also the kernel of

$$T_x \pi : T_x S^{2n+1} \longrightarrow T_{\pi(x)} \mathbf{P}^n(\mathbf{C}),$$

so that the formula

$$\sigma_{[x]}(Y, Z) = \omega_x(\widetilde{Y}, \widetilde{Z})$$

(where $x \in [x]$, $T_x \pi(\widetilde{Y}) = Y$, $T_x \pi(\widetilde{Z}) = Z$) indeed defines a 2-form and that we have shown the following result.

Proposition 5.3.1. *There exists a unique 2-form σ on $\mathbf{P}^n(\mathbf{C})$ such that*

$$\pi^\star \sigma = j^\star \omega.$$

It is a symplectic form. □

Darboux's Theorem

In the same manner that there is only one type of symplectic vector space of dimension $2n$, there is, locally, only one structure of a symplectic manifold of dimension $2n$, as stated in Darboux's famous theorem.

Theorem 5.3.2 (Darboux). *Let x be a point of a symplectic manifold (W, ω). There exist local coordinates $(q_1, \ldots, q_n, p_1, \ldots, p_n)$ centered at x in which*

$$\omega = \sum dp_i \wedge dq_i.$$

It suffices to integrate a well-chosen vector field (following Moser's "path" method [57])... For a complete proof, we refer the readers to their favorite symplectic geometry books, for example [50] or [5].

5.4 Hamiltonian Vector Fields, Hamiltonian Systems

If $H : W \to \mathbf{R}$ is a function, then the symplectic form allows us to associate with it a vector field, a kind of gradient: the *Hamiltonian vector field* X_H (sometimes called the "symplectic gradient" of H). It is the vector field defined by the relation

$$\omega_x(Y, X_H(x)) = (dH)_x(Y) \quad \text{for every } Y \in T_x W$$

(or by $\iota_{X_H}\omega = -dH$).

Note that the vector field X_H is zero at x if and only if x is a critical point of the function H:

$$X_H(x) = 0 \iff (dH)_x = 0.$$

In particular, the singularities (or zeros) of a Hamiltonian vector field are the critical points of a function.

The Hamiltonian system is the differential system associated with this vector field, that is,

$$\dot{x}(t) = X_H(x(t)).$$

Note that the function H is constant on the trajectories (or integral curves) of the vector field X_H: since ω_x is alternating, we have

$$(dH)(X_H) = 0 \quad \text{or} \quad X_H \cdot H = 0.$$

Hamilton's Equations

In $\mathbf{R}^{2n}$ with the symplectic form $\sum dp_i \wedge dq_i$, in terms of the coordinates (q_i, p_i), the differential system takes on the form

$$\dot{q}_i = \frac{\partial H}{\partial p_i}, \quad \dot{p}_i = -\frac{\partial H}{\partial q_i}.$$

These are the classical "Hamilton's equations".

Example 5.4.1 ("Classical" Hamiltonians). In $\mathbf{R}^{2n}$ with its standard symplectic structure, we consider the function

$$H(p,q) = \frac{1}{2}\|p\|^2 + V(q)$$

(think of the total energy, the sum of the kinetic and potential energies). The associated Hamiltonian system is

$$\dot{q} = p, \quad \dot{p} = -\frac{\partial V}{\partial q},$$

so that p indeed appears as the speed (or the impulse) of the particle whose position is given by q.

Proposition 5.4.2. *The time t of the flow of a Hamiltonian vector field is a diffeomorphism that preserves the symplectic form. It is called a Hamiltonian diffeomorphism.*

Proof. We have[3]

$$\frac{d}{dt}\left((\psi^t)^\star \omega\right) = (\psi^t)^\star \mathcal{L}_{X_H}\omega$$
$$= (\psi^t)^\star (di_{X_H}\omega)$$
$$= (\psi^t)^\star (-ddH) = 0.$$

Hence $(\psi^t)^\star \omega$ does not depend on t and $(\psi^t)^\star\omega = (\psi^0)^\star\omega = \omega$ for every t. $\quad\square$

Periodic Orbits

If a trajectory of the flow of X_H is periodic with period 1, then for each of its points we have

$$\psi^1(x) = x.$$

They are therefore all fixed points of ψ^1. For example, the critical points of H are periodic trajectories. Therefore the symplectic diffeomorphism ψ^1 has at least as many fixed points as the function H has critical points.

Example 5.4.3 (Quadratic Hamiltonians). Let us consider the case of a quadratic Hamiltonian H on $\mathbf{R}^{2n}$,

$$H = \frac{1}{2}\sum a_{ij}p_ip_j + \sum b_{ij}p_iq_j + \frac{1}{2}\sum c_{ij}q_iq_j,$$

---

[3] See Appendix A.4.b, if necessary.

where the matrices a and c are symmetric. Then X_H is a linear vector field

$$X_H(p, q) = -\sum_{i=1}^{n} \frac{\partial H}{\partial q_i} \frac{\partial}{\partial p_i} + \sum_{i=1}^{n} \frac{\partial H}{\partial p_i} \frac{\partial}{\partial q_i}$$

$$= A \cdot \begin{pmatrix} p \\ q \end{pmatrix},$$

where A is the matrix

$$A = \begin{pmatrix} -{}^t b & -c \\ a & b \end{pmatrix} = \begin{pmatrix} 0 & -\mathrm{Id} \\ \mathrm{Id} & 0 \end{pmatrix} \begin{pmatrix} a & b \\ {}^t b & c \end{pmatrix} = J_0 \begin{pmatrix} a & b \\ {}^t b & c \end{pmatrix}.$$

Therefore, up to multiplication by the invertible matrix J_0, the matrix A is the Hessian of H at 0, the matrix of the quadratic form H. The flow of X_H is given by

$$\psi^t(p, q) = e^{tA} \cdot \begin{pmatrix} p \\ q \end{pmatrix}.$$

Note that $\psi^1 = e^A$. Hence, if ψ^1 does not have an eigenvalue 1, A does not have an eigenvalue 0 and the quadratic form H is nondegenerate; that is, the critical point of H at 0 is a nondegenerate critical point.

Note that the converse is false: A could have eigenvalues $2ik\pi$ for $k \in \mathbf{Z}$; see for example Exercise 18 on p. 520.

Time-Dependent Hamiltonians

We will now consider "time-dependent" Hamiltonians, that is, functions

$$H : W \times \mathbf{R} \longrightarrow \mathbf{R},$$

and the Hamiltonian vector fields X_t defined by

$$X_t = X_{H_t}, \quad \text{if we set } H(x, t) = H_t(x).$$

The associated differential system is no longer autonomous; it is the system

$$\dot{x}(t) = X_t(x(t)).$$

As in the autonomous case, the solutions of the system allow us to define a family of symplectic diffeomorphisms ψ^t such that

$$\frac{d}{dt} \psi^t = X_t \circ \psi^t \quad \text{and} \quad \psi^0 = \mathrm{Id}.$$

As in Proposition 5.4.2 (and with the same proof), ψ^t preserves the symplectic form.

Nondegenerate Periodic Solutions

A periodic solution of period 1 of the differential system corresponds to a fixed point of the diffeomorphism ψ^1. If we moreover suppose that the Hamiltonian H is periodic of period 1, then the fixed points come from the periodic solutions.

Definition 5.4.4. A periodic solution x is called *nondegenerate* if the differential of ψ^1 does not have eigenvalue 1, that is, in mathematical symbols, if

$$\det(\mathrm{Id} - T_{x(0)}\psi^1) \neq 0.$$

In the specific case where the time-dependent Hamiltonian H does not depend on the time, the critical points of H are (constant) periodic solutions of the Hamiltonian system. Example 5.4.3 illustrates the following statement.

Proposition 5.4.5. *If a critical point of H is nondegenerate as a periodic solution of the Hamiltonian system, then it is nondegenerate as a critical point of the function H.*

Proof. We can use Darboux's theorem in the neighborhood of the critical point, the Taylor expansion of order 2 of H, and deduce the result of the explicit computation carried out above. Here is another proof. We begin by noting that if Y and Z are two vectors tangent to W at x, then

$$(d^2 H)_x(Y, Z) = \omega_x([X_H, Z]_x, Y)$$

(we let Z denote any vector extending the vector Z in the neighborhood of x). Indeed, by extending Y to a Hamiltonian vector field X_f in the neighborhood of x, we have

$$
\begin{aligned}
\omega([X_H, Z], Y) &= \omega([X_H, Z], X_f) \\
&= df([X_H, Z]) \\
&= [X_H, Z] \cdot f \\
&= X_H \cdot (Z \cdot f) - Z \cdot (X_H \cdot f) \\
&= X_H \cdot (Z \cdot f) + Z \cdot (X_f \cdot H).
\end{aligned}
$$

Computed at the critical point x of H, the first term is zero and the second one is exactly

$$(d^2 H)_x(X_f(x), Z(x)) = (d^2 H)_x(Y, Z).$$

We now suppose that x is nondegenerate as a trajectory of X_H. This means that for every $Z \neq 0$, we have

$$T_x\psi^1(Z) - Z \neq 0.$$

Since $\psi^0 = \mathrm{Id}$, there must be a t such that

$$\frac{d}{dt} T_x \psi^t(Z) \neq 0,$$

but this derivative equals

$$T_x \psi^t([X_H, Z]),$$

hence for every $Z \neq 0$, there exists a t such that $T_x \psi^t([X_H, Z]) \neq 0$. It follows that for every $Z \neq 0$, we have $[X_H, Z] \neq 0$. By the earlier relation, this implies that x is nondegenerate as a critical point of H. $\square$

Remark 5.4.6. In local coordinates, the matrix of $T_x \psi^1$ is the Jacobian matrix $\mathrm{Jac}_x \psi^1$, that is, $\exp(J_0 \mathrm{Hess}_x(H))$ (see Exercise 8 on p. 517, if necessary), where Hess denotes the Hessian matrix. The nondegeneracy of x as a periodic orbit is therefore equivalent to the invertibility of $\exp(J_0 \mathrm{Hess}_x(H)) - \mathrm{Id}$, that is, to the fact that the Hessian of H does not have any eigenvalues in $2\pi\mathbf{Z}$.

Remark 5.4.7. If the Hamiltonian H is "sufficiently" $\mathcal{C}^2$-small, more precisely, if the norm of its Hessian is less than 2π, then the previous remark shows that the converse of Proposition 5.4.5 is true: the two notions of nondegeneracy coincide.

Remark 5.4.8. The nondegenerate constant periodic solutions (of period 1) are therefore isolated; there are no infinitesimally close periodic solutions. This is more generally true for the nondegenerate solutions. Here is another way to understand this fact. Let

$$S^1 \longrightarrow W$$
$$t \longmapsto x(t)$$

be a periodic trajectory of the vector field X_t on W. As is true for all linear differential systems of order $2n$, the vector space of solutions of the differential equation linearized[4] along the solution x has dimension $2n$. If $Y_1, \ldots, Y_{2n}$ is a basis of $T_{x(0)}W$, then there exists a unique basis $Y_1(t), \ldots, Y_{2n}(t)$ of $T_{x(t)}W$ such that

$$\begin{cases} Y_i(t) \text{ is a solution} \\ Y_i(0) = Y_i. \end{cases}$$

Then $Y_1(1), \ldots, Y_{2n}(1)$ is also a basis of $T_{x(0)}W$, because x is periodic of period 1. It can be derived from $Y_1, \ldots, Y_{2n}$ through a linear isomorphism that is none other than $T_{x(0)}\psi^1$ (see Appendix A.4.c). In the theory of linear differential equations, this isomorphism is the *monodromy* of the equation

---

[4] See Appendix A.4.c, if necessary.

along the trajectory x. When, as in our case, this solution has periodic coefficients, the eigenvalues of the monodromy are *Floquet multipliers*. The fact that the monodromy does not have eigenvalue 1 (this is our nondegeneracy hypothesis) is equivalent to the fact that the linearized equation does not have a periodic solution. This nondegeneracy is also a type of transversality; see Exercise 6 on p. 516.

5.5 Complex Structures

We now show that all symplectic manifolds have (almost) complex structures that are compatible with their symplectic structures in a sense that we first specify.

On a Vector Space

If E is a vector space endowed with a symplectic form ω, then we say that an endomorphism J of E is a complex structure calibrated by ω if $J^2 = -\mathrm{Id}$ (J is a complex structure),

$$\omega(Jv, Jw) = \omega(v, w)$$

(J is symplectic) and

$$g(v, w) = \omega(v, Jw)$$

is a (positive definite) inner product on E.

It is easy to show that every symplectic vector space admits calibrated complex structures. They are isometries and are antisymmetric for the inner product they define. We can simply use a symplectic basis of the vector space, say $(e_1, \ldots, e_{2n})$ with

$$\omega(e_i, e_{j+n}) = \delta_{i,j}, \quad i, j \leq n.$$

The formula

$$J_0(x_1 e_1 + \cdots + x_n e_n + y_1 e_{n+1} + \cdots + y_n e_{2n})$$
$$= (-y_1 e_1 - \cdots - y_n e_n + x_1 e_{n+1} + \cdots + x_n e_{2n})$$

then defines a complex structure.

In the case where the vector space is $\mathbf{R}^{2n}$ and we use the canonical basis, remembering that $\mathbf{R}^{2n} = \mathbf{C}^n$, this J_0 is the multiplication by i.

Conversely, if the complex vector space $\mathbf{C}^n$ is endowed with a Hermitian structure, then it admits a symplectic form. If we decompose the Hermitian inner product into real and imaginary parts (the Euclidean inner product on $\mathbf{C}^n = \mathbf{R}^{2n}$ and the symplectic form, respectively), then we find

$$
\begin{aligned}
\langle u, v \rangle &= \left\langle \sum u_i e_i, \sum v_j e_j \right\rangle \\
&= \sum u_i \bar{v}_j \langle e_i, e_j \rangle \\
&= \sum u_j \bar{v}_j \\
&= \sum (a_j + i b_j)(x_j - i y_j) \\
&= \sum (a_j x_j + b_j y_j) - i \sum (a_j y_j - b_j x_j) \\
&= (u, v) - i\omega(u, v).
\end{aligned}
$$

We have

$$
\begin{aligned}
\langle u, v \rangle &= i\langle u, iv \rangle \\
&= i((u, iv) - i\omega(u, iv)) \\
&= \omega(u, iv) + i(u, iv),
\end{aligned}
$$

hence $\omega(u, iv)$ is also the Euclidean inner product of u and v. Moreover, $\omega(iu, iv) = \omega(u, v)$: the multiplication by i is an "isometry" of ω. This is what the definition on a manifold will imitate.

Remark 5.5.1. The general linear group $\mathrm{GL}(2n; \mathbf{R})$ acts on the space of complex structures on $\mathbf{R}^{2n}$ through $g \cdot J = gJg^{-1}$. Using a J-complex basis, we see that this action is transitive and that the stabilizer of the complex structure J_0 is the group of *complex* automorphisms (for J_0). In other words, the set of almost complex linear structures on the space $\mathbf{R}^{2n}$ can be identified with the homogeneous space

$$
\mathfrak{I}_n = \mathrm{GL}(2n; \mathbf{R}) / \mathrm{GL}(n; \mathbf{C}).
$$

Calibrated Almost Complex Structures on a Symplectic Manifold

An *almost complex* structure J on a manifold is an endomorphism of the tangent bundle that satisfies $J^2 = -\mathrm{Id}$.

Examples 5.5.2.

(1) If W is a complex manifold (that is, a manifold that is locally diffeomorphic to $\mathbf{C}^n$ with analytic transition maps), then its tangent space $T_x W$ at every point is a complex vector space and the multiplication by i is

an almost complex structure. This is the situation that is mimicked by the definition of an almost complex structure: J plays the role of the multiplication by i.

(2) For example, let W be an oriented surface endowed with a Riemannian metric, so that we have a notion of rotation by $+\pi/2$ in each tangent plane. This family of rotations defines an almost complex structure on W. In this manner, all orientable surfaces have almost complex structures.[5]

(3) It is not true that all manifolds, or even all manifolds of even dimension, have almost complex structures. For example, the sphere S^4 does not have any almost complex structure (and therefore does not have any symplectic structure!).

(4) The sphere S^6, and likewise all orientable hypersurfaces in $\mathbf{R}^7$, has almost complex structures. See Exercise 13 on p. 519.

An almost complex manifold (W, J) is said to be *calibrated* by the symplectic form ω if J is an isometry of ω and if the symmetric bilinear form $\omega(X, JY)$ is positive definite at every point; that is, if J_x is calibrated by ω_x for every x.

(1) The almost complex structure J_0 constructed on a symplectic vector space using a symplectic basis, as above, is calibrated by the symplectic form.

(2) On a complex Kähler manifold, the complex structure is calibrated by the Kähler form.

In order to prove the existence of calibrated almost complex structures on all symplectic manifolds, let us return to the case of vector spaces to once more prove, this time without using a basis, that there exist calibrated complex structures on all symplectic vector spaces. Let (E, ω) be such a space. We begin by choosing an inner product (X, Y). Since $(\,,\,)$ and ω are nondegenerate, the relation $(X, AY) = \omega(X, Y)$ defines an isomorphism $A : E \to E$. We then write down the polar decomposition of A, that is, $A = BJ$, where B is a positive definite symmetric endomorphism, A and B commute and J is an isometry.

Lemma 5.5.3. *The endomorphism A is antisymmetric, J is an isometry of ω and satisfies $J^2 = -1$ and $JB = BJ$.*

---

[5] We can prove, following Gauß, that the almost complex structures on the surfaces are in fact complex structures. An accessible reference is [44, Theorem 3.1.11], which proves the (equivalent) statement under the form "every oriented surface endowed with a Riemannian metric is a Riemann surface".

Proof. We have

$$(X, AY) = \omega(X, Y) = -\omega(Y, X) = -(AX, Y),$$

hence A is antisymmetric. We also have $J = B^{-1}A$, and therefore

$${}^t J = {}^t A {}^t B^{-1} = -AB^{-1} = -B^{-1}A = -J.$$

Since J is an isometry, ${}^t J J = 1$, so that J is indeed a complex structure. Moreover,

$$BJ = A = -{}^t A = -{}^t(BJ) = -{}^t J {}^t B = -{}^t J B = JB,$$

hence B and J commute, and therefore A and J also commute, giving the result

$$\omega(JX, JY) = (JX, AJY) = (JX, JAY) = (X, AY) = \omega(X, Y). \qquad \square$$

The inner product defined by B is

$$(\!(X, Y)\!) = (BX, Y) = \omega(X, JY).$$

We have thus shown the existence of calibrated complex structures on all symplectic vector spaces. Note that the form $(\!(\,,\,)\!) - i\omega(\,,\,)$ is Hermitian. Since the proof uses only the symplectic form and the inner product, it can be generalized to the case of a symplectic manifold endowed with a Riemannian metric.

We can also note that this same construction of J, carried out fiber by fiber, gives the structure of a complex vector bundle on every symplectic vector bundle, in particular on the tangent bundle of a symplectic manifold.

The result in Corollary 5.5.5 is very important because it will allow us to use these complex structures without worrying too much about the way they were constructed. Let $\mathcal{J}_c(\omega)$ denote the space of complex structures calibrated by ω.

Proposition 5.5.4. *Let j be a complex structure on $\mathbf{R}^{2n}$ calibrated by the form ω. The map*

$$J \longmapsto (J + j)^{-1} \circ (J - j)$$

is a diffeomorphism from $\mathcal{J}_c(\omega)$ onto the open unit ball in the vector space of symmetric matrices S with $jS + Sj = 0$.

Corollary 5.5.5. *The space $\mathcal{J}_c(\omega)$ is contractible.* $\qquad \square$

A proof of these classical results can, for example, be found in [3, 18, 50, 5].

Now, let W be a manifold of dimension $2n$ endowed with a symplectic form ω. Choosing a Riemannian metric on W (constructed using a partition of unity) allows us to construct a calibrated almost complex structure, as noted earlier.

Taking its tangent bundle, we associate with it the bundle

$$\mathcal{J}_c(\omega) \longrightarrow W$$

of calibrated almost complex structures on W, whose fiber at x is $\mathcal{J}_c(\omega_x)$. A calibrated complex structure is a section of the fiber bundle $\mathcal{J}_c(\omega) \to W$. Since the fibers of this bundle are contractible, we have the following result.

Proposition 5.5.6. *The space of almost complex structures calibrated by ω on W is nonempty and contractible.* □

We also note the following result.

Proposition 5.5.7. *The tangent space of $\mathcal{J}_c(\omega)$ at J is*

$$T_J \mathcal{J}_c(\omega) = \{S \in \operatorname{End}(TW) \mid JS + SJ = 0 \text{ and } \omega(S\xi, \eta) + \omega(\xi, S\eta) = 0\}.$$

Proof. The first equality is the infinitesimal version of the fact that $J^2 = -\operatorname{Id}$, the second says that S is symmetric (for the metric g defined by J):

$$\begin{aligned}
g(S\xi, \eta) &= \omega(S\xi, J\eta) \\
&= -\omega(\xi, SJ\eta) \\
&= \omega(\xi, JS\eta) \\
&= g(\xi, S\eta),
\end{aligned}$$

and also that JS is symmetric:

$$\begin{aligned}
\omega(S\xi, \eta) + \omega(\xi, S\eta) &= g(S\xi, -J\eta) + g(\xi, -JS\eta) \\
&= -g(S\xi, J\eta) - g(\xi, JS\eta) \\
&= -g(JS\xi, -\eta) - g(\xi, JS\eta) \\
&= g(JS\xi, \eta) - g(\xi, JS\eta).
\end{aligned}$$
□

Examples 5.5.8.

(1) The Euclidean space $\mathbf{R}^{2n}$ has already been studied at length.
(2) The torus $T^{2n} = \mathbf{R}^{2n}/\mathbf{Z}^{2n}$ inherits all structures (symplectic, almost complex) that $\mathbf{R}^{2n}$ is endowed with because these are invariant under translation.

(3) The complex projective space $\mathbf{P}^n(\mathbf{C})$ is endowed with the symplectic structure deduced from that of $\mathbf{C}^{n+1}$, which we described earlier (see Proposition 5.3.1). It inherits an almost complex structure deduced from that of $\mathbf{C}^{n+1}$, which, for $\xi \in T_{[x]}\mathbf{P}^n(\mathbf{C})$, is defined by

$$J\xi = T_x\pi(i\xi'), \text{ if } \xi \text{ is the image of } \xi' \in \mathbf{C}^{n+1}, \text{ with } \langle \xi', x \rangle = 0.$$

It is clear that the result does not depend on the choice of $x \in [x]$: if

$$\xi = T_x\pi(\widetilde{\xi}) \quad \text{with } \widetilde{\xi} = \xi' + \lambda ix,$$

then

$$\xi = T_{u \cdot x}\pi(u\widetilde{\xi}) \quad \text{and} \quad u\widetilde{\xi} = u\xi' + \lambda(iu \cdot x).$$

We of course also have $J(J\xi) = T_x\pi(-\xi') = -\xi$.

Gradient and Hamiltonian Vector Field

If W is endowed with a symplectic form ω, with a calibrated almost complex structure J and with the Riemannian metric $g(X, Y) = \omega(X, JY)$, then given any function $H : W \to \mathbf{R}$, we can associate with it two vector fields: the Hamiltonian vector field X_H and the gradient $\operatorname{grad} H$. We have

$$\omega(Y, X_H) = dH(Y) = g(Y, \operatorname{grad} H) = \omega(Y, J \operatorname{grad} H),$$

so that

$$X_H = J \operatorname{grad} H \quad \text{and} \quad \operatorname{grad} H = -JX_H.$$

5.6 The Symplectic Group

We now consider $\mathbf{R}^{2n}$ endowed with the usual symplectic form ω and a (linear) complex structure that identifies it with $\mathbf{C}^n$. We denote this by J_0.

The symplectic group, denoted by $\operatorname{Sp}(2n)$, is the group of isometries, or symplectic transformations of ω. A transformation g of $\mathbf{C}^n$ is called *symplectic* if it satisfies

$$\omega(gZ, gZ') = \omega(Z, Z') \quad \text{for all } Z, Z' \in \mathbf{C}^n.$$

Example 5.6.1 (The Group Sp(2)). The symplectic group of $\mathbf{C}$ is isomorphic to $\operatorname{SL}(2; \mathbf{R})$.

5.6.a Relations Between Subgroups of $GL(2n; \mathbf{R})$

We view the groups $O(2n)$, $GL(n; \mathbf{C})$, $U(n)$ and $Sp(2n)$ as subgroups of $GL(2n; \mathbf{R})$.

Proposition 5.6.2. *We have the equalities*

$$Sp(2n) \cap O(2n) = Sp(2n) \cap GL(n; \mathbf{C}) = O(2n) \cap GL(n; \mathbf{C}) = U(n).$$

Proof. Let us highlight the different types of elements of $GL(2n; \mathbf{R})$:

(1) $g \in GL(n; \mathbf{C})$ if and only if g is $\mathbf{C}$-linear, that is, if and only if

$$g(iZ) = ig(Z) \quad \text{for every } Z$$

(for a matrix A, this means that $AJ_0 = J_0 A$).

(2) $g \in Sp(2n)$ if and only if g preserves ω, that is, if and only if

$$\omega(gZ, gZ') = \omega(Z, Z') \text{ for all } Z \text{ and } Z'.$$

For a matrix A, this means that

$$^tAJ_0A = J_0.$$

(3) $g \in O(2n)$ if and only if $(gZ, gZ') = (Z, Z')$. For a matrix A, this means that $^tAA = \mathrm{Id}$.

Any two of these conditions always imply the third one:

- (2) and (3) imply that
$$\langle gZ, gZ' \rangle = \langle Z, Z' \rangle$$
and therefore that $g \in U(n) \subset GL(n; \mathbf{C})$.
- (3) and (1) imply that

$$\omega(gZ, gZ') = \omega(gZ, -ig(iZ')) = (gZ, g(iZ')) = (Z, iZ') = \omega(Z, Z')$$

and therefore that $g \in Sp(2n)$.
- Likewise, (1) and (2) imply (3).

In terms of matrices, the intersection $Sp(2n) \cap O(2n)$ consists of the matrices

$$\begin{pmatrix} U & -V \\ V & U \end{pmatrix} \in GL(2n; \mathbf{R})$$

with

$$\begin{cases} ^tUV = {}^tVU \\ ^tUU + {}^tVV = \mathrm{Id} . \end{cases}$$

This is exactly the condition for $U + iV$ to be a unitary matrix. $\qquad \square$

5.6.b The Eigenvalues of the Elements of $\mathrm{Sp}(2n)$

Let $A \in \mathrm{Sp}(2n)$. This means that ${}^t A J_0 A = J_0$, or equivalently that

$$ {}^t A = J_0 A^{-1} J_0^{-1} = -J_0 A^{-1} J_0. $$

In particular, ${}^t A$ and A^{-1} are similar (since ${}^t A$ and A are) and therefore A and A^{-1} are similar.

Proposition 5.6.3. *If $A \in \mathrm{Sp}(2n)$, then A, A^{-1} and ${}^t A$ are similar.* □

Note that λ is an eigenvalue of A if and only if λ^{-1} is also one. Figure 5.2 shows the positions of the eigenvalues of a symplectic matrix in $\mathbf{C}$. As a consequence of the following result, even the multiplicities of λ and λ^{-1} coincide.

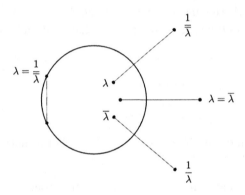

Fig. 5.2

Proposition 5.6.4. *The characteristic polynomial of $A \in \mathrm{Sp}(2n)$ is symmetric (in the sense that its coefficients are symmetric); that is,*

$$ \text{for } A \in \mathrm{Sp}(2n), \quad \det(A - \lambda \, \mathrm{Id}) = \lambda^{2n} \det\left(A - \frac{1}{\lambda}\right). $$

Proof. In fact, we have $A = -J_0 \, {}^t A^{-1} J_0$ and

$$
\begin{aligned}
\det(A - \lambda \, \mathrm{Id}) &= \det(-J_0 \, {}^t A^{-1} J_0 - \lambda \, \mathrm{Id}) \\
&= \det(-{}^t A^{-1} + \lambda \, \mathrm{Id}) \quad \text{because } J_0^2 = -\mathrm{Id} \\
&= \det({}^t A^{-1}) \det(\mathrm{Id} - \lambda \, {}^t A) \\
&= \det(\lambda \, {}^t A - \mathrm{Id}) \quad \text{because } \det A = 1 \text{ (Corollary 5.6.10)} \\
&= \lambda^{2n} \det\left(A - \frac{1}{\lambda} \, \mathrm{Id}\right)
\end{aligned}
$$

□

Remark 5.6.5. The multiplicities of λ, λ^{-1}, $\overline{\lambda}$ and $\overline{\lambda}^{-1}$ as eigenvalues of A are all equal.

5.6.c The Eigenspaces of Elements of $\mathrm{Sp}(2n)$

In order to study the eigenspaces of $A \in \mathrm{Sp}(2n; \mathbf{R})$, we need to complexify the space $\mathbf{R}^{2n}$ (into $\mathbf{C}^{2n}$!). We therefore consider $A \in \mathrm{GL}(2n; \mathbf{C})$ and "extend" the symplectic form ω into a $\mathbf{C}$-bilinear form

$$\omega : \mathbf{C}^{2n} \times \mathbf{C}^{2n} \longrightarrow \mathbf{C}.$$

Proposition 5.6.6. *Let λ and μ be two eigenvalues of A with $\lambda\mu \neq 1$, and let r and s be two (nonzero) integers. If $X \in \mathrm{Ker}(A - \lambda\,\mathrm{Id})^r$ and $Y \in \mathrm{Ker}(A - \mu\,\mathrm{Id})^s$, then $\omega(X, Y) = 0$.*

Proof. Let $P_{r,s}$ denote the desired property. We first prove $P_{1,s}$ by induction on s:

- We have $P_{1,1}$ because
$$\omega(X, Y) = \omega(AX, AY) = \lambda\mu\omega(X, Y).$$

- Next, we assume that $P_{1,s}$ is true. Let X be an eigenvector of A and let $Y \in \mathrm{Ker}(A - \mu\,\mathrm{Id})^{s+1}$. We have
$$\begin{aligned}
\omega(X, Y) &= \omega(AX, AY) \\
&= \lambda\omega(X, (A - \mu\,\mathrm{Id})Y) + \lambda\mu\omega(X, Y) \\
&= \lambda\mu\omega(X, Y)
\end{aligned}$$

because $(A - \mu\,\mathrm{Id})Y \in \mathrm{Ker}(A - \mu\,\mathrm{Id})^s$.

In the same manner, we have property $P_{r,1}$. To show $P_{r,s}$ by induction, we verify that
$$P_{r,s+1} \text{ and } P_{r+1,s} \implies P_{r+1,s+1}.$$
Therefore, let $X \in \mathrm{Ker}(A - \lambda\,\mathrm{Id})^{r+1}$ and $Y \in \mathrm{Ker}(A - \mu\,\mathrm{Id})^{s+1}$. We have
$$\begin{aligned}
\omega(X, Y) &= \omega(AX, AY) \\
&= \omega((A - \lambda\,\mathrm{Id})X, AY) + \lambda\omega(X, AY) \\
&= \lambda\omega(X, AY)
\end{aligned}$$

because $P_{r,s+1}$ is assumed to be true. Next,
$$\begin{aligned}
\lambda\omega(X, AY) &= \lambda\omega(X, (A - \mu\,\mathrm{Id})Y) + \lambda\mu\omega(X, Y) \\
&= \lambda\mu\omega(X, Y)
\end{aligned}$$

by applying $P_{r+1,s}$. Finally,

$$w(X, Y) = \lambda\mu w(X, Y),$$

so that $w(X, Y) = 0$ and $P_{r+1,s+1}$ is true.   □

We let E_λ denote the subspace of $\mathbf{C}^{2n}$ defined by

$$E_\lambda = \bigcup_r \mathrm{Ker}(A - \lambda\,\mathrm{Id})^r.$$

We call this the *generalized eigenspace* for λ. It is well known that E_λ is a complex vector space of dimension the multiplicity $m(\lambda)$ of the eigenvalue λ and that $\mathbf{C}^{2n}$ is the direct sum of the subspaces E_λ. The following is an immediate consequence of the proposition.

Corollary 5.6.7.

(1) *If $\lambda\mu \neq 1$, then $w(E_\lambda, E_\mu) = 0$.*
(2) *The restrictions of w to E_1 and E_{-1} are nondegenerate. In particular, the restrictions of w to $E_{\pm 1} \cap \mathbf{R}^{2n}$ are symplectic forms and the multiplicities $m(1)$ and $m(-1)$ are even.*
(3) *For every $\lambda \in \mathrm{Spec}(A) - \{-1, +1\}$, the restriction of w to $E_\lambda \oplus E_{1/\lambda}$ is nondegenerate.*   □

Remark 5.6.8. The map $X \mapsto \overline{X}$ is an isomorphism (of real vector spaces) from E_λ onto $E_{\overline{\lambda}}$.

5.6.d The Polar Decomposition

We have seen that the group $\mathrm{U}(n)$ is a subgroup of $\mathrm{Sp}(2n)$. It is well known that it is its maximal compact subgroup. In fact, the polar decomposition of $\mathrm{GL}(n; \mathbf{R})$ gives a homeomorphism

$$\mathrm{Sp}(2n) \longrightarrow \mathrm{U}(n) \times C_n$$
$$A \longmapsto US,$$

where C_n denotes the open subset of symmetric positive definite symplectic matrices. Recall that $S = \sqrt{{}^t A A}$ and $U = AS^{-1}$.

Proposition 5.6.9. *The group $\mathrm{Sp}(2n)$ retracts onto $\mathrm{U}(n)$. In particular, it is pathwise connected and its fundamental group is isomorphic to $\mathbf{Z}$.*

Proof. Let us show that the open set C_n is contractible. Let $A \in C_n$; then A, like all symmetric matrices, has real eigenvalues (which are positive) and admits a basis of eigenvectors. Consider an eigenvalue λ, its inverse λ^{-1}

and the sum of the associated eigenspaces, $E_\lambda \oplus E_{\lambda^{-1}}$ (there is no difference between the eigenspaces and the characteristic spaces for these diagonalizable matrices).

We have seen that if $\lambda\mu \neq 1$, then the eigenvectors associated with these two eigenvalues are orthogonal for ω. Assume that λ does not equal 1. We have said that the restriction of ω to $E_\lambda \oplus E_{\lambda^{-1}}$ is nondegenerate. The vectors of E_λ are all mutually orthogonal (because $\lambda^2 \neq 1$), so a vector E_λ cannot be orthogonal to all vectors of $E_{\lambda^{-1}}$. We can therefore find a symplectic basis of $E_\lambda \oplus E_{\lambda^{-1}}$ whose first vectors are eigenvectors for λ, followed by eigenvectors for λ^{-1}. By considering all pairs of eigenvalues, we obtain a symplectic basis of $\mathbf{R}^{2n}$ in which the matrix A is a diagonal block matrix with blocks of the form

$$(\lambda, \ldots, \lambda, \lambda^{-1}, \ldots, \lambda^{-1}).$$

Writing $\lambda = \log \ell$, we obtain a diagonal matrix (in the same symplectic basis) whose exponential is A. It follows that A is the exponential of a diagonalizable symmetric matrix. And, moreover, that there is a continuous map $A \mapsto \log A$, so that we can retract C_n onto the identity using the retraction

$$(A, t) \longmapsto \exp(t \log A). \qquad \square$$

Corollary 5.6.10. *The determinant of a symplectic matrix is 1.*

Indeed, it is clearly ± 1 and the group is pathwise connected. $\qquad \square$

See also Exercises 16 and 35 (pages 520 and 526, respectively). The isomorphism of the fundamental group of $\mathrm{Sp}(2n)$ with $\mathbf{Z}$ can be obtained by taking the composition of the projection onto $\mathrm{U}(n)$ given by the proposition above and the (complex) determinant, a map

$$\mathrm{Sp}(2n) \longrightarrow S^1.$$

Chapter 6
The Arnold Conjecture and the Floer Equation

In this chapter, we arrive at the heart of our subject: the Arnold conjecture. We state this conjecture, which gives a lower bound for the number of fixed points of certain Hamiltonian diffeomorphisms. We then identify these fixed points with periodic orbits of Hamiltonian systems and with critical points of the "action functional". We describe this functional, a function on the space of the contractible loops on the original symplectic manifold, as well as the differential equation defining the flow of the gradient of this functional, called the Floer equation. This is a partial differential equation because it involves both the loop's variable and that of the gradient's flow. We begin studying the space of solutions of this equation by showing a compactness property.

6.1 The Arnold Conjecture

The general setting of the Arnold conjecture (stated by Arnold in [1, 2]) is that of a symplectic diffeomorphism of a symplectic manifold; the problem is the estimation of its number of fixed points. Of course, constructing symplectic manifolds and symplectic diffeomorphisms on them that have *no* fixed points is easy. Take a rotation on a torus, for example (see Exercise 22 on p. 522).

Conversely, we have seen (in Section 5.4) that the flow at "time 1" of a Hamiltonian vector field, in turn, has at least as many fixed points as the function that generated it has critical points. By applying Proposition 4.4.3, we deduce the following result.

Proposition 6.1.1. *The number of periodic solutions of period 1 of a non-degenerate autonomous Hamiltonian system on a compact symplectic mani-*

M. Audin, M. Damian, *Morse Theory and Floer Homology,*
Universitext, DOI 10.1007/978-1-4471-5496-9_6,
© Springer-Verlag London 2014

fold W is greater than or equal to the sum

$$\sum_i \dim HM_i(W; \mathbf{Z}/2).$$ $\square$

The Arnold conjecture that we are going to study here is exactly the same statement, except that the Hamiltonian is no longer assumed to be autonomous; it now depends on time.

Conjecture 6.1.2 (Arnold). *Let W be a compact symplectic manifold and let*

$$H : W \times \mathbf{R} \longrightarrow \mathbf{R}$$

be a time-dependent Hamiltonian. Suppose that the solutions of period 1 of the associated Hamiltonian system are nondegenerate. Then their number is greater than or equal to the sum

$$\sum_i \dim HM_i(W; \mathbf{Z}/2).$$

Recall that a solution of period 1 is called nondegenerate if the differential of the flow at time 1 does not have any fixed vectors (see Definition 5.4.4).

Remark 6.1.3. In this statement, H can also be assumed to be periodic, in the sense that $H(x, t+1) = H(x, t)$. Indeed,

$$\frac{d}{dt}(\varphi^{\alpha(t)}) = \frac{d\alpha}{dt} X_{H_{\alpha(t)}}(\varphi^{\alpha(t)}(x)) = X_{\alpha'(t)H_{\alpha(t)}}(\varphi^{\alpha(t)}(x)),$$

so that $t \mapsto \varphi^{\alpha(t)}$ is the flow of the Hamiltonian vector field associated with the function $K_t = \alpha'(t)H_{\alpha(t)}$. If α is a function from $[0,1]$ to $[0,1]$ that is zero (and flat) near 0 and equal to 1 (and flat) near 1, then this equality gives both the fact that $\varphi^{\alpha(1)} = \varphi^1$ and the fact that K_t can be extended to a periodic function of the time t. $\square$

Remarks 6.1.4. We could add numerous remarks. The "correct" conjecture is that the number of fixed points of a diffeomorphism that is a "time 1" as above is greater than or equal to the minimal number of critical points of a function on the manifold, and that if these fixed points are *nondegenerate*, then their number is greater than or equal to the minimal number of critical points of a *Morse* function on this manifold.[1]

There are a great many variants, such as the one where the fixed points of symplectic diffeomorphisms are replaced by intersection points of Lagrangian submanifolds...

---

[1] We saw in Remark 4.4.5 that the minimal number of critical points of a function may be less than the minimal number of critical points of a Morse function.

It is customary to draw up a chronological list of the results that have been obtained. The conjecture has now been proved in all generality (in its homological form); many mathematicians have contributed to this proof. In chronological order, fearing that we may have forgotten contributions, let us nevertheless try to give a list: Eliashberg for dimension 2, Conley and Zehnder for the tori. Then comes Floer's revolution, for aspherical manifolds ($\pi_2 = 0$) and then for monotone manifolds (which include the complex projective spaces), using methods that were then extended and exploited by Hofer, Salamon and, independently, by Ono for the weakly monotone case and then by Fukaya and Ono, by Liu and Tian and by Hofer and Salamon for the general case. We refer to the overview [66] by Salamon for precise references to these works.

Proof for a Hamiltonian That Is Independent of Time and "Small"

This result is not only an example where the conjecture is easy to prove. It will also play an essential role in the computation of the Floer homology in Chapter 10.

Proposition 6.1.5. *Let H be a function on $\mathbf{R}^{2n}$, so that X_H is a vector field on $\mathbf{R}^{2n}$. If $\|dX_H\|_{L^2} < 2\pi$, then the only solutions of period 1 of the Hamiltonian system associated with H are the constant solutions (critical points of H).*

Note that when the Hamiltonian H is "$\mathcal{C}^2$-small", proving the inequality in the Arnold conjecture corresponds to proving the Morse inequalities (see Remark 5.4.7).

Proof. We take up the proof given in [49]. Consider a solution x of period 1 and take its Fourier expansion (this is a vector in $\mathbf{C}^n$) as well as those of its derivatives $\dot{x}$ and $\ddot{x}$:

$$x(t) = \sum_n c_n(x) e^{2in\pi t} : \quad \dot{x} = \sum_n 2ni\pi c_n(x) e^{2in\pi t}, \quad \text{etc.}$$

Next, Parseval's identity gives

$$\|\ddot{x}\|_{L^2}^2 = \sum 4\pi^2 n^2 \left|c_n(\dot{x})\right|^2 \geq 4\pi^2 \sum_{n \neq 0} \left|c_n(\dot{x})\right|^2 = 4\pi^2 \|\dot{x}\|_{L^2}^2$$

because $c_0(\dot{x}) = 0$. We therefore have

$$\|\dot{x}\|_{L^2} \leq \frac{1}{2\pi} \|\ddot{x}\|_{L^2}.$$

Since $\ddot{x} = (dX_H)_x \cdot \dot{x}$, the condition $\|dX_H\|_{L^2} < 2\pi$ gives

$$\|\ddot{x}\|_{L^2} < 2\pi \, \|\dot{x}\|_{L^2} \quad \text{if } \dot{x} \neq 0,$$

so that $\dot{x} = 0$ and x is constant.   □

In fact, this proposition holds more generally for a vector field that is not necessarily Hamiltonian, but whose Lipschitz constant is less than 2π. Likewise, the following proposition remains true for a $\mathcal{C}^1$-small vector field.

Proposition 6.1.6. *Let W be a compact symplectic manifold and let $H : W \to \mathbf{R}$ be a function. If H is sufficiently small in the $\mathcal{C}^2$ sense, then the only solutions of period 1 of the Hamiltonian system associated with H are the constant solutions.*

Proof. First note that for a Hamiltonian vector field X_H on a disk $D^{2n} \subset \mathbf{R}^{2n}$, we have

$$\forall x \in D^{2n}, \ \forall t \in [0,1], \quad \left\| \varphi^t(x) - x \right\| \leq \sup_{y \in D^{2n}} \|X_H(y)\|$$

by the mean value theorem.

It follows that if $H : W \to \mathbf{R}$ is sufficiently small in the $\mathcal{C}^2$ sense, then there exists a finite cover of the compact manifold W by relatively compact Darboux charts such that:

- Every trajectory of period 1 is contained in a chart.
- $\|dX_H\| < 2\pi$ on every chart (for the metric on $\mathbf{R}^{2n}$).

We then apply Proposition 6.1.5 in each chart.   □

6.2 Outline of the Proof, Floer Homology

The main tool that we will use to prove the Arnold conjecture (under a restrictive condition) is Floer homology. Floer's idea [28, 29, 30, 31] is to "count" the periodic solutions of H, or the fixed points of its flow at time $t = 1$, to give a lower bound for their number in a manner analogous to the one that allowed us to give a lower bound for the number of critical points of a Morse function on a manifold (Proposition 4.4.3).

(1) We begin by defining a "function", the *action functional* (Section 6.3), on a suitable space (which can be seen as an infinite-dimensional manifold; see Section 6.3.a). The critical points of this functional will be exactly the desired periodic solutions.

(2) With these critical points, we will construct a complex. We first take the vector spaces over $\mathbf{Z}/2$ that they generate. To define a grading on these spaces, we will need an analogue of the index of a critical point, which we will define in Chapter 7 and which will be the index in the Morse sense (up to a translation) when the Hamiltonian is not time dependent (Corollary 7.2.2).

(3) To define the differential of the complex, we will use a vector field, the gradient (or its negative) of the functional, which we will describe, together with the metric that defines it, in Section 6.4.

(4) The idea is then to "count" its trajectories. In Section 6.5.a, we will highlight a property, the finiteness of the energy, which is automatically satisfied for a pseudo-gradient field on a compact manifold and which will be useful here.

(5) We will show that the trajectories of finite energy indeed connect two critical points (Theorem 6.5.6).

(6) We will need a compactness property for the space of trajectories of finite energy (Gromov's compactness, Theorem 6.5.4).

(7) As in the Morse case (Section 3.2.b), we will need another compactness property to define the differential ∂ (In Subsection 9.1.c).

(8) And of course, we will need these spaces of trajectories to be manifolds, as well as a genericness property such as the Smale property for a sufficiently close vector field (Theorem 2.2.5), which we will achieve in Chapter 8.

(9) Having thus defined the differential of the supposed complex, we will still need to verify that $\partial \circ \partial = 0$. In the Morse case, we used a gluing property (Section 3.2.c). We will prove an analogous property in Chapter 9.

(10) Using the same methods as in Section 3.4, we will show that the homology of the complex we have finally defined depends neither on the choice of the functional nor on that of the vector field.

(11) And finally, by considering the case of an autonomous $\mathcal{C}^2$-small Hamiltonian, this independence will tell us that the homology we have thus constructed, the Floer homology, coincides with the Morse homology of the manifold. The obvious inequality between the dimensions of the vector spaces involved in the complex will give the expected result, in a manner that is completely analogous to the Morse inequalities (Proposition 4.4.3).

The Assumptions

We will assume that the symplectic manifold W satisfies the following two conditions.

Assumption 6.2.1. *For every $\mathcal{C}^\infty$ map $w : S^2 \to W$, we have*

$$\int_{S^2} w^\star \omega = 0.$$

In the literature, this condition is sometimes called "symplectic asphericity" (the symplectic form is zero on spheres). It can be expressed as

$$\langle \omega, \pi_2(W) \rangle = 0.$$

Assumption 6.2.2. *For every $\mathcal{C}^\infty$ map $w : S^2 \to W$, there exists a symplectic trivialization of the fiber bundle $w^\star TW$.*

This condition can be expressed as

$$\langle c_1(TW), \pi_2(W) \rangle = 0,$$

where $c_1(TW)$ denotes the first Chern class of the complex vector bundle TW (see Section B.2).

These two conditions are satisfied, for example, when all maps from S^2 to W extend to the ball B^3, that is, when $\pi_2(W) = 0$.

6.3 The Action Functional

6.3.a The Loop Space

We are looking for periodic trajectories of a particular vector field, in particular $\mathcal{C}^\infty$ maps

$$x : \mathbf{R}/\mathbf{Z} \longrightarrow W.$$

We will therefore have to consider the space of these maps (instead of the manifold V).

The Connected Component of the Fixed Points.

Of course, the space of all loops is not connected in general: it is clear that two loops that are not homotopic do not lie in the same connected component. We will therefore restrict ourselves to one connected component, and it is natural to consider the one containing the constant loops, since these correspond to the critical points in the autonomous case. Let $\mathcal{L}W$ be the space of *contractible* loops on the manifold W, that is, the space of $\mathcal{C}^\infty$ maps

$$x : S^1 \longrightarrow W$$

(of free loops[2]) homotopic to the constant map.

---

[2] This means that the base point of the loop is not fixed. Moreover, the homotopies between these loops are free.

This space is endowed with the $\mathcal{C}^\infty$ topology and with a distance function d_∞ that defines this topology (see Appendix A.3.b, if necessary). It is pathwise connected (we can connect each loop to the constant loop using a path that is a homotopy between the two).

Fundamental Group.

Let us fix a base point in the loop space, namely the constant loop equal to a point x_0 chosen in W. We will also denote this loop by x_0. A loop with base point x_0 in $\mathcal{L}W$ is a map

$$\gamma : [0,1] \times S^1 \longrightarrow W$$
$$(s,t) \longmapsto \gamma(s,t)$$

with

$$\gamma(0,t) = \gamma(1,t) = x_0(t) = x_0.$$

This can be viewed as a map $\widetilde{\gamma} : S^2 \to W$ (Figure 6.1).

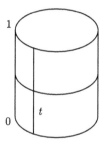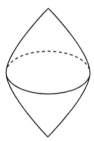

Fig. 6.1

Manifold Structure, Tangent Space.

It is natural to treat $\mathcal{L}W$ as a manifold. At first, we will hardly need to give the manifold structure explicitly: it is used in a rather formal manner, the equations and reasoning take place in W. To prepare for the deliberations of Chapter 8, we will describe the structure at the end of this chapter (Section 6.8). For now, the only thing we need to understand is what a tangent vector at a point $x \in \mathcal{L}W$ is. If a tangent vector at x is viewed as an equivalence class of curves passing through x, then we need to consider a curve $s \mapsto u(s) \in \mathcal{L}W$ with $u(0) = x$, in this case,

$$\mathbf{R} \times S^1 \longrightarrow W$$
$$(s,t) \longmapsto u(s,t) \quad \text{with } u(0,t) = x(t).$$

We then have

$$\frac{\partial}{\partial s}u(s,t)|_{s=0} \in T_{x(t)}W,$$

so that it is natural to view a vector tangent to $\mathcal{L}W$ at x as a vector field tangent to W defined along x, that is, a section Y of $x^\star TW$,

$$Y(t) \in T_{x(t)}W \quad \text{for every } t \in S^1.$$

We can also think of Y as a map

$$Y : \mathbf{R} \longrightarrow TW \quad \text{such that} \begin{cases} Y(t) \in T_{x(t)}W \\ Y(t+1) = Y(t) \end{cases} \quad \forall t \in \mathbf{R}$$

(see also Exercise 24 on p. 522).

A 1-form α, for example the differential of a function, defines a linear form on the set of these tangent vectors at x.

6.3.b The Action Functional

Here W is a manifold endowed with a symplectic form ω and H is a time-dependent Hamiltonian,

$$W \times \mathbf{R} \longrightarrow \mathbf{R}$$
$$(x,t) \longmapsto H_t(x)$$

that we assume to be periodic in t, that is, to satisfy

$$H_{t+1}(x) = H_t(x) \quad \forall t \in \mathbf{R},$$

as authorized by Remark 6.1.3. Consider the expression

$$\mathcal{A}_H(x) = -\int_D u^\star\omega + \int_0^1 H_t(x(t))\, dt,$$

where u is an extension of $x : S^1 \to W$ to the disk, that is, a map $D = \{z \in \mathbf{C} \mid |z| \le 1\} \to W$ such that $u(e^{2i\pi t}) = x(t)$.

The second integral is well defined but *a priori* depends on the choice of u. If v is another extension, then

$$\int_D u^\star\omega - \int_D v^\star\omega = \int_{S^2} w^\star\omega,$$

where w is defined by gluing the two disks along their common boundary (Figure 6.2). Assumption 6.2.1 means that the de Rham cohomology class of

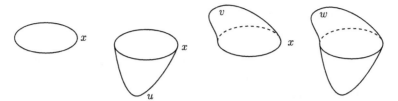

Fig. 6.2

the symplectic form ω is zero on π_2, which, as we noted, can also be written as

$$\langle \omega, \pi_2(W) \rangle = 0.$$

It is satisfied, in particular, if $\pi_2(W) = 0$, that is, if $\mathcal{L}W$ is simply connected (see also Section 6.7, an appendix to this chapter). To conclude, under Assumption 6.2.1, the functional $\mathcal{A}_H$ is well defined.

Example 6.3.1. Consider the case $W = \mathbf{R}^{2n}$ with the symplectic form

$$\omega = \sum dp_i \wedge dq_i = d \sum p_i \, dq_i.$$

Then on any disk whose boundary is our loop x, we have

$$\int_{D^2} u^\star \omega = \int_{S^1} x^\star(p \, dq),$$

so that

$$\mathcal{A}_H(x) = \int_0^1 (H_t \, dt - p \, dq)$$

... the physicists' *action* functional.[3]

Remark 6.3.2. There are many symplectic manifolds other than $\mathbf{R}^{2n}$ that satisfy Assumption 6.2.1, for example the tori $\mathbf{T}^{2n}$, the surfaces of genus at least 1, the cotangent bundles (by Exercise 4 on p. 516). However, neither the sphere S^2 nor any of its cousins $\mathbf{P}^n(\mathbf{C})$ have this property (this time by Exercise 5 on p. 516).

Under our condition, $\mathcal{A}_H$ indeed defines a map

$$\mathcal{L}W \longrightarrow \mathbf{R}.$$

We have the following result.

---

[3] This is why this functional is called $\mathcal{A}_H$.

Proposition 6.3.3. *A loop x is a critical point of A_H if and only if $t \mapsto x(t)$ is a periodic solution of the Hamiltonian system $\dot{x} = X_t(x(t))$.*

Proof. Let us compute the differential of A_H at the point $x(t)$ and on a tangent vector $Y(t)$. We extend x to $\tilde{x}(s,t)$, defined for s in a neighborhood of 0 in such a way that

$$\begin{cases} \tilde{x}(0,t) = x(t) \\ \dfrac{\partial \tilde{x}}{\partial s}(0,t) = Y(t). \end{cases}$$

We then have

$$(dA_H)_x(Y) = \frac{\partial}{\partial s} A_H(\tilde{x})|_{s=0}.$$

Let us study this derivative.

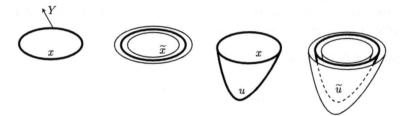

Fig. 6.3

To do this, we choose an extension of u to $\tilde{u}(s,z)$ in such a way that

$$\begin{cases} \tilde{u}(0,z) = u(z) \\ \tilde{u}(s, e^{2i\pi t}) = \tilde{x}(s,t), \end{cases}$$

and we extend Y by setting

$$Y(z) = \frac{\partial \tilde{u}}{\partial s}(0,z).$$

We then have

$$A_H(\tilde{x}(s,t)) = -\int_D \tilde{u}^\star \omega + \int_0^1 H_t(\tilde{x}(s,t))\, dt.$$

Differentiating the first term gives

$$-\int_D \left(\frac{d}{ds}\tilde{u}^\star \omega\right)\Big|_{s=0} = -\int_D u^\star(\mathcal{L}_{Y(z)}\omega) = -\int_D u^\star(di_{Y(z)}\omega)$$

$$= -\int_{S^1} x^\star(i_{Y(t)}\omega) = -\int_0^1 \omega(Y(t), \dot{x}(t))\, dt$$

$$= \int_0^1 \omega(\dot{x}(t), Y(t))\, dt.$$

Differentiating the second term gives

$$\int_0^1 \frac{\partial}{\partial s} H_t(\tilde{x}(s,t))|_{s=0}\, dt = \int_0^1 (dH_t)_{\tilde{x}(0,t)}(Y(t))\, dt$$

$$= \int_0^1 \omega_{x(t)}(Y(t), X_t(x(t)))\, dt.$$

Together, these give

$$(d\mathcal{A}_H)_x(Y) = \int_0^1 \omega(\dot{x}(t) - X_t(x), Y)\, dt.$$

It follows that the differential $(d\mathcal{A}_H)_x$ is zero if and only if

$$\omega(\dot{x}(t) - X_t(x), Y) = 0 \quad \forall Y,$$

that is, by the nondegeneracy of ω, if and only if $\dot{x} = X_t(x)$, which is the desired result. $\square$

We will call x a *nondegenerate* critical point of $\mathcal{A}_H$ if it is a nondegenerate trajectory (in the sense given in Definition 5.4.4).

Remarks 6.3.4 (Case of an Autonomous Hamiltonian).

(1) We have seen that if x is a critical point of H, then the constant trajectory x is a critical point of $\mathcal{A}_H$ (and that the converse holds for "small" H).

(2) We have also seen (Proposition 5.4.5) that if x is nondegenerate for $\mathcal{A}_H$, then it is nondegenerate for H (and that the converse is true for "small" H—this is Remark 5.4.7).

(3) If x is a critical point of $\mathcal{A}_H$ and a *nonconstant* trajectory, then it is degenerate, because the field X_H is a fixed point of $T_x\varphi^1$.

Our last remark is that the values of $\mathcal{A}_H$ at two distinct critical points (geometrically distinct, in the sense where they are two geometrically different trajectories) may be assumed to be different. Let us state this as a lemma (which we will use later).

Lemma 6.3.5. *If x and y are geometrically distinct critical points of $\mathcal{A}_H$, then there exists a function $\tilde{H}$, close to H for the $\mathcal{C}^2$ topology, such that $\mathcal{A}_{\tilde{H}}$ has the same critical points as $\mathcal{A}_H$, with different critical values.*

Proof. It suffices to modify the Hamiltonian H by adding a function H_0 that is constant in the neighborhood of the 1-periodic orbits of X_t, is $\mathcal{C}^2$-small and is such that for all distinct critical points x and y of $\mathcal{A}_H$, we have

$$\mathcal{A}_H(x) + H_0(x(0)) \neq \mathcal{A}_H(y) + H_0(y(0)).$$

If H_0 is sufficiently small, then the critical points of $\mathcal{A}_{H+H_0}$ are those of $\mathcal{A}_H$ and for a critical point x, we have

$$\mathcal{A}_{H+H_0}(x) = \mathcal{A}_H(x) + \int_0^1 H_0(x(t))\, dt = \mathcal{A}_H(x) + H_0(x(0)). \qquad \square$$

6.4 The Gradient, the Floer Equation

As in the Morse case, we need a vector field (the one whose trajectories will define the differential of the complex). We will use the gradient for a particular metric on the space $\mathcal{L}W$ of contractible loops. Be careful, the gradient depends on the metric; the flexibility that we will have if we need to change the vector field (think of the Smale property in Chapter 2) will be available through the metrics (and therefore through the almost complex structures).

Let us begin by fixing an almost complex structure J on W calibrated by ω (see Section 5.5). It defines a Riemannian metric g on W, namely

$$g(X, Y) = \omega(X, J(Y)).$$

This induces a metric on $\mathcal{L}W$, defined by

$$\langle Y, Z \rangle = \int_0^1 g(Y(t), Z(t))\, dt$$

(here Y and Z denote vector fields defined along a loop x). It is clear that this formula defines a symmetric bilinear form; since g_t is positive definite, this form also equals

$$\langle Y, Y \rangle = \int_0^1 g(Y(t), Y(t))\, dt \geq 0,$$

with equality if and only if $Y = 0$, so that $\langle \cdot, \cdot \rangle$ is positive definite. It can also be written as

$$\langle Y, Z \rangle = \int_0^1 \omega_{x(t)}(Y(t), J(Z(t)))\, dt.$$

If $f : \mathcal{L}W \to \mathbf{R}$ is a function, then its gradient is the vector field $\operatorname{grad} f$ defined by

$$\langle \operatorname{grad}_x f, Y \rangle_x = \int_0^1 g_t((\operatorname{grad}_x f)(t), Y(t))\, dt$$

$$= \int_0^1 \omega_{x(t)}((\operatorname{grad}_x f)(t), JY(t))\, dt = (df)_x(Y).$$

Since we also have

$$(dA_H)_x(Y) = \int_0^1 \omega_{x(t)}(\dot{x}(t) - X_t(x), Y(t))\, dt$$

(see Subsection 6.3.b), the gradient of A_H is

$$-X_H(t) = (\mathrm{grad}_x\, A_H)(t) = J_{x(t)}(\dot{x}(t)) + \mathrm{grad}_{x(t)} H_t$$

(the gradient of H_t is computed for the metric g). The trajectories of the

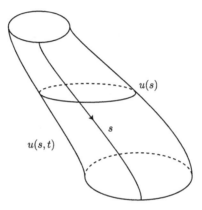

Fig. 6.4

vector field $X = X_H$ (the negative gradient, to be consistent with earlier chapters) are therefore the solutions

$$\mathbf{R} \longrightarrow \mathcal{L}W$$
$$s \longmapsto u(s)$$

(where it is understood that for every s, $u(s)$ is a loop, whose value at time t will be denoted by $u(s,t)$) of the differential equation

$$\frac{\partial u}{\partial s} = -J_{u(s,t)}\left(\frac{\partial u}{\partial t}\right) - \mathrm{grad}_{u(s,t)} H_t(u(s,t))$$

... or, more succinctly, of the (partial) differential equation

$$\frac{\partial u}{\partial s} + J(u)\frac{\partial u}{\partial t} + \mathrm{grad}\, H_t(u) = 0.$$

This equation is the *Floer equation*. Recall that it is its $\mathcal{C}^\infty$ contractible solutions of period 1 in t that interest us.

Remarks 6.4.1.

(1) If H does not depend on t, then the solutions u that also do not depend on t satisfy

$$\frac{du}{ds} + \operatorname{grad} H(u) = 0.$$

These are the trajectories of the (negative) gradient of H.

(2) In general, the solutions u that do not depend on s satisfy

$$\frac{\partial u}{\partial t} = J(u) \operatorname{grad} H_t(u) = X_t(u).$$

This is the (expected) fact that the stationary trajectories of the flow of the gradient are the periodic solutions of the Hamiltonian system.

(3) If $H_t \equiv 0$, then the equation is simply

$$\frac{\partial u}{\partial s} + J(u)\frac{\partial u}{\partial t} = 0;$$

this is the Cauchy–Riemann equation. We then call $(s + it) \mapsto u(s,t)$ a *J-holomorphic curve*.

6.5 The Space of Solutions

Here we study the spaces of solutions of the Floer equation

$$\frac{\partial u}{\partial s} + J(u)\frac{\partial u}{\partial t} + \operatorname{grad} H_t(u) = 0.$$

We use the two points of view represented in Figure 6.5: the solutions of the equation on W are also the trajectories of the vector field $-\operatorname{grad} \mathcal{A}_H$ on $\mathcal{L}W$.

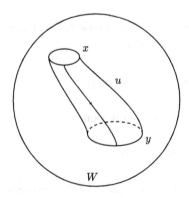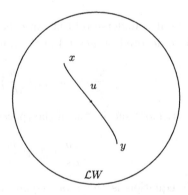

Fig. 6.5

6.5.a Definition of the Energy

In the case of a function and an adapted pseudo-gradient field on a compact manifold V without boundary, all trajectories of the vector field connect two critical points.

This is not automatically the case in the context in which we find ourselves now. Here is an analogy to illustrate the problems we may come across. If V is a manifold with boundary, then there can be trajectories of the pseudo-gradient field that arrive at a critical point without coming from one (and conversely) because they come from the boundary. The trajectories that stay away from the boundary do connect two critical points.

Note that in the compact-manifold–Morse case,[4] if $u : \mathbf{R} \to V$ is a solution of the differential equation

$$\frac{du}{ds} + X(u) = 0,$$

that is, a trajectory of the pseudo-gradient field X, then we can define its *energy*

$$E(u) = -\int_{-\infty}^{+\infty} u^\star df.$$

If u connects two critical points a and b in the sense that $\lim_{s \to -\infty} u(s) = a$ and $\lim_{s \to +\infty} u(s) = b$, then the energy is simply

$$E(u) = f(a) - f(b)$$

(the minus sign in the definition ensures that the energy is positive, since the point a lies above the point b for the function f).

Remark 6.5.1 (Closed Forms). In this definition, it is possible to replace the exact form df by a closed 1-form α. We will see in Section 6.7 that in this case it is still possible to construct an adapted pseudo-gradient field, but it is clear that not all trajectories of such a vector field connect zeros of the form. In this case, the trajectories of finite energy are exactly those that connect two zeros of the form. This is also what happens with the action functional.

In the case of the action functional that we are interested in here, we define the energy of a solution in an analogous manner. This comes down to integrating the square of the norm of the gradient along a solution (whence

---

[4] See also Exercise 27 on p. 523.

the name):

$$E(u) = -\int_{-\infty}^{+\infty} \frac{d}{ds} \mathcal{A}_H(u(s)) \, ds$$

$$= -\int_{-\infty}^{+\infty} -\|\operatorname{grad} \mathcal{A}_H\|^2 \, ds$$

$$= \int_{-\infty}^{+\infty} \left(\int_{S^1} \left| \frac{\partial u}{\partial s} \right|^2 dt \right) ds$$

$$= \frac{1}{2} \int_{-\infty}^{+\infty} \left(\int_{S^1} \left(\left| \frac{\partial u}{\partial s} \right|^2 + \left| \frac{\partial u}{\partial t} - X_t(u) \right|^2 \right) dt \right) ds.$$

Note that since u is a solution, the two terms in the integral are equal, so that

$$E(u) = \int_{\mathbf{R} \times S^1} \left| \frac{\partial u}{\partial s} \right|^2 ds \, dt.$$

Remarks 6.5.2.

(1) The energy is positive.

(2) The energy of a solution is zero if and only if $\partial u / \partial s$ is zero, that is, if u does not depend on s... and u is a solution of the Floer equation, that is, if and only if u is a critical point of the action functional $\mathcal{A}_H$.

(3) If the solution u in question connects two critical points, that is, if there exist critical points x and y of $\mathcal{A}_H$ such that

$$\lim_{s \to -\infty} u_s(t) = x, \qquad \lim_{s \to +\infty} u_s(t) = y,$$

then

$$E(u) = \mathcal{A}_H(x) - \mathcal{A}_H(y) < +\infty.$$

The solutions that connect two critical points have finite energy.

Let us therefore consider the space $\mathcal{M}$ defined by

$$\mathcal{M} = \{ u : \mathbf{R} \times S^1 \to W \mid$$

$$u \text{ is a contractible } \mathcal{C}^\infty \text{ solution of finite energy} \}.$$

In order to avoid problems with the definition of the topology on this space, we will always view the compact symplectic manifold W as being embedded in a Euclidean space $\mathbf{R}^m$ (for m sufficiently large). We will use the $\mathcal{C}^\infty$ topology for the maps from S^1 to $\mathbf{R}^m$ and the $\mathcal{C}^\infty$ uniform convergence

topology on the compact subsets of $\mathbf{R} \times S^1$, with the following notation:
$\mathcal{C}^\infty(S^1; W)$, $\mathcal{C}^\infty(S^1; \mathbf{R}^m)$, $\mathcal{C}^\infty_{\mathrm{loc}}(\mathbf{R} \times S^1; W)$, $\mathcal{C}^\infty_{\mathrm{loc}}(\mathbf{R} \times S^1; \mathbf{R}^m)$.

A strong elliptic regularity result allows us to prove the essential property contained in the following proposition.

Proposition 6.5.3. *Every solution of class* $\mathcal{C}^1$ *of the Floer equation is of class* $\mathcal{C}^\infty$. *Moreover, on* $\mathcal{M}$, *the topologies* $\mathcal{C}^0_{\mathrm{loc}}$, $\mathcal{C}^1_{\mathrm{loc}}$ *and* $\mathcal{C}^\infty_{\mathrm{loc}}$ *coincide.*

Proof. The proof is an immediate consequence of the elliptic regularity lemma (Lemma 12.1.1) and Proposition 6.6.2. □

An important property of this space $\mathcal{M}$ is its compactness. It is an essential property, which we will prove later (in Section 6.6) and which we now state.

Theorem 6.5.4 (Gromov compactness). *Suppose that the compact symplectic manifold* (W, ω) *satisfies Assumption 6.2.1; that is,*

$$\forall f : S^2 \longrightarrow W, \quad \int_{S^2} f^\star \omega = 0.$$

Then $\mathcal{M}$ *is compact in* $\mathcal{C}^\infty_{\mathrm{loc}}(\mathbf{R} \times S^1, W)$.

Remark 6.5.5. In this entire section, we will work in $\mathcal{M}$. We have not proved that the Floer equation has any solutions (be careful, this is not a Cauchy problem).

6.5.b The Finite Energy Solutions Tend Toward Critical Points

We will show a converse to the last of Remarks 6.5.2, namely the following theorem.

Theorem 6.5.6. *Suppose that all periodic trajectories of* X_t *are nondegenerate; then for every* $u \in \mathcal{M}$, *there exist two critical points* x *and* y *of* $\mathcal{A}_H$ *such that*

$$\lim_{s \to -\infty} u(s, \cdot) = x, \quad \lim_{s \to +\infty} u(s, \cdot) = y$$

in $\mathcal{C}^\infty(S^1; W)$. *Moreover,*

$$\lim_{s \to \pm\infty} \frac{\partial u}{\partial s}(s, t) = 0$$

uniformly in t.

Along a Trajectory, the Function Tends Toward a Critical Value. Uniform Bound on the Energy

Let us begin by proving a weaker result.

Proposition 6.5.7. *Let $u \in \mathcal{M}$. There exist two critical points x and y of $\mathcal{A}_H$ such that*

$$\lim_{s \to -\infty} \mathcal{A}_H(u_s) = \mathcal{A}_H(x), \quad \lim_{s \to +\infty} \mathcal{A}_H(u_s) = \mathcal{A}_H(y).$$

Remark 6.5.8. An obvious consequence of this proposition is the fact that if $\mathcal{M}$ is nonempty, then $\mathcal{A}_H$ has critical points.

Corollary 6.5.9. *There exists a real number $C > 0$ such that for every $u \in \mathcal{M}$, we have*

$$-C \leq \mathcal{A}_H(u) \leq C \quad and \quad 0 \leq E(u) \leq C.$$

Proof. The set of critical points of $\mathcal{A}_H$ is finite (and nonempty), hence $\mathcal{A}_H$ is bounded on this set.[5] To conclude we need to use:

- that $s \mapsto \mathcal{A}_H(u_s)$ is decreasing
- and that for u in $\mathcal{M}$ and critical points x and y as in the statement of Proposition 6.5.7 (that is, such that $\mathcal{A}_H(u_s)$ goes from $\mathcal{A}_H(x)$ to $\mathcal{A}_H(y)$), we have
$$E(u) = \mathcal{A}_H(x) - \mathcal{A}_H(y). \qquad \square$$

Proof of Proposition 6.5.7. We will restrict ourselves to the case $s \to +\infty$ since the other case is analogous. The (real) function (in one real variable) $s \mapsto \mathcal{A}_H(u_s)$ is decreasing (its derivative is the negative of the norm of the gradient, and therefore negative). Consequently, it suffices to show that there exist a critical point y in $\mathcal{A}_H$ and a sequence s_k of real numbers tending to infinity such that

$$\lim_{k \to +\infty} \mathcal{A}_H(u_{s_k}) = \mathcal{A}_H(y).$$

We will prove this in three steps:

(1) There exists a sequence s_k such that u_{s_k} converges, for the $\mathcal{C}^0(S^1; W)$ topology, to a limit y.
(2) This limit y is $\mathcal{C}^\infty$ and is a critical point of $\mathcal{A}_H$.
(3) $\mathcal{A}_H(u_{s_k})$ indeed tends to $\mathcal{A}_H(y)$.

---

[5] See also Exercise 30 on p. 524 where the nondegeneracy assumption is left out.

First Step.

Let $u \in \mathcal{M}$. Since

$$\int_{-\infty}^{+\infty} \left(\int_{S^1} \left| \frac{\partial u}{\partial t} - X_t(u) \right|^2 dt \right) ds < +\infty,$$

the integral of the L^2 norm of $\partial u/\partial t - X_t(u)$ is finite. There therefore exists a sequence (s_k) with $\lim_{k \to \infty} s_k = +\infty$ (respectively $-\infty$) such that

$$\lim_{k \to \infty} \left\| \frac{\partial u}{\partial t}(s_k, t) - X_t(u(s_k, t)) \right\|_{L^2} = 0.$$

To simplify the notation, let us set $u_{s_k} = u_k$. And to help us understand this, note that the norm in the integrals that we just wrote down is, in principle, the norm defined by J... but the manifold W is compact and embedded in $\mathbf{R}^m$, so that the operator norm of the tangent map of the embedding is bounded by the norm defined by J at the source, and by the Euclidean norm at the target, which implies that we can work with the Euclidean norm.

We therefore have

$$\lim_{k \to +\infty} \int_0^1 \| \dot{u}_k - X_t(u_k) \|^2 \, dt = 0,$$

that is,

$$\lim_{k \to +\infty} \| \dot{u}_k - X_t(u_k) \|_{L^2(S^1; \mathbf{R}^m)} = 0.$$

Since the manifold W is compact, $X_t(u(s_k, t))$ is bounded and there exists a $B > 0$ such that

$$\| \dot{u}_k \|_{L^2} \le B.$$

The family (u_k) is therefore equicontinuous:

$$\| u_k(t_1) - u_k(t_0) \| = \left\| \int_{t_0}^{t_1} \dot{u}_k(t) \, dt \right\|$$

$$\le \int_{S^1} \mathbf{1}_{[t_0, t_1]} \| \dot{u}_k \|$$

$$\le \sqrt{t_1 - t_0} \, \| \dot{u}_k \|_{L^2} \quad \text{(by the Cauchy–Schwarz inequality)}$$

$$\le B\sqrt{t_1 - t_0}.$$

The image of u_k is contained in W, which is compact. The sequence u_k is therefore a candidate for the Arzelà–Ascoli theorem[6] and we conclude that

---

[6] See Section C.1.

the sequence u_k has a limit y in the $\mathcal{C}^0(S^1; \mathbf{R}^m)$ topology, that is, in the $\mathcal{C}^0(S^1; W)$ topology. This completes the first step of this proof.

Second Step.

Let us show that the limit y is $\mathcal{C}^\infty$ and is a solution of the Hamiltonian system $\dot{x} = X_t(x)$.

Lemma 6.5.10. *The limit y satisfies*

$$y(t) - y(0) = \int_0^t X_t(y(\tau))\, d\tau.$$

The expected result follows from the lemma because it implies that since y is continuous, it is $\mathcal{C}^1$, and therefore $\mathcal{C}^2$, ... and that it is a solution. It is therefore $\mathcal{C}^\infty$ (this is clearly a case of "bootstrapping"[7]). We thus obtain convergence, in the $\mathcal{C}^0$ sense, to a $\mathcal{C}^\infty$ solution.

Proof of Lemma 6.5.10. Let us study the difference

$$y(t) - y(0) - \int_0^t X_t(y(\tau))\, d\tau = \lim_{k \to +\infty} \left(u_k(t) - u_k(0) - \int_0^t X_t(y(\tau))\, d\tau \right)$$

(this is the advantage of being in $\mathbf{R}^m$, a vector space). This also equals

$$y(t) - y(0) - \int_0^t X_t(y(\tau))\, d\tau = \lim_{k \to +\infty} \left(\int_0^t \dot{u}_k(\tau)\, d\tau - \int_0^t X_t(y(\tau))\, d\tau \right)$$

$$= \lim_{k \to +\infty} \left(\int_0^t \dot{u}_k(\tau) - X_t(u_k(\tau))\, d\tau \right)$$

$$+ \lim_{k \to +\infty} \left(\int_0^t (X_t(u_k(\tau)) - X_t(y(\tau)))\, d\tau \right).$$

Both terms tend to 0. The fact that u_k tends to y in the $\mathcal{C}^0$ sense implies that the second term tends to 0. For the first term, we use the fact that $\|\dot{u}_k - X_t(u_k)\|_{L^2}$ tends to 0, and the Cauchy–Schwarz inequality, which gives

$$\left| \int_0^t (\dot{u}_k(\tau) - X_\tau(u_k))\, d\tau \right| = \left| \int_0^1 1_{[0,t]}(\dot{u}_k - X_t(u_k)) \right| \leq \sqrt{t}\, \|\dot{u}_k - X_t(u_k)\|_{L^2},$$

which indeed tends to 0.   □

---

[7] This expression refers to the ability to raise yourself, to levitate, by just pulling on your bootstraps. In general, in this book it refers to what the French call the "elliptic regularity", where a weak solution, in the sense of distributions, of a partial differential equation is automatically a $\mathcal{C}^\infty$ function. See Appendix C.

The $\mathcal{C}^1$ (and even $\mathcal{C}^\infty$) convergence follows from these arguments.

Third Step.

Let us show that $\mathcal{A}_H(u_k)$ tends to $\mathcal{A}_H(y)$. The integral part of the Hamiltonian clearly does not pose any problems, and

$$\int_0^1 H_t(u_k)\, dt \text{ tends to } \int_0^1 H_t(y(t))\, dt$$

because u_k tends to y for the $\mathcal{C}^0$ topology.

Let us therefore study the other piece of the action functional. For this we choose extensions $\widetilde{u}_k$ and $\widetilde{u}_y$ of u_k and y (respectively) to the disk. We must show that

$$\lim_{k \to +\infty} \left(\int_{D^2} \widetilde{u}_k^\star \omega - \int_{D^2} \widetilde{u}_y^\star \omega \right) = 0.$$

If the form ω were exact, $\omega = d\lambda$, then we would have

$$\int_{D^2} \widetilde{u}_k^\star \omega - \int_{D^2} \widetilde{u}_y^\star \omega = \int_{S^1} u_k^\star \lambda - \int_{S^1} y^\star \lambda$$

$$= \int_0^1 (\lambda(\dot{u}_k) - \lambda(\dot{y}))\, dt$$

$$= \int_0^1 \lambda(\dot{u}_k - X_t(u_k))\, dt + \int_0^1 \lambda(X_t(u_k) - X_t(y))\, dt.$$

The last integral tends to 0 because u_k tends to y. For the first integral, we have

$$\left| \int_0^1 (\lambda(\dot{u}_k) - X_t(u_k))\, dt \right| \leq \sup \|\lambda\|\, \|\dot{u}_k - X_t(u_k)\|_{L^1}$$

... for the L^1 norm that we can replace by the L^2 norm owing to the compactness of S^1. The expected result follows because this L^2 norm tends to 0, as we noted in the first step.

Except that W is compact and that ω is therefore not exact. We choose a neighborhood $\mathcal{U}$ of the image of y in W that retracts onto y, so that $\omega|_{\mathcal{U}}$ is exact. For k sufficiently large, the image of u_k is contained in $\mathcal{U}$. Next, we make an S^2 sphere by gluing:

- a cylinder $C \to \mathcal{U}$ that is a homotopy between u_k and y and is contained in $\mathcal{U}$
- the disk $\widetilde{u}_y$ with boundary y
- the disk $\widetilde{u}_k$ with boundary u_k.

Under Assumption 6.2.1, by which the integral of ω is zero on spheres, it is clear that the difference

$$\int_{D^2} \widetilde{u}_k^\star \omega - \int_{D^2} \widetilde{u}_y^\star \omega$$

is the integral of ω over the cylinder C, on which ω is exact and where the previous computation is valid. □

The Trajectories Tend Toward Critical Points.

Let us now show that the trajectories tend to critical *points*, that is, Theorem 6.5.6. The important point is the fact that the space $\mathcal{M}$ is *compact*, (Theorem 6.5.4, which we will prove later).

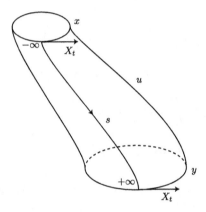

Fig. 6.6

Let us therefore assume that all periodic trajectories of X_t are nondegenerate.

Lemma 6.5.11. *Under the assumption of nondegeneracy, there are finitely many critical points of A_H, or periodic trajectories of X_t.*

Proof. These critical points are the intersection points in the compact manifold $W \times W$ of the two following submanifolds (each of half the dimension, that is, dimension $2n$):

- the diagonal $\Delta = \{(x, x) \mid x \in W\}$
- and the graph of the flow of X_t at time 1.

The nondegeneracy assumption is equivalent to the transversality[8] of these two submanifolds. Their intersection is then a closed submanifold of dimension 0 of W, hence a finite number of points since it is compact. □

---

[8] As in Morse theory, the nondegeneracy translates into transversality.

Remark 6.5.12. The additive group $\mathbf{R}$ acts on the right on $\mathcal{M}$ as follows:

$$(u \cdot \sigma)(s, t) = u(s + \sigma, t).$$

This means that if u is a solution of the Floer equation, then $u \cdot \sigma$ is also (this is straightforward), as in the case of a gradient flow. This action is continuous; that is, if (u_n) tends to u and (σ_n) tends to σ, then the sequence $(u_n \cdot \sigma_n)$ tends to $u \cdot \sigma$. We will come back to its properties later.

To prove Theorem 6.5.6, we begin with a lemma.

Lemma 6.5.13. *Let $u \in \mathcal{M}$ and let (s_k) be a sequence of real numbers tending to $+\infty$. There exist a subsequence $(s_{k'})$ of (s_k) and a critical point y of $\mathcal{A}_H$ such that*

$$\lim_{k' \to +\infty} u(s_{k'}) = y.$$

Proof. Let $u_k = u \cdot s_k$. Since $\mathcal{M}$ is compact (Theorem 6.5.4), there exists a subsequence of (u_k) (that we will also denote by (u_k)) that converges to a $v \in \mathcal{M}$. In other words, for every $s \in \mathbf{R}$, $\lim u_k(s, t) = v(s, t)$. Let us therefore fix an s_0 and set $v_{s_0}(t) = v(s_0, t)$. We have

$$\mathcal{A}_H(v_{s_0}) = \lim_{k \to +\infty} \mathcal{A}_H(u_{s_0 + s_k}) = \lim_{s \to +\infty} \mathcal{A}_H(u_s),$$

because we saw in Proposition 6.5.7 that this limit exists (and even that $\mathcal{A}_H(u_s)$ tends to a critical value). Therefore the energy of the trajectory v is zero, and consequently v is a periodic orbit y (Remark 6.5.2 (2)).

To conclude, $u_k(0) = u_{s_k}$ tends to $v = y$ in $\mathcal{C}^\infty(S^1, W)$. $\square$

Proof of Theorem 6.5.6. We will again restrict ourselves to the case $s \to +\infty$. Recall that d_∞ denotes the $\mathcal{C}^\infty$ distance in the space $\mathcal{L}W$ (see Appendix A.3.b). For a critical point x of $\mathcal{A}_H$, we consider the open ball

$$B(x, \varepsilon) = \{\gamma \in \mathcal{L}W \mid d_\infty(x, \gamma) < \varepsilon\}.$$

As we said before, there are finitely many[9] critical points of $\mathcal{A}_H$, so that for $\varepsilon > 0$ sufficiently small, the balls $B(x, \varepsilon)$ are disjoint. Let U_ε be their (disjoint) union:

$$U_\varepsilon = \bigcup_{x \in \operatorname{Crit} \mathcal{A}_H} B(x, \varepsilon) \subset \mathcal{L}W.$$

For every sufficiently small ε, there exists an s_ε such that

$$u([s_\varepsilon, +\infty[\times S^1) \subset U_\varepsilon$$

---

[9] This is where the nondegeneracy is used.

(if this assertion were not true, then there would exist an $\varepsilon_0 > 0$ and a sequence (s_k) tending to $+\infty$ and such that $u_{s_k} \notin U_{\varepsilon_0}$, but by Lemma 6.5.13, a subsequence of u_{s_k} must tend to a critical point, giving a contradiction).

Once more by Lemma 6.5.13, there exists a critical point y of $\mathcal{A}_H$ such that

$$u([s_\varepsilon, +\infty[\times S^1) \cap B(y, \varepsilon) \neq \varnothing.$$

Since $u([s_\varepsilon, +\infty[\times \cdot)$ is connected in $\mathcal{L}W$ and since the balls $B(x, \varepsilon)$ are disjoint, we have

$$u([s_\varepsilon, +\infty[\times \cdot) \subset B(y, \varepsilon),$$

or, in other words, $\lim_{s \to +\infty} u(s) = y$.

We still need to prove the statement concerning $\partial u / \partial s$. But u is a solution, so

$$\frac{\partial u}{\partial s} = -J\left(\frac{\partial u}{\partial t}\right) - \operatorname{grad}_u H_t(u).$$

Lemma 6.5.14. *In* $\mathcal{C}^\infty(S^1; TW)$, *we have*

$$\lim_{s \to +\infty} \frac{\partial u}{\partial t} = \dot{y}.$$

Proof. Suppose that the statement is not true. Then there exists a sequence s_k tending to $+\infty$ such that $\partial u_{s_k}/\partial t$ does not tend to $\dot{y}$ when k tends to $+\infty$. Let $u_k = u_{s + s_k}$. Then u_k and $y \in \mathcal{M}$, and u_k tends to y in the $\mathcal{C}^0$ sense. Elliptic regularity (Proposition 6.5.3) then implies that u_k tends to y in the $\mathcal{C}^\infty$ sense, giving a contradiction. $\qquad\square$

By taking the limit, we therefore obtain

$$\lim_{s \to +\infty} \frac{\partial u}{\partial s}(s, t) = -J(\dot{y}) - \operatorname{grad}_y H_t(y)$$

$$= -J(\dot{y}) + JX_t$$

$$= J\left(X_t(y) - \dot{y}\right) = 0. \qquad\square$$

We also have the following result.

Proposition 6.5.15. *Let* u *be a solution of the Floer equation; then (seen in* $\mathbf{R}^m$*) the partial derivatives*

$$\frac{\partial^2 u}{\partial s \, \partial t} \quad and \quad \frac{\partial^2 u}{\partial s^2}$$

tend to 0, *uniformly in* t, *when* s *tends to* $\pm\infty$.

Indeed, it suffices to write

$$\frac{\partial u}{\partial s} = -J\left(\frac{\partial u}{\partial t} - X_t\right)$$

(since u is a solution). But

$$\frac{\partial u}{\partial t} - X_t \text{ tends to 0 in the } \mathcal{C}^\infty \text{ sense}$$

since $X_t(u)$ tends to $X_t(y)$ and $\partial u/\partial t$ tends to $\dot{y}$. By differentiating the relation with respect to t, we find that $\partial^2 u/\partial s\,\partial t$ tends to 0. We then differentiate the same relation with respect to s, applying the above. □

Remark 6.5.16. In the same manner, using induction, we can prove that for $k \geq 1$,

$$\lim_{s \to \pm\infty} \frac{\partial^m u}{\partial^k s\, \partial^{m-k} t} = 0.$$

Let

$$\mathcal{M}(x, y) = \left\{ u \in \mathcal{M} \mid \lim_{s \to -\infty} u(s, \cdot) = x \text{ and } \lim_{s \to +\infty} u(s, \cdot) = y \right\}.$$

We have noted (Remarks 6.5.2) that for $u \in \mathcal{M}(x, y)$,

$$E(u) = \mathcal{A}_H(x) - \mathcal{A}_H(y).$$

We also have $\mathcal{M}(x, x) = \{x\}$. Indeed, every solution connecting x to itself must have energy zero, and therefore be constant with respect to s.

6.6 Proof of the Compactness

We will now prove Theorem 6.5.4. As we have already noted (Remarks 6.4.1), when H is zero, the Floer equation is none other than a Cauchy–Riemann equation, whose solutions are simply the J-holomorphic curves introduced by Gromov [42]. Gromov's compactness theorem (see also [62]) remains true in our situation, where the Hamiltonian is nonzero. For this section, we follow the presentation of [49] quite closely.

Remark 6.6.1. We have already used the asphericity Assumption 6.2.1 to define the action functional. We will see that it is an important condition for the compactness (we will explain exactly where we use it).

The theorem is a consequence of the following proposition.

Proposition 6.6.2. *Under Assumption 6.2.1 (that is, $\langle[\omega], \pi_2(W)\rangle = 0$), there exists a constant $A > 0$ such that*

$$\forall u \in \mathcal{M}, \ \forall (s,t) \in \mathbf{R} \times S^1, \quad \left\|\mathrm{grad}_{(s,t)} u\right\| \leq A.$$

Proof of Theorem 6.5.4. As before, our strategy is to show that given a sequence $u_n \in \mathcal{M}$, we have the following results:

- First of all, u_n admits a subsequence that converges to u_0 in $\mathcal{C}^0_{\mathrm{loc}}(\mathbf{R} \times S^1; W)$.
- Next, the limit u_0 is of class $\mathcal{C}^\infty$ and is a solution of the Floer equation.
- Finally, u_n indeed tends to u_0 in $\mathcal{C}^\infty(\mathbf{R} \times S^1; W)$.

Proposition 6.6.2 gives the equicontinuity of the elements of $\mathcal{M}$. Consequently, the closure of $\mathcal{M}$ in the set of continuous maps from $\mathbf{R} \times S^1$ to W is compact (again by Arzelà–Ascoli), which completes the first step. An elliptic regularity argument allows us to prove the other two steps. Note that we cannot use Proposition 6.5.3 because u_0 is only continuous; we will need a more general statement, which will be given in Lemma 12.1.1. Finally, by Proposition 12.1.4, the $\mathcal{C}^0_{\mathrm{loc}}$ and $\mathcal{C}^\infty_{\mathrm{loc}}$ topologies coincide on $\mathcal{M}$. The manifold is therefore also compact for the $\mathcal{C}^\infty$ topology.   □

Proof of Proposition 6.6.2. Let $u : \mathbf{R} \times S^1 \to W$ be a solution. It is more convenient to view it as a (periodic) map (in the variable t) from $\mathbf{R} \times \mathbf{R}$ to W, which we will do. We give a proof by contradiction by assuming that the conclusion of the proposition is false. This means that there exist a sequence (u_k) of elements of $\mathcal{M}$ and a sequence (s_k, t_k) of elements of $\mathbf{R}^2$ such that

$$\lim_{k \to \infty} \left\|\mathrm{grad}_{(s_k, t_k)} u_k\right\| = +\infty.$$

In this proof, we therefore consider a divergent sequence of elements of $\mathcal{M}$ and show that it will in fact yield something whose existence is prohibited under our assumptions, namely the bubble shown in Figures 6.7 and 6.8.

Let (ε_k) be a sequence of positive numbers tending to 0 such that

$$\lim_k \varepsilon_k \left\|\mathrm{grad}_{(s_k, t_k)} u_k\right\| = +\infty.$$

We apply the lemma below, called the "half maximum" lemma,[10] to the function $g = \|\mathrm{grad}\, u\|$.

Lemma 6.6.3. *Let $g : X \to \mathbf{R}^+$ be a continuous function on a complete metric space. Let $x_0 \in X$ and let $\varepsilon_0 > 0$. There exist a $y \in X$ and an*

---

[10] This is a classical lemma in this theory. It seems that its origin lies with Ekeland. The beginning of Chapter IV of his book [26] contains variations on this theme.

$\varepsilon \in \left]0, \varepsilon_0\right]$ *such that*

$$
\begin{cases}
d(y, x_0) \le 2\varepsilon \\
\varepsilon g(y) \ge \varepsilon_0 g(x_0) \\
g(x) \le 2g(y) \qquad \forall x \in B(y, \varepsilon).
\end{cases}
$$

Proof. If $g(x) \le 2g(x_0)$ on the entire ball $B(x_0, \varepsilon_0)$, then there is no need to do anything, it suffices to set $y = x_0$ and $\varepsilon = \varepsilon_0$. If this is not the case, then there exists an x_1 in the ball such that $g(x_1) > 2g(x_0)$. Let $\varepsilon_1 = \varepsilon_0/2$. We then have

$$\varepsilon_1 g(x_1) > \varepsilon_0 g(x_0).$$

If x_1 and ε_1 are suitable, then we are done. Otherwise, we continue. In this manner we construct a sequence x_n of points in the ball and a sequence ε_n of positive numbers such that

$$
\begin{cases}
\varepsilon_n = \dfrac{\varepsilon_{n-1}}{2} \\[2mm]
\varepsilon_n g(x_n) \ge \varepsilon_0 g(x_0).
\end{cases}
$$

Obviously, the first line makes ε_n tend to 0 and x_n tend to a limit (our space is complete), so that the second line prohibits the process from continuing indefinitely: after a finite number of trials, we will find an x_n and an ε_n that are suitable. $\qquad\qquad\square$

The lemma provides a(nother) sequence ε_k and a(nother) sequence (s_k, t_k) such that

$$\lim_{k \to \infty} \varepsilon_k \big\| \mathrm{grad}_{(s_k, t_k)} u_k \big\| = +\infty$$

and $\qquad 2\big\| \mathrm{grad}_{(s_k, t_k)} u_k \big\| \ge \big\| \mathrm{grad}_{(s, t)} u_k \big\| \quad$ for $(s, t) \in B((s_k, t_k), \varepsilon_k)$.

Let $R_k = \big\| \mathrm{grad}_{(s_k, t_k)} u_k \big\|$; then $\varepsilon_k R_k \to +\infty$ and

$$v_k(s, t) = u_k\left(\frac{(s, t)}{R_k} + (s_k, t_k) \right),$$

so that

$$\mathrm{grad}_{(s, t)} v_k = \frac{1}{R_k} \mathrm{grad}_{\frac{(s, t)}{R_k} + (s_k, t_k)} u_k,$$

and in particular, for $(s, t) = (0, 0)$, we have

$$\mathrm{grad}_{(0, 0)} v_k = \frac{1}{R_k} \mathrm{grad}_{(s_k, t_k)} u_k.$$

Thus by construction, $\|\mathrm{grad}_{(0,0)}v_k\| = 1$ and on $B(0,\varepsilon_k R_k)$, we have

$$\|\mathrm{grad}_{(s,t)}v_k\| = \frac{1}{R_k}\left\|\mathrm{grad}_{\frac{(s,t)}{R_k}+(s_k,t_k)}u_k\right\|$$

$$\leq \frac{2}{R_k}\left\|\mathrm{grad}_{(s_k,t_k)}u_k\right\| \leq 2,$$

so that the gradient is uniformly bounded. Finally, the u_k are solutions, so that v_k satisfies

$$\frac{\partial v_k}{\partial s} + J(v_k)\frac{\partial v_k}{\partial t} + \frac{1}{R_k}\,\mathrm{grad}_{(t_k+\frac{t}{R_k},v_k)}H = 0.$$

We now apply the elliptic regularity lemma (Lemma 12.1.1); after extracting a subsequence, if necessary, the sequence v_k tends to a limit v that is in $\mathcal{C}^\infty_{\mathrm{loc}}(\mathbf{R}^2;W)$ and that is a solution of the Floer equation. Moreover,

$$\begin{cases} \|\mathrm{grad}_{(0,0)}v\| = 1, & \text{in particular, } v \text{ is not constant,} \\[2mm] \|\mathrm{grad}_{(s,t)}v\| \leq 2 & \text{for all } (s,t) \in \mathbf{R}^2, \\[2mm] \dfrac{\partial v}{\partial s} + J(v)\dfrac{\partial v}{\partial t} = 0, & \text{hence } v \text{ is } J\text{-holomorphic.} \end{cases}$$

Let us finally show that v has finite energy. Let $B_k = B((s_k,t_k),\varepsilon_k)$. We have

$$\int_{B(0,\varepsilon_k R_k)} \|\mathrm{grad}\,v_k\|^2 = \int_{B_k} \|\mathrm{grad}\,u_k\|^2\,dt\,ds$$

$$= \int_{B_k}\left(\left\|\frac{\partial u_k}{\partial s}\right\|^2 + \left\|\frac{\partial u_k}{\partial t}\right\|^2\right)dt\,ds$$

$$= \int_{B_k}\left(\left\|\frac{\partial u_k}{\partial s}\right\|^2 + \left\|\frac{\partial u_k}{\partial t} - X_t(u_k) + X_t(u_k)\right\|^2\right)dt\,ds$$

$$\leq \int_{B_k}\left(\left\|\frac{\partial u_k}{\partial s}\right\|^2 + \left\|\frac{\partial u_k}{\partial t} - X_t(u_k)\right\|^2\right)dt\,ds$$

$$\quad + \int_{B_k}\left(\|X_t(u_k)\|^2 + 2\left\|\frac{\partial u_k}{\partial t} - X_t(u_k)\right\|\,\|X_t(u_k)\|\right)dt\,ds$$

$$\leq \int_{B_k}\left(\left\|\frac{\partial u_k}{\partial s}\right\|^2 + 2\left\|\frac{\partial u_k}{\partial t} - X_t(u_k)\right\|^2 + 2\,\|X_t\|^2\right)dt\,ds$$

$$\leq 3E(u_k) + 2\int_{B_k}\|X_t\|^2\,dt\,ds \leq 3C + 2\int_{B_k}\|X_t\|^2\,dt\,ds,$$

where C is the constant given by Corollary 6.5.9 (which is a consequence of Proposition 6.5.7).

The last integral tends to 0 when k tends to infinity (B_k is a ball with radius ε_k that tends to 0), so that for k sufficiently large,

$$\int_{B(0,\varepsilon_k R_k)} \left\| \frac{\partial v_k}{\partial s} \right\|^2 + \left\| \frac{\partial v_k}{\partial t} \right\|^2 \leq 4C$$

and in the limit, $B(0, \varepsilon_k R_k)$ covers the whole of $\mathbf{R}^2$, so that v has finite energy by Fatou's lemma.[11]

We are witnessing the formation of a "bubble", which will be prohibited by our assumption on the spheres: around the point (s_k, t_k), the boundary loop of the ball with radius ε_k is increasingly small, while the gradient of u_k at this point explodes. This is why we have chosen a new parametrization (the trick of using $\varepsilon_k R_k$), as shown in Figure 6.7.

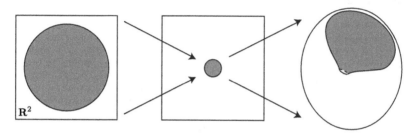

Fig. 6.7

Since a clear computation is worth more than a long discourse, we will now estimate the symplectic area of the image of v.

Lemma 6.6.4. *The symplectic area of v is finite and nonzero.*

Proof.

$$
\begin{aligned}
\int_{\mathbf{R}^2} v^\star \omega &= \int_{\mathbf{R}^2} \omega\left(\frac{\partial v}{\partial s}, \frac{\partial v}{\partial t}\right) ds\, dt \\
&= \int_{\mathbf{R}^2} \omega\left(-J(v)\frac{\partial v}{\partial t}, \frac{\partial v}{\partial t}\right) ds\, dt \quad \text{because } \frac{\partial v}{\partial t} = -J(v)\frac{\partial v}{\partial s} \\
&= \int_{\mathbf{R}^2} \omega\left(\frac{\partial v}{\partial t}, J(v)\frac{\partial v}{\partial t}\right) ds\, dt \\
&= \int_{\mathbf{R}^2} \left\| \frac{\partial v}{\partial t} \right\|^2 ds\, dt < +\infty
\end{aligned}
$$

using the earlier estimate. Furthermore, this area is nonzero because v is not constant. □

---

[11] See, for example, [64].

Lemma 6.6.5. *There exists a sequence r_k tending to $+\infty$ such that the length of the image $v(\partial B(0, r_k))$ tends to 0 when k tends to $+\infty$.*

Let us admit the lemma. Then the image of the boundary of the ball is crushed into one point $w_0 \in W$. For k sufficiently large, it is therefore contained in a Darboux chart U of W. In U, the form ω is a closed form on $\mathbf{R}^{2n}$, it admits a primitive, $\omega = d\lambda$. We may, and do, even assume that U is a closed ball. The curve $v(\partial B_r)$ is the boundary of a small disk D_r in U. The union of $v(B_r)$ and D_r is a sphere S_r^2 and, by our assumption that the spheres have symplectic area zero, we have

$$0 = \int_{S_r^2} \omega = \int_{D_r} \omega + \int_{v(B_r)} \omega.$$

The first integral is

$$\int_{D_r} \omega = \int_{D_r} d\lambda = \int_{v(\partial B_r)} \lambda;$$

hence

$$\left| \int_{D_r} \omega \right| \leq \left| \int_{v(\partial B_r)} \lambda \right| \leq \ell(v(\partial B_r)) \sup_U \|\lambda\|$$

(ℓ is the length) tends to 0 when r tends to infinity.

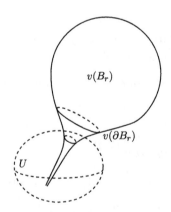

Fig. 6.8 A bubble

The second integral, in turn, converges to the area of $v(\mathbf{R}^2)$, which is nonzero. This is the contradiction we were looking for. The concentric circles $v(\partial B_r)$ have increasingly small circumferences, which is why such an object is called a bubble; see Figure 6.8.

Proof of Lemma 6.6.5. Since v is J-holomorphic, the form $v^\star\omega$ is a symplectic form on $\mathbf{R}^2$. It can therefore be written as

$$v^\star\omega_{(\rho,\theta)} = f(\rho,\theta)\rho\,d\theta \wedge d\rho$$

for a positive function f. Since v is J-holomorphic, this symplectic form, with the usual almost complex structure, gives a Riemannian metric on $\mathbf{R}^2$, namely $f(\rho,\theta)(d\rho^2 + \rho^2 d\theta^2)$, that allows us to compute the length $\ell(r)$ of the boundary $v(\partial B_r)$:

$$\ell(r) = r\int_0^{2\pi} \sqrt{f(r,\theta)}\,d\theta.$$

Likewise,

$$A(r) = \int_{B_r} v^\star\omega = \int_0^{2\pi}\left(\int_0^r f(\rho,\theta)\rho\,d\theta\right)d\rho.$$

Consequently,

$$A'(r) = \frac{dA}{dr} = \int_0^{2\pi} f(r,\theta)r\,d\theta.$$

By applying the Cauchy–Schwarz inequality, we obtain

$$\ell(r) = r\int_0^{2\pi} \sqrt{f(r,\theta)}\,d\theta \leq r\sqrt{\int_0^{2\pi} d\theta \int_0^{2\pi} f(r,\theta)\,d\theta}$$

$$= r\sqrt{2\pi\frac{A'(r)}{r}}$$

and therefore

$$\ell(r)^2 \leq 2\pi r A'(r).$$

We still need to verify that since the function $r \mapsto A(r)$ is *bounded* and differentiable, there exists a sequence r_k tending to $+\infty$ such that $\lim r_k A'(r_k) = 0$. This is an easy exercise: since A is bounded, we have

$$\lim_{k\to+\infty} \frac{A(k^2) - A(k)}{\ln k} = 0.$$

This quotient can also be written as

$$\frac{A(k^2) - A(k)}{\ln k} = \frac{A(k^2) - A(k)}{\ln k^2 - \ln k} = \frac{A'(r_k)}{(1/r_k)}$$

for an r_k lying between k and k^2 (and therefore tending to infinity) by the mean value theorem. □

This concludes the proof of Proposition 6.6.2 and therefore also that of the compactness theorem. □

6.6.a An Example of a Bubble in $\mathbf{P}^2(\mathbf{C})$

We have just shown that because the symplectic manifold W does not contain any spheres of nonzero symplectic area, there cannot be any bubbles. If, on the other hand, we do have $\omega|_{\pi_2(W)} \neq 0$, then an argument involving a "removable singularity" allows us to extend v to $\mathbf{C} \cup \{\infty\}$, giving what we call a "bubble".

To clarify the situation, let us give a classical example of a bubble, in the complex projective plane. Note that in this symplectic manifold, there are spheres: a projective line is a $\mathbf{P}^1(\mathbf{C})$ and therefore also a sphere S^2. Moreover, the symplectic form that we constructed in Section 5.3 gives a positive area to all projective lines: a projective line is a complex (holomorphic) curve and in particular, the symplectic form restricted to such a curve is a volume form. Consequently, the complex projective space does not satisfy our condition. The example we give here is the simplest one possible: we observe a family of smooth conics degenerating to the union of two lines.

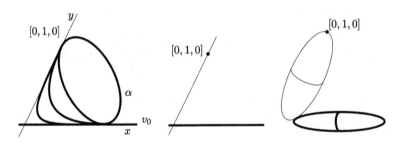

Fig. 6.9

For every $\alpha \in \mathbf{C}$, we consider the curve (conic)

$$v_\alpha : \mathbf{P}^1(\mathbf{C}) \longrightarrow \mathbf{P}^2(\mathbf{C})$$
$$[x, y] \longmapsto [x^2, \alpha y^2, xy].$$

This is simply the completion of

$$v_\alpha : \mathbf{C} \longrightarrow \mathbf{C}^2$$
$$z \longmapsto (z, \alpha/z).$$

For $\alpha = 0$, the image is the "x-axis". For $\alpha \neq 0$, it is a conic. All image curves of v_α contain the point at infinity of the y-axis, which is the point $[0, 1, 0]$ in homogeneous coordinates. When α tends to 0, this point "draws a bubble to itself". Figure 6.9 illustrates this situation by showing different states of the conic $v_\alpha(\mathbf{P}^1(\mathbf{C}))$ and the limit "curve", that is, the x-axis and y-axis, which are shown:

- once as two intersecting lines
- another time as a "curve with bubble", a figure in which each of the two complex projective lines is represented as a sphere S^2.

We also note that:

- The limit curve is *not* the image of a map $v_0 : \mathbf{P}^1(\mathbf{C}) \to \mathbf{P}^2(\mathbf{C})$.
- It does, however, have a limit on the complement of the point $0 = [0, 1]$, namely $z \mapsto (z, 0)$.
- The circle $|z|^2 = \alpha$ is the boundary of a disk ($|z|^2 \le \alpha$) that takes up more and more space in the image; see Figure 6.10.

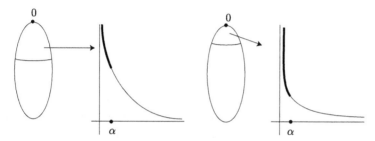

Fig. 6.10

6.7 Appendix: Functions, Closed Forms, Covers

The question we consider here is whether it is possible to extend the definition of the action functional to symplectic manifolds for which the symplectic form is not zero on the π_2; in other words, can we get rid of Assumption 6.2.1?

We begin by recalling the relations between the fundamental group, covers and closed 1-forms.

6.7.a Cover Associated with a Closed Form

From a local point of view, there is no difference between closed and exact forms, for example between a closed 1-form α and the differential of a function f. Indeed, by the Poincaré lemma[12] every closed form, that is, every

---

[12] See for example [45, Chapter V].

form α such that $d\alpha = 0$, is locally exact. In other words, locally, there exists a function f such that $\alpha = df$.

Globally, it is another matter. Consider, for example (this is not an innocent example) the closed 1-form (that we will see is incorrectly) called $d\theta$ (or dz/iz) on the circle S^1. It satisfies

$$\int_{S^1} d\theta = 2\pi$$

and is therefore not exact (there is no function "θ" on the circle). However, the form $d\theta$ lifted to the cover $\exp : \mathbf{R} \to S^1$ is exact: on $\mathbf{R}$ there is indeed a function θ.

More generally, consider a closed 1-form α on a manifold V. Since α is closed, it defines a homomorphism

$$\varphi_\alpha : \pi_1(V) \longrightarrow \mathbf{R}$$
$$[\gamma] \longmapsto \int_\gamma \alpha$$

(we assume that V is connected and do not indicate the base point). The kernel of φ_α is a (normal) subgroup of $\pi_1(V)$. There is therefore a connected (Galois) cover $\pi : \widetilde{V} \to V$ associated with it. By definition, the form $\pi^\star \alpha$ has the property that

$$\varphi_{\pi^\star \alpha}[\gamma] = 0 \quad \text{for every } [\gamma] \in \pi_1 \widetilde{V}.$$

Hence $\pi^\star \alpha$ is an exact form: a primitive $\widetilde{f}$ can be defined by choosing a point $y_0 \in \widetilde{V}$ and setting

$$\widetilde{f}(y) = \int_{y_0}^y \pi^\star \alpha,$$

where we integrate along any path connecting y_0 to y, since the result does not depend on this choice. We of course have $d\widetilde{f} = \pi^\star \alpha$.

The cover $\widetilde{V} \to V$ is "the smallest cover[13] of V on which α is exact", and is called the *integration cover* of α. We now compare the critical points of $\pi^\star \alpha$ and those of $\widetilde{f}$. Since

$$(d\widetilde{f})_y = 0 \iff \alpha_{\pi(y)} = 0,$$

the critical points are the same—as are the properties of nondegeneracy and the indices.

---

[13] For the theory of covers, we refer to [4].

A pseudo-gradient field for α (the definition is analogous to the one given in the case of a function) lifts to a pseudo-gradient field for $\tilde{f}$. It is therefore possible to try to construct a complex with the critical points of α, as we did in Chapter 3. This is what Latour does in [46]. The only big difference is that there is no reason for $\tilde{V}$ to be compact, in fact, it never is (if the form α is not exact).

To understand the problem stemming from this generalization, note that the pseudo-gradient field for $\tilde{f}$ and the trajectories between two zeros of α with consecutive indices come from trajectories connecting the points of $\pi^{-1}(c)$ to points of $\pi^{-1}(d)$. There can therefore be infinitely many of them.

6.7.b The Action Form

Let α_H be the form defined on the space of contractible loops $\mathcal{L}W$ of W by

$$(\alpha_H)_x(Y) = \int_0^1 \omega(\dot{x}(t) - X_t(x(t)), Y(t))\, dt.$$

This is a closed form: we can easily verify (Exercise 26 on p. 523) that α_H is locally exact.

We have seen (this is the computation of $d\mathcal{A}_H$ in Proposition 6.3.3; see Exercise 26) that if the symplectic manifold (W, ω) satisfies Assumption 6.2.1, then the function $\mathcal{A}_H$ is a primitive of α_H, so that α_H is an exact form.

Let us now remove Assumption 6.2.1 and consider the space

$$\mathcal{D}W = \{(x, u) \mid x \in \mathcal{L}W \text{ and } u : D \to W \text{ is an extension to the disk}\}.$$

Let us say that $(x, u) \sim (x, v)$ if

$$\int_D u^\star \omega = \int_D v^\star \omega$$

and let $\widetilde{\mathcal{L}W}$ denote the quotient of $\mathcal{D}W$ by the equivalence relation $\sim$. It is endowed with a projection

$$\pi : \widetilde{\mathcal{L}W} \longrightarrow \mathcal{L}W$$

(forgetting the disk) that turns it into a cover of the group $\pi_2(W)/\operatorname{Ker}(\omega : \pi_2(W) \to \mathbf{R})$. The expression

$$\mathcal{A}_H(x, u) = -\int_D u^\star \omega + \int_0^1 H_t(x(t))\, dt$$

defines a function on $\widetilde{\mathcal{L}W}$ that satisfies the relation

$$\pi^\star \alpha_H = d\mathcal{A}_H.$$

The cover $\pi : \widetilde{\mathcal{L}W} \to \mathcal{L}W$ is the integration cover of the action form.

See also Exercise 34 on p. 525.

6.8 Appendix: Structure of a Banach Manifold on $\mathcal{L}W$

The spaces of $\mathcal{C}^\infty$ functions are not Banach spaces (they are Fréchet spaces). We will restrict ourselves to spaces of loops of class $W^{1,p}$, which we will now describe in detail.

Recall that every symplectic fiber bundle on S^1 can be trivialized. In particular, this is the case for

$$x^\star TW = \left\{ (t, Y) \in S^1 \times TW \mid x(t) = p(Y) \right\},$$

where $x \in \mathcal{L}W$. Let φ be a trivialization

$$\varphi : x^\star TW \longrightarrow S^1 \times \mathbf{R}^{2n}.$$

It allows us to associate with any section Y of the bundle $x^\star TW$, a section φY of the trivial bundle $S^1 \times \mathbf{R}^{2n}$, that is, a map $\varphi Y : S^1 \to \mathbf{R}^{2n}$. For $p > 1$, let

$$W^{1,p}(x^\star TW) = \left\{ Y \mid \varphi Y \in W^{1,p}(S^1; \mathbf{R}^{2n}) \right\}$$

(the definition of the Sobolev spaces $W^{1,p}$ is recalled in Appendix C.4—let us, however, point out that $W^{1,p}$ is contained in $\mathcal{C}^0$, which is reassuring). Another trivialization ψ differs from φ by a map

$$g : S^1 \longrightarrow \mathrm{GL}(2n; \mathbf{R}).$$

Moreover, for $Y \in W^{1,p}(S^1; \mathbf{R}^{2n})$, we have

$$\|gY\|_{W^{1,p}} \le c(g) \, \|Y\|_{W^{1,p}}$$

for some constant $c(g)$ that is the operator norm of g. Consequently, φ and ψ define the same topology of Banach space on $W^{1,p}(x^\star TW)$ (this therefore does not depend on the choice of φ, as the notation already suggested).

The analogue $W^{1,p}$ of the space of vector fields along x, of which we saw (in Section 6.3.a) that it should be the tangent space at x of the loop space, is thus endowed with the structure of a Banach space. The idea of the following is to use these tangent spaces to define local charts on the loop space itself. To do this, we use the exponential of a fixed Riemannian metric on W (see Appendix A.5). This is defined on a neighborhood $\mathcal{D}$ of the zero section in TW (a disk bundle).[14] For every loop x of class $\mathcal{C}^\infty$, we have

$$\exp_x : W^{1,p}(x^\star \mathcal{D}) \longrightarrow \mathcal{C}^0(S^1; W)$$
$$Y \longmapsto (\exp_x Y : t \mapsto \exp_{x(t)} Y(t)).$$

Recall that $W^{1,p}(S^1; \mathbf{R}^{2n}) \subset \mathcal{C}^0(S^1; \mathbf{R}^{2n})$ for $p > 1$. In the formula, x is of class $\mathcal{C}^\infty$, Y is of class $W^{1,p}$ and $\exp_x Y$ is of class $W^{1,p}$, and in particular continuous.

We therefore consider the set of all pairs

$$\left(W^{1,p}(x^\star \mathcal{D}), \exp_x\right) \quad \text{for } x \in \mathcal{L}W$$

and the space, denoted by $\mathcal{L}^{1,p}W$, of continuous maps $y : S^1 \to W$ such that there exist an $x \in \mathcal{L}W$ and a $Y \in W^{1,p}(x^\star \mathcal{D})$ with $y(t) = \exp_{x(t)} Y(t)$.

Theorem 6.8.1. *The space $\mathcal{L}^{1,p}W$ is endowed with the structure of a manifold of class $\mathcal{C}^\infty$ through the atlas*

$$\left(W^{1,p}(x^\star \mathcal{D}), \exp_x\right)_{x \in \mathcal{L}W}.$$

The resulting structure does not depend on the Riemannian metric that is used. Moreover,

$$\mathcal{L}W = \mathcal{C}^\infty(S^1; W) \subset \mathcal{L}^{1,p}W \subset \mathcal{C}^0(S^1; W),$$

where each space is dense in the next one.

Here is the idea of the proof; we refer to [68] for the details. For $x \in W$, the map $\exp_x$ is a diffeomorphism from the fiber $\mathcal{D}_x \subset T_x W$ onto its image. So for every t, the equality $\exp_{x(t)} Y(t) = \exp_{x(t)} Z(t)$ implies that $Y(t) = Z(t)$. The "transition map"

$$Y \longmapsto \exp_{x'}^{-1}(\exp_x Y)$$

sends a $W^{1,p}$ section onto a $W^{1,p}$ section because the exponential is $\mathcal{C}^\infty$ and this transition map is as differentiable as the loops x and x' that define it. This indeed gives the structure of a manifold on $\mathcal{L}^{1,p}W$.

The compatibility of the atlases defined by different Riemannian metrics comes, once again, from the fact that the exponential of any Riemannian

---

[14] The maximal radius of the disks of such a fiber bundle is the *injectivity radius* of the Riemann manifold W.

metric is a $\mathcal{C}^\infty$ map, which gives the desired differentiability to the composition

$$W^{1,p}(x^\star \mathcal{D}_g) \xrightarrow{\ (\exp_g)_x\ } \mathcal{C}^0(S^1; W) \xrightarrow{\ (\exp_{g'})^{-1}_{x'}\ } W^{1,p}(x'^\star \mathcal{D}_{g'})$$

(with the obvious notation).

Finally, the inclusions are clear and the last assertion follows from the density of $\mathcal{C}^\infty(S^1; W)$ in $\mathcal{C}^0(S^1; W)$.   □

Note that, by construction, the tangent space of this Banach manifold at the point $y \in \mathcal{L}^{1,p}W$ is

$$T_y \mathcal{L}^{1,p}W = W^{1,p}(y^\star TW).$$

Chapter 7

The Geometry of the Symplectic Group, the Maslov Index

In this chapter, we are going to define the *index* of the critical points of the action functional.

Traditionally, the *Maslov index* is an integer associated with a loop in the Grassmannian Λ_n of all Lagrangian subspaces of $\mathbf{R}^{2n}$. This is because the fundamental group of this Grassmannian is isomorphic to $\mathbf{Z}$ (see for example Exercise 40 on p. 528 or the book [50]) and, ultimately, because the fundamental group of the unitary group $\mathrm{U}(n)$ is also isomorphic to $\mathbf{Z}$. The index we will talk about here is an integer associated with paths in the symplectic group $\mathrm{Sp}(2n)$. The latter retracts onto $\mathrm{U}(n)$ and therefore also has an infinite cyclic fundamental group. In this setting, we also call it the Conley–Zehnder index (see [67, 66], [49], which we used for inspiration, and the recent paper [43] for references).

7.1 Toward the Definition of the Index

The setting is that of the previous chapter; we have a time-dependent Hamiltonian

$$H : W \times S^1 \longrightarrow \mathbf{R}$$

and a periodic solution $x(t)$ of $\dot{x} = X_t(x)$ of period 1 that we assume to be a contractible loop. We have seen that these loops are the critical points of $\mathcal{A}_H$. We therefore want to define an *index* for these critical points.

We will do this in three steps. We begin with a nondegenerate (and contractible) orbit x.

(1) We associate with it a *path* $t \mapsto A(t)$ of *symplectic* matrices, with $A(0) = \mathrm{Id}$ and $1 \notin \mathrm{Spec}\, A(1)$.

M. Audin, M. Damian, *Morse Theory and Floer Homology*,
Universitext, DOI 10.1007/978-1-4471-5496-9_7,
© Springer-Verlag London 2014

(2) With each such path we associate a path $\gamma : [0,1] \to S^1$ with $\gamma(0) = 1$ and $\gamma(1) = \pm 1$.

(3) And with each such path (with values in S^1), we associate an integer.

Given a nondegenerate critical point x, we will thus have associated with it an integer $\mu(x) \in \mathbf{Z}$.

7.1.a First Step

We have fixed the periodic orbit $x(t) = \varphi^t(x(0))$. We choose a symplectic basis

$$Z(0) = (Z_1(0), \ldots, Z_{2n}(0))$$

of $T_{x(0)}W$. Recall (see Section 5.4) that φ^t preserves ω. In particular, the matrix $A(1)$ of the linear map $T_{x(0)}\varphi^1$ in the basis $Z(0)$ is a symplectic matrix, $A(1) \in \mathrm{Sp}(2n)$ (see Section 5.6 for the symplectic group $\mathrm{Sp}(2n)$) and 1 is not an eigenvalue of $A(1)$ because the solution x is assumed to be nondegenerate.

By the following classical theorem (see for example [75]), there exists a family of symplectic bases

$$Z(t) = (Z_1(t), \ldots, Z_{2n}(t))$$

of $T_{x(t)}W$ that is $\mathcal{C}^\infty$ in t.

Theorem 7.1.1. *For every continuous map*

$$\psi : D^k \longrightarrow W,$$

the symplectic fiber bundle $\psi^* TW$ can be trivialized and all its trivializations are homotopic.   □

We will not prove this theorem, it follows from the contractibility of the disk D^k. For example, the homotopic equivalence of all trivializations follows from the fact that two trivializations are linked by a map $D^k \to \mathrm{Sp}(2n)$ and simply uses the fact (Proposition 5.6.9) that $\mathrm{Sp}(2n)$ is pathwise connected.

But let us get back to the point. Our periodic orbit x is contractible, we extend it to a map $u : D^2 \to W$; from the theorem, we deduce a trivialization, that is, a symplectic frame $Z(z)$ for $z \in D^2$ and in particular a symplectic frame along x.

In this manner, for every t, we can consider the matrix $A(t)$ of the linear map $T_{x(0)}\varphi^t$ in the bases $Z(0)$ (of $T_{x(0)}W$) and $Z(t)$ (of $T_{x(t)}W$), and the map

$$t \longmapsto A(t)$$

is a path with $A(0) = \mathrm{Id}$ for which $A(1)$ does not have eigenvalue 1.

Let us therefore set

$$\mathrm{Sp}(2n)^{\star} = \{A \in \mathrm{Sp}(2n) \mid \det(A - \mathrm{Id}) \neq 0\}$$

and let $\mathcal{S}$ be the space of paths connecting Id to an element of $\mathrm{Sp}(2n)^{\star}$:

$$\mathcal{S} = \{\gamma : [0,1] \longrightarrow \mathrm{Sp}(2n) \mid \gamma(0) = \mathrm{Id} \ \text{and} \ \gamma(1) \in \mathrm{Sp}(2n)^{\star}\}.$$

If Z' is another symplectic frame along x, then the paths $A(t)$ and $A'(t)$ are homotopic in $\mathcal{S}$. More generally, if v is another extension of x to the disk D^2 and if Z' is a trivialization along v, then by gluing u and v, we can construct a map $w : S^2 \to W$ (as in Subsection 6.3.b; see Figure 6.2). We therefore have:

- The path $A(t)$ given by the trivialization Z along u
- The path $A'(t)$ given by Z' along v
- And a path $A''(t)$ given by a trivialization Z'' along w, thanks to Assumption 6.2.2,

and these three paths are homotopic in $\mathcal{S}$.

We have thus completed the first step, that is, associated with the orbit x a path in $\mathcal{S}$ that is unique up to homotopy.

Remark 7.1.2. In the case of a critical point x of an autonomous Hamiltonian H, we have already constructed the path $t \mapsto A(t)$ (in Section 5.4 and in Exercise 8 on p. 517): it is

$$A(t) = e^{t J_0 \, \mathrm{Hess}_x}$$

where Hess_x is the Hessian of H at x, which we will denote by S for the sake of simplicity. In particular, if S is nonsingular with $\|S\| < 2\pi$, then $J_0 S$ does not have eigenvalue $2ik\pi$ and therefore $e^{J_0 S}$ does not have eigenvalue 1.

7.1.b Second Step (Beginning)

For step two, with a path $A(t) \in \mathcal{S}$, we must associate a path

$$\gamma : [0,1] \longrightarrow S^1 \quad \text{with } \gamma(0) = 1 \text{ and } \gamma(1) = \pm 1.$$

To do this, we need a few properties of the symplectic group, namely those seen in Chapter 5, and some additional details.

In Section 5.6.d, we said that there exists a map $\mathrm{Sp}(2n) \to S^1$ that induces an isomorphism on the fundamental groups. In this section, we give more details about the properties of such a map ρ. The construction given here is based on the use of [38] by Salamon and Zehnder in [67]. We give a slightly different, though equivalent, description and write down detailed proofs of the linear algebra results we use.

Theorem 7.1.3 ([67]). *For every $n \in \mathbf{N}^\star$, there exists a continuous map*

$$\rho : \mathrm{Sp}(2n) \longrightarrow S^1$$

satisfying the following properties:

(1) *Naturality: If A and $T \in \mathrm{Sp}(2n; \mathbf{R})$, then*

$$\rho(TAT^{-1}) = \rho(A).$$

(2) *Product: If $A \in \mathrm{Sp}(2m; \mathbf{R})$ and $B \in \mathrm{Sp}(2n; \mathbf{R})$, then*

$$\rho \begin{pmatrix} A & 0 \\ 0 & B \end{pmatrix} = \rho(A)\rho(B).$$

(3) *Determinant: If $A \in \mathrm{U}(n) = \mathrm{Sp}(2n; \mathbf{R}) \cap \mathrm{O}(2n)$, then*

$$\rho(A) = \det{}_{\mathbf{C}}(X + iY), \quad \text{where } A = \begin{pmatrix} X & -Y \\ Y & X \end{pmatrix}.$$

In particular, ρ induces an isomorphism

$$\rho_\star : \pi_1(\mathrm{Sp}(2n); \mathbf{R}) \longrightarrow \pi_1(S^1) = \mathbf{Z}.$$

(4) *Normalization: If $\mathrm{Spec}(A) \subset \mathbf{R}$, then*

$$\rho(A) = (-1)^{m_0/2},$$

where m_0 is the total multiplicity of the negative real eigenvalues.
(5) $\rho({}^t A) = \rho(A^{-1}) = \overline{\rho(A)}.$

The construction of such a map ρ is rather technical. We give the details in the appendix to this chapter (Section 7.3). Even so, let us already say that for a matrix A whose eigenvalues are all distinct, this is "simply"

$$\rho(A) = (-1)^{m_0/2} \prod_{\substack{\lambda \in \mathrm{Spec}(A) \cap S^1 \\ \mathrm{Im}(\lambda) > 0}} \lambda^{\mathrm{sign\,Im}\,\omega(\overline{X}, X)}$$

(we have chosen an eigenvector X for every λ).

7.1.c The Subset $\mathrm{Sp}(2n)^\star$

Let us get back to our construction of the index μ for the periodic orbit x.

The Transformations That Do Not Have Eigenvalue 1.

The symplectic transformations that we need to consider do not have eigenvalue 1 (this is our nondegeneracy assumption). This is why we consider the open set

$$\mathrm{Sp}(2n)^\star = \{A \in \mathrm{Sp}(2n) \mid \det(A - \mathrm{Id}) \neq 0\},$$

which is the complement of the hypersurface Σ defined by

$$\Sigma = \{A \in \mathrm{Sp}(2n) \mid \det(A - \mathrm{Id}) = 0\}.$$

This brings us closer to the usual definition of the Maslov index in the Grassmannian of the Lagrangians.

It is clear that $\mathrm{Sp}(2n)^\star$ cannot be connected, because it is the union of the two disjoint open sets defined by $\det(A - \mathrm{Id}) > 0$ and $\det(A - \mathrm{Id}) < 0$. Also note that the sign of $\det(A - \mathrm{Id})$ is the same as that of the product $\prod(\lambda_i - 1)$ over the λ_i that are the positive real eigenvalues of A.

Example: $\mathrm{Sp}(2)$.

In the case $n = 1$, $\mathrm{Sp}(2) = \mathrm{SL}(2; \mathbf{R})$. This group is the (affine real) quadric made up of the real matrices $\left(\begin{smallmatrix} a & b \\ c & d \end{smallmatrix}\right)$ with $ad - bc = 1$, a submanifold of dimension 3. The polar decomposition makes it retract onto the circle consisting of matrices $\left(\begin{smallmatrix} \cos\theta & -\sin\theta \\ \sin\theta & \cos\theta \end{smallmatrix}\right)$ (this is the group $\mathrm{U}(1)$). The hypersurface Σ of matrices with eigenvalue 1 consists of the $\left(\begin{smallmatrix} a & b \\ c & d \end{smallmatrix}\right)$ with $ad - bc = 1$ and $a + d = 2$. It is smooth outside of the point Id. The complement of Σ consists of the two open sets defined by

$$\mathrm{tr}\, A > 2 \quad \text{and} \quad \mathrm{tr}\, A < 2,$$

respectively. One easily sees that these two open sets are connected because:

- The matrices with trace greater than 2 are the ones that are similar to

$$\begin{pmatrix} \lambda & 0 \\ 0 & \lambda^{-1} \end{pmatrix} \text{ (with } \lambda > 0).$$

- Those with trace less than 2 are the ones that are similar to

$$\begin{pmatrix} \cos\theta & -\sin\theta \\ \sin\theta & \cos\theta \end{pmatrix}, \quad \begin{pmatrix} \lambda & 0 \\ 0 & \lambda^{-1} \end{pmatrix} \text{ (with } \lambda < 0), \quad \text{or} \quad \begin{pmatrix} -1 & a \\ 0 & -1 \end{pmatrix} \cdots$$

all matrices that can be connected to $-\mathrm{Id}$ without any problem.

Remark. The map $A \mapsto \rho(A)$ is not equal to the complex determinant of U, where $A = US$ is the polar decomposition (see 5.6.d). Here is a counter-example: Take

$$U = \begin{pmatrix} \cos \pi/3 & -\sin \pi/3 \\ \sin \pi/3 & \cos \pi/3 \end{pmatrix} \quad \text{and} \quad S = \begin{pmatrix} 4 & 0 \\ 0 & 1/4 \end{pmatrix}.$$

Then $\mathrm{tr}(A) > 2$ and therefore $\rho(A) = 1$, according to (4) in Theorem 7.1.3.

Topology of $\mathrm{Sp}(2n)^{\star}$

The following proposition is due to Conley and Zehnder.

Proposition 7.1.4 ([21]). *The open set* $\mathrm{Sp}(2n)^{\star}$ *has two connected components. The inclusion of each of these in* $\mathrm{Sp}(2n)$ *induces the zero homomorphism on the fundamental groups.*

Proof. We have already said that $\mathrm{Sp}(2n)^{\star}$ is not connected. We still need to show that each of the subspaces

$$\mathrm{Sp}(2n)^{+} = \{A \in \mathrm{Sp}(2n; \mathbf{R}) \mid \det(A - \mathrm{Id}) > 0\}$$

and $\quad\quad \mathrm{Sp}(2n)^{-} = \{A \in \mathrm{Sp}(2n; \mathbf{R}) \mid \det(A - \mathrm{Id}) < 0\}$

is pathwise connected. The proof of this fact is based on the following lemma.

Lemma 7.1.5. *Let* $A \in \mathrm{Sp}(2n)^{\star}$. *There exists a path in* $\mathrm{Sp}(2n)^{\star}$ *that connects* A *to a matrix* B *whose eigenvalues are all distinct and that has exactly zero (if* $A \in \mathrm{Sp}(2n)^{+}$*) or two (if* $A \in \mathrm{Sp}(2n)^{-}$*) real positive eigenvalues.*

Admitting this lemma (for the moment), we use it to show that every matrix A of $\mathrm{Sp}(2n)^{\star}$ can be connected by a path in $\mathrm{Sp}(2n)^{\star}$ to the matrix

$$\begin{cases} -\mathrm{Id} \in \mathrm{Sp}(2n)^{+} & \text{if } A \in \mathrm{Sp}(2n)^{+}, \\ \left(\begin{array}{cc|c} 2 & 0 & \\ 0 & 1/2 & 0 \\ \hline & 0 & -\mathrm{Id} \end{array} \right) & \text{otherwise.} \end{cases}$$

We first connect A to a matrix B as authorized by the lemma. We then still need to connect B to one of the two matrices above. We choose a basis of eigenvectors of B that is symplectic and invariant under complex conjugation. Since the eigenvalues of B are distinct, we can call X_λ "the" eigenvector associated with λ. For every eigenvalue λ of B that is not real and positive, we choose a path $\lambda(s)$ that connects λ to -1 while avoiding 1 and is such that if $\lambda(s)$ is the path chosen for λ, then:

- The path chosen for $\overline{\lambda}$ is $\overline{\lambda}(s)$...
- And the path chosen for $1/\lambda$ is $1/\lambda(s)$.

We define the path $s \mapsto B(s)$ by setting

$$B(s) \cdot X_\lambda = \begin{cases} \lambda(s)X_\lambda & \text{if } \lambda \notin \mathbf{R}_+ \\ \lambda X_\lambda & \text{if } \lambda \in \mathbf{R}_+. \end{cases}$$

The resulting matrix $B(s)$ is real and in $\mathrm{Sp}(2n)^\star$, $B(0) = B$ and

$$B(1) \cdot X_\lambda = \begin{cases} -X_\lambda & \text{if } \lambda \notin \mathbf{R}_+ \\ \lambda X_\lambda & \text{if } \lambda \in \mathbf{R}_+. \end{cases}$$

There are therefore two possibilities:

- Either B does not have any positive real eigenvalue, in which case $B(1) = -\mathrm{Id}$
- Or B has two positive real eigenvalues, λ and $1/\lambda$. In this case, the matrix $B(1)$ in the symplectic basis of eigenvectors X_λ (with a suitable ordering) is

$$B(1) = \left(\begin{array}{cc|c} \lambda & 0 & \\ 0 & 1/\lambda & 0 \\ \hline & 0 & -\mathrm{Id} \end{array} \right).$$

Since the group $\mathrm{Sp}(2n; \mathbf{R})$ is pathwise connected, we can find a path that connects this matrix to the matrix of the same form in the canonical basis, and then to the matrix

$$\left(\begin{array}{cc|c} 2 & 0 & \\ 0 & 1/2 & 0 \\ \hline & 0 & -\mathrm{Id} \end{array} \right).$$

Consequently, the two open sets $\mathrm{Sp}(2n)^\pm$ are indeed the connected components of $\mathrm{Sp}(2n)^\star$.

Let us now show that the inclusion of each of them in $\mathrm{Sp}(2n; \mathbf{R})$ induces the trivial morphism on the fundamental groups. It suffices to lift the map ρ, as authorized by the following lemma.

Lemma 7.1.6. *There exist two continuous maps $\widetilde{\rho}_\pm : \mathrm{Sp}(2n)^\pm \to \mathbf{R}$ such that the diagrams*

$$\begin{array}{ccc} & & \mathbf{R} \\ & \nearrow{\widetilde{\rho}_\pm} & \downarrow{\exp} \\ \mathrm{Sp}(2n)^\pm \xrightarrow{\ \ i\ \ } \mathrm{Sp}(2n) \xrightarrow{\ \ \rho\ \ } & & S^1 \end{array}$$

commute.

Indeed, we have shown that ρ induces an isomorphism on the fundamental groups. Consequently, since

$$\rho_\star \circ i_\star = \exp_\star \circ (\widetilde{\rho}_\pm)_\star = 0,$$

the morphism

$$i_\star : \pi_1 \operatorname{Sp}(2n)^\pm \longrightarrow \pi_1(\operatorname{Sp}(2n))$$

is zero.   □

Lemma 7.1.6 relies on the details of the construction of ρ. The proofs of the two Lemmas 7.1.6 and 7.1.5 are elementary in the sense that they only use elementary linear algebra. Still, we feel that it is useful to write them out in detail. They can be found in the appendix to this chapter, where they should be, right after the construction of ρ (Section 7.3.d).

We have finished the second step; we now only need to define the index, an integer.

7.2 The Maslov Index of a Path

7.2.a Definition of the Maslov Index

Let W^+ and W^- be fixed matrices in $\operatorname{Sp}(2n)^+$ and $\operatorname{Sp}(2n)^-$, respectively, for example those we used in the proofs of the previous section, namely

$$W^+ = -\operatorname{Id}, \quad W^- = \left(\begin{array}{cc|c} 2 & 0 & 0 \\ 0 & 1/2 & \\ \hline 0 & & -\operatorname{Id} \end{array} \right).$$

For every path $\gamma : [0,1] \to \operatorname{Sp}(2n)$, we choose a lift $\alpha : [0,1] \to \mathbf{R}$ of $\rho \circ \gamma$,

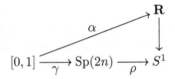

and we let

$$\Delta(\gamma) = \frac{\alpha(0) - \alpha(1)}{\pi}.$$

If $A \in \operatorname{Sp}(2n)^\star$, then we choose a path γ_A (in $\operatorname{Sp}(2n)^\star$) from A to the matrix $W^\pm$ in $\operatorname{Sp}(2n)^\pm$. By Proposition 7.1.4, the homotopy class of γ_A is well defined and, in particular, $\Delta(\gamma_A)$ relies only on A. We therefore set $r(A) = \Delta(\gamma_A)$.

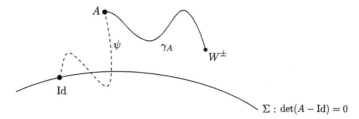

Fig. 7.1

Let ψ be a path connecting Id to an element of $\mathrm{Sp}(2n)^\star$. We define the Maslov index $\mu(\psi)$ of this path by setting

$$\mu(\psi) = \Delta(\psi) + r(\psi(1)).$$

This is the number of *clockwise* "half turns" that the image under ρ of the path composed of ψ and γ_A makes on the circle.

Proposition 7.2.1. *The Maslov index is an integer. Two paths ψ_0 and ψ_1 are homotopic with endpoint in $\mathrm{Sp}(2n)^\star$ if and only if they have the same index. Moreover, we have:*

- *The sign of $\det(\psi(1) - \mathrm{Id})$ is $(-1)^{\mu(\psi)-n}$.*
- *If S is an invertible symmetric matrix with norm $\|S\| < 2\pi$ and if $\psi(t) = \exp(tJ_0 S)$, then*

$$\mu(\psi) = \mathrm{Ind}(S) - n,$$

  where $\mathrm{Ind}(S)$ denotes the number of negative eigenvalues of S.

Proof. We begin by taking the composition of our path ψ with a path in $\mathrm{Sp}(2n)^\star$ that connects $\psi(1)$ to the matrix $W^\pm$, as authorized by Proposition 7.1.4. Let γ be the composed path. We have

$$\mu(\psi) = \Delta(\gamma) \in \mathbf{Z}$$

because $\rho(W^\pm) = \pm 1$.

Moreover, by the same proposition, two paths ψ_0 and ψ_1 are homotopic if and only if the two extensions γ_0 and γ_1 are homotopic (with fixed endpoints). The map ρ induces an isomorphism on the fundamental groups, hence this is equivalent to the equality $\Delta(\gamma_0) = \Delta(\gamma_1)$, that is, to the equality of the Maslov indices of ψ_0 and ψ_1.

Let ψ be a path and let γ be an extension as above. If $\psi(1) \in \mathrm{Sp}(2n)^+$, that is, if $\det(\psi(1) - \mathrm{Id}) > 0$, then the endpoint of γ is at $W^+ = -\mathrm{Id}$ and therefore $\rho(\gamma(1)) = (-1)^n$. In this case, $\mu(\psi) - n$ is even. If, on the other hand, $\det(\psi(1) - \mathrm{Id}) < 0$, then γ goes to W^- and $\rho(\gamma(1)) = (-1)^{n-1}$, so that $\mu(\psi) - n$ is odd.

We still need to prove the statement on the symmetric matrices. One easily verifies (Exercise 15 on p. 519) that if S is symmetric, then $\exp(tJ_0S)$ is symplectic. Next, since S is symmetric, it is diagonalizable in an orthonormal basis and there exists a path $\lambda \mapsto P(\lambda)$ of matrices in $O^+(2n)$ such that $P(0) = \mathrm{Id}$ and $S(1) = {}^tP(1)SP(1)$ is a diagonal matrix. Let

$$S(\lambda) = {}^tP(\lambda)SP(\lambda) \quad \text{and} \quad \psi_\lambda(t) = \exp(tJS_0(\lambda)).$$

The index (in the sense of quadratic forms) of the symmetric matrix S_λ does not depend on λ. The fact that the norm of S is less than 2π guarantees that $\exp(J_0S(\lambda))$ does not have eigenvalue 1. We can therefore compute the Maslov index of the path ψ_λ for any λ (because the index does not depend on it and $\psi_\lambda \in \mathcal{S}$) and we have consequently reduced the problem to proving the desired equality in the case where the symmetric matrix is simply diagonal. Using the same argument, we may, and do, further assume that S has eigenvalues π and $-\pi$. We then decompose $\mathbf{R}^{2n}$ into a sum of n symplectic planes, so that it suffices to compute the Maslov index for the symmetric matrices

$$\begin{pmatrix} \pi & 0 \\ 0 & \pi \end{pmatrix}, \quad \begin{pmatrix} \pi & 0 \\ 0 & -\pi \end{pmatrix}, \quad \begin{pmatrix} -\pi & 0 \\ 0 & -\pi \end{pmatrix}.$$

Indeed, the multiplicativity of ρ in Theorem 7.1.3 translates into the additivity of the Maslov index.

For the first matrix,

$$\exp(tJ_0S) = \begin{pmatrix} \cos \pi t & -\sin \pi t \\ \sin \pi t & \cos \pi t \end{pmatrix}$$

is a rotation by $t\pi$. This matrix is the unitary matrix $\exp(it\pi)$, so that its image under ρ is $\exp(it\pi)$. This gives Maslov index

$$\mu(\exp(tJ_0S)) = -1 \,(= \mathrm{Ind}(S) - 1).$$

The same computation for the third matrix gives

$$\exp(tJ_0S) = \begin{pmatrix} \cos \pi t & \sin \pi t \\ -\sin \pi t & \cos \pi t \end{pmatrix},$$

a rotation by $-t\pi$ this time, so that its image under ρ is $\exp(-it\pi)$. This gives Maslov index

$$\mu(\exp(tJ_0S)) = 1 (= \mathrm{Ind}(S) - 1).$$

The second symmetric matrix gives

$$\exp(tJ_0S) = \begin{pmatrix} \cosh \pi t & \sinh \pi t \\ \sinh \pi t & \cosh \pi t \end{pmatrix},$$

a matrix whose eigenvalues are $e^{\pi t}$ and $e^{-\pi t}$, two positive real numbers, so that ρ sends this matrix onto 1 and

$$\mu(\exp(tJ_0S)) = 0 \ (= \mathrm{Ind}(S) - 1).$$

So we have the stated formula (with $n = 1$) for these three cases and therefore in general by the additivity.   □

7.2.b Summary, Third Step

Under Assumption 6.2.2, we have thus associated an integer with any non-degenerate contractible periodic orbit of period 1, namely its *Maslov index*.

The computation of the Maslov index carried out for the symmetric matrices above gives the following result in the case of an autonomous Hamiltonian and a stationary orbit.

Corollary 7.2.2. *Let W be a symplectic manifold of dimension $2n$, let*

$$H : W \longrightarrow \mathbf{R}$$

be a(n autonomous) Hamiltonian and let x be a critical point of H. We assume that H is small for the C^2 topology, in this case $\|\mathrm{Hess}_x(H)\| < 2\pi$. Then the Maslov index $\mu(x)$ of x as a periodic solution of the Hamiltonian system and its index $\mathrm{Ind}(x)$ as a critical point of the function H are connected by

$$\mu(x) = \mathrm{Ind}(x) - n.$$ □

7.2.c Link Between Symplectic and Symmetric Matrices

We know (by Exercise 15 on p. 519 and Proposition 7.2.1) that when S is a symmetric matrix, $\exp(tJ_0S)$ is a symplectic matrix. More generally, we have the following result.

Lemma 7.2.3. *Let $S : [0,1] \to M(2n; \mathbf{R})$ be a continuous path of symmetric matrices. Then the path $R : [0,1] \to M(2n; \mathbf{R})$ that is a solution of*

$$\frac{d}{dt}R(t) = J_0S(t)R(t), \quad R(0) = \mathrm{Id}$$

is in $\mathrm{Sp}(2n)$. Conversely, if $R : [0,1] \to \mathrm{Sp}(2n)$ is a path of class C^1, then the path

$$S(t) = -J_0R'(t)R(t)^{-1}$$

consists of symmetric matrices.

Proof. We let $'$ denote the derivative with respect to t. We first have

$$^tR(t)' = -^tR(t)S(t)J_0,$$

and then

$$\begin{aligned}
\left(^tRJ_0R\right)' &= {}^tR'J_0R + {}^tRJ_0R' \\
&= -^tRSJ_0^2R + {}^tRJ_0^2SR \\
&= {}^tRSR - {}^tRSR = 0,
\end{aligned}$$

which shows that $^tRJ_0R = J_0$ for every $t \in [0,1]$, and therefore that $R(t) \in \mathrm{Sp}(2n)$.

Conversely, we have another computation:

$$\begin{aligned}
^tS = -^t(J_0R'R^{-1}) &= -^tR^{-1}\,{}^tR'\,{}^tJ_0 \\
&= {}^tR^{-1}\,{}^tR'J_0 \quad \text{because } J_0 \text{ is antisymmetric} \\
&= {}^tR^{-1}(^tRJ_0)' \\
&= {}^tR^{-1}(J_0R^{-1})' \quad \text{because } {}^tRJ_0R = J_0 \Rightarrow {}^tRJ_0 = J_0R^{-1} \\
&= {}^tR^{-1}J_0(R^{-1})' \\
&= J_0R(R^{-1})' \quad \text{because, likewise, } {}^tR^{-1}J_0 = J_0R \\
&= -J_0R'R^{-1} \quad \text{because } RR^{-1} = \mathrm{Id} \Rightarrow R'R^{-1} + RR'^{-1} = 0 \\
&= S. \qquad\qquad\qquad\qquad\qquad\qquad\qquad\qquad\qquad\qquad\qquad\qquad \square
\end{aligned}$$

7.2.d Paths With Prescribed Maslov Index

Lemma 7.2.4. *For every $k \in \mathbf{Z}$, there exists a diagonal matrix $S_k \in M(2n; \mathbf{R})$ such that the associated path $R(t) = \exp(tJ_0S_k)$ is in $\mathcal{S}$ and satisfies*

$$\mu(R(t)) = k.$$

Proof. We begin by generalizing a computation already carried out in dimension 2 on p. 197. We choose an odd integer ℓ and consider the diagonal matrix $S = \left(\begin{smallmatrix} \ell\pi & 0 \\ 0 & \ell\pi \end{smallmatrix}\right)$. Then

$$e^{tJ_0S} = \begin{pmatrix} \cos \ell\pi t & -\sin \ell\pi t \\ \sin \ell\pi t & \cos \ell\pi t \end{pmatrix}$$

is a path in $\mathcal{S}$ that ends up at $-\mathrm{Id} = W^+ \in \mathrm{Sp}(2)^+$. The matrix e^{tJ_0S} is the unitary matrix $e^{i\ell t} \in U(1) \subset \mathrm{Sp}(2)$, so that $\mu(e^{tJ_0S}) = -\ell$. For $S = \left(\begin{smallmatrix} 1 & 0 \\ 0 & -1 \end{smallmatrix}\right)$, we have

$$e^{tJ_0S} = \begin{pmatrix} \cosh t & \sinh t \\ \sinh t & \cosh t \end{pmatrix},$$

a path in $\mathcal{S}$ consisting of matrices whose eigenvalues e^t and e^{-t} are real, positive and distinct for $t > 0$, so that $\mu(e^{tJ_0S}) = 0$.

In the coordinates $p_1, q_1, \ldots, p_n, q_n$, consider the diagonal matrices

$$
S_k = \begin{bmatrix}
\begin{bmatrix} -\pi & 0 \\ 0 & -\pi \end{bmatrix} & & & & \\
& \ddots & & & \\
& & \begin{bmatrix} -\pi & 0 \\ 0 & -\pi \end{bmatrix} & & \\
& & & \begin{bmatrix} -\pi & 0 \\ 0 & -\pi \end{bmatrix} & \\
& & & & \begin{bmatrix} (n-k-1)\pi & 0 \\ 0 & (n-k-1)\pi \end{bmatrix}
\end{bmatrix}
$$

if $k \equiv n \bmod 2$ and

$$
S_k = \begin{bmatrix}
\begin{bmatrix} -\pi & 0 \\ 0 & -\pi \end{bmatrix} & & & & \\
& \ddots & & & \\
& & \begin{bmatrix} -\pi & 0 \\ 0 & -\pi \end{bmatrix} & & \\
& & & \begin{bmatrix} 1 & 0 \\ 0 & -1 \end{bmatrix} & \\
& & & & \begin{bmatrix} (n-k-2)\pi & 0 \\ 0 & (n-k-2)\pi \end{bmatrix}
\end{bmatrix}
$$

if $k \equiv n - 1 \bmod 2$. By the additivity of the Maslov index, these define paths with Maslov index k. $\qquad\square$

Remark 7.2.5. If we replace any of the first $(n-1)$ diagonal blocks in the matrices above as follows:

- $\begin{bmatrix} -\pi & 0 \\ 0 & -\pi \end{bmatrix}$ with $\begin{bmatrix} -\pi\varepsilon & 0 \\ 0 & -\pi\varepsilon \end{bmatrix}$
- $\begin{bmatrix} 1 & 0 \\ 0 & -1 \end{bmatrix}$ with $\begin{bmatrix} \varepsilon & 0 \\ 0 & -\varepsilon \end{bmatrix}$,

for some small $\varepsilon > 0$, their Maslov index remains unchanged: the paths between Id and $W^\pm$ used to compute the Maslov index are the same.

We will use these matrices S_k again, with this notation (but sometimes modified blocks as in Remark 7.2.5), in Chapter 8.

7.3 Appendix: Construction and Properties of ρ

7.3.a Preliminaries

Let B be the form

$$\mathbf{C}^{2n} \times \mathbf{C}^{2n} \longrightarrow \mathbf{R}$$

defined by

$$B(X_1, X_2) = \operatorname{Im} \omega(\overline{X}_1, X_2).$$

Lemma 7.3.1. *The form B is an $\mathbf{R}$-bilinear, symmetric and nondegenerate form. Moreover, it satisfies*

$$B(iX_1, iX_2) = B(X_1, X_2) \quad and \quad B(\overline{X}_1, \overline{X}_2) = -B(X_1, X_2).$$

Proof. It is clear that B is $\mathbf{R}$-bilinear. Proving that it is symmetric is straightforward:

$$\begin{aligned}
B(X_2, X_1) &= \operatorname{Im} \omega(\overline{X}_2, X_1) \\
&= -\operatorname{Im} \omega(X_1, \overline{X}_2) \\
&= \operatorname{Im} \overline{\omega(X_1, \overline{X}_2)} \\
&= \operatorname{Im} \omega(\overline{X}_1, X_2) = B(X_1, X_2).
\end{aligned}$$

To show that it is nondegenerate, we suppose that X satisfies $B(X, Y) = 0$ for every Y. We then have

$$\operatorname{Im} \omega(\overline{X}, Y) = 0 \quad \forall Y \in \mathbf{C}^{2n},$$

and therefore also

$$\operatorname{Im} \omega(\overline{X}, iY) = 0 \quad \forall Y \in \mathbf{C}^{2n},$$

and consequently

$$\omega(\overline{X}, Y) = 0 \quad \forall Y \in \mathbf{C}^{2n},$$

so that $\overline{X} = 0$ because ω is nondegenerate.

The two equalities also have straightforward proofs:

$$B(iX_1, iX_2) = \operatorname{Im} \omega(-i\overline{X}_1, iX_2) = \operatorname{Im} \omega(\overline{X}_1, X_2) = B(X_1, X_2)$$

for the first, and

$$B(\overline{X}_1, \overline{X}_2) = \operatorname{Im} \omega(X_1, \overline{X}_2)$$
$$= -\operatorname{Im} \overline{\omega(X_1, \overline{X}_2)}$$
$$= -\operatorname{Im} \omega(\overline{X}_1, X_2)$$
$$= -B(X_1, X_2)$$

for the second. □

Corollary 7.3.2. *The quadratic form $Q(X) = B(X,X) = \operatorname{Im} \omega(\overline{X}, X)$ is nondegenerate and its signature is zero.* □

We use the terminology where the *signature* of a quadratic form is the difference

$$\sigma(Q) = m_+(Q) - m_-(Q),$$

where m_+, resp. m_-, is the maximal dimension of the subspace on which Q is positive definite, or negative definite respectively (m_- is what we called the index in the context of critical points).

Lemma 7.3.3. *Let λ and μ be two eigenvalues of A. If $\overline{\lambda}\mu \neq 1$, then the generalized eigenspaces E_λ and E_μ are orthogonal for B.*

This is an immediate consequence of Proposition 5.6.6: if $X_1 \in E_\lambda$ and $X_2 \in E_\mu$, then $\overline{X}_1 \in E_{\overline{\lambda}}$ and $\omega(\overline{X}_1, X_2) = 0$. □

Corollary 7.3.4.

(1) *Let $\lambda \in S^1$; then the restrictions of B and Q to E_λ are nondegenerate.*
(2) *Let $\lambda \in \mathbf{C} - S^1$; then the restrictions of B and Q to $E_\lambda \oplus E_{1/\overline{\lambda}}$ are nondegenerate. Moreover, the signature of the restriction of Q to this subspace is zero.*

Proof. The only assertion that deserves a verification is the one concerning the signature. We know that the restriction of ω to $E_\lambda \oplus E_{1/\lambda}$ is nondegenerate (Corollary 5.6.7) and that the two generalized eigenspaces are isotropic. We can therefore find a basis $(X_1, \ldots, X_k)$ of E_λ and a basis $(Y_1, \ldots, Y_k)$ of $E_{\overline{\lambda}}$ such that $(X_1, \ldots, X_k, \overline{Y}_1, \ldots, \overline{Y}_k)$ is a symplectic basis of $E_\lambda \oplus E_{1/\lambda}$. Let

$$u_j = X_j + iY_j, \quad v_j = X_j - iY_j.$$

We then have

$$\begin{aligned}
B(u_j, u_k) &= B(X_j + iY_j, X_k + iY_k) \\
&= B(iY_j, X_k) + B(iY_k, X_j) \\
&= \operatorname{Im} \omega(-i\overline{Y}_j, X_k) + \operatorname{Im} \omega(-i\overline{Y}_k, X_j) \\
&= 2\delta_{j,k},
\end{aligned}$$

so that Q is positive definite on the subspace generated by the u_j, and

$$\begin{aligned}
B(u_j, v_k) &= B(X_j + iY_j, X_k - iY_k) \\
&= B(iY_j, X_k) - B(iY_k, X_j) \\
&= 0,
\end{aligned}$$

so that the subspaces generated by the u_j and by the v_j are orthogonal. Finally,

$$\begin{aligned}
B(v_j, v_k) &= B(X_j - iY_j, X_k - iY_k) \\
&= -B(iY_j, X_k) - B(iY_k, X_j) \\
&= -2\delta_{j,k},
\end{aligned}$$

so that Q is negative on the subspace generated by the v_j and therefore has signature zero.   □

7.3.b Definition of ρ

Let us now define the map ρ. If $\lambda \in S^1 - \mathbf{R}$ is an eigenvalue, then we can write the generalized eigenspace

$$E_\lambda = E_\lambda^+ \oplus E_\lambda^-$$

as the sum of two real vector subspaces of $\mathbf{C}^{2n}$ on which the form Q is positive definite and negative definite, respectively. Since $Q(iX) = Q(X)$, the two subspaces are stable under multiplication by i and are in fact *complex* vector subspaces of $\mathbf{C}^{2n}$.

We let $m_+(\lambda)$ and $m_-(\lambda)$ be the complex dimensions of these spaces,

$$m_+(\lambda) = \dim_{\mathbf{C}} E_\lambda^+, \quad m_-(\lambda) = \dim_{\mathbf{C}} E_\lambda^-,$$

so that

$$m_+(\lambda) + m_-(\lambda) = \dim_{\mathbf{C}} E_\lambda = m(\lambda),$$

the multiplicity of λ. We then define the *signature* of the eigenvalue λ to be

$$\sigma(\lambda) = m_+(\lambda) - m_-(\lambda).$$

Recall that the multiplicity of -1 as a (potential) eigenvalue is even, because E_{-1} is symplectic (Corollary 5.6.7), so that the sum of the multiplicities of the negative real eigenvalues is even, that is,

$$m_0 = \sum_{\lambda \in \text{Spec}(A) \cap \mathbf{R}_-} m(\lambda) \in 2\mathbf{N}.$$

Consequently, we can finally set

$$\rho(A) = (-1)^{m_0/2} \prod_{\lambda \in \text{Spec}(A) \cap (S^1 - \mathbf{R})} \lambda^{m_+(\lambda)}.$$

This is the map that was announced in Theorem 7.1.3, as we will prove. We begin by noting that we could have used only the eigenvalues with positive imaginary part.

Proposition 7.3.5.

$$\rho(A) = (-1)^{m_0/2} \prod_{\substack{\lambda \in \text{Spec}(A) \cap S^1 \\ \text{Im}(\lambda) > 0}} \lambda^{\sigma(\lambda)}.$$

Proof. We have already said (Remark 5.6.8) that $X \mapsto \overline{X}$ is an isomorphism of real vector subspaces from E_λ onto $E_{\overline{\lambda}}$. Since $Q(\overline{X}) = -Q(X)$, we have, for $\lambda \in S^1$,

$$\begin{cases} m_+(\overline{\lambda}) = m_-(\lambda) \\ m_-(\overline{\lambda}) = m_+(\lambda) \\ \sigma(\overline{\lambda}) = -\sigma(\lambda), \end{cases}$$

so that

$$\lambda^{m_+(\lambda)} \cdot \overline{\lambda}^{m_+(\lambda)} = \lambda^{\sigma(\lambda)} = \overline{\lambda}^{\sigma(\overline{\lambda})}.$$

By grouping the eigenvalues of absolute value 1 into pairs $(\lambda, \overline{\lambda})$ in the definition of ρ, we obtain the stated formula. $\qquad\square$

7.3.c Properties of ρ

Let us now begin verifying the desired properties of ρ, that is, proving Theorem 7.1.3.

Continuity of ρ

Let $(A_k)_{k \in \mathbf{N}}$ be a sequence in $\text{Sp}(2n; \mathbf{R})$ that converges to a matrix $A \in \text{Sp}(2n)$. We are going to show that the sequence consisting of the $\rho(A_k)$ converges to $\rho(A)$. It is clear that it suffices to show this for a subsequence of (A_k). We are going to use the fact that the eigenvalues depend continuously on the coefficients of the matrix, a classical fact that can be stated as follows.[1]

Proposition 7.3.6. *Let $(A_k)_{k\in\mathbf{N}}$ be a sequence of square $m \times m$ matrices tending to a limit A. Let $\lambda_1, \dots, \lambda_m$ be the eigenvalues of A, repeated according to their multiplicities. Then there exists a numbering $\lambda_1^k, \dots, \lambda_m^k$ of the eigenvalues of A_k such that*

$$\forall\, i \in [1, m] \quad \lim_{k\to+\infty} \lambda_i^k = \lambda_i.$$

We will also need a result on the continuity of the generalized eigenspaces.

Proposition 7.3.7. *With the same assumptions, let λ be an eigenvalue of A. Then after extracting a subsequence, if necessary,*

$$\lim_{\substack{k\to+\infty \\ \lim \lambda_i^k = \lambda \\ i\neq j \Rightarrow \lambda_i^k \neq \lambda_j^k}} \bigoplus E_{\lambda_i^k}(A_k) = E_\lambda(A).$$

In this statement, the convergence of a sequence of vector subspaces (of $\mathbf{C}^m$) of the same dimension to a subspace of this dimension is defined (that is, as the convergence in the corresponding Grassmannian) by $\lim V_k = V$ if for every k there exists a unitary basis $\mathcal{B}_k$ of V_k such that the sequence of the $\mathcal{B}_k$ converges to a basis $\mathcal{B}$ of V.

Proof of Proposition 7.3.7. Let $\lambda_1^k, \lambda_2^k, \dots, \lambda_{r_k}^k$ denote the (distinct) eigenvalues of A_k whose generalized eigenspaces occur in the direct sum. By Proposition 7.3.6, we know that the sum of their multiplicities is the multiplicity of the limit λ. Let V_k be this direct sum and note that

$$V_k \subset \mathrm{Ker}(A_k - \lambda_1^k\,\mathrm{Id})^{m(\lambda_1^k)}(A_k - \lambda_2^k\,\mathrm{Id})^{m(\lambda_2^k)} \cdots (A_k - \lambda_{r_k}^k\,\mathrm{Id})^{m(\lambda_{r_k}^k)}.$$

In fact, $(A_k - \lambda_j^k\,\mathrm{Id})^{m(\lambda_j^k)}$ is zero on the generalized eigenspace $E_{\lambda_j^k}(A_k)$ (by the definition of the generalized eigenspaces). Consequently, if $v_k \in V_k$ is a sequence of vectors that converges to v, then

$$(A - \lambda\,\mathrm{Id})^{m(\lambda)} v = 0,$$

and therefore $v \in E_\lambda(A)$. $\square$

From Proposition 7.3.6, we deduce without difficulty the following useful result.

---

[1] The proof is left as an exercise for willing readers; in Exercise 43 on p. 529, we propose a proof based on Rouché's theorem.

Proposition 7.3.8. *If $(V_k)_{k \in \mathbf{N}}$ is a sequence of vector subspaces of $\mathbf{C}^m$ of the same dimension that converges to a subspace V and if Q is a quadratic form on $\mathbf{C}^m$ whose restriction to each of the V_k and to V is nondegenerate, then for k sufficiently large, the signature of $Q|_{V_k}$ is constant and equals that of $Q|_V$.*

Proof. We choose a sequence of unitary bases of V_k that converges to a unitary basis of V. The matrix of the restriction of Q to V_k tends to that of the restriction of Q to V. The number of positive eigenvalues counted with their multiplicities is therefore constant for k sufficiently large. $\qquad\square$

Let us now prove the continuity of ρ. Let $(A_k)_{k \in \mathbf{N}}$ be a sequence of symplectic matrices that converges to $A \in \mathrm{Sp}(2n)$ and let $\lambda \in S^1 \cap \{\mathrm{Im}(z) > 0\}$ be an eigenvalue of A. With the notation used above, we let

$$E_\lambda(A) = \lim_{k \to +\infty} E_{\lambda_1^k}(A_k) \oplus \cdots \oplus E_{\lambda_{r_k}^k}(A_k).$$

The eigenvalue λ can be approximated by a sequence $(\lambda^k)_{k \in \mathbf{N}}$ of eigenvalues of A_k that lie on the circle or by a sequence $(\mu^k)_{k \in \mathbf{N}}$ of numbers outside of the circle, in which case it can also be approximated by the sequence $(1/\overline{\mu}^k)_{k \in \mathbf{N}}$. This is illustrated by Figure 7.2.

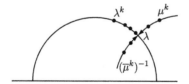

Fig. 7.2

Let $\lambda_1^k, \ldots, \lambda_{s_k}^k$ (for $s_k \leq r_k$) be the eigenvalues that lie on the circle for k sufficiently large. Here is a corollary to Proposition 7.3.8.

Corollary 7.3.9.

$$\lim_{k \to +\infty} (\lambda_1^k)^{\sigma(\lambda_1^k)} \cdots (\lambda_{s_k}^k)^{\sigma(\lambda_{s_k}^k)} = \lambda^{\sigma(\lambda)}.$$

Proof. This is an immediate consequence of Proposition 7.3.8 when $s_k = r_k$, because in that case

$$\sigma(\lambda_1^k) + \cdots + \sigma(\lambda_{s_k}^k) = \sigma(\lambda)$$

for k sufficiently large, which gives the desired result. If $s_k < r_k$, then the eigenvalues $\lambda_{s_k+1}^k, \ldots, \lambda_{r_k}^k$ can be grouped into pairs $\mu, \overline{\mu}^{-1}$ with the same multiplicity (as indicated in Figure 7.2). However, by Corollary 7.3.4, the signature of Q on $E_\mu(A_k) \oplus E_{\overline{\mu}^{-1}}(A_k)$ is zero. The relation between the signatures is once again satisfied and the corollary is proved.   □

To finish the proof of the continuity, we need to analyze the sequences of eigenvalues of the matrices A_k that tend to a real eigenvalue λ of A.

We begin with the case $\lambda > 0$. If $\lambda \neq 1$, then λ_i^k and λ do not play a role in the definition of ρ. If $\lambda = 1$, then the only sequences that play a role in the definition of ρ are those that lie on $S^1 \cap \{\mathrm{Im}(z) > 0\}$ for k sufficiently large (Figure 7.3). For each of these,

$$\lim_{k \to +\infty} (\lambda^k)^{\sigma(\lambda_k)} = 1 \quad \text{because} \quad \lim_{k \to +\infty} \lambda^k = 1.$$

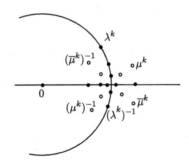

Fig. 7.3

Let us now move on to the case of a $\lambda < 0$ (Figures 7.4 and 7.5). Let:

- (As above) $\lambda_1^k, \ldots, \lambda_{s_k}^k$ be the sequences of eigenvalues of A_k that are in $S^1 \cap \{\mathrm{Im}(z) > 0\}$ for k sufficiently large (if there is at least one, then $\lambda = -1$)
- $\lambda_{s_k+1}^k, \ldots, \lambda_{t_k}^k$ be the real sequences
- $\lambda_{t_k+1}^k, \ldots, \lambda_{r_k}^k$ be the remaining sequences.

We will prove the following result.

Proposition 7.3.10.

$$\lim_{k \to +\infty} (\lambda_1^k)^{\sigma(\lambda_1^k)} \cdots (\lambda_{s_k}^k)^{\sigma(\lambda_{s_k}^k)} \cdot (-1)^{(m(\lambda_{s_k+1}^k)+\cdots+m(\lambda_{t_k}^k))/2} = (-1)^{m(\lambda)/2}.$$

Proof. If $\lambda \neq -1$, then $s_k = 0$ and the eigenvalues $\lambda_{t_k+1}^k, \ldots, \lambda_{r_k}^k$ can be grouped into quadruples $\mu, 1/\mu, \overline{\mu}, 1/\overline{\mu}$ (Figure 7.4), so that

$$m(\mu) + m(1/\mu) + m(\overline{\mu}) + m(1/\overline{\mu}) = 4m(\mu).$$

Therefore, for k sufficiently large, the continuity of the eigenvalues (Proposition 7.3.6) implies that

$$\frac{m(\lambda)}{2} = \sum_{i=1}^{r_k} \frac{m(\lambda_i^k)}{2} \quad \text{and} \quad \sum_{i=1}^{t_k} \frac{m(\lambda_i^k)}{2}$$

have the same parity, concluding the proof in this case.

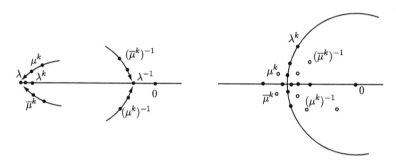

Fig. 7.4   **Fig. 7.5**

If $\lambda = -1$, then the eigenvalues $\lambda_{t_k+1}, \ldots, \lambda_{r_k}$ are either the conjugates $\overline{\lambda}_1^k, \ldots, \overline{\lambda}_{s_k}^k$ or quadruples $\mu, 1/\mu, \overline{\mu}, 1/\overline{\mu}$ (Figure 7.5). This time, for k sufficiently large, and modulo 2, we have

$$\frac{m(\lambda)}{2} \equiv \sum_{i=1}^{s_k} \frac{m(\lambda_i^k)}{2} + \sum_{i=1}^{s_k} \frac{m(\overline{\lambda}_i^k)}{2} + \sum_{i=s_k+1}^{t_k} \frac{m(\lambda_i^k)}{2}$$

$$\equiv \sum_{i=1}^{s_k} m(\lambda_i^k) + \sum_{i=s_k+1}^{t_k} \frac{m(\lambda_i^k)}{2}$$

$$\equiv \sum_{i=1}^{s_k} \sigma(\lambda_i^k) + \sum_{i=s_k+1}^{t_k} \frac{m(\lambda_i^k)}{2},$$

because m and σ have the same parity. This is the stated result. □

This (that is, Corollary 7.3.9 and Proposition 7.3.10) concludes the proof of the continuity of ρ. □

Let us now show that the resulting continuous map ρ satisfies all the properties announced in Theorem 7.1.3.

Naturality

The matrices TAT^{-1} and A have the same spectrum, including the multiplicities. Moreover, the generalized eigenspaces correspond through

$$E_\lambda^{TAT^{-1}} = T(E_\lambda^A).$$

Finally, since T is not just any invertible matrix, but an element of $\mathrm{Sp}(2n; \mathbf{R})$, it preserves the symplectic form ω and everything that is deduced from it. In particular, $Q(T(X)) = Q(X)$, so that

$$m_\pm^{TAT^{-1}}(\lambda) = m_\pm^A(\lambda) \quad \text{and finally } \rho(TAT^{-1}) = \rho(A). \qquad \square$$

Product

The spectrum of $\left(\begin{smallmatrix} A & 0 \\ 0 & B \end{smallmatrix}\right)$ is the union of the spectra of A and B (with multiplicities) and, likewise (with the convention that $E_\lambda = 0$ if λ is not an eigenvalue),

$$E_\lambda \begin{pmatrix} A & 0 \\ 0 & B \end{pmatrix} = E_\lambda(A) \oplus E_\lambda(B).$$

The $m_\pm$ also add up, and therefore

$$\rho \begin{pmatrix} A & 0 \\ 0 & B \end{pmatrix} = \rho(A)\rho(B). \qquad \square$$

Normalization

This property ($\rho = \pm 1$ if the eigenvalues are real) is an immediate consequence of the definition of ρ. $\qquad \square$

Determinant

Let $A \in \mathrm{Sp}(2n; \mathbf{R}) \cap \mathrm{O}(2n) = \mathrm{U}(n)$, then

$$A = \begin{pmatrix} M & -N \\ N & M \end{pmatrix}, \quad \text{which is identified with } U = M + iN \in \mathrm{U}(n).$$

First note that the eigenvalues of A are indeed the eigenvalues of U. On the one hand, we have

$$U(z) = \lambda z \Longrightarrow A \begin{pmatrix} z \\ -iz \end{pmatrix} = \lambda \begin{pmatrix} z \\ -iz \end{pmatrix}$$

and on the other hand, we have

$$\begin{pmatrix} M & -N \\ N & M \end{pmatrix} \begin{pmatrix} v \\ w \end{pmatrix} = \lambda \begin{pmatrix} v \\ w \end{pmatrix} \Longrightarrow (M + iN)(v + iw) = \lambda(v + iw)$$

(if we happen to have $v + iw = 0$, then $(M + iN)v = \lambda v$, so that λ is indeed an eigenvalue of U). In particular, like those of U (because they are the same), the eigenvalues of A are elements of S^1.

Lemma 7.3.11. Let $A \in \mathrm{Sp}(2n; \mathbf{R}) \cap \mathrm{O}(2n) = \mathrm{U}(n)$ and let λ be a nonreal eigenvalue of A. Then

$$m_+^A(\lambda) = m^U(\lambda) \quad and \quad m^A(-1) = 2m^U(-1).$$

Proof. The matrices A and U are diagonalizable over $\mathbf{C}$, hence the generalized eigenspaces E_λ are just the usual eigenspaces. Let J_0 be the complex structure

$$J_0 = \begin{pmatrix} 0 & -\mathrm{Id} \\ \mathrm{Id} & 0 \end{pmatrix}, \quad \text{so that } J_0^2 = -\mathrm{Id}, \ AJ_0 = J_0A$$

and $\omega(X, J_0 Y) = (X, Y)$, the inner product on $\mathbf{R}^{2n}$. Since A commutes with J_0, we have

$$J_0(E_\lambda^A) = E_\lambda^A.$$

Moreover, $J_0 \in \mathrm{Sp}(2n; \mathbf{R}) \cap \mathrm{O}(2n)$ is also diagonalizable over $\mathbf{C}$, its eigenvalues are i and $-i$, with multiplicity n each, and its eigenspaces are

$$E_i^{J_0} = \left\{ \begin{pmatrix} x \\ ix \end{pmatrix} \mid x \in \mathbf{C}^n \right\} \quad \text{and} \quad E_{-i}^{J_0} = \left\{ \begin{pmatrix} x \\ -ix \end{pmatrix} \mid x \in \mathbf{C}^n \right\}.$$

In particular, for $v \in E_i^{J_0}$, we have

$$\omega(\overline{v}, v) = \omega(\overline{v}, -iJ_0 v) = -i\omega(\overline{v}, J_0 v) = -i(\|\mathrm{Re}\, v\|^2 + \|\mathrm{Im}\, v\|^2),$$

so that Q is negative definite on $E_i^{J_0}$. An analogous computation shows that it is positive definite on $E_{-i}^{J_0}$. It follows that the eigenspaces of A satisfy

$$E_\lambda^+ = E_\lambda \cap E_{-i}^{J_0}, \quad E_\lambda^- = E_\lambda \cap E_i^{J_0}.$$

Consequently,

$$E_\lambda^+ = \left\{ \begin{pmatrix} x \\ -ix \end{pmatrix} \in \mathbf{C}^{2n} \mid \begin{pmatrix} M & -N \\ N & M \end{pmatrix} \begin{pmatrix} x \\ -ix \end{pmatrix} = \lambda \begin{pmatrix} x \\ -ix \end{pmatrix} \right\}$$

$$= \{ x \in \mathbf{C}^n \mid (M + iN)x = \lambda x \},$$

which is exactly the eigenspace of the matrix U for λ. Consequently, we indeed have $m_+^A(\lambda) = m^U(\lambda)$. The eigenvalue -1 case can be treated in an analogous manner: we can verify that

$$\begin{pmatrix} v \\ w \end{pmatrix} \in E_{-1}^A \cap \mathbf{R}^{2n} \iff (v + iw) \in E_{-1}^U,$$

so that the eigenspaces of A and of U for the eigenvalue -1 are isomorphic as real vector spaces, and that

$$m^A(-1) = \dim_{\mathbf{R}}(E^A_{-1} \cap \mathbf{R}^{2n}) = \dim_{\mathbf{R}} E^U_{-1} = 2\dim_{\mathbf{C}} E^U_{-1} = 2m^U(-1)$$

... which concludes the proof of the lemma...   □

and which proves that $\rho(A) = \det_{\mathbf{C}}(U)$.   □

Taking the Inverse

We have seen that ${}^t A = J_0^{-1} A^{-1} J_0$, hence, owing to the naturality, $\rho({}^t A) = \rho(A^{-1})$. Moreover, λ is an eigenvalue of A^{-1} if and only if $1/\lambda$ is an eigenvalue of A and the generalized eigenspaces are the same:

$$E_\lambda(A^{-1}) = E_{1/\lambda}(A).$$

In particular,

$$m^{A^{-1}}_+(\lambda) = m^A_+(1/\lambda) \quad \text{and} \quad m^{A^{-1}}(-1) = m^A(-1), \quad \text{so that } m^{A^{-1}}_0 = m^A_0.$$

We then compute

$$\rho(A^{-1}) = (-1)^{m^{A^{-1}}_0/2} \prod_{\substack{\lambda \in \mathrm{Spec}(A^{-1}) \\ \lambda \in S^1 - \mathbf{R}}} \lambda^{m^{A^{-1}}_+(\lambda)}$$

$$= (-1)^{m^A_0/2} \prod_{\substack{\lambda \in \mathrm{Spec}(A^{-1}) = \mathrm{Spec}(A) \\ \lambda \in S^1 - \mathbf{R}}} \lambda^{m^A_+(1/\lambda)}.$$

Changing λ to $1/\lambda$, we find that

$$\rho(A^{-1}) = (-1)^{m^A_0/2} \prod_{\substack{\lambda \in \mathrm{Spec}(A) \\ \lambda \in S^1 - \mathbf{R}}} \left(\frac{1}{\lambda}\right)^{m^A_+(\lambda)} = \frac{1}{\rho(A)} = \overline{\rho(A)}.$$

7.3.d The Lemmas Concerning $\mathrm{Sp}(2n)^\star$

Proof of Lemma 7.1.6. We use the precise description of ρ given in Proposition 7.3.5 to construct $\tilde\rho$ and statements analogous to those proving the continuity of ρ to prove that of the lift.

For $\lambda \in S^1$ *nonreal*, we let $\arg(\lambda)$ denote the number

$$\arg(\lambda) \in {]0, 2\pi[} \text{ such that } \exp(i\arg(\lambda)) = \lambda.$$

We define $\widetilde{\rho} : \mathrm{Sp}(2n)^\star \to \mathbf{R}$ using the formulas

$$\widetilde{\rho}(A) = \begin{cases} \displaystyle\sum_{\substack{\lambda\in\mathrm{Spec}(A) \\ \lambda\in S^1-\mathbf{R}}} m_+(\lambda)\arg(\lambda) + \displaystyle\sum_{\substack{\lambda\in\mathrm{Spec}(A) \\ \lambda\notin S^1-\mathbf{R}}} \frac{\pi}{2}m(\lambda) & \text{if } A\in\mathrm{Sp}(2n)^+ \\[3mm] \displaystyle\sum_{\substack{\lambda\in\mathrm{Spec}(A) \\ \lambda\in S^1-\mathbf{R}}} m_+(\lambda)\arg(\lambda) + \displaystyle\sum_{\substack{\lambda\in\mathrm{Spec}(A) \\ \lambda\notin S^1-\mathbf{R}}} \frac{\pi}{2}m(\lambda) + \pi & \text{if } A\in\mathrm{Sp}(2n)^-. \end{cases}$$

Note that the first sum can be written using only the eigenvalues with positive imaginary part:

$$\sum_{\substack{\lambda\in\mathrm{Spec}(A) \\ \lambda\in S^1-\mathbf{R}}} m_+(\lambda)\arg(\lambda) = \sum_{\substack{\lambda\in\mathrm{Spec}(A) \\ \lambda\in S^1\cap\{\mathrm{Im}(z)>0\}}} \left(m_+(\lambda)\arg(\lambda) + m_+(\overline{\lambda})\arg(\overline{\lambda})\right)$$

$$= \sum_{\substack{\lambda\in\mathrm{Spec}(A) \\ \lambda\in S^1\cap\{\mathrm{Im}(z)>0\}}} \left(m_+(\lambda)\arg(\lambda) + m_-(\lambda)(2\pi - \arg(\lambda))\right)$$

$$= \sum_{\substack{\lambda\in\mathrm{Spec}(A) \\ \lambda\in S^1\cap\{\mathrm{Im}(z)>0\}}} \left(m_-(\lambda)(2\pi) + \sigma(\lambda)\arg(\lambda)\right).$$

Moreover, the nonreal eigenvalues of $A \in \mathrm{Sp}(2n)$ can be grouped into pairs $\lambda,\overline{\lambda}$ with the same multiplicity. From this we deduce an expression for $\widetilde{\rho}$ that only involves the eigenvalues with positive imaginary part:

- For $A \in \mathrm{Sp}(2n)^+$,

$$\widetilde{\rho} = \sum_{\substack{\lambda\in\mathrm{Spec}(A) \\ \lambda\in S^1\cap\{\mathrm{Im}(z)>0\}}} \left(2\pi m_-(\lambda) + \sigma(\lambda)\arg(\lambda)\right)$$

$$+ \sum_{\substack{\lambda\in\mathrm{Spec}(A) \\ \lambda\in\{\mathrm{Im}(z)>0\}-S^1}} \pi m(\lambda) + \sum_{\lambda\in\mathrm{Spec}(A)\cap\mathbf{R}} \frac{\pi}{2}m(\lambda).$$

- And for $A \in \mathrm{Sp}(2n)^-$,

$$\widetilde{\rho} = \sum_{\substack{\lambda\in\mathrm{Spec}(A) \\ \lambda\in S^1\cap\{\mathrm{Im}(z)>0\}}} \left(2\pi m_-(\lambda) + \sigma(\lambda)\arg(\lambda)\right)$$

$$+ \sum_{\substack{\lambda\in\mathrm{Spec}(A) \\ \lambda\in\{\mathrm{Im}(z)>0\}-S^1}} \pi m(\lambda) + \sum_{\lambda\in\mathrm{Spec}(A)\cap\mathbf{R}} \frac{\pi}{2}m(\lambda) + \pi.$$

Let us now verify that $\widetilde{\rho}$ has the required properties. Let $A \in \mathrm{Sp}(2n)^+$. The eigenvalues of A that are neither real nor of absolute value 1 occur in groups of four with the same multiplicity. The total multiplicity of the positive real eigenvalues is also divisible by 4: they occur in pairs $(\lambda, 1/\lambda)$ and

$$0 < \det(A - \mathrm{Id}) = \prod_{\lambda \in \mathrm{Spec}(A)} (\lambda - 1)$$

has the same sign as

$$\prod_{\lambda \in \mathrm{Spec}(A) \cap \mathbf{R}_+} (\lambda - 1).$$

It follows that

$$\exp\left(i \sum_{\substack{\lambda \in \mathrm{Spec}(A) \\ \lambda \notin S^1 - \mathbf{R}}} m(\lambda)\frac{\pi}{2} \right) = \exp\left(i \frac{m_0}{2}\pi \right) = (-1)^{m_0/2}$$

(recall that m_0 is the total multiplicity of the negative real eigenvalues of A). We therefore indeed have

$$\exp\left(i\widetilde{\rho}(A) \right) = \rho(A) \quad \forall A \in \mathrm{Sp}(2n)^+.$$

For the case of $\mathrm{Sp}(2n)^-$, by the same argument, the total multiplicity of the positive real eigenvalues of A is an integer of the form $4k + 2$, but we also have an additional π in the formula defining $\widetilde{\rho}$, so that

$$\exp\left(i \sum_{\substack{\lambda \in \mathrm{Spec}(A) \\ \lambda \in S^1 - \mathbf{R}}} m(\lambda)\frac{\pi}{2} + \pi \right) = \exp\left(i \left(\frac{m_0}{2}\pi + 2\ell\pi \right) \right) = (-1)^{m_0/2},$$

and once again

$$\exp\left(i\widetilde{\rho}(A) \right) = \rho(A) \quad \forall A \in \mathrm{Sp}(2n)^-.$$

Consequently, $\widetilde{\rho}_\pm$ is a lift of ρ.

Let us now show that this map $\widetilde{\rho}$ is continuous, using arguments similar to those we have already used to show the continuity of ρ. We do this only for $\mathrm{Sp}^+(2n)$, since the proof for $\mathrm{Sp}(2n)^-$ is completely analogous. We therefore proceed as for the continuity of ρ, with a sequence $(A_k)_{k \in \mathbf{N}}$ that converges to A in $\mathrm{Sp}(2n)^+$. If λ is an eigenvalue of A, then as before, let $\lambda_1^k, \ldots, \lambda_{r_k}^k$ denote the (distinct) eigenvalues of A_k such that $\lim_{k \to +\infty} \lambda_i^k = \lambda$. We once more need to distinguish between several cases. In each of them, we use the formula giving ρ as a function of only the eigenvalues with a positive imaginary part:

(1) $\lambda \in \{\mathrm{Im}(z) > 0\} - S^1$. In this case, once again by the continuity of the eigenvalues,

$$\sum_{i=1}^{r_k} \pi m(\lambda_i^k) = \pi m(\lambda).$$

(2) $\lambda \in \{\mathrm{Im}(z) > 0\} \cap S^1$. As in Corollary 7.3.9, let $\lambda_1^k, \ldots, \lambda_{s_k}^k$ denote the sequences that are on S^1 (for k sufficiently large). The others are grouped into pairs $\mu, 1/\overline{\mu}$ (as in Figure 7.2). Recall (Corollary 7.3.4) that the signature of Q on a space $E_\mu \oplus E_{1/\overline{\mu}}$ is zero, so that for k sufficiently large, we have

$$\sum_{i=1}^{s_k} \sigma(\lambda_i^k) = \sigma(\lambda)$$

(as in the proof of Corollary 7.3.9). By applying the fact that

$$m_-(Q|_{E_\mu \oplus E_{1/\overline{\mu}}}) = m_+(Q|_{E_\mu \oplus E_{1/\overline{\mu}}}) = m(\mu) = \frac{1}{2}(m(\mu) + m(1/\overline{\mu})),$$

we find

$$\lim_{k \to +\infty} \left(\sum_{i=1}^{s_k} (2\pi m_-(\lambda_i^k) + \sigma(\lambda_i^k)\arg(\lambda_i^k)) + \sum_{i=s_k+1}^{r_k} \pi m(\lambda_i^k) \right)$$

$$= \lim_{k \to +\infty} \left((2\pi m_-(Q|_{\oplus_{i=1}^{r_k} E_{\lambda_i^k}(A_k)})) + \left(\sum_{i=1}^{s_k} \sigma(\lambda_i^k) \right) \arg(\lambda) \right)$$

$$= 2\pi m_-(\lambda) + \sigma(\lambda)\arg(\lambda).$$

(3) $\lambda \in \mathbf{R}$, $|\lambda| \neq 1$. Let $\lambda_1^k, \ldots, \lambda_{t_k}^k$ denote the eigenvalues of A_k that are real for k sufficiently large. The others occur in quadruples $\mu, \overline{\mu}, 1/\mu, 1/\overline{\mu}$ (as in Figure 7.4), where all elements of the quadruple have the same multiplicity. Once again using the continuity of the eigenvalues, we have

$$\frac{\pi}{2} m(\lambda) = \sum_{i=1}^{r_k} \frac{\pi}{2} m(\lambda_i^k) = \sum_{i=1}^{t_k} \frac{\pi}{2} m(\lambda_i^k) + \pi \sum_{\substack{i=t_k+1 \\ \mathrm{Im}(\lambda_i^k)>0}}^{r_k} m(\lambda_i^k).$$

(4) $\lambda = -1$. We first have the eigenvalues $\lambda_1^k, \ldots, \lambda_{s_k}^k$ that lie on S^1 for k sufficiently large: they can be grouped into pairs $\mu, \overline{\mu}$ (see Figure 7.5). For a sequence of this type with $\mathrm{Im}(\lambda_i^k) > 0$, we have

$$\lim_{k \to +\infty} \left(2\pi m_-(\lambda_i^k) + \sigma(\lambda_i^k)\arg(\lambda_i^k) \right) - \pi m(\lambda_i^k)$$

$$= \lim_{k \to +\infty} \left(\sigma(\lambda_i^k)(\arg(\lambda_i^k) - \pi) + \pi \left(2m_-(\lambda_i^k) + \sigma(\lambda_i^k) - m(\lambda_i^k) \right) \right) = 0.$$

There are also eigenvalues $\lambda_{s_k+1}^k, \ldots, \lambda_{t_k}^k$ that are real for k sufficiently large, and the remaining eigenvalues $\lambda_{t_k+1}^k, \ldots, \lambda_{r_k}^k$ that are neither real nor of absolute value 1 and that occur in quadruples $\mu, \overline{\mu}, 1/\mu, 1/\overline{\mu}$ (see

Figure 7.5). This time, we find

$$\frac{\pi}{2} m(\lambda) = \lim_{k \to +\infty} \frac{\pi}{2} \sum_{i=1}^{r_k} m(\lambda_i^k)$$

$$= \lim_{k \to +\infty} \frac{\pi}{2} \left(\sum_{i=1}^{s_k} m(\lambda_i^k) + \sum_{i=s_k+1}^{t_k} m(\lambda_i^k) + \sum_{i=t_k+1}^{r_k} m(\lambda_i^k) \right)$$

$$= \lim_{k \to +\infty} \frac{\pi}{2} \left(2 \sum_{\substack{i=1 \\ \mathrm{Im}(\lambda_i^k)>0}}^{s_k} m(\lambda_i^k) + \sum_{i=s_k+1}^{t_k} m(\lambda_i^k) + 2 \sum_{\substack{i=t_k+1 \\ \mathrm{Im}(\lambda_i^k)>0}}^{r_k} m(\lambda_i^k) \right)$$

$$= \lim_{k \to +\infty} \left(\sum_{\substack{i=1 \\ \mathrm{Im}(\lambda_i^k)>0}}^{s_k} (2\pi m_-(\lambda_i^k) + \sigma(\lambda_i^k)\arg(\lambda_i^k)) \right.$$

$$\left. + \frac{\pi}{2} \sum_{i=s_k+1}^{t_k} m(\lambda_i^k) + \pi \sum_{\substack{i=t_k+1 \\ \mathrm{Im}(\lambda_i^k)>0}}^{r_k} m(\lambda_i^k) \right).$$

The relations we obtain in these four cases give the continuity of $\widetilde{\rho}$.   □

Proof of Lemma 7.1.5. We begin with a symplectic matrix A that does not have eigenvalue 1, and we want to connect it to a matrix B with the same properties, distinct eigenvalues and exactly two positive real eigenvalues.

We begin by connecting A to a symplectic matrix whose eigenvalues are all distinct. We only need to do something if A has multiple eigenvalues:

(1) We first consider the case of a multiple eigenvalue $\lambda \in \mathbf{C} - (S^1 \cup \mathbf{R})$.
Let X and Y be eigenvectors for λ and $1/\lambda$, respectively, chosen such that $\omega(X,Y) = 1$ (this is possible because ω is symplectic on $E_\lambda \oplus E_{1/\lambda}$).
The subspace F of $\mathbf{C}^{2n}$ generated by $X, Y, \overline{X}, \overline{Y}$ is symplectic and these four vectors form a symplectic basis of it.
Let $\beta : [0,\varepsilon] \to \mathbf{C}^\star$ be a path of class $\mathcal{C}^\infty$ with origin 1. For $s \in [0,\varepsilon]$, we define $A(s)$ by setting

$$A(s)(X) = \beta(s)\lambda X, \qquad A(s)(\overline{X}) = \overline{\beta}(s)\overline{\lambda}\overline{X},$$

$$A(s)(Y) = \frac{1}{\beta(s)\lambda}Y, \qquad A(s)(\overline{Y}) = \frac{1}{\overline{\beta}(s)\overline{\lambda}}\overline{Y}$$

and $A(s) = A$ on the symplectic orthogonal complement F° of F. One easily verifies that $A(s)$ is real and symplectic. We have

$$\begin{cases} A(s)|_{E_\mu} = A|_{E_\mu} & \text{for } \mu \notin \{\lambda, 1/\lambda, \overline{\lambda}1/\overline{\lambda}\}, \\ A(s)|_{E_\mu \cap F^\circ} = A|_{E_\mu \cap F^\circ} & \text{for } \mu \in \{\lambda, 1/\lambda, \overline{\lambda}, 1/\overline{\lambda}\} \end{cases}$$

(for s sufficiently small). Consequently, by choosing β well, we will have, for s sufficiently small, $\beta(s)\lambda \in \mathbf{C} - (S^1 \cup \mathbf{R})$, $A(s) \in \mathrm{Sp}(2n)^\star$. Moreover,

$$\dim_{\mathbf{C}} E_\mu(A(s)) = \begin{cases} \dim_{\mathbf{C}} E_\mu(A) & \text{if } \mu \in \mathrm{Spec}(A) \\ & \text{and } \mu \notin \{\lambda, 1/\lambda, \overline{\lambda}, 1/\overline{\lambda}\} \\ \dim_{\mathbf{C}} E_\mu(A) - 1 & \text{if } \mu \in \{\lambda, 1/\lambda, \overline{\lambda}, 1/\overline{\lambda}\} \\ 1 & \text{if } \mu \in \{\beta\lambda, 1/\beta\lambda, \overline{\beta\lambda}, 1/\overline{\beta\lambda}\}, \end{cases}$$

so that we have lowered the multiplicity of λ by 1 without increasing the multiplicities of the other eigenvalues.

(2) Let us now consider the case of a multiple eigenvalue in $S^1 - \mathbf{R}$. Let X be an eigenvector of A for the eigenvalue λ. Then $\overline{X}$ is an eigenvector for $\overline{\lambda}$. The subspace generated by X and $\overline{X}$ can either be symplectic or not:

- If $\omega(X, \overline{X}) \neq 0$, then we can proceed exactly as above, that is, choose a path β with values in S^1 and define $A(s) \in \mathrm{Sp}(2n)^\star$ in such a way that it multiplies X by $\beta(s)\lambda$ and $\overline{X}$ by its conjugate and that it is identical to A on the symplectic orthogonal complement, which lowers the multiplicity of the eigenvalue λ by 1.

- If $\omega(X, \overline{X}) = 0$, then since ω is symplectic on $E_\lambda \oplus E_{\overline{\lambda}}$, there exists a vector Y in the generalized eigenspace $E_\lambda(A)$ such that $\omega(X, \overline{Y}) = 1$ and $\omega(Y, \overline{Y}) = 0$. The four vectors $X, \overline{Y}, \overline{X}, Y$ form a symplectic basis of the subspace F they generate. We again use a path of class $\mathcal{C}^\infty$, $\beta : [0, \varepsilon] \to \mathbf{C}$, with $\beta(0) = 1$ and $\beta(s) \in \mathbf{C} - S^1$ for $s > 0$, to set

$$A(s)X = \beta(s)\lambda X, \qquad A(s)\overline{X} = \overline{\beta}(s)\overline{\lambda}\overline{X},$$
$$A(s)Y = \frac{1}{\overline{\beta}(s)}AY, \qquad A(s)\overline{Y} = \frac{1}{\beta(s)}A\overline{Y}$$

and $A(s) = A$ on F°. As before, $A(s) \in \mathrm{Sp}(2n)^\star$ and the dimensions of the generalized eigenspaces for the eigenvalues other than λ and $\overline{\lambda}$ remain the same. We have introduced new eigenvalues, $\beta(s)\lambda$ and $\overline{\beta}(s)\overline{\lambda}(s) \in \mathbf{C} - (S^1 - \mathbf{R})$ for the matrix $A(s)$, so that $1/\beta(s)\lambda(s)$ and $1/\overline{\beta}(s)\overline{\lambda}(s)$ are also eigenvalues. The dimension of the generalized eigenspace for λ (and likewise for $\overline{\lambda}$) has been lowered by 2, so that the new eigenvalues must each have multiplicity 1.

(3) Let us now assume that λ is a real multiple eigenvalue other than ± 1; then $1/\lambda$ is also an eigenvalue, with the same multiplicity. Let X be a real eigenvector of A for the eigenvalue λ. We know (Corollary 5.6.7) that $E_\lambda \oplus E_{1/\lambda}$ is a symplectic subspace. There therefore exists, in $E_{1/\lambda}$, a vec-

tor X' such that $\omega(X, X') = 1$. Since $\lambda \in \mathbf{R}$, we may, and do, further assume that X' is real. We choose a (nonconstant) path $\beta : [0, \varepsilon] \to \,]0, +\infty[$ with $\beta(0) = 1$ and define $A(s)$ by setting

$$A(s)(X) = \beta(s)\lambda X, \qquad A(s)(X') = \frac{1}{\beta(s)}A(X')$$

and $A(s) = A$ on the (symplectic) orthogonal complement of the (symplectic) plane generated by X and X'. The matrix $A(s)$ is real, symplectic, and $\beta(s)\lambda$ is one of its eigenvalues, as is, of course, $1/(\beta(s)\lambda)$ (Proposition 5.6.3). Moreover, these two eigenvalues each have multiplicity 1 (for $s \neq 0$) because $\dim_{\mathbf{C}} E_\lambda(A(s)) = \dim_{\mathbf{C}} E_\lambda(A) - 1$, and likewise for $1/\lambda$. Finally, $A(s) \in \mathrm{Sp}(2n)^\star$ (by choosing a suitable β).

(4) We still need to consider the case where -1 is an eigenvalue of A. This eigenvalue has an even multiplicity; in particular, it is a multiple eigenvalue. Recall that $E_{-1}(A)$ is a symplectic subspace, so that it contains two vectors X and Y with $\omega(X, Y) = 1$. We may, and do, assume that X is an eigenvector and that X and Y are real. Let F be the complex subspace generated by them. We now choose a path β in $\mathbf{R}$ with $\beta(0) = 1$ and set

$$A(s)X = \beta(s)A(X), \qquad A(s)Y = \frac{1}{\beta(s)}A(Y)$$

and $A(s) = A$ on F°. The matrix $A(s)$ is again an element of $\mathrm{Sp}(2n)^\star$ and $-\beta(s)$ is one of its eigenvalues (so that $-1/\beta(s)$ is also). Once again, the dimension of the generalized eigenspace has been lowered by 2, and therefore the eigenvalues $-\beta(s)$ and $-1/\beta(s)$ each have multiplicity 1.

It is clear that by repeating the processes described above often enough, we can connect A to a matrix A' whose eigenvalues are distinct, and moreover that we can do this using a path in $\mathrm{Sp}(2n)^\star$. We now only need to connect A' to a matrix with zero or two positive real eigenvalues.

If A' has two eigenvalues λ and μ in $]1, +\infty[$, then we begin by connecting them to reduce to the case of a double eigenvalue μ: we choose a real eigenvector X for λ and an $X' \in E_{1/\lambda}$ such that $\omega(X, X') = 1$. We modify A' on the subspace they generate by setting

$$A'(s)(X) = ((1 - s)\lambda + s\mu)X, \qquad A'(s)(X') = \frac{1}{(1 - s)\lambda + s\mu}X',$$

so that $A'(0) = A'$, and $A'(1)$ no longer has eigenvalues λ and $1/\lambda$ but instead has μ and $1/\mu$ with multiplicity 2. Note that $A'(1)$ is diagonalizable because it admits the same basis of eigenvectors as $A'(0) = A'$.

Let X and Y be two independent eigenvectors of $A'(1)$ for the eigenvalue μ. The generalized eigenspaces E_λ and $E_{1/\lambda}$ are isotropic and their sum is symplectic (by Corollary 5.6.7). There exist vectors X' and Y' in $E_{1/\lambda}$ such that

$$\omega(X, X') = \omega(Y, Y') = 1, \quad \omega(X, Y') = \omega(Y, X') = 0,$$

that is, such that X, X', Y, Y' is a symplectic basis of the complex vector subspace F that these vectors generate. Since these vectors are in generalized eigenspaces corresponding to real eigenvalues, we can choose them to be real. We again choose a path $\beta(s)$ with $\beta(0) = 1$ and $\beta(s) \in \mathbf{C} - \mathbf{R}$ for $s > 0$ and we define $A(s)$ by setting

$$A(s)(X + iY) = \beta(s)\mu(X + iY), \qquad A(s)(X - iY) = \overline{\beta}(s)\mu(X - iY),$$

$$A(s)(X' + iY') = \frac{1}{\overline{\beta}(s)}A(X' + iY'), \quad A(s)(X' - iY') = \frac{1}{\beta(s)}A(X' - iY'),$$

and $A(s) = A$ on F° (we have written $A'(1) = A$ to simplify). Once more, the matrix $A(s)$ is real, symplectic, and in $\mathrm{Sp}(2n)^\star$ for a suitable β. It has eigenvalues $\beta(s)\mu$, $\overline{\beta}(s)\mu$, and therefore also their inverses. As before, these eigenvalues each have multiplicity 1 because

$$\dim_{\mathbf{C}} E_\mu(A(s)) = \dim_{\mathbf{C}} E_\mu(A) - 2$$

(and likewise for $1/\mu$).

This process allows us to remove all quadruples of eigenvalues of the form

$$\{\lambda, \mu, 1/\lambda, 1/\mu\} \subset \mathbf{R}_+ - \{1\}.$$

The matrix A' is left with at most two positive real eigenvalues, and in fact, none if $\det(A - \mathrm{Id}) > 0$ (this sign is the same as that of $\det(A' - \mathrm{Id})$) and exactly two if $\det(A - \mathrm{Id}) < 0$. □

Chapter 8
Linearization and Transversality

In this chapter, we show that the spaces of solutions of the Floer equation
possess a regularity property. More precisely, if H is a Hamiltonian on W,
and if x and y are two periodic orbits of H (of period 1), then for every almost
complex structure J, we can consider the space $\mathcal{M}(x, y)$ of the solutions of the
Floer equation connecting the orbit x to the orbit y. We show that by taking
a perturbation of H, if necessary (without modifying it close to x and y, so
that these remain periodic orbits), we may assume that the space $\mathcal{M}(x, y)$
is a manifold of dimension $\mu(x) - \mu(y)$. The strategy consists in describing
the space $\mathcal{M}(x, y)$ as the set of zeros of a section of a vector bundle on
a(n infinite-dimensional) Banach manifold $\mathcal{P}(x, y)$. We will use the infinite-
dimensional analogue of Sard's theorem (the Sard–Smale theorem, here 8.5.7)
to show that, after taking a perturbation of H, the space $\mathcal{M}(x, y)$ is the
inverse image of a regular value of a certain map. In this setting, applying
Sard's theorem requires the assumption that the tangent maps are Fredholm
operators. We will prove this and compute the index of these operators, which
will be $\mu(x) - \mu(y)$—the dimension of the space $\mathcal{M}(x, y)$.

8.1 The Results

We use the Floer map

$$\mathcal{F} : \mathcal{C}^\infty(\mathbf{R} \times S^1; W) \longrightarrow \mathcal{C}^\infty(\mathbf{R} \times S^1; TW)$$

$$u \longmapsto \frac{\partial u}{\partial s} + J\frac{\partial u}{\partial t} + \operatorname{grad}_u(H_t),$$

or, more exactly, a $W^{1,p}$ version of this map (whose details we will give in
Section 8.2.d). The space of solutions $E = \mathcal{C}^\infty(\mathbf{R} \times S^1; TW)$ is the total

M. Audin, M. Damian, *Morse Theory and Floer Homology*,
Universitext, DOI 10.1007/978-1-4471-5496-9_8,
© Springer-Verlag London 2014

space of a vector bundle $E \to \mathcal{C}^\infty(\mathbf{R} \times S^1; W)$ whose fiber E_u at u is the space of vector fields tangent to W along u. By abuse of notation, we will write $\mathcal{F}(u) = 0$ to say that $\mathcal{F}(u)$ is in the zero section of E. We can also use embeddings

$$W \subset \mathbf{R}^m \quad \text{and} \quad TW \subset W \times \mathbf{R}^m$$

(and avoid the abuse of notation).

Note that if $\mathcal{F}$ were transversal to the zero section of E, then the space of solutions of the Floer equation would be a manifold. This transversality in a solution u in the inverse image of the zero section is equivalent to the surjectivity of the projection from $\operatorname{Im}(d\mathcal{F})_u$ onto the fiber E_u. Again, by abuse of notation we will use the notation $(d\mathcal{F})_u$ to denote the composition $\operatorname{pr}_{E_u} \circ (d\mathcal{F})_u$ with the projection. The other option is to view $\mathcal{F}$ as having values in $\mathcal{C}^\infty(\mathbf{R} \times S^1; \mathbf{R}^m)$ (see Section 8.4).

The Floer equation involves an almost complex structure J and a Hamiltonian H. Our aim is to take a perturbation of H (with fixed J) for which this transversality property holds. We will call a pair (H, J) *regular* if it satisfies this property and we let $(\mathcal{H} \times \mathcal{J})_{\mathrm{reg}}$ denote the set of all regular pairs. In order to make (H, J) regular, we define a Banach space $\mathcal{C}_\varepsilon^\infty(H)$ of perturbations of H that have the same periodic orbits as H (Section 8.3). We will then give the proof in two steps:

- We will first prove that the space $\mathcal{Z}(x, y, J)$ of solutions going from x to y for all perturbations of the Hamiltonian is a(n infinite-dimensional) Banach manifold.
- We will then prove that the Sard–Smale theorem can be applied to the projection

$$\pi : \mathcal{Z}(x, y, J) \longrightarrow \mathcal{C}_\varepsilon^\infty(H),$$

allowing us to conclude the proof because, by definition,

$$\mathcal{M}(x, y, J, H) = \pi^{-1}(H).$$

In these two steps, the Fredholm property of the linearization $(d\mathcal{F})_u$ is crucial. To obtain this property, we must replace the source and target spaces of the map $\mathcal{F}$ by larger Banach manifolds modeled on $W^{1,p}$ and L^p Sobolev spaces, respectively. In this setting, we will have

$$(d\mathcal{F})_u : W^{1,p}(u^\star TW) \longrightarrow L^p(u^\star TW)$$

(the space of $W^{1,p}$, or L^p, respectively, vector fields tangent to W along u, defined using the embedding $TW \subset W \times \mathbf{R}^m$; see Section 8.2.c)... where, as specified above, $(d\mathcal{F})_u$ denotes the composition with the projection onto the fiber E_u of the bundle E, which we will make precise in Section 8.2.

The results are as follows.

Theorem 8.1.1. *Let H_0 be a fixed nondegenerate Hamiltonian. There exist a neighborhood of 0 in $\mathcal{C}_\varepsilon^\infty(H_0)$ and a countable intersection of dense open subsets $\mathcal{H}_{\mathrm{reg}}$ in this neighborhood such that if $h \in \mathcal{H}_{\mathrm{reg}}$, then $H = H_0 + h$ is nondegenerate and the map $(d\mathcal{F})_u$ is surjective for every $u \in \mathcal{M}(H_0 + h, J)$.*

The notion of nondegeneracy used here is the one defined in Section 5.4 (Definition 5.4.4). From this result, we will deduce the one that is the purpose of this chapter, which is the following.

Theorem 8.1.2. *For every $h \in \mathcal{H}_{\mathrm{reg}}$ and for all contractible orbits x and y of period 1 of H_0, $\mathcal{M}(x, y, H_0 + h)$ is a manifold of dimension $\mu(x) - \mu(y)$.*

Proposition 8.1.3. *Let*

$$\mathcal{Z}(x, y, J) = \{(u, H = H_0 + h) \mid h \in \mathcal{C}_\varepsilon^\infty(H_0) \text{ and } u \in \mathcal{M}(x, y, J, H)\}.$$

For $x \neq y$, $\mathcal{Z}(x, y, J)$ is a (Banach) manifold.

This will be a consequence, *via* the implicit function theorem, of the following result known as the transversality property.

Proposition 8.1.4. *If $(u, H) \in \mathcal{Z}(x, y)$, then*

$$\Gamma : W^{1,p}(\mathbf{R} \times S^1; \mathbf{R}^{2n}) \times \mathcal{C}_\varepsilon^\infty(H_0) \longrightarrow L^p(\mathbf{R} \times S^1; \mathbf{R}^{2n})$$
$$(Y, h) \longmapsto (d\mathcal{F}^H)_u(Y) + \mathrm{grad}_u\, h$$

(where $H = H_0 + h$ and $\mathcal{F}^H$ is the corresponding Floer operator) is surjective and admits a continuous right inverse.

We will give the details of the definition of Γ, and in particular the fact that it is defined on the spaces we are considering, in Section 8.5.a. To conclude the proof of Theorems 8.1.1 and 8.1.2, we still need to prove the following result.

Theorem 8.1.5. *For every nondegenerate Hamiltonian H, every almost complex structure J calibrated by ω and every $u \in \mathcal{M}(x, y, J, H)$, $(d\mathcal{F})_u$ is a Fredholm operator of index $\mu(x) - \mu(y)$.*

Recall that a (continuous) linear operator $L : E \to F$ from a Banach space E to a Banach space F is a *Fredholm operator* if its image is closed and its kernel and cokernel are finite-dimensional. *The index* of a Fredholm operator is the difference

$$\operatorname{Ind} L = \dim \operatorname{Ker} L - \dim \operatorname{Coker} L.$$

A differentiable map from one Banach space into another is a *Fredholm map* if at every point its differential is a Fredholm operator. The useful properties of Fredholm operators are gathered in Appendix C.2.

This chapter is organized as follows: to begin, we describe the spaces of trajectories that interest us, using the Sobolev $(1, p)$ norms (in Section 8.2). We then define the Banach space of perturbations of the Hamiltonian (in Section 8.3), after which we arrive at the proofs themselves:

- In Section 8.4, we compute the differential of the Floer map.
- In Section 8.5, we prove the transversality property (that is, Propositions 8.1.3 and 8.1.4) modulo a few properties of the solutions of the Floer equation—using the Fredholm property (here Theorem 8.1.5) of the Floer map...
- ... which we prove in Section 8.7.
- Prior to that, in Section 8.6, we establish the properties of the solutions of the Floer equation ("injectivity", continuation principle) that we have used.
- The computation of the index is the object of Section 8.8.
- In Section 8.9, we prove an essential property of (exponential) decay at infinity of the solutions of the Floer equation.

We could just as well have adopted the section order 8.4, 8.7, 8.8, 8.9, 8.6, 8.5...

The following diagram should help the readers find their way in the labyrinth of statements in this chapter.

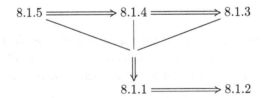

8.2 The Banach Manifold $\mathcal{P}^{1,p}(x,y)$

8.2.a The Sobolev Spaces We Use

We need to work in Banach spaces, which the spaces of $\mathcal{C}^\infty$ maps are not. Just as we considered loops of class $W^{1,p}$ in W in Section 6.8, we will now consider an analogous structure on the space of u's. This is a bit more complicated, for two reasons:

- First, because the u's are defined on a space of dimension 2, the space $\mathbf{R} \times S^1$ of (s,t)'s
- Second, because the variable s varies in the noncompact space $\mathbf{R}$.

The functional spaces that we use are completions of the spaces of $\mathcal{C}^\infty$ sections (with sufficient decay at infinity), for the "Sobolev norms"

$$\|Y\|_{L^p} = \left(\int_{-\infty}^{+\infty} \int_0^1 \|Y(s,t)\|^p \, ds \, dt \right)^{1/p}$$

and

$$\|Y\|_{W^{1,p}} = \left(\int_{-\infty}^{+\infty} \int_0^1 \|Y(s,t)\|^p + \left\| \frac{\partial Y}{\partial s}(s,t) \right\|^p + \left\| \frac{\partial Y}{\partial t}(s,t) \right\|^p ds \, dt \right)^{1/p}$$

for $p \in \,]1,+\infty[$, on the Sobolev spaces (which, by definition, are Banach spaces)

$$L^p(\mathbf{R} \times S^1; \mathbf{R}^{2n}) \quad \text{and} \quad W^{1,p}(\mathbf{R} \times S^1; \mathbf{R}^{2n}),$$

respectively.

Remark 8.2.1. The Sobolev spaces $W^{1,p}$ can also be defined as distribution spaces. This is the best point of view, because then an element of $W^{1,p}$ is not an equivalent class of Cauchy sequences of $\mathcal{C}^\infty$ functions but a distribution, so that as such it has a derivative etc. See Appendix C.4.

Let us right away point out a difficulty. In dimension 1, that is, for a bounded interval I in $\mathbf{R}$, $W^{1,p}(I)$ is contained in the space of continuous functions on $\overline{I}$, for all $p \geq 1$. This is no longer true in dimension at least 2 (and unfortunately, our source space $\mathbf{R} \times S^1$ has dimension 2). For bounded U (with sufficiently regular boundary) in $\mathbf{R}^m$, we only have

$$W^{1,p}(U) \subset C^0(\overline{U})$$

for $p > m$ (see Appendix C.4). One of the difficulties we come across comes from the fact that the elements of $W^{1,2}(\mathbf{R} \times S^1; \mathbf{R}^{2n})$ are not continuous functions.[1] Despite our desire to stay in this sympathetic Hilbert space, we

---

[1] And we want to work with continuous functions in order to use the regularity and compactness results Proposition 6.5.3 and Theorem 6.5.4.

will need to work with $W^{1,p}$ for $p > 2$ (for detailed explanations of how we use this crucial condition, see Section 12.1.b).

8.2.b The Norms That Will Play a Role

The symplectic manifold W is still embedded in a large $\mathbf{R}^m$. We let $T_W \mathbf{R}^m$ denote the restriction of the tangent bundle $T\mathbf{R}^m$ (we have $T_W \mathbf{R}^m \cong W \times \mathbf{R}^m$) to W. On W, we have the Riemannian metric g defined by ω and J which is

$$g_a(v, w) = \omega_a(v, Jw) \quad \text{for } a \in W, \; v, w \in T_a W.$$

Using a partition of unity, we can extend this metric to $T_W \mathbf{R}^m$, giving

$$\widetilde{g} : W \times \mathbf{R}^m \times \mathbf{R}^m \longrightarrow \mathbf{R}$$

such that for every a in W, $\widetilde{g}(a, \cdot, \cdot)$ is a positive definite symmetric bilinear form. The usual inner product on $\mathbf{R}^m$ is denoted by $\langle , \rangle$ (or sometimes simply by $\cdot$).

8.2.c The Spaces of Trajectories

As above, we let $\|\cdot\|_{W^{1,p}}$ or $\|\cdot\|_{L^p}$ denote the Sobolev norms on $W^{1,p}(\mathbf{R} \times S^1; \mathbf{R}^m)$ and $W^{1,p}(\mathbf{R} \times S^1; \mathbf{R}^{2n})$, or $L^p(\mathbf{R} \times S^1; \mathbf{R}^m)$ and $L^p(\mathbf{R} \times S^1; \mathbf{R}^{2n})$ respectively. Note that the norm on the spaces $\mathbf{R}^N$ ($\mathbf{R}^m$ or $\mathbf{R}^{2n}$) that occurs in the definitions of $\|\cdot\|_{W^{1,p}}$ and $\|\cdot\|_{L^p}$ is the Euclidean norm, not the one defined by $\widetilde{g}$.

Finally, for linear operators between Banach spaces, when this is needed for the sake of clarity, we will let $\|\cdot\|^{\mathrm{op}}$ denote the operator norm:

$$\|A\|^{\mathrm{op}} = \sup_{\|x\|=1} \|Ax\|.$$

If x and y are contractible loops in W, which are critical points of $\mathcal{A}_H$, then $\mathcal{C}^\infty_\searrow(x, y)$ denotes the set of $\mathcal{C}^\infty$ maps

$$u : \mathbf{R} \times S^1 \longrightarrow W$$

such that

$$\lim_{s \to -\infty} u(s, t) = x(t), \quad \lim_{s \to +\infty} u(s, t) = y(t),$$

$$\left| \frac{\partial u}{\partial s}(s, t) \right| \leq K e^{-\delta|s|} \quad \text{and} \quad \left| \frac{\partial u}{\partial t}(s, t) - X_H(u) \right| \leq K e^{-\delta|s|},$$

for positive constants K and δ (that depend on u).

Definition 8.2.2. For $p > 2$, $\mathcal{P}^{1,p}(x,y)$ (or $\mathcal{P}(x,y)$ with the exponents being implied) denotes the space of maps of the form

$$(s,t) \longmapsto \exp_{w(s,t)} Y(s,t),$$

where $Y \in W^{1,p}(w^\star TW)$, $w \in \mathcal{C}^{\infty}_{\searrow}(x,y)$.

Before going into the definition of the spaces $W^{1,p}(w^\star TW)$, let us note the following result.

Proposition 8.2.3. If x and y are contractible loops and nondegenerate critical points of the action functional $\mathcal{A}_H$, then we have

$$\mathcal{M}(x,y) \subset \mathcal{C}^{\infty}_{\searrow}(x,y) \subset \mathcal{P}^{1,p}(x,y).$$

Proof. This is a consequence of the exponential decay (that is, of Theorem 8.9.1 and Remark 8.9.2).   □

Definition of $W^{1,p}(w^\star TW)$

If $w : \mathbf{R} \times S^1 \to W$ is a map of class $\mathcal{C}^{\infty}$, then here is the definition of $W^{1,p}(w^\star TW)$ (that we sometimes also denote by $W^{1,p}(\mathbf{R} \times S^1; u^\star TW)$). The symplectic manifold W is embedded in a space $\mathbf{R}^m$. We will say that $Y \in W^{1,p}(w^\star TW)$ if Y is a *continuous*[2] map

$$Y : \mathbf{R} \times S^1 \longrightarrow TW$$

such that $Y(s,t) \in T_{w(s,t)}W$ for every (s,t) and the composition

$$\mathbf{R} \times S^1 \xrightarrow{Y} TW \subset T\mathbf{R}^m = \mathbf{R}^m \times \mathbf{R}^m \xrightarrow{\mathrm{pr}_2} \mathbf{R}^m$$

is in $W^{1,p}(\mathbf{R} \times S^1; \mathbf{R}^m)$.

We can also define this space using a trivialization[3] of $w^\star TW$ rather than an embedding of W in $\mathbf{R}^m$. Consider the map $\overline{w} : \overline{\mathbf{R}} \times S^1 \to W$ defined by

$$\overline{w}(s,t) = \begin{cases} x(t) & s = -\infty \\ w(s,t) & s \in \mathbf{R} \\ y(t) & s = +\infty \end{cases}$$

---

[2] We therefore assume that $p > 2$.

[3] We have seen that there is one, because the loops x and y are contractible and our manifold satisfies Assumption 6.2.2.

as well as an orthonormal frame $(Z_i(s,t))_{i=1,\dots,2n}$ along $\overline{w}$. In this frame, Y can be written as

$$Y(s,t) = \sum_{i=1}^{2n} y_i(s,t) Z_i(s,t),$$

where the coordinates $y_i : \mathbf{R} \times S^1 \to \mathbf{R}^{2n}$ are defined by $y_i = \langle Y, Z_i \rangle$. The vector field Y along $\overline{w}$ is in $W^{1,p}(w^\star TW)$ if and only if the vector $(y_1, \dots, y_{2n})$ is in $W^{1,p}(\mathbf{R} \times S^1; \mathbf{R}^{2n})$.

The equivalence of the two definitions is a consequence of the following easy lemma.

Lemma 8.2.4. *Let $f \in W^{1,p}(\mathbf{R} \times S^1; \mathbf{R})$ and let $g \in \mathcal{C}^\infty(\mathbf{R} \times S^1; \mathbf{R})$ be such that g and its derivatives $\partial g/\partial s$, $\partial g/\partial t$ are bounded on $\mathbf{R} \times S^1$. Then the product fg is in $W^{1,p}(\mathbf{R} \times S^1; \mathbf{R})$ and satisfies the inequality*

$$\|fg\|_{W^{1,p}} \le \|f\|_{W^{1,p}} \left(\sup_{\mathbf{R} \times S^1} \left(|g|, |\partial g/\partial s|, |\partial g/\partial t| \right) \right).$$

Likewise, if $f \in L^p(\mathbf{R} \times S^1; \mathbf{R})$ and if $g \in \mathcal{C}^0(\mathbf{R} \times S^1; \mathbf{R})$ is a bounded function (and, in particular, if $g \in W^{1,p}(\mathbf{R} \times S^1; \mathbf{R})$), then the product fg is in $L^p(\mathbf{R} \times S^1; \mathbf{R})$ and satisfies the inequality

$$\|fg\|_{L^p} \le \|f\|_{L^p} \sup |g|.$$

Using a simplified notation, the two inequalities could also be written (which we will do) as

$$\|fg\|_{W^{1,p}} \le \|f\|_{W^{1,p}} \|g\|_{\mathcal{C}^1} \quad \text{and} \quad \|fg\|_{L^p} \le \|f\|_{L^p} \|g\|_{\mathcal{C}^0}.$$

Proof of Lemma 8.2.4. It is based on the inequalities

$$\left(\int_{\mathbf{R} \times S^1} |fg|^p \right)^{1/p} \le \left(\int_{\mathbf{R} \times S^1} |f|^p (\sup |g|)^p \right)^{1/p} = \|f\|_{L^p} \sup |g|,$$

and

$$\left(\int_{\mathbf{R} \times S^1} |\partial(fg)/\partial s|^p \right)^{1/p} \le \left(\int_{\mathbf{R} \times S^1} \left(|\partial f/\partial s| |g| + |\partial g/\partial s| |f| \right)^p \right)^{1/p}$$
$$\le \sup(|g|, |\partial g/\partial s|) \, \| |\partial f/\partial s| + |f| \|_{L^p}$$
$$\le \sup(|g|, |\partial g/\partial s|) \left(\| \partial f/\partial s \|_{L^p} + \|f\|_{L^p} \right)$$
$$\le \sup(|g|, |\partial g/\partial s|, |\partial g/\partial t|) \, \|f\|_{W^{1,p}}$$

and likewise for $\partial(fg)/\partial t$. $\square$

8.2.d Structure of a Banach Manifold on $\mathcal{P}(x,y)$

The space $\mathcal{P}^{1,p}(x,y)$ (Definition 8.2.2) is a Banach manifold modeled on $W^{1,p}(\mathbf{R} \times S^1; \mathbf{R}^{2n})$. This Banach property is analogous to that of $\mathcal{L}^{1,p}(W)$ (see Section 6.8). Let us therefore define an atlas in an analogous manner. As above, let $w \in \mathcal{C}^\infty_\curlyvee(x,y)$ and let (Z_i) be an orthonormal frame along w, so that $W^{1,p}(w^\star TW)$ is identified with $W^{1,p}(\mathbf{R} \times S^1; \mathbf{R}^{2n})$. Since we have assumed that $p > 2$, we know that

$$W^{1,p}(\mathbf{R} \times S^1; \mathbf{R}^{2n}) \longhookrightarrow L^\infty(\mathbf{R} \times S^1; \mathbf{R}^{2n})$$

and that this injection is continuous (Theorem C.4.9). Consequently,

$$\forall Y \in W^{1,p}(\mathbf{R} \times S^1; \mathbf{R}^{2n}), \quad \|Y\|_{L^\infty} \le K \|Y\|_{W^{1,p}}.$$

Let ρ_{inj} be the injectivity radius (see Appendix A.5, if necessary) of the metric defined on W. Let us fix an $r_0 < \rho_{\mathrm{inj}}$. Let

$$\Phi_w : \left\{ Y \in W^{1,p}(w^\star TW) \mid \|Y\|_{W^{1,p}} \le \frac{r_0}{K} \right\} \longrightarrow \mathcal{P}(x,y)$$
$$(w, Y) \longmapsto \exp_w(Y).$$

This is a bijection on its image and, as in Section 6.8, that is, as in [68], the Φ_w (for $w \in \mathcal{C}^\infty_\curlyvee(x,y)$) form an atlas for $\mathcal{P}^{1,p}(x,y)$.

Let us include the almost complex structure J and the Hamiltonian H that define the Floer equation in question in the notation by writing:

- $\mathcal{M}(J,H)$ for the space of contractible solutions of finite energy
- $\mathcal{M}(x,y,J,H)$ for those connecting x to y—be careful, x and y are periodic trajectories of $X_t = X_{H_t}$ and, in this notation, depend on the Hamiltonian H.

The Floer Map

We now want to define the "Floer map"

$$\mathcal{F} : \mathcal{P}^{1,p}(x,y) \longrightarrow \mathcal{L}^p(x,y)$$

by setting

$$\mathcal{F}(u) = \frac{\partial u}{\partial s} + J(u)\frac{\partial u}{\partial t} + \mathrm{grad}\, H_t(u).$$

Here, $\mathcal{L}^p(x,y)$ is a fiber bundle on $\mathcal{P}^{1,p}(x,y)$ whose fiber at u is the space $L^p(u^\star TW)$ that can be defined in a manner analogous to $W^{1,p}(u^\star TW)$. By the definition of $\mathcal{P}^{1,p}(x,y)$, its elements u can be written as $u = \exp_w(X)$ for a $w \in \mathcal{C}^\infty(\mathbf{R} \times S^1; W)$ with exponential decay and $X \in W^{1,p}(w^\star TW)$. We therefore need to verify that $\mathcal{F}$ takes on its values in L^p, that is, that

$$\mathcal{F}(\exp_w X) \in L^p(\mathbf{R} \times S^1; \mathbf{R}^m),$$

which we will do in Section 13.3 (Lemma 13.3.1 and Remark 13.3.2).

8.3 The Space of Perturbations of H

We want to show that, arbitrarily close (in the sense of the $\mathcal{C}^\infty$ topology) to a fixed Hamiltonian H, there exists a Hamiltonian with exactly the same periodic orbits and for which the $\mathcal{M}(x, y)$ are manifolds of the expected dimension.

We will now construct the space $\mathcal{C}_\varepsilon^\infty(H)$ of perturbations of H announced at the beginning of this chapter.

Let us fix a sequence $\varepsilon = (\varepsilon_n)$ of positive real numbers (that we will make explicit later on) and let

$$\|h\|_\varepsilon = \sum_{k \geq 0} \varepsilon_k \sup_{(x,t) \in W \times S^1} \left| d^k h(x, t) \right|.$$

Some additional details are necessary here. First of all, we use $\left| d^k h(x, t) \right|$ to denote the maximum of the $|d^\alpha h(x, t)|$ over all multi-indices α of length k. Next, to compute the higher-order derivatives, we need charts. We therefore fix, once and for all, a finite number of diffeomorphisms

$$\Psi_i : B_i \longrightarrow \overline{B}(0, 1),$$

with $\bigcup_i \overset{\circ}{B}_i = W \times S^1$. The sup in the formula is then

$$\sup_{(x,t) \in W \times S^1} \left| d^k h(x, t) \right| = \sup_{i, z \in B(0,1)} \left| d^k (h \circ \Psi_i^{-1})(z) \right|.$$

The space $\mathcal{C}_\varepsilon^\infty$ of $\mathcal{C}^\infty$ functions on $W \times S^1$ with finite norm $\|\cdot\|_\varepsilon$ is clearly a normed and complete vector space.

We still need to verify that this space is dense in the space of $\mathcal{C}^\infty$ functions when the sequence ε is well chosen. This is what the following proposition asserts.

Proposition 8.3.1. *We can choose the sequence ε in such a manner that the space of $\mathcal{C}_\varepsilon^\infty$ functions is dense in $\mathcal{C}^\infty(W \times S^1)$ for the $\mathcal{C}^1$ topology.*

Proof. We will use the following result.

Lemma 8.3.2. *The space* $\mathcal{C}^\infty(W \times S^1)$, *endowed with the* $\mathcal{C}^1$ *topology, is separable.*

Proof. By considering an embedding of $W \times S^1$ in a cube $[-M, M]^m \subset \mathbf{R}^m$, we see that it suffices to prove the result for $\mathcal{C}^\infty([-M, M]^m)$. The Stone–Weierstrass theorem guarantees that this space is separable for the $\mathcal{C}^0$ topology since it asserts that its countable subspace $\mathbf{Q}[X_1, \ldots, X_m]$ is dense.

To prove the analogous assertion for the $\mathcal{C}^1$ topology, we fix a function $\chi \in \mathcal{C}^\infty([-M, M]^m)$ of integral 1 and with support in $B(0, 1)$. We consider the sequence (χ_k) defined by $\chi_k(x) = k^m \chi(kx)$. We can easily prove that for a function $f \in \mathcal{C}^\infty(\mathbf{R}^m)$, the sequence of convolutions

$$ f \star \chi_k(x) = \int_{\mathbf{R}^m} f(x - y) \cdot \chi_k(y) \, dy $$

tends to f (in the $\mathcal{C}^0_{\mathrm{loc}}$ sense) (see for example [13, Section 3.4]). Next, for each fixed k, if g_ℓ tends to f for $\ell \to +\infty$ and for the $\mathcal{C}^\infty_{\mathrm{loc}}$ topology, then we have

$$ \lim_{\ell \to +\infty} g_\ell \star \chi_k = f \star \chi_k $$

for the $\mathcal{C}^1_{\mathrm{loc}}$ topology. Indeed, note that for every compact K, we have

$$ \sup_K \left| \frac{\partial}{\partial x_i}(g_\ell - f) \star \chi_k \right| = \sup_K \left| (g_\ell - f) \star \frac{\partial \chi_k}{\partial x_i} \right| $$
$$ \leq \sup_K |g_\ell - f| \cdot \int_{\mathbf{R}^m} \left| \frac{\partial \chi_k}{\partial x_i} \right| dx, $$

so that the set

$$ \{ P \star \chi_k \mid P \in \mathbf{Q}[X_1, \ldots, X_m], \ k \in \mathbf{N} \} $$

is a countable subset of $\mathcal{C}^\infty([-M, M]^m)$ that is dense for the $\mathcal{C}^1$ topology. $\square$

The proof of Proposition 8.3.1 can now be concluded. Let (f_n) be a sequence in $\mathcal{C}^\infty(W \times S^1)$ that is dense for the $\mathcal{C}^1$ topology (the lemma asserts that one exists). Let

$$ \varepsilon_n = 1/(2^n \max_{k \leq n} \|f_k\|_{\mathcal{C}^n(W \times S^1)}), $$

with the same convention as before using the diffeomorphisms Ψ_i to compute the $\mathcal{C}^n$ norm of f_k.

For a fixed k and $n \geq k$, we therefore have

$$\varepsilon_n \sup_{(x,t) \in W \times S^1} |d^n f_k(x,t)| \leq \frac{1}{2^n},$$

so that with this choice of the sequence ε, $f_k \in \mathcal{C}_\varepsilon^\infty$ for every k, giving the desired result. $\qquad\square$

Remark 8.3.3. The same proof would give the density of $\mathcal{C}_\varepsilon^\infty$ for the $\mathcal{C}^\infty$ topology, but we will only be using the $\mathcal{C}^1$ density.

We will also need a version of Proposition 8.3.1 with compact support. The following is a precise statement of this.

Proposition 8.3.4. *There exists a sequence ε for which the following property is true. Let $(x_0, t_0) \in W \times S^1$ and let U be a neighborhood of (x_0, t_0). There exists a neighborhood $V \subset U$ of (x_0, t_0) such that every $h \in \mathcal{C}^\infty(W \times S^1)$ with support in V can be approximated, for the $\mathcal{C}^1$ topology, by functions in $\mathcal{C}_\varepsilon^\infty$ with support in U.*

Proof. We begin by fixing a function β of class $\mathcal{C}^\infty$ on $\mathbf{R}^n$, with support in $B(0,1)$ and with value 1 on $B(0,1/2)$. For $z_0 \in B(0,1)$ and for $\sigma \in \,]0,1[$, we set

$$\beta_{z_0,\sigma}(z) = \beta\left(\frac{z - z_0}{\sigma}\right).$$

Let $(x_0, t_0) \in W \times S^1$ and let B_i be the open set of one of the charts we fixed, containing (x_0, t_0) in its interior. Let $z_0 = \Psi_i(x_0, t_0)$. We choose a $\sigma > 0$ such that

$$\Psi_i^{-1}(B(z_0, \sigma)) \subset \overset{\circ}{B_i} \cap U$$

and set $V = \Psi_i^{-1}(B(z_0, \sigma/2))$.

Let $h \in \mathcal{C}^\infty(W \times S^1)$ with support in V and let us show that it satisfies the conclusion of the proposition. By Proposition 8.3.1, we know that for some sequence ε and for every $n \in \mathbf{N}$, there exists an $h_n \in \mathcal{C}^\infty(W \times S^1)$, such that

$$\lim_{n \to +\infty} h_n = h \quad \text{for the } \mathcal{C}^1 \text{ topology.}$$

Let $g_n = (\beta_{z_0,\sigma} \circ \Psi_i) \cdot h_n$ on $\Psi_i^{-1}(B(z_0, \sigma))$ and extend it by 0 elsewhere. It is clear that g_n has support in U and that the sequence g_n tends to $(\beta_{z_0,\sigma} \circ \Psi_i) \cdot h = h$ in the $\mathcal{C}^1$ topology.

It therefore suffices to modify the sequence ε so that g_n is in $\mathcal{C}_\varepsilon^\infty$ (for this new sequence). Let us therefore study the sup of $d^k g_n$. We begin with the chart Ψ_i (writing h_n for $h_n \circ \Psi_i^{-1}$). We have

$$
\begin{aligned}
\sup_{(x,t) \in B_i} \left| d^k g_n \right| &= \sup_{z \in B(0,1)} \left| d^k (\beta_{z_0,\sigma} \cdot h_n)(z) \right| \\
&\leq 2^k \sum_{\ell=0}^{k} \sup_{B(0,1)} \left| d^{k-\ell} \beta_{z_0,\sigma} \right| \sup_{B(0,1)} \left| d^\ell h_n \right| \\
&\leq 2^k \sum_{\ell=0}^{k} \frac{1}{\sigma^{k-\ell}} \sup_{B(0,1)} \left| d^{k-\ell} \beta \right| \sup_{B(0,1)} \left| d^\ell h_n \right| \\
&\leq \frac{2^k}{\sigma^k} \|\beta\|_{\mathcal{C}^k(B(0,1))} \sum_{\ell=0}^{k} \sup_{B(0,1)} \left| d^\ell h_n \right|.
\end{aligned}
$$

We therefore change the sequence ε into the sequence ε' defined by

$$
\varepsilon'_k = \frac{1}{k^k} \cdot \frac{\min_{\ell=0,\dots,k} \varepsilon_\ell}{\|\beta\|_{\mathcal{C}^k(B(0,1))}}
$$

(with the convention that $0^0 = 1$). We then have

$$
\begin{aligned}
\varepsilon'_k \sup_{(x,t) \in B_i} \left| d^k g_n \right| &\leq \left(\frac{2}{\sigma k} \right)^k \sum_{\ell=0}^{k} \varepsilon_\ell \sup_{B(0,1)} \left| d^\ell h_n \right| \\
&\leq \left(\frac{2}{\sigma k} \right)^k \|h_n\|_\varepsilon .
\end{aligned}
$$

The sequence whose general term is the right-hand side (obviously) converges. To prove that $\|g_n\|_{\varepsilon'} < +\infty$, we need to establish an estimate of this type in all charts whose open sets B_i meet U. This can be done in an analogous manner, by replacing

$$
\|\beta\|_{\mathcal{C}^k(B(0,1))} \quad \text{by} \quad \min_j \left\| \beta \circ \Psi_i \circ \Psi_j^{-1} \right\|_{\mathcal{C}^k(\Psi_j(B_i \cap B_j))}
$$

in the definition of ε'. $\qquad \square$

Let us fix a (time-dependent) Hamiltonian H_0 whose periodic orbits we assume to be nondegenerate. The space of "perturbations" of H_0 that we are going to use is the space $\mathcal{C}_\varepsilon^\infty(H_0)$ of maps $h : W \times S^1 \to \mathbf{R}$ such that $\|h\|_\varepsilon < +\infty$ and

$$
h(x,t) = 0 \quad \text{in a neighborhood of the 1-periodic orbits of } H_0.
$$

Since the support of h is "far" from the periodic solutions of H_0, at least when $\|h\|_\varepsilon$ is sufficiently small, the periodic solutions of $H_0 + h$ are exactly the periodic solutions of H_0 itself—and they are nondegenerate.

8.4 Linearization of the Floer Equation: Computation of the Differential of $\mathcal{F}$

In order to spare beginners the painful differentiations of vector fields and the use of the Levi-Cività connection, we will use an embedding of the manifold W in $\mathbf{R}^m$ (m is very large, in any case larger than the dimension $2n$ of the manifold). With

$$TW \subset \mathbf{R}^m \times \mathbf{R}^m \xrightarrow{\text{pr}_2} \mathbf{R}^m,$$

the vectors Z_i, as well as all vectors tangent to W along u and even along a neighborhood B of u, can be viewed as vectors in $\mathbf{R}^m$. In the same manner, $\mathcal{F}$ is considered to have values in a vector space of maps with values in $\mathbf{R}^m$, namely $\mathcal{C}^\infty(\mathbf{R} \times S^1; \mathbf{R}^m)$ or $L^p(\mathbf{R} \times S^1; \mathbf{R}^m)$. To compute the differential of $\mathcal{F}$, we therefore fix a solution

$$u \in \mathcal{M}(x,y) \subset \mathcal{C}^\infty_{\text{loc}}(\mathbf{R} \times S^1; W)$$

of the Floer equation. The cylinder

$$u : \mathbf{R} \times S^1 \longrightarrow W$$

can be completed into a sphere: the loops x and y are contractible, we extend them to disks, giving a map

$$\tilde{u} : S^2 \longrightarrow W$$

as in Figure 8.1.

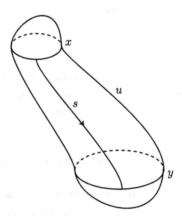

Fig. 8.1

As in Chapter 7, the fiber bundle $\widetilde{u}^*TW$ can be trivialized as a symplectic fiber bundle (owing to Assumption 6.2.2). We therefore choose a trivialization, that is, a basis $(Z_1, \ldots, Z_{2n}) \in T_{u(s,t)}W$, that depends in a $\mathcal{C}^\infty$ manner on s and t (here we view the cylinder $\mathbf{R} \times S^1$ of the (s,t)'s as a subset of the sphere, as in Figure 8.1). We will require this trivialization to be symplectic and orthonormal, that is, that the basis consisting of the Z_i be a symplectic and orthonormal basis, and that the vectors Z_i have a limit when s tends to $\pm\infty$. We will also need that

$$\lim_{s \to \pm\infty} \frac{\partial Z_i}{\partial s} = 0, \qquad \lim_{s \to \pm\infty} \frac{\partial^2 Z_i}{\partial s^2} = 0, \qquad \lim_{s \to \pm\infty} \frac{\partial^2 Z_i}{\partial s\, \partial t} = 0.$$

There exist such trivializations, as we can convince ourselves using cylinders near the spherical caps in Figure 8.1.

This frame defines a chart (centered at u) of the Banach manifold $\mathcal{P}^{1,p}(x,y)$:

$$i : W^{1,p}(\mathbf{R} \times S^1; \mathbf{R}^{2n}) \longrightarrow \mathcal{P}^{1,p}(x,y)$$

$$(y_1, \ldots, y_{2n}) \longmapsto \exp_u\left(\sum y_i Z_i\right).$$

Note that

$$(di)_0(y_1, \ldots, y_{2n}) = \sum y_i Z_i$$

(because $(d\exp)_0 = \mathrm{Id}$; see Appendix A.5, if necessary).

Let us now consider the following map, which we also call $\mathcal{F}$:

$$\mathcal{F} : \mathcal{P}^{1,p}(x,y) \xrightarrow{\ \mathcal{F}\ } L^p(\mathbf{R} \times S^1; TW) \longrightarrow L^p(\mathbf{R} \times S^1; \mathbf{R}^m)$$

$$u \longmapsto \frac{\partial u}{\partial s} + J(u)\left(\frac{\partial u}{\partial t} - X_t(u)\right)$$

and let us compute its differential at u. Let

$$Y(s,t) = (y_1(s,t), \ldots, y_{2n}(s,t)) \in \mathbf{R}^{2n} \subset \mathbf{R}^m$$

be a vector. We view $Y = \sum y_i Z_i$ as a vector in $\mathbf{R}^m$ tangent to W. Let us write

$$\mathcal{F}(u + Y) = \frac{\partial(u+Y)}{\partial s} + J(u+Y)\frac{\partial(u+Y)}{\partial t} - J(u+Y)X_t(u+Y).$$

The part of this expression that is linear in Y is

$$(d\mathcal{F})_u(Y) = \frac{\partial Y}{\partial s} + (dJ)_u(Y)\frac{\partial u}{\partial t} + J(u)\frac{\partial Y}{\partial t} - (dJ)_u(Y)X_t - J(u)(dX_t)_u(Y).$$

Lemma 8.4.1. *For every map J with values in the endomorphisms of $\mathbf{R}^m$ and all maps Y and v with values in $\mathbf{R}^m$, we have*

$$(dJ)(Y) \cdot v = d(Jv)(Y) - Jdv(Y).$$

Proof. It suffices to differentiate the map $x \mapsto J(x) \cdot v(x)$, which gives

$$J(x+Y) \cdot v(x+Y) = (J(x) + (dJ)_x(Y)) \cdot (v(x) + (dv)_x(Y))$$

to order 1, so that

$$d(J \cdot v)_x(Y) = (dJ)_x(Y) \cdot v(x) + J(x) \cdot (dv)_x(Y). \qquad \square$$

Remark 8.4.2. For every map $u : \mathbf{R} \times S^1 \to W$ of class $\mathcal{C}^\infty$,

$$(d\mathcal{F})_u(Y) = \left(\frac{\partial Y}{\partial s} + J(u)\frac{\partial Y}{\partial t} \right) + \left((dJ)_u(Y)\frac{\partial u}{\partial t} - (dJ)_u(Y)X_t - J(u)(dX_t)_u(Y) \right)$$

is the sum of a differential operator of order 1 and one of order 0. Let us now use the chart defined by the basis $(Z_1, \ldots, Z_{2n})$ and write

$$Y = \sum y_i Z_i.$$

In this chart, we have

$$(d\mathcal{F})_u(Y) = \sum \left(\frac{\partial y_i}{\partial s} Z_i + \frac{\partial y_i}{\partial t} J(u) Z_i \right)$$
$$+ \sum y_i \left(\frac{\partial Z_i}{\partial s} + J(u)\frac{\partial Z_i}{\partial t} + (dJ)_u(Z_i)\frac{\partial u}{\partial t} \right.$$
$$\left. - J(u)(dX_t)_u Z_i - (dJ)_u(Z_i)X_t \right).$$

The terms on the first line are "of order 0", that is, they do not differentiate the y_i. We begin by studying the "order 1" terms, the remaining ones. It is easy to see that they reduce to

$$\sum \left(\frac{\partial y_i}{\partial s} + J_0 \frac{\partial y_i}{\partial t} \right) Z_i,$$

where J_0 is the standard complex structure on $\mathbf{R}^{2n} = \mathbf{C}^n$.

We can also say that the linearized Floer equation is the sum of the Cauchy–Riemann operator and an operator of order 0. Indeed, we have:

- Since we have assumed that the basis $Z_1, \ldots, Z_{2n}$ is symplectic and orthonormal, the term of order 1 is $\overline{\partial}(y_1, \ldots, y_{2n})$, where $\overline{\partial}$ denotes the Cauchy–Riemann operator for the standard complex structure[4] J_0.
- The two other terms do not differentiate the y_i (this is indeed an operator of order 0).

Remark 8.4.3 (Concerning the Notation). As always, to write the differential of a map defined on a manifold, we need a chart of this manifold. Here we have used

$$F_u : W^{1,p}(\mathbf{R} \times S^1; \mathbf{R}^{2n}) \longrightarrow \mathcal{P}^{1,p}(x, y) \xrightarrow{\ \mathcal{F}\ } L^p(\mathbf{R} \times S^1; \mathbf{R}^m),$$

where the first map is the chart (denoted by i on p. 235) centered at u. Of course, $(d\mathcal{F})_u$ denotes that which in coordinates is $(dF_u)_0$. We did not think that using the notation $(dF_u)_0$ would contribute to the clarity of this text, so we did not use it.

The equality in Remark 8.4.2 shows that, in this chart, $(d\mathcal{F})_u$ can be decomposed into

$$(d\mathcal{F})_u(Y) = \overline{\partial} Y + SY,$$

where S is a linear operator of order 0, which can be seen as a smooth map

$$S : \mathbf{R} \times S^1 \longrightarrow \operatorname{End}(\mathbf{R}^n).$$

In the case where u is a solution of the Floer equation, the operator of order 0 has a specific property.

Proposition 8.4.4. *If u is a solution of the Floer equation, then the differential of $\mathcal{F}$ in u is a sum*

$$(d\mathcal{F})_u = \overline{\partial} + S(s, t),$$

where S is a linear operator that tends to a symmetric operator when s tends to $\pm\infty$ and satisfies

$$\lim_{s \to \pm\infty} \frac{\partial S}{\partial s}(s, t) = 0$$

(uniformly in t).

---

[4] Up to a factor 2: the usual $\overline{\partial}$ is

$$\frac{1}{2}\left(\frac{\partial}{\partial s} + J_0 \frac{\partial}{\partial t}\right).$$

Proof. We begin with the expression given in Remark 8.4.2; the operator S is the part of order 0:

$$S(y_1, \ldots, y_{2n}) = \sum y_i \left[\frac{\partial Z_i}{\partial s} + (dJ)_u(Z_i) \left(\frac{\partial u}{\partial t} - X_t(u) \right) \right.$$
$$\left. + J(u) \frac{\partial Z_i}{\partial t} - J(u)(dX_t)_u(Z_i) \right].$$

When s tends to $\pm\infty$

$$\lim \left(\frac{\partial u}{\partial t} - X_t(u) \right) = 0$$

because u is a solution and $\partial u/\partial s$ tends to 0 (when $s \to \pm\infty$) uniformly, as do its derivatives (see Theorem 6.5.6 and Proposition 6.5.15). Then, we have chosen Z_i such that

$$\lim_{s \to \pm\infty} \frac{\partial Z_i}{\partial s} = 0,$$

as well as its derivatives. We get

$$\lim_{s \to \pm\infty} \frac{\partial S}{\partial s} = 0.$$

By the same argument, it suffices to prove the symmetry, for $s \to \pm\infty$, of the operator

$$A(y_1, \ldots, y_{2n}) = \sum y_i \left(J(u) \frac{\partial Z_i}{\partial t} - J(u)(dX_t)_u(Z_i) \right).$$

The jth component of $A(y_1, \ldots, y_{2n})$ is

$$\sum y_i \left\langle J(u) \frac{\partial Z_i}{\partial t} - J(u)(dX_t)_u(Z_i), Z_j \right\rangle;$$

so let us show that

$$\lim_{s \to \pm\infty} \left\langle J(u) \frac{\partial Z_i}{\partial t} - J(u)(dX_t)_u(Z_i), Z_j \right\rangle - \left\langle J(u) \frac{\partial Z_j}{\partial t} - J(u)(dX_t)_u Z_j, Z_i \right\rangle = 0.$$

We have (using that the frame (Z_i) is unitary)

$$0 = \frac{\partial}{\partial t} \langle J(u) Z_i, Z_j \rangle$$
$$= \left\langle (dJ)_u \left(\frac{\partial u}{\partial t} \right) Z_i, Z_j \right\rangle + \left\langle J(u) \frac{\partial Z_i}{\partial t}, Z_j \right\rangle + \left\langle J(u) Z_i, \frac{\partial Z_j}{\partial t} \right\rangle$$
$$= \left\langle (dJ)_u \left(\frac{\partial u}{\partial t} \right) Z_i, Z_j \right\rangle + \left\langle J(u) \frac{\partial Z_i}{\partial t}, Z_j \right\rangle - \left\langle Z_i, J(u) \frac{\partial Z_j}{\partial t} \right\rangle.$$

Therefore it suffices to prove that

$$\lim_{s \to \pm\infty} \Big(-\langle J(u)(dX_t)_u(Z_i), Z_j \rangle + \langle J(u)(dX_t)_u(Z_j), Z_i \rangle$$
$$-\Big\langle (dJ)_u \Big(\frac{\partial u}{\partial t}\Big) Z_i, Z_j \Big\rangle \Big) = 0.$$

Using again the fact that

$$\lim_{s \to \pm\infty} \Big(\frac{\partial u}{\partial t} - X_t(u) \Big) = 0,$$

this is equivalent to

$$\lim_{s \to \pm\infty} \Big(-\langle J(u)(dX_t)_u(Z_i), Z_j \rangle + \langle J(u)(dX_t)_u(Z_j), Z_i \rangle$$
$$- \langle (dJ)_u(X_t)Z_i, Z_j \rangle \Big) = 0.$$

Note that, for a fixed (s,t), this expression only depends on the values of the Z_i's at the points $u(s,t)$. We prove the following lemma.

Lemma 8.4.5. *Let $p \in W$ and let $(Z_i)_{i=1,\dots,2n}$ be a unitary basis of T_pW. Then:*

$$-\langle J(p)(dX_t)_p(Z_i), Z_j \rangle + \langle J(p)(dX_t)_p(Z_j), Z_i \rangle - \langle (dJ)_p(X_t)Z_i, Z_j \rangle = 0.$$

Proof. Extend $(Z_i)_{i=1,\dots,2n}$ to a unitary frame of TW on a chart domain containing p. Using Lemma 8.4.1, the expression above writes

$$-\langle J(dX_t)(Z_i), Z_j\rangle + \langle J(dX_t)(Z_j), Z_i\rangle + \langle J(dZ_i)(X_t), Z_j\rangle - \langle d(JZ_i)(X_t), Z_j\rangle$$
$$= \langle J[X_t, Z_i], Z_j \rangle + \langle J(dX_t)(Z_j), Z_i \rangle - \langle d(JZ_i)(X_t), Z_j \rangle.$$

We now use the relation
$$X_t\langle JZ_i, Z_j \rangle = 0,$$

which writes[5]

$$\langle d(JZ_i)(X_t), Z_j \rangle + \langle JZ_i, (dZ_j)(X_t) \rangle = 0,$$

to transform this expression into

$$\langle J[X_t, Z_i], Z_j \rangle + \langle J(dX_t)(Z_j), Z_i \rangle + \langle JZ_i, (dZ_j)(X_t) \rangle$$
$$= \langle J[X_t, Z_i], Z_j \rangle + \langle J(dX_t)(Z_j) - J(dZ_j)(X_t), Z_i \rangle$$
$$= \langle J[X_t, Z_i], Z_j \rangle - \langle J[X_t, Z_j], Z_i \rangle$$
$$= \omega([X_t, Z_i], Z_j) - \omega([X_t, Z_j], Z_i).$$

---

[5] The derivation along X_t is actually the derivation D_{X_t} given by the Levi-Città connection; see Section A.5.

The symmetry follows from the fact that the form ω is closed,

$$
\begin{aligned}
0 = {}& d\omega(X_t, Z_i, Z_j)\\
= {}& X_t \cdot \omega(Z_i, Z_j) - Z_i \cdot \omega(X_t, Z_j) + Z_j \cdot \omega(X_t, Z_i)\\
& - \omega([X_t, Z_i], Z_j) + \omega([X_t, Z_j], Z_i) - \omega([Z_i, Z_j], X_t)\\
= {}& -X_t \cdot \langle Z_i, JZ_j \rangle + Z_i \cdot (dH_t)(Z_j) - Z_j \cdot (dH_t)(Z_i)\\
& - (dH_t)([Z_i, Z_j]) - \omega([X_t, Z_i], Z_j) + \omega([X_t, Z_j], Z_i)\\
= {}& d(dH_t)(Z_i, Z_j) - \omega([X_t, Z_i], Z_j) + \omega([X_t, Z_j], Z_i)\\
= {}& -\omega([X_t, Z_i], Z_j) + \omega([X_t, Z_j], Z_i) \qquad\qquad \square
\end{aligned}
$$

And this ends the proof of Proposition 8.4.4. $\qquad\qquad\qquad\qquad \square$

Let $Y \mapsto S \cdot Y$ the order zero part of $(d\mathcal{F})_u$, so that S is a map

$$
\mathbf{R} \times S^1 \longrightarrow \mathrm{End}(\mathbf{R}^{2n}).
$$

Denote by $S^\pm$ the symmetric operators defined by $S^\pm = \lim_{s \to \pm\infty} S(s, \cdot)$. Let us prove the following result.

Proposition 8.4.6. *The equation*

$$
\frac{\partial Y}{\partial t} = J_0 S^\pm Y
$$

is the linearization of Hamilton's equation

$$
\dot{z} = X_t(z)
$$

at $x = \lim_{s \to -\infty} u$ *(for* S^-*) or at* $y = \lim_{s \to +\infty} u$ *(for* S^+*), respectively.*

Proof. According to Subsection A.4.c, the linearized equation at x is

$$
\frac{dY}{dt} = (dX_t)_x Y.
$$

Writing $Y = \sum y_i Z_i$, we get

$$
\begin{aligned}
\sum_i \frac{\partial y_i}{\partial t} Z_i &= \sum_i y_i \left(-\frac{\partial Z_i}{\partial t} + (dX_t)(Z_i) \right)\\
&= \sum_i \sum_j y_i \left\langle -\frac{\partial Z_i}{\partial t} + (dX_t)(Z_i), Z_j \right\rangle Z_j\\
&= \sum_i \sum_j y_j \left\langle -\frac{\partial Z_i}{\partial t} + (dX_t)(Z_j), Z_i \right\rangle Z_i,
\end{aligned}
$$

so that

$$\frac{\partial y_i}{\partial t} = \sum_j \left\langle -\frac{\partial Z_j}{\partial t} + (dX_t)(Z_j), Z_i \right\rangle y_j.$$

Therefore, the linearization of Hamilton's equation at x, for $Y = (y_1, \dots, y_{2n})$, is

$$\frac{\partial Y}{\partial t} = B^- \cdot Y, \qquad \text{where } B^- = (b_{ij})$$

is given by

$$b_{ij} = \left\langle -\frac{\partial Z_j}{\partial t} + (dX_t)_x(Z_j), Z_i \right\rangle.$$

Now, the proof of Proposition 8.4.4 shows that, at $s = -\infty$, the zero order part of $(d\mathcal{F})_u$ is given by

$$A\left(\sum y_i Z_i \right) = \sum_i \left(J(x)\frac{\partial Z_i}{\partial t} - J(x)(dX_t)_x(Z_i) \right)$$

$$= \sum_i \sum_j y_i \left\langle J\frac{\partial Z_i}{\partial t} - J(dX_t)(Z_i), Z_j \right\rangle Z_j$$

$$= \sum_i \sum_j y_j \left\langle J\frac{\partial Z_j}{\partial t} - J(dX_t)(Z_j), Z_i \right\rangle Z_i$$

$$= \sum_i \sum_j \left\langle -\frac{\partial Z_j}{\partial t} + (dX_t)(Z_j), JZ_i \right\rangle y_j Z_i.$$

We deduce that $S^- = (s_{ij})$, where

$$s_{ij} = \left\langle -\frac{\partial Z_j}{\partial t} + (dX_t)_x(Z_j), J(x)Z_i \right\rangle.$$

Now $JZ_i = Z_{i+n}$ for $i \le n$ and $JZ_i = -Z_{i-n}$ for $i \ge n+1$, so that

$$s_{ij} = b_{i+n,j} \quad \text{for } i \le n \qquad \text{and} \qquad s_{ij} = -b_{i-n,j} \quad \text{for } i \ge n+1.$$

This is equivalent to

$$S^- = -J_0 B^-,$$

and this proves our assertion. $\qquad \square$

Remark 8.4.7. If u is a solution of the Floer equation, then we have already said (Remark 6.5.12) that the product $u \cdot s$ defined by

$$(u \cdot s)(\sigma, t) = u(\sigma + s, t)$$

is also a solution. Consequently, $\mathcal{F}(u \cdot s) = 0$ for every s and therefore

$$0 = \frac{d}{ds}\mathcal{F}(u \cdot s) = (d\mathcal{F})_u\left(\frac{\partial u}{\partial s}\right),$$

so that $\partial u/\partial s$ is a solution of the linearized equation. In particular, along a (nonconstant) solution connecting x to y, the kernel of $(d\mathcal{F})_u$ has dimension greater than or equal to 1.

8.5 The Transversality

We now prove the transversality property (Proposition 8.1.4), using the Fredholm property for $(d\mathcal{F})_u$, that is, modulo the first part of Theorem 8.1.5. The almost complex structure J is fixed, as is the nondegenerate Hamiltonian H_0. We fix an $h_0 \in \mathcal{C}^\infty_\varepsilon(H_0)$ and a solution u of the Floer equation for J and $H = H_0 + h_0$:

$$\mathcal{F}(u) = \frac{\partial u}{\partial s} + J\frac{\partial u}{\partial t} + \mathrm{grad}_u(H) = 0.$$

The differential of $\mathcal{F}$ is computed, as we have just explained, in a fixed unitary trivialization along u; we write it as

$$(d\mathcal{F})_u(Y) = \frac{\partial Y}{\partial s} + J_0\frac{\partial Y}{\partial t} + S \cdot Y.$$

8.5.a Definition of Γ

We fix two distinct critical points x and $y \in \mathrm{Crit}\,\mathcal{A}_{H_0}$. To show that $\mathcal{Z}(x, y, J)$ is a manifold, we describe it as the set of zeros of a section of a fiber bundle. On the space $\mathcal{P}(x, y) \times \mathcal{C}^\infty_\varepsilon(W, H_0)$, we define the vector bundle

$$\mathcal{E} = \{(u, h, Y) \mid Y \in L^p(u^*TW)\}.$$

We can view $\mathcal{E}$ as a fiber bundle

$$\mathcal{E} \longrightarrow \mathcal{P}(x, y) \times \mathcal{C}^\infty_\varepsilon(H_0)$$

(through $(u, h, Y) \mapsto (u, h)$). The map

$$\mathcal{P}(x, y) \times \mathcal{C}^\infty_\varepsilon(H_0) \xrightarrow{\sigma} \mathcal{E}$$

$$(u, h) \longmapsto \frac{\partial u}{\partial s} + J(u)\frac{\partial u}{\partial t} + \mathrm{grad}_u(H_0 + h)$$

is a section of this bundle. The fact that the section σ takes on its values in $\mathcal{E}$, that is, the fact that

$$\frac{\partial u}{\partial s} + J\frac{\partial u}{\partial t} + \operatorname{grad}_u(H)$$

is in $L^p(\mathbf{R} \times S^1; u^\star TW)$, as we have already noted in Section 8.2.d, is proved in Chapter 13 (more precisely, in Lemma 13.3.1 and Remark 13.3.2).

The zeros of σ are exactly the points of $\mathcal{Z}(x, y, J)$ (more exactly, of its $W^{1,p}$ version); note that the data (H_0, J) are now $\mathcal{C}^\infty$ while (u, Y) are weak solutions. To conclude, it suffices to show that σ is transversal to the zero section, that is, that the linearized map $(d\sigma)_{(u,h)}$ composed with the projection onto the fiber is surjective when $\sigma(u, h) = 0$.

Note that σ is linear in h and that its differential is

$$(d\sigma)_{(u,h)}(Y, \eta) = (d\mathcal{F})_u(Y) + \operatorname{grad}_u(\eta).$$

The map

$$\Gamma : W^{1,p}(\mathbf{R} \times S^1; \mathbf{R}^{2n}) \times \mathcal{C}^\infty_\varepsilon(H_0) \longrightarrow L^p(\mathbf{R} \times S^1; \mathbf{R}^{2n}),$$

whose surjectivity is claimed by Proposition 8.1.4, is the composition of $(d\sigma)_{(u,h)}$ and the projection from $T_{\sigma(u,h)}\mathcal{E}$ onto the tangent space of $\mathcal{E}$ at the fiber in (u, h). Consequently, Proposition 8.1.3 follows immediately from Proposition 8.1.4. Note that the trivialization Z_i of TW along u allows us to identify the tangent space of the fiber with the space $L^p(\mathbf{R} \times S^1; \mathbf{R}^{2n})$.

8.5.b Proof of Proposition 8.1.4

Assume that Γ is not surjective. We then have the following result.

Lemma 8.5.1. *Let $q > 0$ satisfy $1/p + 1/q = 1$. There exists a nonzero vector field $Z \in L^q(\mathbf{R} \times S^1; \mathbf{R}^{2n})$ of class $\mathcal{C}^\infty$ such that for every $h \in \mathcal{C}^\infty_\varepsilon(H_0)$ and for every $Y \in W^{1,p}(\mathbf{R} \times S^1; \mathbf{R}^{2n})$, we have*

$$\langle Z, (d\mathcal{F})_u(Y) \rangle = 0 \quad and \quad \langle Z, \operatorname{grad}_u(h) \rangle = 0.$$

In this statement, $\langle \, , \, \rangle$ denotes the product (pairing of L^q and L^p)

$$\langle Z, Y \rangle = \int_{\mathbf{R} \times S^1} \langle Z(s,t), Y(s,t) \rangle \, ds \, dt$$

and, as above, we have identified $W^{1,p}(\mathbf{R} \times S^1; u^\star TW)$ with $W^{1,p}(\mathbf{R} \times S^1; \mathbf{R}^{2n})$ by choosing a unitary trivialization (and likewise for L^q!).

Proof of Lemma 8.5.1. We first show that the image of Γ is a closed subspace of $L^p(\mathbf{R} \times S^1; \mathbf{R}^{2n})$. The operator Γ is not a Fredholm operator (see Exercise 44 on p. 530), but $(d\mathcal{F})_u$ is, as we will show in Section 8.7.c. Consequently, its image is closed and finite-codimensional. This image is, of course, contained in that of Γ. Hence there exists a finite-dimensional subspace G that is the complement of $\mathrm{Im}(d\mathcal{F})_u$, that is,

$$\mathrm{Im}(d\mathcal{F})_u \oplus G = L^p(\mathbf{R} \times S^1; \mathbf{R}^{2n})$$

and continuous projections[6]

$$\pi_1 : L^p(\mathbf{R} \times S^1; \mathbf{R}^{2n}) \longrightarrow \mathrm{Im}(d\mathcal{F})_u \quad \text{and} \quad \pi_2 : L^p(\mathbf{R} \times S^1; \mathbf{R}^{2n}) \longrightarrow G.$$

The subspace

$$G_1 = G \cap \mathrm{Im}(\Gamma) \subset G$$

has finite dimension in G, which is also finite-dimensional; it therefore admits a complement G_2. We then have

$$\mathrm{Im}(\Gamma) = \mathrm{Im}(d\mathcal{F})_u \oplus G_1, \quad \text{so that} \quad \mathrm{Im}(\Gamma) \oplus G_2 = L^p(\mathbf{R} \times S^1; \mathbf{R}^{2n}).$$

There therefore exists a continuous projection

$$\pi_2' : L^p(\mathbf{R} \times S^1; \mathbf{R}^{2n}) \longrightarrow G_2.$$

It follows that $\mathrm{Im}(\Gamma)$ is closed: if a sequence (y_n) of points of $\mathrm{Im}(\Gamma)$ converges to a limit $y_\star$ in $L^p(\mathbf{R} \times S^1; \mathbf{R}^{2n})$, then $\pi_2'(y_\star) = 0$, and therefore $y_\star \in \mathrm{Im}(\Gamma)$.

Consequently, the image of Γ is closed, and by the Hahn–Banach theorem,[7] there exists a nonzero continuous linear form φ on $L^p(\mathbf{R} \times S^1; \mathbf{R}^{2n})$ that is zero on $\mathrm{Im}(\Gamma)$. The Riesz representation theorem[8] states that φ is of the form

$$\varphi(Y) = \langle Z, Y \rangle$$

for a vector field $Z \in L^q(\mathbf{R} \times S^1; \mathbf{R}^{2n})$.

For every $Y \in W^{1,p}(\mathbf{R} \times S^1; \mathbf{R}^{2n})$ and for every $h \in \mathcal{C}_\varepsilon^\infty(H_0)$, we therefore have

$$\langle Z, (d\mathcal{F})_u(Y) \rangle = 0 \quad \text{and} \quad \langle Z, \mathrm{grad}_u(h) \rangle = 0.$$

We still need to prove that the vector field Z is of class $\mathcal{C}^\infty$. Let

$$L : W^{1,p}(\mathbf{R} \times S^1; \mathbf{R}^{2n}) \longrightarrow L^p(\mathbf{R} \times S^1; \mathbf{R}^{2n})$$

---

[6] See [17, Chapter 2], if necessary.

[7] Once again [17, Chapter 1], if necessary.

[8] This time, [17, Chapter 4].

denote the operator $(d\mathcal{F})_u$. Recall (Proposition 8.4.4) that

$$LY = \frac{\partial Y}{\partial s} + J_0 \frac{\partial Y}{\partial t} + S \cdot Y$$

(here $Y \in u^\star TW$; we should use the orthonormal frame (Z_i) to define L on $W^{1,p}(\mathbf{R} \times S^1; \mathbf{R}^{2n})$, but we refrain from doing this so as not to weigh down the reading). We define a map $L^\star$ by setting

$$L^\star : W^{1,q}(\mathbf{R} \times S^1; \mathbf{R}^{2n}) \longrightarrow L^q(\mathbf{R} \times S^1; \mathbf{R}^{2n})$$

$$X \longmapsto -\frac{\partial X}{\partial s} + J_0 \frac{\partial X}{\partial t} + {}^t S \cdot X.$$

It is clear that $L^\star$ is a bounded operator. It is the adjoint of L: with a proof analogous to the one given below, we can show that for $Y \in W^{1,p}(\mathbf{R} \times S^1; \mathbf{R}^{2n})$ and $X \in W^{1,q}(\mathbf{R} \times S^1; \mathbf{R}^{2n})$, we have

$$\int_{\mathbf{R} \times S^1} \langle LY, X \rangle = \int_{\mathbf{R} \times S^1} \langle Y, L^\star X \rangle.$$

The vector field Z should therefore satisfy $L^\star Z = 0$... but *a priori*, it lives in $L^q(\mathbf{R} \times S^1; \mathbf{R}^{2n})$, which is larger than the space on which $L^\star$ is defined. Let us therefore show the following result.

Lemma 8.5.2. *In the sense of distributions, we have $L^\star Z = 0$.*

Proof. It suffices to establish the equality above for $Y \in \mathcal{C}_0^\infty(\mathbf{R} \times S^1; \mathbf{R}^{2n})$ and for $X = Z$. We first write

$$\int_{-\infty}^{+\infty} \int_0^1 \langle LY, Z \rangle \, dt \, ds = \int_0^1 \left(\int_{-\infty}^{+\infty} \left\langle \frac{\partial Y}{\partial s}, Z \right\rangle ds \right) dt$$

$$+ \int_{-\infty}^{+\infty} \int_0^1 \left\langle J_0 \frac{\partial Y}{\partial t}, Z \right\rangle dt \, ds + \int_{-\infty}^{+\infty} \int_0^1 \langle SY, Z \rangle \, dt \, ds.$$

Let us consider the three integrals one by one. First, by a simple integration by parts (in fact, properties of weak derivatives),

$$\int_0^1 \left(\int_{-\infty}^{+\infty} \left\langle \frac{\partial Y}{\partial s}, Z \right\rangle ds \right) dt = - \int_0^1 \left(\int_{-\infty}^{+\infty} \left\langle Y, \frac{\partial Z}{\partial s} \right\rangle ds \right) dt$$

(note that this is true, or, naively, that the so-called "fully integrated" term is zero, because we have assumed that $\lim_{s \to \pm\infty} Y(s, t) = 0$). For the second integral, we have

$$\int_{-\infty}^{+\infty} \int_0^1 \left\langle J_0 \frac{\partial Y}{\partial t}, Z \right\rangle dt \, ds = - \int_{-\infty}^{+\infty} \int_0^1 \left\langle \frac{\partial Y}{\partial t}, J_0 Z \right\rangle dt \, ds$$

$$= \int_{-\infty}^{+\infty} \int_0^1 \left\langle Y, \frac{\partial J_0 Z}{\partial t} \right\rangle dt \, ds = \int_{-\infty}^{+\infty} \int_0^1 \left\langle Y, J_0 \frac{\partial Z}{\partial t} \right\rangle dt \, ds$$

(this time the fully integrated term is zero by the periodicity in t). Next, we have

$$\int_{-\infty}^{+\infty} \int_0^1 \langle SY, Z\rangle \, dt \, ds = \int_{-\infty}^{+\infty} \int_0^1 \langle Y, {}^tSZ\rangle \, dt \, ds.$$

Summarizing,

$$\int_{-\infty}^{+\infty} \int_0^1 \langle LY, Z\rangle \, dt \, ds = \int_{-\infty}^{+\infty} \int_0^1 \left\langle Y, -\frac{\partial Z}{\partial s} + J_0 \frac{\partial Z}{\partial t} + {}^tSZ\right\rangle \, ds \, dt$$

$$= \langle Y, L^\star Z\rangle \text{ in the sense of distributions.}$$

Therefore $\langle Z, LY\rangle = 0$ implies that

$$\int_{-\infty}^{+\infty} \int_0^1 \langle Y, L^\star Z\rangle \, dt \, ds = 0,$$

in other words, that $L^\star Z = 0$ in the sense of distributions, which we wanted to prove.   □

It now follows from elliptic regularity (Theorem 12.1.3) that Z is of class $\mathcal{C}^\infty$.   □

To obtain a contradiction, let us show that a vector field satisfying the two conditions of the lemma is necessarily zero. The second condition can also be written as

$$\int_{\mathbf{R} \times S^1} dh_t(Z) \, ds \, dt = 0.$$

This relation is satisfied when $Z(s,t) = \lambda(t)\partial u/\partial s$:

$$\int_{\mathbf{R} \times S^1} dh_t\left(\lambda(t)\frac{\partial u}{\partial s}\right) ds \, dt = \int_{S^1} \lambda(t) \int_{\mathbf{R}} \frac{\partial}{\partial s} h_t(u(s,t)) \, ds \, dt = 0$$

since, by the definition of $\mathcal{C}_\varepsilon^\infty(H_0)$, h is zero near the 1-periodic orbits of X_H. Conversely, we have the following result.

Lemma 8.5.3. *If $Z \in L^q(\mathbf{R} \times S^1; u^\star TW)$ is of class $\mathcal{C}^\infty$ and satisfies*

$$\forall\, h \in \mathcal{C}_\varepsilon^\infty(H_0), \quad \langle Z, \operatorname{grad}_u h\rangle = 0,$$

then there exists a $\mathcal{C}^\infty$ function $\lambda : S^1 \to \mathbf{R}$ such that

$$Z(s,t) = \lambda(t)\frac{\partial u}{\partial s}(s,t).$$

Proof. The proof relies on a theorem of Floer, Hofer and Salamon that guarantees that every solution of the Floer equation is "somewhere injective", a notion whose details we will give in the definitions that follow and in Theorem 8.5.4; we will prove the property in Section 8.6.

Let $u \in \mathcal{M}(x, y, J, H)$. A point $(s_0, t_0) \in \mathbf{R} \times S^1$ is called a *critical point* of u if $\partial u / \partial s(s_0, t_0) = 0$. A point (s_0, t_0) is *regular* if it is not critical and if $u(s_0, t_0) \neq u(s, t_0)$ for every $s \neq s_0$ (even if $s = \pm \infty$, that is, if $u(s_0, t_0) \neq x(t_0)$ or $u(s_0, t_0) \neq y(t_0)$). The set of critical points is denoted by $C(u) \subset \mathbf{R} \times S^1$. We let $R(u)$ denote the set of regular points of u.

Theorem 8.5.4 ([32]). *The set $C(u)$ of critical points is discrete and the set $R(u)$ of regular points is a dense open subset of $\mathbf{R} \times S^1$.*

We will prove this theorem in Section 8.6.

Let $(s_0, t_0) \in R(u)$. Suppose that $\partial u / \partial s(s_0, t_0)$ and $Z(s_0, t_0)$ are linearly independent. We will construct an $h \in \mathcal{C}_\varepsilon^\infty(H_0)$ such that $\langle Z, \text{grad}_u h \rangle \neq 0$, giving a contradiction. We define a map

$$\widetilde{u} : \mathbf{R} \times S^1 \longrightarrow W \times S^1$$
$$(s, t) \longmapsto (u(s, t), t).$$

We view Z as a vector field over $W \times S^1$ along $\widetilde{u}$ (whose component in the direction $\partial / \partial t \in TS^1$ is zero). We view h as a map defined on $W \times S^1$. We write

$$\int_{\mathbf{R} \times S^1} dh_t(Z) \, ds \, dt = \int_{\mathbf{R} \times S^1} dh(Z) \, ds \, dt,$$

and we construct an $h \in \mathcal{C}_\varepsilon^\infty(H_0)$ such that this integral is not zero. Note that it suffices to define h on the integral curves of the vector field Z in the neighborhood of the image of $\widetilde{u}$.

We choose a real number $\delta > 0$ that is sufficiently small for the square

$$C_\delta = \left\{ (s, t) \in \mathbf{R} \times S^1 \mid |s - s_0| \leq \delta \text{ and } |t - t_0| \leq \delta \right\}$$

to be contained in the dense open set $R(u)$ of regular values of u. Then

$$\widetilde{u} : C_\delta \longrightarrow W \times S^1$$

is an embedding (if δ is chosen sufficiently small, which it is). We may, and do, also assume (by decreasing δ) that $Z(s, t)$ and $\partial u / \partial s(s, t)$ are linearly independent as vectors of $T_{u(s,t)} W$ when $(s, t) \in C_\delta$. Seen in $W \times S^1$, this condition translates into the fact that $Z(s, t)$ is transversal to the plane tangent to the image $\widetilde{u}(C_\delta)$.

Since $\widetilde{u} : C_\delta \to W \times S^1$ is an embedding, after decreasing δ again, if necessary, we can consider a local parametrization

$$\psi : C_\delta \times D_\varepsilon \longrightarrow W \times S^1$$

(here $D_\varepsilon = \{y \in \mathbf{R}^{2n-1} \mid \|y\| \leq \varepsilon\}$) such that $\psi|_{C_\delta \times \{0\}} = \widetilde{u}$. We use B (for "box") to denote the image of ψ. This box is shown on the left in Figure 8.2.

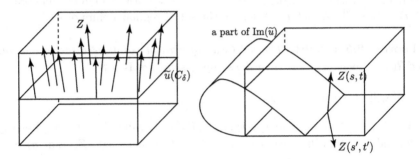

Fig. 8.2

We are going to construct h with support in B by prescribing its values on the integral curves of Z along $\widetilde{u}(C_\delta)$. This will be difficult if the cylinder $\mathrm{Im}(\widetilde{u})$ intersects B outside of $\widetilde{u}(C_\delta)$ (as on the right in Figure 8.2). We exclude this possibility through an auxiliary lemma.

Lemma 8.5.5. *For ε sufficiently small, $\widetilde{u}(s,t) \in \mathrm{Im}(\psi)$ if and only if $(s,t) \in C_\delta$.*

Proof. If the property announced in the lemma is not true, then there exist a sequence ε_n tending to 0 and a sequence (s_n, t_n) in $\mathbf{R} \times S^1 - C_\delta$ such that

$$\widetilde{u}(s_n, t_n) = \psi(s'_n, t'_n, y_n) \quad \text{for } (s'_n, t'_n, y_n) \in C_\delta \times D_{\varepsilon_n},$$

and
$$\lim_{n \to +\infty} (s'_n, t'_n, y_n) = (s_\star, t_\star, 0) \in C_\delta \times \mathbf{R}^{2n-1}.$$

After extracting a subsequence, if necessary, the sequence (s_n, t_n) tends to $(-\infty, t_\#)$, $(+\infty, t_\#)$ or $(s_\#, t_\#) \in \mathbf{R} \times S^1$. We necessarily have $t_\# = t_\star$ and either $x(t_\star) = u(s_\star, t_\star)$, $y(t_\star) = u(s_\star, t_\star)$ or $u(s_\#, t_\star) = u(s_\star, t_\star)$. Now each of these three equalities contradicts the fact that $(s_\star, t_\star)$ is a regular point of u, which it must be because $(s_\star, t_\star) \in C_\delta \subset R(u)$. $\qquad \square$

We can now define h. Outside of B, we choose $h \equiv 0$. Note that h is then zero near the 1-periodic orbits of X_H. To define h inside B, we choose a positive function β of class $\mathcal{C}^\infty$ on C_δ with value 1 on a square $C_{\delta'}$ for some $\delta' < \delta$ and value zero in the neighborhood of the boundary of C_δ. Let $\gamma_{s,t} : [-\varepsilon_0, \varepsilon_0] \to B$ be a curve such that

$$\gamma_{s,t}(0) = \widetilde{u}(s,t) \quad \text{and} \quad \gamma'_{s,t}(0) = Z(s,t).$$

The formula $h(\gamma_{s,t}(\sigma)) = \sigma\beta(s,t)$ defines a function on a subset of the box diffeomorphic to $[-\varepsilon_0, \varepsilon_0] \times C_\delta$ because Z is transversal to the image $\tilde{u}(C_\delta)$. Moreover, on this subset of B, we have

$$(dh)_{\tilde{u}(s,t)}(Z(s,t)) = \beta(s,t).$$

We extend h arbitrarily to a function with support in B. Using the auxiliary lemma 8.5.5, we finally obtain

$$\int_{\mathbf{R} \times S^1} (dh)_{\tilde{u}}(Z)\,ds\,dt = \int_{C_\delta} (dh)_{\tilde{u}}(Z)\,ds\,dt = \int_{C_\delta} \beta(s,t)\,ds\,dt > 0.$$

Since the functions in $\mathcal{C}_\varepsilon^\infty(H_0)$ with support in B are dense in the $\mathcal{C}^\infty$ function with support in B (Proposition 8.3.4), we can approximate h by a function in $\mathcal{C}_\varepsilon^\infty(H_0)$ in such a way that the integral remains positive.

The assumption that $\partial u/\partial s(s_0, t_0)$ and $Z(s_0, t_0)$ are linearly independent has lead us to a contradiction. There therefore exists a function $\lambda : R(u) \to \mathbf{R}$ such that for every $(s,t) \in R(u)$,

$$Z(s,t) = \lambda(s,t)\frac{\partial u}{\partial s}(s,t).$$

To conclude the proof of our lemma (Lemma 8.5.3), we must now show that $\lambda(s,t)$ does not depend on s.

The function λ can then be expressed by the formula

$$\lambda(s,t) = \frac{\langle Z(s,t), \partial u/\partial s(s,t)\rangle}{\|\partial u/\partial s(s,t)\|^2},$$

which shows that it is a $\mathcal{C}^\infty$ function on $R(u)$. This formula also allows us to extend λ to the complement of $C(u)$ in $\mathbf{R} \times S^1$. Since $R(u)$ is dense in $\mathbf{R} \times S^1$, the relation $Z = \lambda \partial u/\partial s$ still holds on $\mathbf{R} \times S^1 - C(u)$. For every $h \in \mathcal{C}_\varepsilon^\infty(H_0)$, we have

$$\int_{\mathbf{R} \times S^1} (dh)_{\tilde{u}}(Z)\,ds\,dt = \int_{\mathbf{R} \times S^1} \lambda(s,t)(dh)_{\tilde{u}}\left(\frac{\partial u}{\partial s}\right)\,ds\,dt$$

$$= \int_{\mathbf{R} \times S^1} \lambda(s,t)\frac{\partial}{\partial s}(h(u(s,t),t))\,ds\,dt.$$

Suppose that there exists a point (s_0, t_0) of $\mathbf{R} \times S^1 - C(u)$ where $\partial\lambda/\partial s$ is not zero. This property still holds on a square C_δ centered at (s_0, t_0) and contained in $\mathbf{R} \times S^1 - C(u)$. As before, we construct a box B in $W \times S^1$ such that if h has support in B, then

$$\int_{\mathbf{R} \times S^1} (dh)_{\tilde{u}}(Z)\,ds\,dt = \int_{C_\delta} (dh)_{\tilde{u}}(Z)\,ds\,dt.$$

We once again use the plateau function $\beta : C_\delta \to \mathbf{R}$ chosen above to define

$$h(\widetilde{u}(s,t)) = -\beta(s,t)\frac{\partial \lambda}{\partial s}(s,t) \text{ on } \widetilde{u}(C_\delta)$$

(extending it arbitrarily to a function with support in B). Using integration by parts in B, we therefore have

$$\int_{\mathbf{R}\times S^1} (dh)_{\widetilde{u}}(Z)\,ds\,dt = \int_{C_\delta} (dh)_{\widetilde{u}}(Z)\,ds\,dt$$

$$= \int_{C_\delta} \lambda(s,t)\frac{\partial}{\partial s}(h(u(s,t),t))\,ds\,dt$$

$$= -\int_{C_\delta} \frac{\partial \lambda}{\partial s}(s,t)h(u(s,t),t)\,ds\,dt$$

$$= \int_{C_\delta} \beta(s,t)\left(\frac{\partial \lambda}{\partial s}(s,t)\right)^2 ds\,dt$$

$$\geq \int_{C_{\delta'}} \left(\frac{\partial \lambda}{\partial s}(s,t)\right)^2 ds\,dt > 0.$$

Again by density, we may, and do, assume that $h \in \mathcal{C}_\varepsilon^\infty(H_0)$ as before. We have thus contradicted Lemma 8.5.1, hence the assumption (the existence of a pair (s_0, t_0) where $\partial \lambda/\partial s$ is not zero) is false. We therefore have

$$\forall (s,t) \in \mathbf{R} \times S^1 - C(u), \quad \frac{\partial \lambda}{\partial s}(s,t) = 0.$$

Since $C(u)$ is discrete, $\mathbf{R} \times S^1 - C(u)$ is connected (an assertion left as an exercise for the readers). Hence on $\mathbf{R} \times S^1 - C(u)$, $\lambda(s,t) = \lambda(t)$ does not depend on s. We can then extend this function to a $\mathcal{C}^\infty$ function on $\mathbf{R}^2$, simply by setting

$$\lambda(s_0, t_0) = \lambda(s_0 + \varepsilon, t_0) \text{ if } (s_0, t_0) \in C(u).$$

The relation

$$Z(s,t) = \lambda(t)\frac{\partial u}{\partial s}(s,t)$$

is therefore true on $\mathbf{R} \times S^1$, and Lemma 8.5.3 is proved.   □

Proof of Proposition 8.1.4. Let us show that $\lambda(t) \neq 0$ for every t. If this were not the case, then there would be a t_0 such that $Z(s, t_0) = 0$ for every $s \in \mathbf{R}$. In particular, all derivatives $\partial^k Z/\partial s^k(s, t_0)$ would be zero. Since Z is a solution of $L^\star Z = 0$, we can show by induction that all derivatives of Z would be zero for all s and $t = t_0$. From

$$L^\star Z = -\frac{\partial Z}{\partial s} + J_0\frac{\partial Z}{\partial t} +{}^t S(s,t)Z,$$

we can deduce that Z would then be a solution of a "perturbed Cauchy–Riemann"-type equation and therefore satisfy a continuation principle analogous to the one satisfied by holomorphic maps: if it and all its derivatives are zero on $\mathbf{R} \times \{t_0\}$, then it is zero everywhere. We will explain the notion of a "perturbed Cauchy–Riemann" equation and prove the continuation principle (Proposition 8.6.6).

This continuation principle would then imply that Z is identically zero, which contradicts our assumption.

Hence $\lambda(t) \neq 0$ for every t. We may, and do, moreover assume that

$$\lambda(t) > 0 \quad \text{for all } t.$$

We then have

$$\int_0^1 \left\langle \frac{\partial u}{\partial s}(s, t), Z(s, t) \right\rangle dt = \int_0^1 \lambda(t) \left| \frac{\partial u}{\partial s}(s, t) \right|^2 dt > 0 \quad \text{for all } s \in \mathbf{R};$$

consequently, this function of s is positive and tends to 0 (as does $\partial u/\partial s$) when $s \to \pm\infty$. It would lead to a contradiction if this function were constant. To conclude, let us therefore show that it is, indeed, constant.

Recall that, as we have already noted (Remark 8.4.7), $\partial u/\partial s$ is a solution of $LY = 0$. To simplify the notation, we set

$$Y(s, t) = \frac{\partial u}{\partial s}(s, t).$$

We have $LY = 0$ and $L^\star Z = 0$, that is,

$$\frac{\partial Y}{\partial s} = -J_0 \frac{\partial Y}{\partial t} - SY \quad \text{and} \quad \frac{\partial Z}{\partial s} = J_0 \frac{\partial Z}{\partial t} + {}^t SZ.$$

The derivative of our function in s is therefore

$$\frac{d}{ds} \int_0^1 \langle Y, Z \rangle \, dt = \int_0^1 \left(\left\langle \frac{\partial Y}{\partial s}, Z \right\rangle + \left\langle Y, \frac{\partial Z}{\partial s} \right\rangle \right) dt$$

$$= \int_0^1 \left(\left\langle -J_0 \frac{\partial Y}{\partial t}, Z \right\rangle - \langle SY, Z \rangle + \left\langle Y, J_0 \frac{\partial Z}{\partial t} \right\rangle + \langle Y, {}^t SZ \rangle \right) dt$$

$$= -\int_0^1 \left(\left\langle J_0 \frac{\partial Y}{\partial t}, Z \right\rangle + \left\langle J_0 Y, \frac{\partial Z}{\partial t} \right\rangle \right) dt$$

$$= -\int_0^1 \frac{\partial}{\partial t} \langle J_0 Y, Z \rangle \, dt = 0.$$

This contradiction implies that Z is zero, which concludes the surjectivity part of the proof of Proposition 8.1.4.   □

The proof that Γ admits a continuous right inverse is given by the following abstract lemma.

Lemma 8.5.6. *Let E, F and G be Banach spaces and*

$$L_1 : E \longrightarrow G, \qquad L_2 : F \longrightarrow G$$

be linear operators. Assume that L_1 is Fredholm and that $\Gamma : E \oplus F \to G$, defined by $\Gamma(x,y) = L_1(x) + L_2(y)$, is surjective. Then Γ admits a continuous right inverse.

Proof. Write $G = \operatorname{Im}(L_1) \oplus H$, where H is closed and finite-dimensional. Let E' be a closed subspace of E such that $E = \operatorname{Ker}(L_1) \oplus E'$. The operator $L_1 : E' \to \operatorname{Im}(L_1)$ is obviously bijective. Denote by L_1^{-1} the composition

$$L_1^{-1} : \operatorname{Im}(L_1) \longrightarrow E' \subset E \subset E \oplus F.$$

Let $h_1, \ldots, h_r$ be a basis of H and $x_1, \ldots, x_r \in E \oplus F$ be such that $\Gamma(x_i) = h_i$. Define $\nu : H \to E \oplus F$ by $\nu(h_i) = x_i$. This is a continuous map, since its image is finite-dimensional. Now the map

$$\Pi : \operatorname{Im}(L_1) \oplus H \longrightarrow E \oplus F$$
$$(z, h) \longmapsto (L_1^{-1}(z), 0) + \nu(h)$$

is a right inverse of Γ: it is easy to check that $\Gamma \circ \Pi = \operatorname{Id}$; moreover, Π is continuous since it can be written as

$$\Pi = (L_1^{-1} \circ \operatorname{pr}_{\operatorname{Im}(L_1)}, 0) + \nu \circ \operatorname{pr}_H. \qquad \square$$

8.5.c Toward the Proofs of Theorems 8.1.1 and 8.1.2, the Tangent Space of $\mathcal{Z}(x, y, J)$

The contradiction obtained at the end of the previous proof also concludes the proof of Proposition 8.1.3. We have shown that $\mathcal{Z}(x, y, J)$ is a Banach manifold. Its tangent space at a point (u, h) is the kernel of $(d\sigma)_{(u,h)}$, that is, the space

$$\left\{ (Y, \eta) \in W^{1,p}(\mathbf{R} \times S^1; \mathbf{R}^{2n}) \times \mathcal{C}_\varepsilon^\infty(H_0) \mid (d\mathcal{F})_u Y + \operatorname{grad}_u \eta = 0 \right\}.$$

We consider the projection

$$\pi : \mathcal{Z}(x, y, J) \longrightarrow \mathcal{C}_\varepsilon^\infty(H_0)$$
$$(u, H_0 + h) \longmapsto h$$

and its tangent map

$$(d\pi)_{(u,H)} : T_{(u,H)} \mathcal{Z}(x,y,J) \longrightarrow T_h \mathcal{C}_\varepsilon^\infty(H_0) = \mathcal{C}_\varepsilon^\infty(H_0)$$
$$(Y, \eta) \longmapsto \eta$$

(where $H = H_0 + h$). Note that π is smooth. Let us verify that π is a Fredholm map. The kernel of $(d\pi)_{(u,H_0+h)}$ is exactly that of $L = (d\mathcal{F})_u$, hence has finite dimension. Its image is the inverse image of the image of L under the linear map

$$\mathcal{C}_\varepsilon^\infty(H_0) \longrightarrow L^p(u^*TW)$$
$$\eta \longmapsto \operatorname{grad}_u \eta,$$

and therefore is finite-codimensional (and closed).

We can now apply the Sard–Smale theorem, which is as follows.

Theorem 8.5.7 (Sard–Smale [73]). *Let E and F be two separable Banach spaces, let U be an open subset of E and let*

$$\mathcal{F} : U \longrightarrow F$$

be a (smooth) Fredholm map. Then the set

$$\{y \in F \mid \text{if } y = f(x) \text{ for an } x \in U, \text{ then } T_x\mathcal{F} \text{ is surjective}\}$$

of regular values of $\mathcal{F}$ is a countable intersection of dense open subsets.

Remark 8.5.8. In this theorem, the separability guarantees that we can extract a countable subcover from any open cover. It is essential in order to obtain a *countable* intersection of dense open subsets, and therefore a dense subset.

Let us now prove the following result.

Lemma 8.5.9. *The regular values of π are exactly the $h \in \mathcal{C}_\varepsilon^\infty(H_0)$ such that for every $u \in \mathcal{M}(H_0 + h, J)$, the map $(d\mathcal{F})_u$ is surjective.*

Proof. Let h be a regular value of π and let $u \in \mathcal{M}(H_0 + h, J)$. We will show that $(d\mathcal{F})_u$ is surjective. If this were not the case, then, as in Lemma 8.5.1, there would exist a $Z \in L^q(\mathbf{R} \times S^1; \mathbf{R}^{2n})$ such that

$$\forall Y \in W^{1,p}(\mathbf{R} \times S^1; \mathbf{R}^{2n}), \quad \langle (d\mathcal{F})_u(Y), Z \rangle = 0.$$

Since $(d\pi)_{(u,H)}$ is surjective, for every $\eta \in \mathcal{C}_{\varepsilon}^{\infty}(H_0)$, there exists a vector field $Y \in W^{1,p}(\mathbf{R} \times S^1; \mathbf{R}^{2n})$ such that

$$(d\mathcal{F})_u(Y) + \mathrm{grad}_u \, \eta = 0.$$

Using these two equalities, the proof of Proposition 8.1.4 (see Section 8.5.b) gives $Z = 0$ and a contradiction. Consequently, $(d\mathcal{F})_u$ is surjective.

Conversely, given an $h \in \mathcal{C}_{\varepsilon}^{\infty}(H_0)$, if $(d\mathcal{F})_u$ is surjective for every $u \in \mathcal{M}(H_0 + h, J)$, then given an $\eta \in \mathcal{C}_{\varepsilon}^{\infty}(H_0)$, choose a $Y \in W^{1,p}(\mathbf{R} \times S^1; \mathbf{R}^{2n})$ such that

$$(d\mathcal{F})_u(Y) = -\mathrm{grad}_u \, \eta.$$

Then $(Y, \eta) \in T_{(u,H)} \mathcal{Z}(x, y, J)$ and $(d\pi)_{(u,H)}(Y, \eta) = \eta$, hence $(d\pi)_{(u,H)}$ is surjective, and h is a regular value of π. $\square$

Lemma 8.5.9 immediately gives Theorem 8.1.1 (using the Sard–Smale theorem, that is, Theorem 8.5.7). For this proof to be truly complete, we still need to prove Theorem 8.5.4 and the continuation principle (which we will prove as Proposition 8.6.6).

Admitting these results, let us finally prove (after taking a perturbation of the original Hamiltonian, if necessary) that the space of trajectories from x to y is a manifold of the desired dimension, in other words, let us prove Theorem 8.1.2.

Proof of Theorem 8.1.2. Let $h \in \mathcal{H}_{\mathrm{reg}}$. Then by Lemma 8.5.9, h is a regular value of

$$\pi : \mathcal{Z}(x, y, J) \longrightarrow \mathcal{C}_{\varepsilon}^{\infty}(H_0).$$

Consequently, $\pi^{-1}(h)$ is a manifold and its dimension equals the Fredholm index of π, which is

$$\begin{aligned}
\dim \mathrm{Ker}(d\pi)_{(u,H)} &= \dim \mathrm{Ker}(d\mathcal{F})_u \\
&= \mathrm{Ind}(d\mathcal{F})_u \\
&= \mu(x) - \mu(y).
\end{aligned}$$

The elements of $\pi^{-1}(h)$ are the solutions in $\mathcal{P}^{1,p}$ of the Floer equation for $(H_0 + h_0, J)$. By elliptic regularity (see Proposition 12.1.4), we have

$$\pi^{-1}(h) \subset \mathcal{M}(x, y, H_0 + h).$$

Proposition 8.2.3 gives the inclusion in the other direction, so that

$$\pi^{-1}(h) = \mathcal{M}(x, y, H_0 + h),$$

which we wanted to prove. $\square$

Remark 8.5.10. We have shown that for $h \in \mathcal{H}_{\text{reg}}$ and for all critical points x and y of $\mathcal{A}_{H_0}$, the space $\mathcal{M}(x, y, H_0 + h, J)$ is a submanifold of $\mathcal{P}^{1,p}(x, y)$. On $\mathcal{M}(x, y, H_0 + h, J)$, we use the $\mathcal{C}^{\infty}_{\text{loc}}$ topology. Indeed, since $p > 2$, there is an injection of $\mathcal{P}^{1,p}(x, y)$ into the space of continuous functions that is continuous for the $\mathcal{C}^{0}_{\text{loc}}$ topology and, as we have already noted (in Proposition 6.5.3), on $\mathcal{M}(H_0 + h, J)$ (of which $\mathcal{M}(x, y, H_0 + h, J)$ is a subspace), the $\mathcal{C}^{0}_{\text{loc}}$ and $\mathcal{C}^{\infty}_{\text{loc}}$ topologies coincide.

The dense open set $\mathcal{H}_{\text{reg}}$ whose existence was announced in Theorem 8.1.1 is obtained by taking the intersection of the different dense open subsets obtained by considering the different pairs (x, y) of periodic orbits of period 1.

To conclude the proofs of Theorems 8.1.5 and 8.1.1, we still need to prove that $(d\mathcal{F})_u$ indeed has the Fredholm property and to compute its index, which we will do in Sections 8.7 and 8.8.

8.6 The Solutions of the Floer Equation Are "Somewhere Injective"

8.6.a The Injectivity "in s"

We will now prove Theorem 8.5.4 and a continuation principle that we used in the proof of Proposition 8.1.4 on p. 250 (Proposition 8.6.6 below). Let $z = s + it$ and let u be a solution of the equation

$$\frac{\partial u}{\partial s} + J(t, u)\left(\frac{\partial u}{\partial t} - X(t, u)\right) = 0.$$

Here X is a vector field (that depends periodically on time) on $\mathbf{R}^{2n}$ and X and J are assumed to be of class $\mathcal{C}^{\infty}$. Every solution u of class $W^{1,p}$ (with $p > 2$) is in fact of class $\mathcal{C}^{\infty}$. We begin by transforming this equation into a Cauchy–Riemann equation on $\mathbf{R}^2$.

Proposition 8.6.1. *Let u be a solution of the equation*

$$\frac{\partial u}{\partial s} + J(t, u)\left(\frac{\partial u}{\partial t} - X(t, u)\right) = 0.$$

There exist an almost complex structure J and a diffeomorphism φ on W, as well as a map $v : \mathbf{R}^2 \to W$ of class $\mathcal{C}^{\infty}$, such that

$$\begin{cases} \dfrac{\partial v}{\partial s} + J\dfrac{\partial v}{\partial t} = 0 \\ v(s, t+1) = \varphi(v(s, t)), \end{cases}$$

and for $(s,t) \in \mathbf{R} \times [0,1[$, $C(u) = C(v)$ (u and v have the same critical points) and $R(u) = R(v)$.

Proof. Since $W \times S^1$ is compact, the "flow" ψ_t of X_t is defined on all of W, so that we have a map

$$\psi_t : W \longrightarrow W \quad \text{such that } \frac{d}{dt}\psi_t = X_t \circ \psi_t \text{ and } \psi_0 = \mathrm{Id}.$$

Let $v(s,t) = \psi_t^{-1}(u(s,t))$; then

$$\frac{\partial u}{\partial s} = (d\psi_t)\left(\frac{\partial v}{\partial s}\right) \quad \text{and} \quad \frac{\partial u}{\partial t} = (d\psi_t)\left(\frac{\partial v}{\partial t}\right) + X_t(u),$$

and consequently,

$$\begin{aligned}
0 &= \frac{\partial u}{\partial s} + J\left(\frac{\partial u}{\partial t} - X_t(u)\right) \\
&= (d\psi_t)\left(\frac{\partial v}{\partial s}\right) + J(u)(d\psi_t)\left(\frac{\partial v}{\partial s}\right) \\
&= (d\psi_t)\left(\frac{\partial v}{\partial s} + (d\psi_t)^{-1}J(u)(d\psi_t)\left(\frac{\partial v}{\partial t}\right)\right).
\end{aligned}$$

Setting $(d\psi_t)^{-1}J(u)(d\psi_t) = \psi_t^\star J(v)$, we have seen that v is a solution of

$$\frac{\partial v}{\partial s} + \psi_t^\star J(v)\frac{\partial v}{\partial t} = 0.$$

We conclude by setting $\varphi = \psi_1$ (and renaming the resulting complex structure J). The verification of the properties of φ and v is immediate.   □

We now apply Proposition 8.6.1: proving Theorem 8.5.4 (on the critical points) is equivalent to proving the results expressed in the following two statements. The first one asserts that the set of critical points of v (and therefore also that of u) is discrete.

Lemma 8.6.2. *There exists a constant $\delta > 0$ such that $(dv)_z \neq 0$ for $0 < |z| < \delta$.*

The proof of this lemma uses the "similarity principle" (Lemma 8.6.8) and is postponed to p. 264.

Before stating the second result, we consider a solution $v : \mathbf{R}^2 \to W$ of class $\mathcal{C}^\infty$ with all the properties given by Proposition 8.6.1. Recall that

$$R(v) = \Big\{(s,t) \in \mathbf{R}^2 \mid \frac{\partial v}{\partial s}(s,t) \neq 0,$$
$$v(s,t) \neq x^\pm(t) \text{ and } v(s,t) \notin v(\mathbf{R} - \{s\},t)\Big\}.$$

Definition. We set $v(\pm\infty, t) = x^{\pm}(t)$. Let $(s, t) \in \mathbf{R}^2$. We call a *multiple point* of (s, t) a point (s', t) (with the same t!) with $s' \in \mathbf{R} \cup \{\pm\infty\}$ and $s' \neq s$ such that $v(s', t) = v(s, t)$.

So, by definition, $R(v)$ is the set of points in the complement of $C(v)$ that do not admit multiples.

The "injectivity" result that we have in view is the following.

Proposition 8.6.3. *Let v be a solution of class $\mathcal{C}^{\infty}$ of the Cauchy–Riemann equation satisfying the periodicity condition $v(s, t+1) = \varphi(v(s, t))$, and such that $\partial v / \partial s \not\equiv 0$. Then $R(v)$ is a dense open subset of $\mathbf{R}^2$.*

Proof. We divide the proof into two steps. We show:

- That $R(v)$ is an open subset, which is quite easy since the two conditions occurring in the definition are obviously open conditions
- And (this is the delicate part) that $R(v)$ is dense.

First, $R(v)$ is an open subset; in other words, its complement is closed. If this were not the case, then there would exist a sequence $(s_n, t_n) \notin R(v)$ that converges to a limit $(s, t) \in R(v)$. The first two conditions defining $R(v)$ are open; consequently, for n sufficiently large, we have

$$\frac{\partial v}{\partial s}(s_n, t_n) \neq 0 \quad \text{and} \quad v(s_n, t_n) \neq x^{\pm}(t).$$

It is the injectivity that no longer holds, so that for every n, we have an $s'_n \in \mathbf{R}$ with $s'_n \neq s_n$ and $v(s_n, t_n) = v(s'_n, t_n)$.

Let us show that such a sequence (s'_n) is bounded. If this were not the case, then it would admit a subsequence that tends to $\pm\infty$ and we would have (for this subsequence)

$$v(s, t) = \lim v(s'_n, t_n) = x^{\pm}(t),$$

which is not allowed because $(s, t) \in R(v)$.

Since the sequence (s'_n) is bounded, let us extract a convergent subsequence with limit s'. Since $v(s, t) = v(s', t)$, by the definition of $R(v)$ we must have $s' = s$. We have two sequences (s_n) and (s'_n) with $s_n \neq s'_n$ and $\lim s_n = \lim s'_n = s$. Consequently,

$$\frac{\partial v}{\partial s}(s, t) = \lim_{n \to \infty} \frac{v(s_n, t) - v(s'_n, t)}{s_n - s'_n} = 0,$$

which gives a contradiction with the assumption that $(s, t) \in R(v)$.

We still need to prove that $R(v)$ is dense. Since $C(v)$ is discrete, it suffices to show that $R(v)$ is dense in the complement of $C(v)$. It is clear that every $(s,t) \in \mathbf{R}^2$ with $(s,t) \notin C(v)$ is the limit of a sequence $(s_n, t) \notin C(v)$ with $v(s_n, t) \neq x^{\pm}(t)$. Indeed,

$$\text{if } v(s + 1/n, t) = x^+(t) \text{ (for example), then } \frac{\partial v}{\partial s}(s,t) = 0.$$

Let us therefore show that every point $(s_0, t_0) \in \mathbf{R} \times [0,1]$ with

$$\frac{\partial v}{\partial s}(s_0, t_0) \neq 0 \quad \text{and} \quad v(s_0, t_0) \neq x^{\pm}(t_0)$$

is the limit of a sequence of points of $R(v)$. If this were not the case, then there would exist a small open ball centered at (s_0, t_0) such that

$$B_\varepsilon(s_0, t_0) \cap R(v) = \varnothing.$$

If the radius ε is sufficiently small, then the following two properties are satisfied for a sufficiently large $M \geq 0$:

(1) If $|t - t_0| \leq \varepsilon$ and $|s| \geq M$, then $v(s,t) \notin v(B_\varepsilon(s_0, t_0))$ and $x^{\pm}(t) \notin v(B_\varepsilon(s_0, t_0))$; otherwise, there would exist two sequences t_n and t'_n tending to t_0 and two sequences s_n and s'_n with $\lim s_n = \pm\infty$ and $\lim s'_n = s_0$ such that $v(s_n, t_n) = v(s'_n, t'_n)$, which would then imply that $v(s_0, t_0) = x^{\pm}(t_0)$ (which is false).

(2) If $|t - t_0| \leq \varepsilon$, then the map

$$[s_0 - \varepsilon, s_0 + \varepsilon] \longrightarrow W$$
$$s \longmapsto v(s,t)$$

is an injective immersion; otherwise, there would exist two sequences s_n and s'_n (with $s_n \neq s'_n$) tending to s_0 and a sequence t_n tending to t_0 such that $v(s_n, t_n) = v(s'_n, t_n)$, so that we would have $\partial v/\partial s(s_0, t_0) = 0$. This is illustrated in Figure 8.3 (the s-axis is horizontal): the multiples of the points of the ball $B_\varepsilon(s_0, t_0)$ are not in the shaded areas.

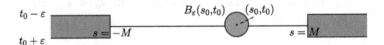

$t_0 - \varepsilon$ $B_\varepsilon(s_0, t_0)$ (s_0, t_0)

$s = -M$ $s = M$

$t_0 + \varepsilon$

Fig. 8.3

Because of these two properties, we in particular have that

$$\forall (s,t) \in B_\varepsilon(s_0, t_0), \quad \frac{\partial v}{\partial s}(s,t) \neq 0 \text{ and } v(s,t) \neq x^\pm(t).$$

In other terms, v is locally constant and $(s_0, t_0) \in C(v)$.

(3) Since $[-M, M] \times [0,1]$ is compact and $C(v)$ is discrete, their intersection is finite. After slightly modifying the point (s_0, t_0), if necessary, we will assume that $v(s_0, t_0) \neq v(s, t)$ for all (s, t) in this finite set (this is possible because v is not constant in a neighborhood of (s_0, t_0) since (s_0, t_0) is not in $C(v)$) and, after decreasing ε, that

$$v(B_\varepsilon(s_0, t_0)) \cap v([-M, M] \times [0,1] \cap C(v)) = \varnothing.$$

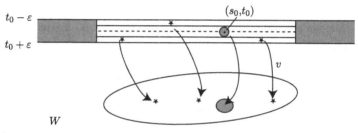

Fig. 8.4

This is sketched in Figure 8.4, where the stars are the points of $C(v)$ and their images. So we no longer consider the case of a multiple point that is also a critical point. Only the injectivity counts from now on and for every $(s,t) \in B_\varepsilon(s_0, t_0)$, there exists an $s' \in \mathbf{R}$ such that $s' \neq s$ and

$$u(s,t) = u(s',t) \quad \text{with } \frac{\partial u}{\partial s}(s',t) \neq 0 \text{ and } |s'| \leq M,\ |s'| > \varepsilon.$$

For every (s,t), the set of points (s', t) that have the same image is finite: otherwise this set would have a limit point, which would imply that $\partial v/\partial s = 0$. Let $s_1, \ldots, s_N \in [-M, M]$ be the points such that

$$v(s_0, t_0) = v(s_1, t_0) = \cdots = v(s_N, t_0).$$

Lemma 8.6.4. *For every $r > 0$, there exists a $\delta > 0$ such that if $|t - t_0| < \delta$ and $|s - s_0| < \delta$, then there exists an $s' \in B_r(s_j)$ with $v(s,t) = v(s',t)$.*

Proof. If this were not the case, then there would exist a sequence (σ_n, t_n) tending to (s_0, t_0) such that the multiple points (σ, t_n) of (σ_n, t_n) satisfy

$\sigma \notin B_r(s_j)$ for $j = 1, \ldots, n$. Let (σ'_n, t_n) be a multiple point of (σ_n, t_n). We know by property (1) above that $|\sigma'_n| \leq M$ and by property (2) that $|\sigma'_n - s_0| \geq \varepsilon$.

The sequence σ'_n has a limit point σ', which is different from $s_0, \ldots, s_N$. Moreover, $v(\sigma'_n, t_n) = v(\sigma_n, t_n)$, so that $v(\sigma', t_0) = v(s_0, t_0)$, giving a contradiction.

This is illustrated in Figure 8.5, where the multiple points of B_δ are in the lightly shaded areas. $\qquad\qquad\qquad\qquad\qquad\qquad\qquad\qquad\qquad\qquad\qquad\qquad\square$

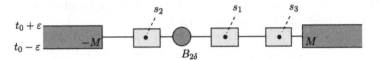

Fig. 8.5

Now that we have the lemma, we fix an $r < \varepsilon/2$ and a corresponding δ. For $j = 1, \ldots, N$, we set

$$\Sigma_j = \left\{ (s,t) \in \overline{B}_\delta(s_0, t_0) \mid v(s,t) \in v(\overline{B}_r(s_j) \times \{t\}) \right\}.$$

The Σ_j are closed and, by the previous lemma,

$$\Sigma_1 \cup \cdots \cup \Sigma_N = \overline{B}_\delta(s_0, t_0),$$

so that at least one of them has a nonempty interior. We assume that it is Σ_1. For a point $(s_\star, t_\star)$ in the interior of Σ_1 and a sufficiently small real number $\rho > 0$, we have

$$B_\rho(s_\star, t_\star) \subset \Sigma_1 \subset B_\delta(s_0, t_0) \subset B_\varepsilon(s_0, t_0).$$

We can therefore choose $r > 0$ sufficiently small so that

$$B_r(s_i) \cap B_\varepsilon(s_0) = \varnothing \quad \text{for every } i = 1, \ldots, N,$$

in particular,

$$B_\rho(s_\star, t_\star) \cap (B_{r_1}(s_1) \times B_\delta(t_0)) = \varnothing.$$

This is illustrated in Figure 8.6, where each point of $B_\rho(s_\star, t_\star)$ has a multiple in the lightly shaded area.

By the definition of Σ_1, for every $(s,t) \in B_\rho(s_\star, t_\star)$, there exists an $s' \in \overline{B}_r(s_1)$ such that $v(s,t) = v(s',t)$. In particular, there exists an $s'_\star \neq s_\star$ with

$$v(s_\star, t_\star) = v(s'_\star, t_\star).$$

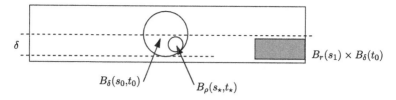

Fig. 8.6

We define two functions v_1 and v_2 on $B_\varepsilon(0,0)$ by setting

$$v_1(s,t) = v(s + s_\star, t + t_\star)$$
$$v_2(s,t) = v(s + s'_\star, t + t_\star).$$

These two functions satisfy the same Cauchy–Riemann equation and coincide at the origin. Moreover, their differentials at the origin are nonzero. Indeed, $(s_\star, t_\star) \in B_\varepsilon(s_0, t_0)$ is not in $C(v)$ and $(s'_\star, t_\star)$ is a multiple of $(s_\star, t_\star)$, hence is also not in $C(v)$ by property (3). So, by construction, for every $(s,t) \in B_\rho(0,0)$, there exists an $s' \in \overline{B}_{2r}(0)$ such that $v_1(s,t) = v_2(s',t)$. We apply the following lemma to these functions. It is a consequence of the continuation principle (we will prove it later).

Lemma 8.6.5. *Let v_1 and v_2 be two solutions of the Cauchy–Riemann equation with $X_t \equiv 0$ on $B_\varepsilon(0)$, with the same value at 0 and such that $(dv_1)_0$ and $(dv_2)_0$ are nonzero. Suppose, moreover, that for every $\varepsilon > 0$, there exists $\delta > 0$ such that*

$$\forall\, (s,t) \in B_\delta(0), \exists\, s' \in \mathbf{R} \text{ such that } (s',t) \in B_\varepsilon(0) \text{ and } v_1(s,t) = v_2(s',t).$$

Then $v_1(s,t) = v_2(s,t)$ for every $z \in B_\varepsilon(0)$.

Hence $v_1(s,t) = v_2(s,t)$, that is, $v(s + s_\star, t + t_\star) = v(s + s'_\star, t + t_\star)$ in a neighborhood of 0. But we want to show that $v_1 = v_2$ on $\mathbf{R}^2$. The maps v_1 and v_2 both satisfy the Cauchy–Riemann equation

$$\frac{\partial w}{\partial s} + J \frac{\partial w}{\partial t} = 0.$$

We define the operator

$$\mathcal{F} : \mathcal{C}^\infty(\mathbf{R} \times S^1; \mathbf{R}^{2n}) \longrightarrow \mathcal{C}^\infty(\mathbf{R} \times S^1; \mathbf{R}^{2n})$$
$$w \longmapsto \frac{\partial w}{\partial s} + J(w) \frac{\partial w}{\partial t}.$$

We then have $\mathcal{F}(v_1) = \mathcal{F}(v_2)$. We can write this as

$$
\begin{aligned}
0 &= \mathcal{F}(v_1) - \mathcal{F}(v_2) \\
&= \int_0^1 \frac{d}{d\tau} \mathcal{F}(v_1 + \tau(v_2 - v_1)) \, d\tau \\
&= \int_0^1 (d\mathcal{F})_{v_1 + \tau(v_2 - v_1)} (v_2 - v_1) \, d\tau.
\end{aligned}
$$

A computation similar to the one carried out in Section 8.4 to linearize the Floer operator gives (for $H = 0$ and J depending on t)

$$
(d\mathcal{F})_{v_1 + \tau(v_2 - v_1)}(Y) = \frac{\partial Y}{\partial s} + J_0 \frac{\partial Y}{\partial t} + \widetilde{S}(\tau, s, t)Y,
$$

where $\widetilde{S}$ is a map

$$
\widetilde{S} : [0, 1] \times \mathbf{R}^2 \longrightarrow \operatorname{End}(\mathbf{R}^{2n}).
$$

Let $Y = v_2 - v_1$ and let $S(s, t) = \int_0^1 \widetilde{S}(\tau, s, t) \, d\tau$. We find that $v_2 - v_1$ is a solution of

$$
\frac{\partial Y}{\partial s} + J_0 \frac{\partial Y}{\partial t} + S \cdot Y = 0,
$$

which, by the above, is zero in a neighborhood of the origin. By applying the continuation principle (Proposition 8.6.6), we have $v_1 = v_2$, that is,

$$
v(s + s_\star, t + t_\star) = v(s + s'_\star, t + t_\star) \quad \text{for every } (s, t) \in \mathbf{R}^2.
$$

By induction, we have $v(s, t) = v(k(s'_\star - s_\star), t)$ for every $k \in \mathbf{Z}$ and, by taking the limit, $v(s, t) = x^\pm(t)$, which contradicts the assumption we made. $\square$

8.6.b The Continuation Principle

We must now prove the continuation principle. We will consider the case of a "perturbed Cauchy–Riemann" equation

$$
\frac{\partial Y}{\partial s} + J_0 \frac{\partial Y}{\partial t} + S \cdot Y = 0
$$

in which J_0 is the standard complex structure on $\mathbf{R}^{2n}$ and

$$
S : \mathbf{R}^2 \longrightarrow \operatorname{End}(\mathbf{R}^{2n})
$$

is a map of class $\mathcal{C}^\infty$. Here is the proposition that we are leading up to.

Proposition 8.6.6 (Continuation Principle). *Let Y be a solution of the perturbed Cauchy–Riemann equation on an open subset U of $\mathbf{R}^2$. Then the* *set*

$$C = \{(s,t) \in U \mid Y \text{ has an infinite-order zero at } (s,t)\}$$

is open and closed in U. In particular, if U is connected and if Y is zero on a nonempty open subset of U, then Y is identically zero on U.

Remarks 8.6.7.

(1) Recall that a function f has an infinite-order zero at a point z_0 if, for every $k \geq 0$,

$$\lim_{r \to 0} \frac{\sup_{|z - z_0| \leq r} |f(z)|}{r^k} = 0.$$

For a function f of class $\mathcal{C}^\infty$, this is equivalent to the derivatives of all orders of f being zero at z_0.

(2) The set of points where a function of class $\mathcal{C}^\infty$ has an infinite-order zero is closed. In the case of a holomorphic function (that is, one satisfying the Cauchy–Riemann equations), this closed set is also open: this is what we call the "analytic continuation principle".

We will prove this proposition by presenting it as a consequence of a version of the Carleman similarity principle, namely the following lemma. We write $\mathbf{R}^{2n} = \mathbf{C}^n$.

Lemma 8.6.8 (Similarity Principle). *Let $Y : B_\varepsilon \to \mathbf{C}^n$ be a solution of class $\mathcal{C}^\infty$ of the perturbed Cauchy–Riemann equation*

$$\frac{\partial Y}{\partial s} + J_0 \frac{\partial Y}{\partial t} + S \cdot Y = 0$$

and let $p > 2$. Then there exist a number $\delta > 0$, $\delta < \varepsilon$, a map $A \in W^{1,p}(B_\delta, \mathrm{GL}(\mathbf{R}^{2n}))$ and a holomorphic map $\sigma : B_\delta \to \mathbf{C}^n$ such that

$$\forall (s,t) \in B_\delta, \quad Y(s,t) = A(s,t)\sigma(s+it) \text{ and } J_0 A(s,t) = A(s,t)J_0.$$

Remark 8.6.9. More generally, we can assume in this statement that $Y \in W^{1,p}(B_\varepsilon; \mathbf{C}^n)$ and $S \in L^p(B_\varepsilon; \mathrm{End}_{\mathbf{R}}(\mathbf{R}^{2n}))$ for $p > 2$.

To prove this similarity principle, we use the fact that the standard $\overline{\partial}$ is a Fredholm operator (this will be Theorem 8.6.11).

Let us now write down the proofs of the statements (Lemma 8.6.2 and Proposition 8.6.6) that use this principle.

Proof of Proposition 8.6.6. It is clear that the set C is closed. We will now show that it is also open. Let $z_0 = s_0 + it_0 \in C$. The similarity principle (Lemma 8.6.8) ensures the existence of a neighborhood $B_\delta(z_0)$ on which

$Y(z) = A(z)\sigma(z)$, where $\sigma : B_\delta(z_0) \to \mathbf{C}^n$ is holomorphic and A has values in the real endomorphisms of $\mathbf{C}^n$.

On $B_\delta(z_0)$, Y has an infinite-order zero if and only if σ also has one. But σ does have an infinite-order zero at z_0. Indeed, for $r < \delta$, we have

$$\sup_{|z-z_0|\leq r} |\sigma(z)| = \sup_{|z-z_0|\leq r} \left| A^{-1}(z) \cdot Y(z) \right|$$
$$\leq K \sup_{|z-z_0|\leq r} |Y(z)|$$

because A^{-1} is continuous (since $A \in W^{1,p}(B_\delta; \mathrm{GL}(\mathbf{R}^{2n}))$ is continuous). Consequently,

$$\lim_{r\to 0} \frac{\sup_{|z-z_0|\leq r} |\sigma(z)|}{r^k} = 0 \quad \text{for every } k.$$

But σ is an analytic function, therefore it is zero on $B_\delta(z_0)$, hence $B_\delta(z_0) \subset C$. $\square$

Proof of Lemma 8.6.2. Obviously, if $(dv)_0 \neq 0$, then the statement is true. Assume that $(dv)_0 = 0$. The map v is a solution of the equation

$$\frac{\partial v}{\partial s} + J\frac{\partial v}{\partial t} = 0.$$

Then, as we have already noted (Remark 8.4.7), $\partial v/\partial s$ is a solution of the linearized Cauchy–Riemann equation. We can therefore apply the similarity principle (Lemma 8.6.8) to $Y = \partial v/\partial s$, giving

$$Y(s,t) = A(s,t)\sigma(s,t)$$

with σ holomorphic in a neighborhood of 0. The lemma follows: the zeros of σ are isolated, hence so are those of $Y = \partial v/\partial s$, and *a fortiori* those of dv. $\square$

From the continuation principle, we now deduce a proof of Lemma 8.6.5.

Proof of Lemma 8.6.5. We choose an $\varepsilon > 0$ that is sufficiently small for $v_2 : B_\varepsilon \to \mathbf{R}^{2n}$ to embed B_ε as a submanifold $\Sigma = v(B_\varepsilon) \subset \mathbf{R}^{2n}$; this is authorized by the fact that $(dv_2)_0 \neq 0$. Using a projection from a neighborhood U_ε of the submanifold Σ onto this submanifold, we deduce a map φ of class $\mathcal{C}^\infty$:

$$\varphi : U_\varepsilon \longrightarrow B_\varepsilon \quad \text{with } \varphi|_\Sigma = v_2^{-1}.$$

For δ sufficiently small, $v_1(B_\delta) \subset \Sigma$ (by assumption), so that we have a map

$$\varphi \circ v_1 : B_\delta \longrightarrow U_\varepsilon \longrightarrow B_\varepsilon$$

that, by our assumption, must be of the form

$$\varphi \circ v_1(s,t) = (f(s,t),t)$$

with f of class $\mathcal{C}^\infty$, defined on $B_\delta(0)$ and with values in $B_\varepsilon(0)$. So for $(s,t) \in B_\delta$, we have $v_1(s,t) = v_2(f(s,t),t)$. Since v_1 is a solution, we also have

$$0 = \frac{\partial v_1}{\partial s}(s,t) + J(t,v_1)\frac{\partial v_1}{\partial t}(s,t) = \frac{\partial v_2}{\partial s}(f(s,t),t)\frac{\partial f}{\partial s}$$
$$+ J(t,v_2(f(s,t),t))\left[\frac{\partial v_2}{\partial s}(f(s,t),t)\frac{\partial f}{\partial t} + \frac{\partial v_2}{\partial t}(f(s,t),t)\right].$$

Next, we use the fact that v_2 is also a solution, that is, that

$$J\frac{\partial v_2}{\partial t} = -\frac{\partial v_2}{\partial s} \quad \text{and} \quad J\frac{\partial v_2}{\partial s} = \frac{\partial v_2}{\partial t},$$

to obtain

$$\frac{\partial v_2}{\partial s}(f,t)\left(\frac{\partial f}{\partial s} - 1\right) + \frac{\partial v_2}{\partial t}(f,t)\frac{\partial f}{\partial t} = 0,$$

a linear relation between the two independent vectors $(\partial v_2/\partial s)(f,t)$ and $(\partial v_2/\partial t)(f,t)$. Consequently,

$$\frac{\partial f}{\partial s} = 1 \quad \text{and} \quad \frac{\partial f}{\partial t} = 0,$$

so that f is of the form $f(s,t) = s + s_0$ for some $s_0 \in]-\varepsilon,\varepsilon[$ that must moreover be zero because $v_2(s_0,0) = v_1(0) = v_2(0)$ and v_2 is injective on $B_\varepsilon(0)$. It follows that $f(s,t) = s$, which means that v_1 and v_2 coincide in the neighborhood of 0 where f is defined. By the continuation principle, v_1 and v_2 must coincide on all of B_ε. □

Proof of Lemma 8.6.8. The last condition that needs to be satisfied is that $A(s,t)$ is a **C**-linear map (namely commutes with multiplication by i, which we have denoted by J_0) for all (s,t).

Let us try to replace S (in the perturbed Cauchy–Riemann equation) by a **C**-linear map. We begin by writing

$$S^+ = \frac{1}{2}(S - J_0SJ_0) \quad \text{and} \quad S^- = \frac{1}{2}(S + J_0SJ_0),$$

so that $S = S^+ + S^-$ and

$$J_0S^+ = \frac{1}{2}(J_0S + SJ_0) = S^+J_0;$$

consequently S^+ is **C**-linear and S^- is anti-**C**-linear. For $(s,t) \in B_\varepsilon$, we define $D(s,t) \in \mathrm{End}_{\mathbf{R}}(\mathbf{C}^n)$ by setting

$$D(s,t) \cdot Z = \begin{cases} \dfrac{1}{\|Y(s,t)\|^2} \cdot (Y(s,t) \cdot {}^tY(s,t)) \cdot \overline{Z} & \text{if } Y(s,t) \neq 0, \\ 0 & \text{if } Y(s,t) = 0. \end{cases}$$

Note that when $Y(s,t) \neq 0$, we have

$$D(s,t) \cdot Z = \frac{\langle Y, Z \rangle}{\|Y\|^2}(s,t) \cdot Y(s,t),$$

where $\langle\,,\,\rangle$ denotes the usual Hermitian inner product on $\mathbf{C}^n$ (see Section 5.5). In particular, $DY = Y$ for all (s,t). Moreover, this map is clearly anti-**C**-linear. Finally, we see that

$$\|D(s,t)\| \leq 1 \quad \text{for all } (s,t),$$

which in particular implies that

$$S^- \cdot D \in L^p(B_\varepsilon, \mathrm{End}_{\mathbf{R}}(\mathbf{R}^{2n})).$$

Next, we set

$$\widetilde{S}(s,t) = S^+(s,t) + S^-(s,t) \cdot D(s,t),$$

thus defining a **C**-linear map $\widetilde{S}$,

$$\widetilde{S} \in L^p(B_\varepsilon, \mathrm{End}_{\mathbf{R}}(\mathbf{R}^{2n})),$$

that satisfies

$$\widetilde{S} \cdot Y = S^+Y + S^- DY = S^+Y + S^-Y = SY,$$

so that Y is also a solution of the equation in which we replace S by $\widetilde{S}$. We can therefore assume that the S in our equation is **C**-linear. The desired result is a consequence of the following lemma.

Lemma 8.6.10. *There exist a $\delta \in \,]0,\varepsilon]$ and an $A \in W^{1,p}(B_\delta; \mathrm{End}(\mathbf{R}^{2n}))$ such that*

$$\frac{\partial A}{\partial s} + J_0 \frac{\partial A}{\partial t} + S \cdot A = 0$$

and $A(0,0) = \mathrm{Id}$.

In this statement, the product $S \cdot A$ is an element of $L^p(B_\delta; \mathrm{End}(\mathbf{R}^{2n}))$ (by Lemma 8.2.4). Let us admit this lemma (for the moment!) and finish the proof of Lemma 8.6.8. Let A be as in the lemma and, if it is not **C**-linear, replace it by

$$A^+ = \frac{1}{2}(A - J_0 A J_0),$$

which is a solution of the same equation (because we have assumed that S is **C**-linear) and which also satisfies $A^+(0,0) = \mathrm{Id}$. We may, and do, therefore assume that A commutes with J_0. Let us now show that it also satisfies the other conditions announced in Lemma 8.6.8. Since $A(0,0) = \mathrm{Id}$, if we choose δ sufficiently small, $A(s,t)$ is invertible for $(s,t) \in B_\delta$. Next, set

$$\sigma = A^{-1} \cdot Y, \quad \text{so that } Y = A \cdot \sigma.$$

Since Y is a solution of the equation, we have

$$\frac{\partial(A\sigma)}{\partial s} + J_0 \frac{\partial(A\sigma)}{\partial t} + S \cdot (A\sigma) = 0,$$

or

$$\frac{\partial A}{\partial s}\sigma + A\frac{\partial \sigma}{\partial s} + J_0\frac{\partial A}{\partial t}\sigma + J_0 A\frac{\partial \sigma}{\partial t} + S \cdot A\sigma = 0,$$

which implies that

$$A\left(\frac{\partial \sigma}{\partial s} + J_0\frac{\partial \sigma}{\partial t}\right) = 0,$$

and therefore that σ is holomorphic (it is continuous because it equals $\sigma = A^{-1} \cdot Y$, and is $\mathcal{C}^\infty$ by the elliptic regularity).

Proof of Lemma 8.6.10. The matrix A we are looking for is a kind of fundamental matrix of solutions of our equation. It suffices to consider the equation for the "vector" $Y \in W^{1,p}(B_\delta; \mathbf{R}^{2n})$,

$$\frac{\partial Y}{\partial s} + J_0\frac{\partial Y}{\partial t} + S \cdot Y = 0,$$

and to show that it has a solution such that $Y(0,0) = v_0$, for every fixed $v_0 \in \mathbf{R}^{2n}$. Using the vectors of the canonical basis, we will obtain the columns of the matrix A.

To do this, consider

$$B_\delta \subset \mathbf{C} \subset \mathbf{C} \cup \{\infty\} = S^2.$$

If Y is a map from S^2 to $\mathbf{C}^n = \mathbf{R}^{2n}$, then $\overline{\partial}Y$ is a section of the vector bundle $\left(\Lambda^{0,1}T^\star S^2\right)^n = \Lambda^{0,1}T^\star S^2 \otimes \mathbf{C}^n$, and the equality $\overline{\partial}Y = 0$ means that Y is a holomorphic sphere in $\mathbf{C}^n$.

We can now use the essential property of $\overline{\partial}$ recalled in the following theorem (which is a consequence of the Calderón–Zygmund inequality; see Theorem C.5.8).

Theorem 8.6.11. *For every $p > 1$, the operator*

$$\bar{\partial} : W^{1,p}(S^2, \mathbf{C}^n) \longrightarrow L^p(\Lambda^{0,1}T^\star S^2 \otimes \mathbf{C}^n)$$

is a surjective Fredholm operator.

The computation that makes up the proof of Lemma 6.6.4 shows that, if $\bar{\partial}Y = 0$,

$$\int_{\mathbf{R}^2} \left\| \frac{\partial Y}{\partial t} \right\|^2 ds\, dt = \int_{S^2} Y^\star \omega = 0$$

(by applying Stokes's formula). Hence the kernel of $\bar{\partial}$ contains only the constants, so that its dimension is $2n$, and, since $\bar{\partial}$ is surjective, its index is also equal to $2n$. Next, consider the operator

$$D : W^{1,p}(S^2; \mathbf{C}^n) \longrightarrow L^p\big((\Lambda^{0,1}T^\star S^2)^n\big) \oplus \mathbf{C}^n$$
$$Y \longmapsto (\bar{\partial}Y, Y(0)).$$

It is the sum of

$$(\bar{\partial}, 0) : W^{1,p}(S^2; \mathbf{C}^n) \longrightarrow L^p\big((\Lambda^{0,1}T^\star S^2)^n\big) \oplus \mathbf{C}^n,$$

which is a Fredholm operator of index 0, and the operator $Y \mapsto (0, Y(0))$, which is compact because there is a continuous injection of $W^{1,p}$ into L^∞. By Theorem C.2.10, we know that it is also a Fredholm operator of index 0. But its kernel consists of the zero constants, and is therefore zero. Consequently, D is bijective.

Let D_δ be the small perturbation of D defined by

$$D_\delta(Y) = (\bar{\partial}Y + S_\delta \cdot Y\, d\bar{Z}, Y(0)),$$

where $S_\delta : \mathbf{C} \cup \{\infty\} \to \operatorname{End}_{\mathbf{R}}(\mathbf{C}^n)$ is, in turn, defined by

$$S_\delta(s, t) = \begin{cases} S(s, t) & \text{if } (s, t) \in B_\delta, \\ 0 & \text{otherwise.} \end{cases}$$

Clearly,

$$\lim_{\delta \to 0} \|S_\delta\|_{L^p} = 0, \quad \text{hence} \quad \lim_{\delta \to 0} \|D_\delta - D\|^{\mathrm{op}} = 0,$$

and therefore D_δ is also bijective when δ is sufficiently small. After fixing such a number δ, we choose a Y such that $D_\delta Y = (0, v_0)$. Its restriction to B_δ satisfies the perturbed Cauchy–Riemann equation and the "initial condition" $Y(0) = v_0$, which proves the lemma (Lemma 8.6.10)... $\qquad \square$

... and the similarity principle (Lemma 8.6.8). $\qquad \square$

We could have used the same method as in the computation of the index (which we will give in Section 8.8): this is the object of Exercise 45.

8.7 The Fredholm Property

We will now attack the proof of Theorem 8.1.5. Let

$$S^{\pm}(t) = \lim_{s \to \pm\infty} S(s,t)$$

and let $R_t^{\pm}$ be the solution of

$$\dot{R} = J_0 S^{\pm} R \quad \text{with } R_0^{\pm} = \mathrm{Id}.$$

The aim of this section is to prove the following result.

Proposition 8.7.1. *If* $\det(\mathrm{Id} - R_1^{\pm}) \neq 0$, *then*

$$L = \bar{\partial} + S(s,t) : W^{1,p}(\mathbf{R} \times S^1; \mathbf{R}^{2n}) \longrightarrow L^p(\mathbf{R} \times S^1; \mathbf{R}^{2n})$$

is a Fredholm operator (for every $p > 1$).

We take inspiration from the proof given in [66] (see also [16]). The main ingredient is the following elliptic regularity theorem, together with a consequence of the Calderón–Zygmund inequality (Theorem C.5.8) stated in the next lemma (a proof can be found in Section 12.2).

Theorem (Theorem 12.1.3). *Let $p > 1$. If $Y \in L^p(\mathbf{R} \times S^1; \mathbf{R}^{2n})$ is a weak solution of the linearized Floer equation $LY = 0$, then $Y \in W^{1,p}(\mathbf{R} \times S^1; \mathbf{R}^{2n})$ (and Y is of class $\mathcal{C}^{\infty}$).*

Lemma 8.7.2. *Let $p > 1$. If $Y \in W^{1,p}(\mathbf{R} \times S^1; \mathbf{R}^{2n})$, then there exists a positive constant C such that*

$$\|Y\|_{W^{1,p}} \leq C(\|LY\|_{L^p} + \|Y\|_{L^p}).$$

The proof is set up as follows: we first consider the case where $S(s,t)$ does not depend on s, where we prove the following stronger result.

Proposition 8.7.3. *If the symmetric operator $S(s,t) = S(t)$ is independent of s and if $\det(\mathrm{Id} - R_1^{\pm}) \neq 0$, then*

$$D = \bar{\partial} + S(t) : W^{1,p}(\mathbf{R} \times S^1; \mathbf{R}^{2n}) \longrightarrow L^p(\mathbf{R} \times S^1; \mathbf{R}^{2n})$$

is bijective (for every $p > 1$).

We first prove this proposition in the case $p = 2$ in Section 8.7.a, and then in the general case in Section 8.7.b. The invertibility of the "asymptotic" operator D allows us to improve the inequality of Lemma 8.7.2 to

$$\|Y\|_{W^{1,p}(\mathbf{R} \times S^1; \mathbf{R}^{2n})} \leq C(\|Y\|_{L^p(\mathbf{R} \times S^1)} + \|Y\|_{L^p([-M,M] \times S^1)})$$

(for a sufficiently large $M > 0$).

Since the restriction $W^{1,p}(\mathbf{R} \times S^1) \to L^p([-M, M] \times S^1)$ is a compact operator (by Rellich's theorem (Theorem C.4.10)), we can then use a general result on so-called "semi-Fredholm" operators (whose proof is given in Appendix C.2.c).

Proposition 8.7.4. *Let E, F and G be three Banach spaces. Let $L : E \to F$ be an operator and let $K : E \to G$ be a compact operator. We suppose that there exists a constant $C > 0$ such that*

$$\forall x \in E, \quad \|x\|_E \leq C \left(\|L(x)\|_F + \|K(x)\|_G \right).$$

Then the kernel of L is finite-dimensional and its image is closed.

We will still need to show that the cokernel of L is finite-dimensional. We will do this by identifying it with the kernel of the adjoint operator

$$L^\star : W^{1,q}(\mathbf{R} \times S^1; \mathbf{R}^{2n}) \longrightarrow L^q(\mathbf{R} \times S^1; \mathbf{R}^{2n}),$$

where q is defined by $1/p + 1/q = 1$. This operator, which we have already come across in the proof of Lemma 8.5.1, also satisfies the conditions of Proposition 8.7.4, and its kernel therefore has finite dimension.

8.7.a Proof of Proposition 8.7.3, First Step, the Case $p = 2$

We consider the operator

$$A = J_0 \frac{\partial}{\partial t} + S : W^{1,2}(S^1; \mathbf{R}^{2n}) \longrightarrow L^2(S^1; \mathbf{R}^{2n})$$

acting on the functions in t.

Lemma 8.7.5. *Under the nondegeneracy assumption, the operator A is invertible.*

Remark 8.7.6. First note that A is the linear operator considered in the proof of Proposition 8.4.6, the one we obtained by linearizing the differential equation $\dot{x} = X_t(x)$ (see Subsections A.4.c and A.4.d).

Proof of Lemma 8.7.5. This is an application of the variation of constants. Inverting the operator comes down to solving, for $Z \in L^2(S^1; \mathbf{R}^{2n})$, the (nonhomogeneous) linear differential equation

$$\dot{Y} = J_0 SY - J_0 Z, \quad \text{with } Y \in W^{1,2}(S^1; \mathbf{R}^{2n}).$$

When $Z = 0$, the solutions are

$$Y(t) = R(t)Y_0, \quad t \in \mathbf{R},$$

where R is the fundamental solution, the matrix satisfying

$$\dot{R} = J_0 SR \quad \text{and} \quad R(0) = \text{Id}$$

(this is the matrix that we assumed without the eigenvalue 1 for $t = 1$). To solve the equation in general, we look for a solution of the form

$$Y(t) = R(t)Y_0(t), \quad t \in [0, 1].$$

Such a Y satisfies the differential equation if and only if

$$\dot{Y}_0(t) = -R^{-1}(t)J_0 Z(t).$$

We must therefore have

$$Y_0(t) = Y_0(0) - \int_0^t R^{-1}(\tau)J_0 Z(\tau) \, d\tau$$

and therefore

$$Y(t) = R(t)\left(Y_0(0) - \int_0^t R^{-1}(\tau)J_0 Z(\tau) \, d\tau\right).$$

We want to be able to extend Y to a periodic function, that is, to have $Y(0) = Y(1)$, or equivalently

$$R(1)\left(-\int_0^1 R^{-1}(\tau)J_0 Z(\tau) \, d\tau + Y_0(0)\right) = Y_0(0),$$

that is,

$$(R(1) - \text{Id})Y_0(0) = R(1)\int_0^1 R^{-1}(\tau)J_0 Z(\tau) \, d\tau.$$

This equation is easy to solve because the operator $\text{Id} - R(1)$ has been assumed to be invertible, giving a unique value for $Y_0(0)$. We have thus shown that A is bijective. $\qquad \square$

Remark 8.7.7. In this proof, we were able to use the values of the elements of $W^{1,2}$ in 0 and 1 because

$$W^{1,2}([0,1]; \mathbf{R}^{2n}) \subset \mathcal{C}^0([0,1]; \mathbf{R}^{2n}).$$

As we have already noted, the analogous inclusion is not true when the source space has dimension ≥ 2. See the results from analysis recalled in the appendices and in particular in Remark C.4.7.

Remainder of the Proof of Proposition 8.7.3 in the Case $p = 2$.

For $Z \in L^2(\mathbf{R} \times S^1; \mathbf{R}^{2n})$, we are looking for a $Y \in W^{1,2}(\mathbf{R} \times S^1; \mathbf{R}^{2n})$ such that

$$\frac{\partial Y}{\partial s} + J_0 \frac{\partial Y}{\partial t} + S(t)Y = Z.$$

In other words, we want to solve the "nonhomogeneous linear differential equation"

$$\frac{\partial Y}{\partial s} = -A \cdot Y(s) + Z(s)$$

in $W^{1,2}(\mathbf{R} \times S^1; \mathbf{R}^{2n})$. Unfortunately, in an infinite-dimensional setting, we cannot apply the variation of constants method as we did to show that A is invertible. We now know that the homogeneous equation

$$\begin{cases} \dfrac{\partial Y}{\partial s} = -AY \\ Y(0) = Y_0 \end{cases}$$

admits solutions defined only on $[0, +\infty[$, and only when the operator A is *monotone*, that is, satisfies

$$\forall x, \quad \langle Ax, x \rangle \geq 0$$

(for the L^2 product, see [17, Chapter 7] and Theorem 8.7.9). Since our A is not monotone, before being able to apply this result, we will need to decompose $L^2(S^1; \mathbf{R}^{2n})$ as a direct sum of spaces on which this monotonicity property does hold.

To simplify, let us denote this Hilbert space by $\mathcal{H}$:

$$\mathcal{H} = L^2(S^1; \mathbf{R}^{2n}).$$

The map A is not defined on $\mathcal{H}$, but on its subspace $W^{1,2}(S^1)$, it is what we call an unbounded operator, simply because it is continuous for the $W^{1,2}$ norm but possibly not for the L^2 norm on this subspace. Also note that the domain of A is dense in $\mathcal{H} = L^2(S^1)$ (because $\mathcal{C}^\infty(S^1) \subset W^{1,2}(S^1)$ is dense) and that A is a closed operator (that is, that its graph

$$\{(Y, AY) \mid Y \in W^{1,2}(S^1)\}$$

is closed in $L^2(S^1) \times L^2(S^1)$, an easy exercise for our readers).

The computation carried out for L in the proof of Lemma 8.5.2 tells us that A is self-adjoint, or more precisely that for the L^2 product, we have

$$\langle AX, Y \rangle = \langle X, AY \rangle \quad \text{for } X, Y \in W^{1,2}(S^1).$$

Let us now consider the operator $T : \mathcal{H} \to \mathcal{H}$ defined as the composition

$$L^2(S^1) \xrightarrow{\ A^{-1}\ } W^{1,2}(S^1) \xrightarrow{\ i\ } L^2(S^1).$$

This operator is continuous (because A^{-1} is continuous by the Banach theorem [17, Theorem 2.6]) and even compact, because the inclusion is compact. Moreover, it is self-adjoint, which easily follows from the similar property of A. We can therefore apply the following result (which is [17, Section 6.4]) to it.

Theorem 8.7.8. *Let $\mathcal{H}$ be a separable Hilbert space and let $T : \mathcal{H} \to \mathcal{H}$ be a compact self-adjoint operator. Then $\mathcal{H}$ admits a Hilbertian basis made up of eigenvectors of T.*

Recall that the set of eigenvalues of the operator A,

$$\{\lambda \in \mathbf{C} \mid A - \lambda \operatorname{Id} \text{ is not injective}\},$$

is contained in the spectrum of A, which, in turn, consists of the λ for which $A - \lambda \operatorname{Id}$ is not bijective. For a compact operator, the set of eigenvalues either is finite or consists of a sequence that tends to 0 (see [17, Section 6.3]). Note that in our case, 0 is not an eigenvalue because A^{-1} is injective. Also note that the eigenvectors of T are in $W^{1,2}(S^1; \mathbf{R}^{2n})$ because $Tv = \lambda v$ implies that

$$\lambda v = A^{-1} v \in W^{1,2}(S^1; \mathbf{R}^{2n}).$$

We have a decomposition

$$\mathcal{H} = \mathcal{H}^+ \oplus \mathcal{H}^-$$

(as a sum of positive and negative eigenspaces of T, respectively) and two orthogonal projections $p^\pm : \mathcal{H} \to \mathcal{H}^\pm$. Let $A^\pm$ be the restriction of A to $\mathcal{H}^\pm$. Each of these is again an unbounded operator. If $Y \in W^{1,2}(S^1)$ is in the eigenspace corresponding to the eigenvalue λ of T, then

$$AY = \frac{1}{\lambda} Y.$$

So the operators A^+ and $-A^-$ are indeed monotone operators (each of them satisfies $\langle Bx, x \rangle \geq 0$)

$$A^\pm : \mathcal{H}^\pm \longrightarrow \mathcal{H}^\pm.$$

The following surprising existence result for solutions (Hille–Yosida theory) applies to these operators.

Theorem 8.7.9. *Let $A : D(A) \subset H \to H$ be a self-adjoint monotone closed operator defined on a dense open subset $D(A)$. Then for every Y_0 in H, there exists a map $Y : [0, +\infty[\to H$ that is continuous, differentiable on $]0, +\infty[$, has image $Y(]0, +\infty[) \subset D(A)$ and satisfies*

$$\begin{cases} \dfrac{\partial Y}{\partial s} = -AY \\ Y(0) = Y_0. \end{cases}$$

Moreover, Y, with these properties, is unique and we have

$$\|Y(s)\| \leq \|Y_0\| \quad and \quad \forall s > 0, \quad \left\| \frac{\partial Y}{\partial s}(s) \right\| = \|AY(s)\| \leq \frac{1}{s} \|Y_0\|.$$

Remarks 8.7.10. We called this result surprising for the following reasons:

(1) It is not a local existence result for solutions of a differential equation: nothing is said *in the neighborhood* of 0.
(2) The initial condition is not assumed to be in the definition space of A (it is true that the latter is dense in H by the previous remark).
(3) It is, however, a global result, as in the case of a linear ordinary differential equation, in the sense that it gives solutions on all of $[0, +\infty[$.
(4) Similarly, as soon as we fix $s > 0$, the map $Y_0 \mapsto Y(s)$ is linear (by the uniqueness of the solution), defining a continuous linear map from H to $D(A)$. Let us call it $\Gamma(s)$. Again by the uniqueness, we have

$$\Gamma(s_1 + s_2) = \Gamma(s_1) \cdot \Gamma(s_2)$$

and, since $Y(0) = Y_0$, $\Gamma(0) = \mathrm{Id}$. We say that Γ is a semiflow (or a semigroup)... and use the notation $\Gamma(s) = e^{-As}$.

Our operators A^+ and $-A^-$ therefore generate "semigroups" of operators on $\mathcal{H}^+$ and $\mathcal{H}^-$, solutions of the differential equations

$$\frac{dY}{ds} = -A^+Y, \quad \frac{dY}{ds} = A^-Y$$

that are well defined for $s \geq 0$ and that we denote by

$$s \longmapsto e^{-A^+ s}, \quad s \longmapsto e^{A^- s}.$$

We then define a "kernel"

$$K(s) = \begin{cases} e^{-A^+ s} p^+ & \text{for } s \geq 0 \\ -e^{A^- (-s)} p^- & \text{for } s < 0, \end{cases}$$

where the $p^{\pm} : \mathcal{H} \to \mathcal{H}^{\pm}$ denote the orthogonal projections.

This is a map $\mathbf{R} \to \mathcal{L}(\mathcal{H})$ (with values in the space $\mathcal{L}(\mathcal{H})$ of continuous operators on $\mathcal{H}$). Note that it is continuous for $s \neq 0$, but not at 0. We also have, for $s \geq 0$,

$$\|K(s) \cdot Y\|_{\mathcal{H}} = \|e^{-A^+ s} p^+ Y\|_{\mathcal{H}} \leq e^{-\mu s} \|Y\|_{\mathcal{H}},$$

where $\mu = \lambda^{-1} > 0$ for $\lambda > 0$ the largest positive eigenvalue of T. The analogous inequality for $s < 0$ gives

$$\|K(s)\|_{\mathcal{L}(\mathcal{H})} \leq e^{-\delta |s|}$$

for some constant $\delta > 0$.

We can therefore define

$$Q : L^2(\mathbf{R}, \mathcal{H}) \longrightarrow W^{1,2}(\mathbf{R} \times S^1; \mathbf{R}^{2n})$$

by setting

$$(Q \cdot Z)(s, t) = \int_{-\infty}^{+\infty} K(-\sigma) Z(s + \sigma, t) \, d\sigma.$$

The integral is convergent in $L^2(\mathbf{R} \times S^1; \mathbf{R}^{2n})$. In fact, the absolute convergence comes from

$$\int_{\mathbf{R}} \|K(-\sigma) Z(s + \sigma, t)\|_{L^2(\mathbf{R} \times S^1)} \, d\sigma$$

$$= \int_{\mathbf{R}} \left(\int_{\mathbf{R}} \|K(-\sigma) Z(s + \sigma)\|_{L^2(S^1)}^2 \, ds \right)^{1/2} d\sigma$$

$$\leq \int_{\mathbf{R}} \left(\int_{\mathbf{R}} e^{-2\delta |\sigma|} \|Z(s + \sigma)\|_{L^2(S^1)}^2 \, ds \right)^{1/2} d\sigma$$

$$= \int_{\mathbf{R}} e^{-2\delta |\sigma|} \|Z\|_{L^2(\mathbf{R} \times S^1)} \, d\sigma < +\infty.$$

Consequently, $Q \cdot Z$ is in $L^2(\mathbf{R} \times S^1; \mathbf{R}^{2n})$. To show that it is in $W^{1,2}(\mathbf{R} \times S^1; \mathbf{R}^{2n})$, it suffices to establish, for $Y = Q \cdot Z$, the equality

$$Z = \frac{dY}{ds} + A \cdot Y.$$

To do this, note that (omitting the variable t in the notation)

$$(Q \cdot Z)(s) = \int_{\mathbf{R}} K(s - \sigma) Z(\sigma) \, d\sigma$$

$$= \int_{-\infty}^{s} e^{-A^+(s-\sigma)} Z^+(\sigma) \, d\sigma - \int_{s}^{+\infty} e^{A^-(\sigma-s)} Z^-(\sigma) \, d\sigma$$

(where the $Z^\pm$ denote the projections onto $\mathcal{H}^\pm$). Let

$$Y = Q \cdot Z = Y^+ + Y^-,$$

so that

$$\frac{dY^+}{ds} = \frac{d}{ds} \int_{-\infty}^{s} e^{-A^+(s-\sigma)} Z^+(\sigma) \, d\sigma$$

$$= e^{-A^+ \cdot 0} \cdot Z^+(s) + \int_{-\infty}^{s} \frac{d}{ds} e^{-A^+(s-\sigma)} Z^+(\sigma) \, d\sigma$$

$$= Z^+(s) + \int_{-\infty}^{s} -A^+ e^{-A^+(s-\sigma)} Z^+(\sigma) \, d\sigma$$

$$= Z^+(s) - A^+ Y^+(s).$$

The analogous computation for Y^- gives

$$\frac{dY^\pm}{ds} + A^\pm Y^\pm = Z^\pm,$$

so that

$$Z = \frac{dY}{ds} + AY.$$

This relation shows that $D \circ Q = \mathrm{Id}$. Let us also show that $Q \circ D = \mathrm{Id}$. Let $Y \in W^{1,2}(\mathbf{R} \times S^1; \mathbf{R}^{2n})$. We decompose it into $Y = Y^+ + Y^-$, so that

$$AY = A^+ Y^+ + A^- Y^-.$$

Note that for $B = A^\pm$, the two expressions

$$B \cdot e^{Bs} Y_0 \quad \text{and} \quad e^{Bs} \cdot BY_0$$

are solutions of

$$\begin{cases} \dfrac{\partial Y}{\partial s} = BY \\ Y(0) = B \cdot Y_0. \end{cases}$$

They are therefore equal (by the uniqueness stated in Theorem 8.7.9). We use this commutativity in the following computation.

Let us determine $Q \cdot (AY)$. We have

$$Q \cdot (AY) = \int_{-\infty}^{s} e^{-A^+(s-\sigma)} A^+ Y^+(\sigma) \, d\sigma - \int_{s}^{+\infty} e^{A^-(\sigma-s)} A^- Y^-(\sigma) \, d\sigma.$$

The first term of the sum equals

$$\int_{-\infty}^{s} A^+ e^{-A^+(s-\sigma)} Y^+(\sigma)\, d\sigma = \int_{-\infty}^{s} -\frac{\partial}{\partial s}\left(e^{-A^+(s-\sigma)} Y^+(\sigma)\right) d\sigma$$

$$= -\frac{\partial}{\partial s} \int_{-\infty}^{s} e^{-A^+(s-\sigma)} Y^+(\sigma)\, d\sigma + Y^+(s)$$

$$= -\frac{\partial}{\partial s} \int_{-\infty}^{0} e^{-A^+(-\sigma)} Y^+(s+\sigma)\, d\sigma + Y^+(s)$$

$$= -\int_{-\infty}^{0} e^{-A^+(-\sigma)} \frac{\partial Y^+}{\partial s}(s+\sigma)\, d\sigma + Y^+(s).$$

Analogously, the second term equals

$$-\int_{s}^{+\infty} A^- e^{A^-(\sigma-s)} Y^-(\sigma)\, d\sigma = \int_{0}^{+\infty} e^{A^-(-\sigma)} \frac{\partial Y^-}{\partial s}(s+\sigma)\, d\sigma + Y^-(s).$$

By taking the sum of the two, we obtain

$$Q(AY) = -Q\left(\frac{\partial Y}{\partial s}\right) + Y,$$

that is, $Q \circ D(Y) = Y$, so that Q is indeed an inverse for D. This concludes the proof of Proposition 8.7.3 for $p = 2$.

8.7.b Proof of Proposition 8.7.3 in the General Case Where $p > 1$

We use the following stronger version of the Calderón–Zygmund inequality (our Lemma 8.7.2) for the operator $D = \bar{\partial} + S(t)$.

Lemma 8.7.11. *Let $p > 1$. There exists a constant $C > 0$ such that for every $k \in \mathbf{R}$ and every $Y \in W^{1,p}(\mathbf{R} \times S^1; \mathbf{R}^{2n})$, we have*

$$\|Y\|_{W^{1,p}([k,k+1]\times S^1)} \leq C\left(\|DY\|_{L^p([k-\frac{1}{2},k+\frac{3}{2}]\times S^1)} + \|Y\|_{L^p([k-\frac{1}{2},k+\frac{3}{2}]\times S^1)}\right).$$

Note that by taking the sum of the inequalities given in this lemma over the $k \in \mathbf{Z}$, we obtain Lemma 8.7.2: this statement is indeed stronger.

Proof. First let $k = 0$. The inequality is then an immediate consequence of Theorem 12.1.2. Next, apply the result to

$$Z(s,t) = Y(s-k, t).$$

The operator D is invariant under translations in s, so that

$$DZ(s,t) = (DY)(s-k, t).$$

This gives the result for every k (with the same constant $C > 0$). □

From now on we assume that $p > 2$. The next lemma is a consequence of the previous one.

Lemma 8.7.12. *Let* $p > 2$. *There exists a constant* $C_1 > 0$ *such that for every* $k \in \mathbf{R}$ *and every* $Y \in W^{1,p}(\mathbf{R} \times S^1; \mathbf{R}^{2n})$, *we have*

$$\|Y\|_{W^{1,p}([k,k+1]\times S^1)} \leq C_1 \left(\|DY\|_{L^p([k-1,k+2]\times S^1)} + \|Y\|_{L^2([k-1,k+2]\times S^1)} \right).$$

Proof. Because of the invariance of D, it suffices, as above, to prove the result for $k = 0$. Since we now have $p > 2$, by Hölder's inequality, we have

$$L^p([-1,2] \times S^1) \subset L^2([-1,2] \times S^1),$$

with, for q defined by $2/p + 1/q = 1$,

$$\|Y\|_{L^2} \leq 3^{1/2q} \|Y\|_{L^p}.$$

Likewise,

$$W^{1,p}([-1,2] \times S^1) \subset W^{1,2}([-1,2] \times S^1), \quad \text{with } \|Y\|_{W^{1,2}} \leq 3^{1/2q} \|Y\|_{W^{1,p}}.$$

The same thing holds in the interval $[-1/2, 3/2]$, by replacing $3^{1/2q}$ by $2^{1/2q}$. Finally, Rellich's theorem (Theorem C.4.10) gives

$$W^{1,2}([-1/2,3/2] \times S^1) \subset L^p([-1/2,3/2] \times S^1), \quad \text{with } \|Y\|_{L^p} \leq C \|Y\|_{W^{1,2}}.$$

We then have (leaving out the factor S^1 to simplify the notation)

$$\begin{aligned}
\|Y\|_{W^{1,p}([0,1])} &\leq C_1 \left(\|DY\|_{L^p([-1/2,3/2])} + \|Y\|_{L^p([-1/2,3/2])} \right) \\
&\leq C_2 \left(\|DY\|_{L^p([-1/2,3/2])} + \|Y\|_{W^{1,2}([-1/2,3/2])} \right) \\
&\leq C_3 \left(\|DY\|_{L^p([-1/2,3/2])} + \|DY\|_{L^2([-1,2])} + \|Y\|_{L^2([-1,2])} \right) \\
&\qquad \text{by the previous lemma with } p = 2, k = -1/2, \text{ and then } k = 1/2 \\
&\leq C_4 \left(\|DY\|_{L^p([-1,2])} + \|Y\|_{L^2([-1,2])} \right).
\end{aligned}$$

This concludes the proof (of this lemma)... □

... and leads us to another lemma.

Lemma 8.7.13. *Let* $p > 2$. *There exists a constant* $C > 0$ *such that if* $Y \in W^{1,2}(\mathbf{R} \times S^1)$ *and* $DY \in L^p(\mathbf{R} \times S^1)$, *then*

$$Y \in W^{1,p}(\mathbf{R} \times S^1) \quad \text{and} \quad \|Y\|_{W^{1,p}} \leq C \|DY\|_{L^p}.$$

Proof. Let us begin by proving that $Y \in W^{1,p}(\mathbf{R} \times S^1)$. By Lemma 8.7.12, it suffices to prove that $Y \in W^{1,p}(K)$ for every compact K, which is a consequence of Theorem 12.1.2.

In the following proof, we will need to view Y as a map

$$Y : \mathbf{R} \longrightarrow L^2(S^1; \mathbf{R}^{2n}) = \mathcal{H}$$

and to use the corresponding $L^p(\mathbf{R}; \mathcal{H})$ norm

$$\|Y\|_{L^p(\mathbf{R};\mathcal{H})} = \left(\int_{\mathbf{R}} \|Y(s, \cdot)\|_{L^2}^p \, ds \right)^{1/p}.$$

Using the previous lemma and the inequality $(a + b)^p \leq 2^p(a^p + b^p)$ (an exercise for our readers), we find

$$\|Y\|_{W^{1,p}([k,k+1])}^p \leq C_1 \left(\|DY\|_{L^p([k-1,k+2])} + \|Y\|_{L^2([k-1,k+2])} \right)^p$$
$$\leq 2^p C_1 \left(\|DY\|_{L^p([k-1,k+2])}^p + \|Y\|_{L^2([k-1,k+2])}^p \right).$$

By applying Hölder's inequality (and using the number q defined by $2/p + 1/q = 1$), we obtain

$$\|Y\|_{L^2([k-1,k+2])}^p = \left(\int_{k-1}^{k+2} \int_{S^1} \|Y(s,t)\|^2 \, dt \, ds \right)^{p/2}$$
$$= \left(\int_{k-1}^{k+2} \|Y(s, \cdot)\|_{L^2}^2 \, ds \right)^{p/2}$$
$$\leq \left(3^{1/q} \left(\int_{k-1}^{k+2} \|Y(s, \cdot)\|_{L^2}^p \, ds \right)^{2/p} \right)^{p/2}$$
$$= 3^{p/2q} \int_{k-1}^{k+2} \|Y(s, \cdot)\|_{L^2}^p \, ds.$$

Consequently,

$$\|Y\|_{W^{1,p}([k,k+1])}^p \leq C_2 \left(\|DY\|_{L^p([k-1,k+2])}^p + \int_{k-1}^{k+2} \|Y(s, \cdot)\|_{L^2}^p \, ds \right)$$

and, taking the sum over $k \in \mathbf{Z}$,

$$\|Y\|_{W^{1,p}(\mathbf{R} \times S^1)}^p \leq C_3 \left(\|DY\|_{L^p(\mathbf{R} \times S^1)}^p + \|Y\|_{L^p(\mathbf{R},\mathcal{H})}^p \right).$$

We now want to give an upper bound for the last term of this sum. We use the inverse

$$Q : L^2(\mathbf{R} \times S^1) \longrightarrow W^{1,2}(\mathbf{R} \times S^1)$$

of D that we defined in Section 8.7.a. Since we have assumed that $Y \in W^{1,2}(\mathbf{R} \times S^1)$, we have

$$\|Y\|_{L^p(\mathbf{R};\mathcal{H})} = \|QDY\|_{L^p(\mathbf{R};\mathcal{H})} .$$

Once again to simplify the notation, let $Z = DY$ and let $\| \ \|$ denote the norm on $\mathcal{H}$. We then have

$$
\begin{aligned}
\|QZ\|_{L^p(\mathbf{R};\mathcal{H})} &= \left(\int_{\mathbf{R}} \|(QZ)(s)\|^p \, ds \right)^{1/p} \\
&= \left(\int_{\mathbf{R}} \left\| \int_{\mathbf{R}} K(s-\sigma) \cdot Z(\sigma) \, d\sigma \right\|^p \, ds \right)^{1/p} \\
&\leq \left(\int_{\mathbf{R}} \left(\int_{\mathbf{R}} \|K(s-\sigma) \cdot Z(\sigma)\| \, d\sigma \right)^p \, ds \right)^{1/p} \\
&\leq \left(\int_{\mathbf{R}} \left(\int_{\mathbf{R}} e^{-\delta|s-\sigma|} \|Z(\sigma)\| \, d\sigma \right)^p \, ds \right)^{1/p} .
\end{aligned}
$$

This is a convolution of $f(s) = e^{-\delta|s|}$ and $g(s) = \|Z(s)\|$. We can apply Young's inequality[9] to find

$$\|QZ\|_{L^p(\mathbf{R};\mathcal{H})} \leq C \|Z\|_{L^p(\mathbf{R};\mathcal{H})} .$$

By Hölder's inequality for $L^p(S^1)$ and $L^2(S^1)$, we have

$$
\begin{aligned}
\|Z\|_{L^p(\mathbf{R};\mathcal{H})} &= \left(\int_{\mathbf{R}} \|DY(s,\cdot)\|_{L^2}^p \, ds \right)^{1/p} \\
&\leq \left(\int_{\mathbf{R}} \|DY(s,\cdot)\|_{L^p}^p \, ds \right)^{1/p} \\
&= \|Z\|_{L^p(\mathbf{R} \times S^1)} .
\end{aligned}
$$

We conclude that

$$\|Y\|_{L^p(\mathbf{R};\mathcal{H})} = \|QZ\|_{L^p(\mathbf{R};\mathcal{H})} \leq C \|Z\|_{L^p(\mathbf{R} \times S^1)} = C \|DY\|_{L^p(\mathbf{R} \times S^1)}$$

and finally that

$$\|Y\|_{W^{1,p}(\mathbf{R} \times S^1)} \leq C_4 \|DY\|_{L^p(\mathbf{R} \times S^1)} ,$$

proving the lemma. $\qquad \square$

The following result is a consequence of this.

---

[9] If necessary, see [17, Chapter 4] for this inequality:

$$\|f \star g\|_{L^p} \leq \|f\|_{L^1} \cdot \|g\|_{L^p} .$$

Proposition 8.7.14. *The operator D is bijective for $p > 2$.*

Proof. The inequality

$$\|Y\|_{W^{1,p}(\mathbf{R}\times S^1)} \leq C \, \|DY\|_{L^p(\mathbf{R}\times S^1)}$$

of the previous lemma holds for every $Y \in W^{1,p}(\mathbf{R}\times S^1) \cap W^{1,2}(\mathbf{R}\times S^1)$ and, in particular, for every $Y \in \mathcal{C}_0^\infty(\mathbf{R}\times S^1)$. Since the $\mathcal{C}^\infty$ functions with compact support are dense[10] in $W^{1,p}$, the inequality remains true for $Y \in W^{1,p}(\mathbf{R}\times S^1)$ (entirely). Hence D is injective. Moreover, since $W^{1,p}$ is complete, its image is closed.

To prove that D is also surjective, it suffices to establish that its image is dense in $L^p(\mathbf{R}\times S^1)$. Let $Z \in L^p(\mathbf{R}\times S^1) \cap L^2(\mathbf{R}\times S^1)$. Note that because this space contains the characteristic functions, it is dense in $L^p(\mathbf{R}\times S^1)$. The surjectivity of D when $p = 2$, established earlier, gives a $Y \in W^{1,2}(\mathbf{R}\times S^1)$ such that $DY = Z$. By the above, this Y is in $W^{1,p}(\mathbf{R}\times S^1)$, proving our proposition. □

To conclude the proof of Proposition 8.7.3, we still need to prove the following result.

Proposition 8.7.15. *The operator*

$$D : W^{1,p}(\mathbf{R}\times S^1) \longrightarrow L^p(\mathbf{R}\times S^1)$$

is bijective for $1 < p < 2$.

Proof. Let us show, as in the previous proposition, that there exists a constant $C > 0$ such that

$$\|Y\|_{W^{1,p}(\mathbf{R}\times S^1)} \leq C \, \|DY\|_{L^p(\mathbf{R}\times S^1)}.$$

As above, because of the density property, it suffices to establish this equality for $Y \in \mathcal{C}_0^\infty(\mathbf{R}\times S^1)$. We use the adjoint operator

$$D^\star : W^{1,q}(\mathbf{R}\times S^1) \longrightarrow L^q(\mathbf{R}\times S^1)$$

$$x \longmapsto -\frac{\partial X}{\partial s} + J_0\frac{\partial X}{\partial t} + S \cdot X,$$

where, as it should be (but not as above), q is defined by $1/p + 1/q = 1$, so that $q > 2$ (and where, recall, S is symmetric). We have already seen (in the proof of Lemma 8.5.2), that for every $X \in W^{1,q}(\mathbf{R}\times S^1)$ and every $Y \in \mathcal{C}_0^\infty(\mathbf{R}\times S^1)$,

$$\langle D^\star X, Y \rangle = \langle X, DY \rangle.$$

---

[10] See [17, Chapter 9], if necessary.

The results that we proved for D and $p > 2$ also apply to $D^\star$, which is of the same form as D, and to q, which is greater than 2. In particular, $D^\star$ is bijective. Let us now write

$$\|Y\|_{W^{1,p}} = \|Y\|_{L^p} + \left\|\frac{\partial Y}{\partial s}\right\|_{L^p} + \left\|\frac{\partial Y}{\partial t}\right\|_{L^p}$$

and give an upper bound for each of the three terms on the right. By Riesz's[11] theorem, we have

$$\|Y\|_{L^p} = \sup_{\substack{Z \in L^q \\ \|Z\|_{L^q}=1}} |\langle Z, Y \rangle|.$$

Since $D^\star$ is bijective, this gives

$$\|Y\|_{L^p} = \sup_{\substack{X \in W^{1,q} \\ \|D^\star X\|_{L^q}=1}} |\langle D^\star X, Y \rangle| = \sup_{\substack{X \in W^{1,q} \\ \|D^\star X\|_{L^q}=1}} |\langle X, DY \rangle|$$

$$\leq \|DY\|_{L^p} \sup_{\substack{X \in W^{1,q} \\ \|D^\star X\|_{L^q}=1}} \|X\|_{L^q}.$$

As in the proof of the previous proposition, we have

$$\|X\|_{L^q} \leq \|X\|_{W^{1,q}} \leq C \|D^\star X\|_{L^q},$$

and therefore

$$\|Y\|_{L^p} \leq C \|DY\|_{L^p}.$$

We proceed as for the derivative with respect to s, using the fact that

$$D^\star \frac{\partial}{\partial s} = \frac{\partial}{\partial s} D^\star$$

(the application of this operator to an element of $W^{1,q}$ should be taken in the sense of distributions). We have

$$\left\|\frac{\partial Y}{\partial s}\right\|_{L^p} = \sup_{\substack{X \in W^{1,q} \\ \|D^\star X\|_{L^q}=1}} \left|\left\langle D^\star X, \frac{\partial}{\partial s} Y \right\rangle\right| = \sup_{\substack{X \in W^{1,q} \\ \|D^\star X\|_{L^q}=1}} \left|\left\langle \frac{\partial}{\partial s} D^\star X, Y \right\rangle\right|$$

$$= \sup_{\substack{X \in W^{1,q} \\ \|D^\star X\|_{L^q}=1}} \left|\left\langle D^\star \frac{\partial}{\partial s} X, Y \right\rangle\right| = \sup_{\substack{X \in W^{1,q} \\ \|D^\star X\|_{L^q}=1}} \left|\left\langle \frac{\partial}{\partial s} X, DY \right\rangle\right|$$

$$\leq \|DY\|_{L^p} \sup_{\substack{X \in W^{1,q} \\ \|D^\star X\|_{L^q}=1}} \left\|\frac{\partial X}{\partial s}\right\|_{L^q} \leq C \|DY\|_{L^p}$$

because

$$\|X\|_{W^{1,q}} \leq C \|D^\star X\|_{L^q}$$

---

[11] See [17, Chapter 4], if necessary.

as before. For the derivative with respect to t, note that for $X \in W^{1,q}$, we have

$$\frac{\partial}{\partial t} D^\star X = D^\star \frac{\partial}{\partial t} X + \frac{\partial}{\partial t} S \cdot X$$

(where the derivatives are still taken in the sense of distributions). It follows that

$$\left\| \frac{\partial Y}{\partial t} \right\|_{L^p} = \sup_{\substack{X \in W^{1,q} \\ \|D^\star X\|_{L^q} = 1}} \left| \left\langle D^\star X, \frac{\partial}{\partial t} Y \right\rangle \right| = \sup_{\substack{X \in W^{1,q} \\ \|D^\star X\|_{L^q} = 1}} \left| \left\langle \frac{\partial}{\partial t} D^\star X, Y \right\rangle \right|$$

$$= \sup_{\substack{X \in W^{1,q} \\ \|D^\star X\|_{L^q} = 1}} \left| \left\langle D^\star \frac{\partial}{\partial t} X + \frac{\partial S}{\partial t} X, Y \right\rangle \right|$$

$$= \sup_{\substack{X \in W^{1,q} \\ \|D^\star X\|_{L^q} = 1}} \left| \left\langle \frac{\partial}{\partial t} X, DY \right\rangle + \left\langle \frac{\partial S}{\partial t} X, Y \right\rangle \right|$$

$$\leq \|DY\|_{L^p} \sup_{\substack{X \in W^{1,q} \\ \|D^\star X\|_{L^q} = 1}} \|X\|_{W^{1,q}} + C \|Y\|_{L^p} \sup_{\substack{X \in W^{1,q} \\ \|D^\star X\|_{L^q} = 1}} \|X\|_{L^q}$$

with $C = \sup_{t \in S^1} \|\partial S / \partial t\|$. As before, the first term of the sum is bounded from above by $C \|DY\|_{L^p}$. Moreover, since we have shown that $\|Y\|_{L^p} \leq \|DY\|_{L^p}$, the second term admits an upper bound of the same form. We have therefore established that

$$\text{for every } Y \in W^{1,p}(\mathbf{R} \times S^1), \quad \|Y\|_{W^{1,p}} \leq C \|DY\|_{L^p}.$$

It follows that, in this case too, the operator D is injective and has a closed image. Otherwise, Riesz's theorem would give a nonzero $Z \in L^q(\mathbf{R} \times S^1)$ such that

$$\text{for every } Y \in W^{1,p}(\mathbf{R} \times S^1), \quad \langle Z, DY \rangle = 0.$$

As in the proof of Lemma 8.5.2, it follows that $D^\star Z = 0$ (still in the sense of distributions), and therefore, by elliptic regularity (that is, Theorem 12.1.3), that $Z \in W^{1,q}(\mathbf{R} \times S^1)$. Hence $Z \in \mathrm{Ker}\, D^\star$, and Z must be zero, which contradicts our assumption. This concludes the proof of our proposition (namely, Proposition 8.7.15). □

8.7.c Proof of Proposition 8.7.1

Since D is bijective, its inverse is a continuous map (by the Banach open mapping theorem). Hence there exists a constant $B > 0$ such that

$$\|Y\|_{W^{1,p}} \leq B \|DY\|_{L^p}.$$

Consequently, since $S(s,t) \to S^{\pm}(t)$ for $s \to \infty$, there exist positive real constants M and C such that for every $Y \in W^{1,p}(\mathbf{R} \times S^1, W)$,

$$\text{if } Y(s,t) = 0 \text{ for } |s| \leq M - 1, \text{ then } \|Y\|_{W^{1,p}} \leq C \|LY\|_{L^p}.$$

Indeed,

$$\|LY - DY\|_{L^p} \leq \sup_{\substack{|s| \geq M \\ t \in S^1}} |S(s,t) - S^{\pm}(t)| \|Y\|_{L^p} \leq \varepsilon \|Y\|_{L^p} \leq \varepsilon \|Y\|_{W^{1,p}}.$$

We study Y separately for $|s|$ large and then for $|s|$ small. To do this, we choose a positive $\mathcal{C}^{\infty}$ function $\beta : \mathbf{R} \to [0,1]$ that is zero for $|s| \geq M$ and equal to 1 for $|s| \leq M - 1$, and we write

$$Y(s,t) = \beta(s)Y(s,t) + (1 - \beta(s))Y(s,t)$$

and of course

$$\|Y\|_{W^{1,p}} \leq \|\beta Y\|_{W^{1,p}} + \|(1 - \beta)Y\|_{W^{1,p}}.$$

The inequality of Lemma 8.7.2 for β and the inequality above for $(1 - \beta)Y$ give

$$\|Y\|_{W^{1,p}} \leq C_1 \left(\|L(\beta Y)\|_{L^p} + \|\beta Y\|_{L^p} + \|L((1 - \beta)Y)\|_{L^p} \right).$$

Since β depends only on s, we have

$$L(\beta Y) = \left(\frac{\partial}{\partial s} + J_0 \frac{\partial}{\partial t} + S \right)(\beta Y) = \beta L(Y) + \beta'(s)Y.$$

The derivative $\beta'(s)$ is bounded;

$$|\beta'(s)| \leq K \text{ for } s \in [-M, M] \quad \text{and} \quad \beta'(s) = 0 \text{ for } |s| \geq M.$$

We therefore have

$$\|L(\beta Y)\|_{L^p} \leq \|L(Y)\|_{L^p} + K \|Y\|_{L^p[-M,M]}$$

and likewise for $L((1 - \beta)Y)$, so that the inequality above gives

$$\|Y\|_{W^{1,p}} \leq C_2 \left(\|Y\|_{L^p[-M,M]} + \|L(Y)\|_{L^p} \right).$$

By Rellich's theorem (Theorem C.4.10), the restriction to $[-M, M]$ defines a *compact* operator

$$W^{1,p}(\mathbf{R} \times S^1; \mathbf{R}^{2n}) \longrightarrow L^p([-M, M] \times S^1; \mathbf{R}^{2n}).$$

We then use Proposition 8.7.4 to deduce that L has a finite-dimensional kernel and a closed image.

We still use the real number q with $1/p + 1/q = 1$. Let us consider the subspace F of $L^q(\mathbf{R} \times S^1)$ consisting of the Z with $\langle \operatorname{Im} L, Z \rangle = 0$ and the adjoint

$$L^\star = -\frac{\partial}{\partial s} + J_0 \frac{\partial}{\partial t} + {}^t S : W^{1,q}(\mathbf{R} \times S^1) \longrightarrow L^q(\mathbf{R} \times S^1).$$

Again, as in the proof of Lemma 8.5.2, $L^\star Z = 0$ in the sense of distributions, so that $Z \in W^{1,q}(\mathbf{R} \times S^1)$ by elliptic regularity (Theorem 12.1.3). Consequently, $F \subset \operatorname{Ker} L^\star$. Moreover, since $L^\star$ is of the same form as L, it also satisfies the assumptions of Proposition 8.7.4, so that it also satisfies its conclusion, namely that its kernel is finite-dimensional.

Let us now show that $\operatorname{Coker} L$ is finite-dimensional. The Hahn–Banach theorem allows us to find linear forms $\varphi : L^p \to \mathbf{R}$ that are zero on $\operatorname{Im} L$; we want to prove that the space of these forms is finite-dimensional. The Riesz representation theorem allows us to write a linear form as

$$\varphi = \varphi_U \quad \text{for a } U \in L^q \text{ with } \varphi_U(V) = \langle U, V \rangle.$$

Since these forms are zero on $\operatorname{Im} L$, the U that represent them must be in F. But this is finite-dimensional. Consequently, so is $\operatorname{Coker} L$, concluding the proof of Proposition 8.7.1. □

8.8 Computing the Index of L

To compute the index of L,

$$L(Y) = \frac{\partial Y}{\partial s} + J_0 \frac{\partial Y}{\partial t} + S(s,t)Y,$$

with $\lim_{s \to \pm\infty} S(s,t) = S^\pm(t)$ uniformly in t, we will:

(1) Replace L by L_0 given by the same formula... except that $S(s,t)$ is replaced by a matrix $\widetilde{S}(s,t)$ that is *exactly* $S^-(t)$ for $s \le -\sigma_0$ and $S^+(t)$ for $s \ge \sigma_0$. The invariance of the index under small perturbations (for σ_0 sufficiently large) will imply that the index of L_0 is the same as that of L. This is Lemma 8.8.4.

(2) Replace L_0 by L_1, still given by the same formula, but where $\widetilde{S}(s,t)$ is replaced by a *diagonal* matrix $S(s)$ (that does not depend on t and) that will be constant for $s \le -\sigma_0$ and $s \ge \sigma_0$. This time L_1 will have the same index as L_0 because of the invariance of the index under homotopy (and the construction of limit diagonal matrices). This is Propositions 8.8.2 and 8.8.3.

The process is sketched in Figure 8.7, which represents the different maps $S(s,t)$ that occur in the operators L, L_0 and L_1 in the space of matrices: the outer "cylinder" is $S(s,t)$ (the original one), the thick cylinder is $\widetilde{S}(s,t)$ (we have approximated S at infinity by true cylinders), the dotted line consisting of the diagonal matrices represents the matrix $S(s)$ (for L_1).

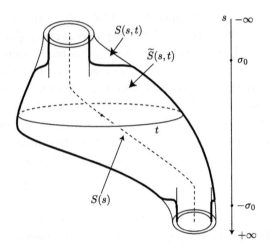

Fig. 8.7

8.8.a The Fredholm Index

We consider the operator

$$L : W^{1,p}(\mathbf{R} \times S^1; \mathbf{R}^{2n}) \longrightarrow L^p(\mathbf{R} \times S^1; \mathbf{R}^{2n})$$

$$Y \longmapsto \frac{\partial Y}{\partial s} + J_0 \frac{\partial Y}{\partial t} + S(s,t)Y.$$

Recall that $S : \mathbf{R} \times S^1 \to M(2n; \mathbf{R})$ satisfies

$$\lim_{s \to \pm\infty} S(s,t) = S^{\pm}(t) \text{ uniformly in } t$$

for symmetric matrices $S^{\pm}(t)$ (for every $t \in S^1$). Consider the symplectic paths

$$R^{\pm} : [0,1] \longrightarrow \mathrm{Sp}(2n; \mathbf{R})$$

associated with these two matrices $S^{\pm}$ (see Subsection 7.2.c). Proposition 8.4.6 shows that these paths are exactly those that define the (Conley–Zehnder) indices $\mu(x)$ and $\mu(y)$. We have proved (Proposition 8.7.1) that if $R^{\pm}$ is in the set $\mathcal{S}$ of paths $R(t)$ with $R(0) = \mathrm{Id}$ and $\det(R(1) - \mathrm{Id}) \neq 0$, then L is a Fredholm operator. We now compute its index.

Theorem 8.8.1. *The index of the Fredholm operator L is*

$$\mu(R^-(t)) - \mu(R^+(t)) = \mu(x) - \mu(y).$$

Let $k^\pm$ denote the index of $R^\pm(t)$. We use the notation of Section 7.2.d and in particular the matrices $S_{k\pm}$ given by Lemma 7.2.4.

The theorem will be a consequence of the following two propositions.

Proposition 8.8.2. *Let s_0 be a positive real number and let*

$$S : \mathbf{R} \longrightarrow M(2n; \mathbf{R})$$

be a path of diagonal matrices such that

$$S(s) = S_{k^-} \ if \ s \le -s_0, \quad S(s) = S_{k^+} \ if \ s \ge s_0.$$

Let

$$L_1 : W^{1,p}(\mathbf{R} \times S^1; \mathbf{R}^{2n}) \longrightarrow L^p(\mathbf{R} \times S^1; \mathbf{R}^{2n})$$

$$Y \longmapsto \frac{\partial Y}{\partial s} + J_0 \frac{\partial Y}{\partial t} + S(s)Y.$$

Then the index of the Fredholm operator L_1 is the same as that of L.

Proposition 8.8.3. *The index of L_1 is $k^- - k^+$.*

To prove Proposition 8.8.2, we modify L within the set of Fredholm operators without changing its index.

Lemma 8.8.4. *The index of L is the same as that of the operator L_0 in which we have replaced $S(s,t)$ by $S^-(t)$ for $s \le -s_0$ and by $S^+(t)$ for $s \ge s_0$.*

Proof. We fix a real number $\varepsilon > 0$. Since the matrix $S(s,t)$ tends to $S^\pm(t)$ for $s \to \pm\infty$, there exists a real number σ_0 such that

$$\begin{cases} \text{for } s \le -\sigma_0, & \|S(s,t) - S^-(t)\| < \varepsilon, \\ \text{for } s \ge \sigma_0, & \|S(s,t) - S^+(t)\| < \varepsilon. \end{cases}$$

We consider a plateau function $\chi : \mathbf{R} \to [0,1]$ with value 1 for $|s| \le \sigma_0$ and 0 for $|s| \ge 2\sigma_0$. Let

$$\Sigma(s,t) = \begin{cases} \chi(s)S(s,t) + (1 - \chi(s))S^-(t) & \text{if } s \le -\sigma_0 \\ S(s,t) & \text{if } |s| \le \sigma_0 \\ \chi(s)S(s,t) + (1 - \chi(s))S^+(t) & \text{if } s \ge \sigma_0, \end{cases}$$

and let L_0 be defined by

$$L_0(Y) = \frac{\partial Y}{\partial s} + J_0 \frac{\partial Y}{\partial t} + \Sigma Y.$$

So $LY = L_0 Y + C(s,t)Y$, where

$$C(s,t) = \begin{cases} (1 - \chi(s))(S(s,t) - S^-(t)) & \text{if } s \leq -\sigma_0 \\ 0 & \text{if } |s| \leq \sigma_0 \\ (1 - \chi(s))(S(s,t) - S^+(t)) & \text{if } s \geq \sigma_0. \end{cases}$$

In particular, $\|C(s,t)\| < \varepsilon$. If ε is sufficiently small, then we know (this is the invariance of the index under small perturbations, Theorem C.2.9) that L_0 is a Fredholm operator and that it has the same index as L.

Now $\Sigma(s,t)$ coincides with $S^\pm(t)$ for $|s| \geq 2\sigma_0$, while we want this property with s_0 instead of σ_0 (σ_0 was determined by the choice of ε). It suffices to connect $\Sigma(s,t)$ to $\Sigma_0(s,t)$ defined in an analogous manner by

$$\Sigma_0(s,t) = \begin{cases} S^-(t) & \text{if } s \leq -s_0 \\ S^+(t) & \text{if } s \geq s_0, \end{cases}$$

using a path that is constant for s sufficiently large. The Fredholm index of the operators defined by this path is constant, as follows from the same property of being locally constant (see Remark C.2.11).   □

We are going to use the link, established in Section 7.2.c, between paths in $\mathrm{Sp}(2n)$ and fundamental matrices $R(t)$ of solutions of the equations

$$\frac{dY}{dt} = J_0 S(t) Y$$

we have already considered in the proof of Lemma 8.7.5, as well as the paths with prescribed Maslov index constructed in Section 7.2.d.

Proof of Proposition 8.8.2. The diagonal matrices S_k of the proof of Lemma 7.2.4 define symplectic paths $R_{k^\pm}(t) = e^{tJS_{k^\pm}}$ that have the same Maslov index ($k^\pm$) as $R^\pm(t)$. There therefore exists (by Proposition 7.1.4) a homotopy $\psi^\pm(\lambda,t)$,

$$\psi^\pm : [0,1] \times [0,1] \longrightarrow \mathrm{Sp}(2n)$$

(with $\psi^\pm(\lambda,\cdot) \in \mathcal{S}$ for every λ) between $R_{k^\pm}(t)$ and $R^\pm(t)$, that we may, and do, assume to be of class $\mathcal{C}^1$.

As we have already noted in Lemma 7.2.3, this path of symplectic matrices generates a path of symmetric matrices

$$S_\lambda^\pm(t) = -J\dot\psi_\lambda^\pm(t)(\psi_\lambda^\pm(t))^{-1}.$$

The only problem is that our variable t is in S^1; we therefore want paths that are periodic in t. To obtain this, we modify the homotopies $\psi^\pm$ as follows. We use an increasing $\mathcal{C}^\infty$ function

$$\chi : [0,1] \longrightarrow [0,1]$$

that is 0 near 0 and equals 1 near 1, and a homotopy χ_λ that connects χ to Id. The path of symmetric matrices associated with $R_{k^\pm}(\chi_\lambda(t))$ is $\dot\chi_\lambda(t)S_{k^\pm}$, it is periodic if we choose the homotopy in such a way that $\dot\chi_\lambda(0) = \dot\chi_\lambda(1)$.

Likewise, we connect the paths $R^\pm(t)$ and $R^\pm(\chi(t))$ by the homotopy $R(\chi_\lambda(t))$ whose associated paths of symmetric matrices are periodic for every λ. We then consider the homotopy $\psi^\pm(\lambda, \chi(t))$. The associated paths of symmetric matrices are zero near $t = 0$ and $t = 1$, and in particular periodic.

We have thus obtained maps

$$S^\pm : [0,1] \times S^1 \longrightarrow M(2n; \mathbf{R})$$

with values in the space of symmetric matrices such that, for every $\lambda \in [0,1]$, $t \mapsto S^\pm(\lambda, t)$ generates a path in S and we have:

- $S^\pm(0, t)$ generates $R^\pm(t)$.
- $S^\pm(1, t) = S_{k^\pm}$ is independent of t and generates $R_{k^\pm}(t)$.

We can then define a continuous map

$$S : [0,1] \times \mathbf{R} \times S^1 \longrightarrow M(2n; \mathbf{R})$$

such that

$$S_\lambda(s, t) = \begin{cases} S(s, t) & \text{if } \lambda = 0 \\ S_\lambda^+(t) & \text{if } s \geq \sigma_0 \\ S_\lambda^-(t) & \text{if } s \leq -\sigma_0 \\ S(s) & \text{if } \lambda = 1. \end{cases}$$

This defines a family of operators

$$L_\lambda : W^{1,p}(\mathbf{R} \times S^1; \mathbf{R}^{2n}) \longrightarrow L^p(\mathbf{R} \times S^1; \mathbf{R}^{2n})$$

$$Y \longmapsto \frac{\partial Y}{\partial s} + J_0\frac{\partial Y}{\partial t} + S_\lambda(s, t)Y,$$

that are all Fredholm operators (still by Proposition 8.7.1) and all have the same index (by the invariance theorem C.2.9). The operator L_1 is the one announced in the proposition. $\qquad\square$

Proof of Proposition 8.8.3. In the proof of Proposition 8.7.1, we used that Coker L_1 is isomorphic to Ker L_1^*, where the adjoint L_1^* of L_1 is

$$L_1^* : W^{1,q}(\mathbf{R} \times S^1; \mathbf{R}^{2n}) \longrightarrow L^q(\mathbf{R} \times S^1; \mathbf{R}^{2n})$$

$$Z \longmapsto -\frac{\partial Z}{\partial s} + J_0 \frac{\partial Z}{\partial t} + {}^t S(s) Z,$$

with $1/p + 1/q = 1$. It therefore suffices to compute the dimension of the kernel of operators of this type. Since

$$J_0 = \begin{pmatrix} \begin{pmatrix} 0 & -1 \\ 1 & 0 \end{pmatrix} & & & \\ & \begin{pmatrix} 0 & -1 \\ 1 & 0 \end{pmatrix} & & \\ & & \ddots & \\ & & & \begin{pmatrix} 0 & -1 \\ 1 & 0 \end{pmatrix} \end{pmatrix} \quad \text{is in } M(2; \mathbf{R}) \times \cdots \times M(2; \mathbf{R}),$$

we can reduce to the case where $n = 1$. We therefore assume that the diagonal matrix $S(s)$ is a 2×2 matrix of the form

$$S(s) = \begin{pmatrix} a_1(s) & 0 \\ 0 & a_2(s) \end{pmatrix}, \quad \text{with } a_i(s) = \begin{cases} a_i^- & \text{if } s \le -s_0, \\ a_i^+ & \text{if } s \ge s_0. \end{cases}$$

We now prove the following result.

Lemma 8.8.5. *Let $p > 2$ and let*

$$F : W^{1,p}(\mathbf{R} \times S^1; \mathbf{R}^2) \longrightarrow L^p(\mathbf{R} \times S^1; \mathbf{R}^2)$$

be defined by

$$F(Y) = \frac{\partial Y}{\partial s} + J_0 \frac{\partial Y}{\partial t} + S(s)Y.$$

We suppose that $a_i^\pm \notin 2\pi \mathbf{Z}$:

(1) Suppose that $a_1(s) = a_2(s)$. Denote $a^\pm = a_1^\pm = a_2^\pm$. Then

$$\dim \operatorname{Ker} F = 2\# \left\{ \ell \in \mathbf{Z} \mid a^- < 2\pi\ell < a^+ \right\}$$
$$\dim \operatorname{Ker} F^* = 2\# \left\{ \ell \in \mathbf{Z} \mid a^+ < 2\pi\ell < a^- \right\}$$

(2) Suppose that $\sup_{s \in \mathbf{R}} \|S(s)\| < 1$. Then

$$\dim \operatorname{Ker} F = \# \left\{ i \in \{1, 2\} \mid a_i^- < 0 \text{ and } a_i^+ > 0 \right\}$$
$$\dim \operatorname{Ker} F^* = \# \left\{ i \in \{1, 2\} \mid a_i^+ < 0 \text{ and } a_i^- > 0 \right\}.$$

Remark 8.8.6. This is quite close to the formula computing the index in the Morse case in terms of the number of eigenvalues that change sign (see the notes on the proof of Proposition 10.2.8).

The proof of Lemma 8.8.5 is an explicit computation of the kernel, which we will give later. Here is how, if we admit the lemma for the moment, we finish the proof of Proposition 8.8.3 by using the lemma to compute the index of L_1. We need to distinguish between four cases, according to the possible parities of $k^+ - n$ and $k^- - n$.

(1) The case where S_{k^-} and S_{k^+} are the diagonal matrices

$$\begin{cases} S_{k^-} = (-\pi, -\pi, \ldots, -\pi, -\pi, (n-1-k^-)\pi, (n-1-k^-)\pi) \\ S_{k^+} = (-\pi, -\pi, \ldots, -\pi, -\pi, (n-1-k^+)\pi, (n-1-k^+)\pi), \end{cases}$$

with $k^- \equiv k^+ \equiv n \bmod 2$. We may take $a_1(s) = a_2(s)$, so $a_1^\pm = a_2^\pm$ and the lemma gives

$$\begin{aligned} \dim \operatorname{Ker} L_1 &= 2\# \left\{ \ell \in \mathbf{Z} \mid n - 1 - k^- < 2\ell < n - 1 - k^+ \right\} \\ &= \begin{cases} k^- - k^+ & \text{if } k^- > k^+, \\ 0 & \text{otherwise,} \end{cases} \end{aligned}$$

and $\dim \operatorname{Ker} L_1^* = 2\# \left\{ \ell \in \mathbf{Z} \mid k^- - n + 1 < 2\ell < k^+ - n + 1 \right\}$

$$= \begin{cases} k^+ - k^- & \text{if } k^+ > k^-, \\ 0 & \text{otherwise.} \end{cases}$$

Consequently,
$$\operatorname{Ind}(L_1) = k^- - k^+.$$

(2) The case where S_{k^-} and S_{k^+} are the diagonal matrices

$$\begin{cases} S_{k^-} = (-\pi, -\pi, \ldots, -\varepsilon\pi, -\varepsilon\pi, (n-1-k^-)\pi, (n-1-k^-)\pi) \\ S_{k^+} = (-\pi, -\pi, \ldots, \varepsilon, -\varepsilon, (n-2-k^+)\pi, (n-2-k^+)\pi), \end{cases}$$

with $k^- \equiv n \bmod 2$ and $k^+ \equiv n - 1 \bmod 2$. In this case, we take $a_1(s) = a_2(s)$ except for the $(n-1)$th block, for which we may suppose that $\sup_{s \in \mathbf{R}} \|S(s)\| < 1$. We get that

$$\begin{aligned} \dim \operatorname{Ker} L_1 &= 2\# \left\{ \ell \in \mathbf{Z} \mid n - 1 - k^- < 2\ell < n - 2 - k^+ \right\} + 1 \\ &= \begin{cases} (k^- - k^+ - 1) + 1 & \text{if } k^- > k^+, \\ 1 & \text{if } k^- < k^+, \end{cases} \end{aligned}$$

and $\dim \operatorname{Ker} L_1^* = 2\# \left\{ \ell \in \mathbf{Z} \mid k^- - n + 1 < 2\ell < k^+ - n + 2 \right\}$

$$= \begin{cases} k^+ - k^- + 1 & \text{if } k^+ > k^-, \\ 0 & \text{otherwise.} \end{cases}$$

Therefore, in this case we also have

$$\operatorname{Ind}(L_1) = k^- - k^+.$$

(3) The case where S_{k^-} and S_{k^+} are the diagonal matrices

$$\begin{cases} S_{k^-} = (-\pi, -\pi, \ldots, \varepsilon, -\varepsilon, (n - 2 - k^-)\pi, (n - 2 - k^-)\pi) \\ S_{k^+} = (-\pi, -\pi, \ldots, -\varepsilon\pi, -\varepsilon\pi, (n - 1 - k^+)\pi, (n - 1 - k^+)\pi), \end{cases}$$

with, this time, $k^- \equiv n - 1 \bmod 2$ and $k^+ \equiv n \bmod 2$. In this case, we again have (by inverting the roles of S_{k^-} and S_{k^+})

$$\dim \operatorname{Ker} L_1 = \begin{cases} k^- - k^+ + 1 & \text{if } k^- > k^+, \\ 0 & \text{otherwise,} \end{cases}$$

and $$\dim \operatorname{Ker} L_1^* = \begin{cases} k^+ - k^- & \text{if } k^+ > k^-, \\ 1 & \text{otherwise,} \end{cases}$$

so that in this case, we also have

$$\operatorname{Ind}(L_1) = k^- - k^+.$$

(4) This leaves the case where S_{k^-} and S_{k^+} are the diagonal matrices

$$\begin{cases} S_{k^-} = (-\pi, -\pi, \ldots, 1, -1, (n - 2 - k^-)\pi, (n - 2 - k^-)\pi) \\ S_{k^+} = (-\pi, -\pi, \ldots, 1, -1, (n - 2 - k^+)\pi, (n - 2 - k^+)\pi), \end{cases}$$

and $k^+ \equiv k^- \equiv n - 1 \bmod 2$. We have (for $a_1(s) = a_2(s)$)

$$\dim \operatorname{Ker} L_1 = \begin{cases} k^- - k^+ & \text{if } k^+ > k^-, \\ 0 & \text{otherwise,} \end{cases}$$

and $$\dim \operatorname{Ker} L_1^* = \begin{cases} k^+ - k^- & \text{if } k^- > k^+, \\ 0 & \text{otherwise,} \end{cases}$$

and, as in the other cases, we again have

$$\operatorname{Ind}(L_1) = k^- - k^+,$$

concluding the proof of Proposition 8.8.3.   □

Proof of Lemma 8.8.5. We start with Assertion (1).

Denote $a(s) = a_1(s) = a_2(s)$. Let

$$Y(s,t) = (Y_1(s,t), Y_2(s,t)) \in \mathbf{R}^2$$
$$= Y_1(s+it) + iY_2(s+it) \in \mathbf{C}.$$

The partial differential equation $F(Y) = 0$ can be written as

$$\frac{\partial}{\partial s}\begin{pmatrix} Y_1 \\ Y_2 \end{pmatrix} + \begin{pmatrix} 0 & -1 \\ 1 & 0 \end{pmatrix}\frac{\partial}{\partial t}\begin{pmatrix} Y_1 \\ Y_2 \end{pmatrix} + \begin{pmatrix} a(s) & 0 \\ 0 & a(s) \end{pmatrix}\begin{pmatrix} Y_1 \\ Y_2 \end{pmatrix} = 0,$$

or

$$\overline{\partial} Y + S(s)Y = 0.$$

Changing the unknown function to $Y = B\widetilde{Y}$ with B a complex invertible matrix satisfying

$$\overline{\partial} B + SB = 0$$

transforms this equation into

$$\overline{\partial}\widetilde{Y} = 0$$

(we are transforming the equation into the Cauchy–Riemann equation, exactly as we did in Section 8.6).

The simplest solution is to let B be the matrix (in $\mathrm{GL}(1;\mathbf{C}) \subset \mathrm{GL}(2;\mathbf{R})$)

$$B = \begin{pmatrix} b(s) & 0 \\ 0 & b(s) \end{pmatrix} \quad \text{with } b' = -ab,$$

that is,

$$b(s) = \exp \int_0^s -a(\sigma)\,d\sigma = \exp(-A(s)),$$

which is what we do here. We should not forget to note that for $s \le -\sigma_0$, $A(s) = C_1 + a^- s$ and, likewise, for $s \ge \sigma_0$, $A(s) = C_2 + a^+ s$ for certain constants C_1 and C_2.

The new unknown function $\widetilde{Y}$ satisfies the Cauchy–Riemann equation $\overline{\partial}\widetilde{Y} = 0$. It is continuous, L^1_{loc}, and therefore smooth because of elliptic regularity (Theorem 12.1.3). Its real and imaginary parts $\widetilde{Y}_1$ and $\widetilde{Y}_2$ are of class $\mathcal{C}^\infty$ and harmonic.

We now identify the $s + it \in \mathbf{R} \times S^1$ with the $u = e^{2\pi z}$, so that Laurent's theorem (for $\widetilde{Y}(u)$ on $\mathbf{C} - \{0\}$) gives the expansion of $\widetilde{Y}$ in z. The solutions of our system are therefore

$$\widetilde{Y}(s+it) = \sum_{\ell \in \mathbf{Z}} c_\ell e^{(s+it)2\pi\ell}$$

(where $c_\ell \in \mathbf{C}$ and the sequence converges for all s and t); in real coordinates, we have

$$\widetilde{Y}(s,t) = \sum_{\ell \in \mathbf{Z}} e^{2\pi s\ell} \left(\alpha_\ell \begin{pmatrix} \cos 2\pi \ell t \\ \sin 2\pi \ell t \end{pmatrix} + \beta_\ell \begin{pmatrix} -\sin 2\pi \ell t \\ \cos 2\pi \ell t \end{pmatrix} \right).$$

Coming back to our unknown vector $Y = B\widetilde{Y}$, we therefore have

$$Y(s,t) = \sum_{\ell \in \mathbf{Z}} e^{2\pi s\ell} \left(\alpha_\ell \begin{pmatrix} e^{-A(s)} \cos 2\pi \ell t \\ e^{-A(s)} \sin 2\pi \ell t \end{pmatrix} + \beta_\ell \begin{pmatrix} -e^{-A(s)} \sin 2\pi \ell t \\ e^{-A(s)} \cos 2\pi \ell t \end{pmatrix} \right).$$

For $s \le -s_0$, we have

$$Y(s,t) = \sum_{\ell \in \mathbf{Z}} \begin{pmatrix} e^{(2\pi \ell - a^-)s + K}(\alpha_\ell \cos 2\pi \ell t - \beta_\ell \sin 2\pi \ell t) \\ e^{(2\pi \ell - a^-)s + K'}(\alpha_\ell \sin 2\pi \ell t + \beta_\ell \cos 2\pi \ell t) \end{pmatrix}$$

for certain constants K and K'. For this solution to be in L^p, it is necessary (and sufficient) that the exponential terms tend to 0 at infinity, that is, that:

- Terms $\ell \ne 0$: $\alpha_\ell = \beta_\ell = 0$ or $2\pi \ell > a^-$
- Term $\ell = 0$: ($\alpha_0 = 0$ or $a^- < 0$) and ($\beta_0 = 0$ or $a^- < 0$).

Likewise, for $s \ge s_0$, we have

$$Y(s,t) = \sum_{\ell \in \mathbf{Z}} \begin{pmatrix} e^{(2\pi \ell - a^+)s + C}(\alpha_\ell \cos 2\pi \ell t - \beta_\ell \sin 2\pi \ell t) \\ e^{(2\pi \ell - a^+)s + C'}(\alpha_\ell \sin 2\pi \ell t + \beta_\ell \cos 2\pi \ell t) \end{pmatrix},$$

which leads to:

- Terms $\ell \ne 0$: $\alpha_\ell = \beta_\ell = 0$ or $2\pi \ell < a^+$
- Term $\ell = 0$: ($\alpha_0 = 0$ or $a^+ > 0$) and ($\beta_0 = 0$ or $a^+ > 0$).

Combining these conditions, we have:

- Terms $\ell \ne 0$: $\alpha_\ell = \beta_\ell = 0$ or $a^- < 2\pi \ell < a^+$
- Term $\ell = 0$: ($\alpha_0 = 0$ or $a^- < 0 < a^+$) and ($\beta_0 = 0$ or $a^- < 0 < a^+$).

There are only a finite number of values of ℓ that satisfy all these conditions, and these conditions are sufficient for the $Y(s,t)$ that we find to be in $W^{1,p}$. The dimension of the resulting space of solutions is

$$\dim \operatorname{Ker} F = 2\# \left\{ \ell \in \mathbf{Z}^\star \mid a^- < 2\pi \ell < a^+ \right\}$$
$$(+2 \text{ if } a^- < 0 < a^+)$$
$$= 2\# \left\{ \ell \in \mathbf{Z} \mid a^- < 2\pi \ell < a^+ \right\}.$$

From this we deduce the dimension of the kernel of $F^\star$. If $Y \in \operatorname{Ker} F^\star$, then $Z(s,t) = Y(-s,t)$ satisfies $\widetilde{F} = 0$, where $\widetilde{F}$ is the operator

$$\widetilde{F} : W^{1,q}(\mathbf{R} \times S^1) \longrightarrow L^q(\mathbf{R} \times S^1)$$

$$Z \longmapsto \frac{\partial Z}{\partial s} + J_0 \frac{\partial Z}{\partial t} + S(-s)Z.$$

The converse is clearly also true, hence

$$\operatorname{Ker} F^\star \cong \operatorname{Ker} \widetilde{F}.$$

The formula that gives the dimension of $\operatorname{Ker} F^\star$ is therefore the one that gives the dimension of $\operatorname{Ker} \widetilde{F}$. This formula is similar to the one that gives the dimension of $\operatorname{Ker} F$, where we have exchanged a^- and a^+.

To prove assertion (2), we use the following lemma.

Lemma 8.8.7. *Suppose that* $\sup_{s \in \mathbf{R}} \|S(s)\| < 1$. *Then the elements of* $\operatorname{Ker} F$ *and* $\operatorname{Ker} F^\star$ *are independent of* t.

The proof is identical to that of Proposition 10.1.7 (which will be given in Subsection 10.4.a).

We have

$$Y = \begin{pmatrix} Y_1 \\ Y_2 \end{pmatrix} \in \operatorname{Ker} F, \text{ hence } \begin{cases} \dfrac{\partial Y_1}{\partial s} = -a_1(s)Y_1 \\ \dfrac{\partial Y_2}{\partial s} = -a_2(s)Y_2. \end{cases}$$

Therefore

$$Y_i(s) = \alpha_i e^{-A_i(s)},$$

where $\alpha_i \in \mathbf{R}$ (for $i = 1, 2$) and

$$A_i(s) = \int_0^s -a_i(\sigma)\, d\sigma.$$

As before, for $s \le -\sigma_0$, $A_i(s) = C_{1,i} + a_i^- \cdot s$, and for $s \ge \sigma_0$, $A_i(s) = C_{2,i} + a_i^+ \cdot s$ (for $i = 1, 2$ and some constants $C_{1,i}$, $C_{2,i}$). This means that $Y_i \in W^{1,p}$ if and only if $a_i^- < 0 < a_i^+$, and the formula dor $\dim \operatorname{Ker} F$ is established. The relation for $\dim \operatorname{Ker} F^\star$ follows from it, using the operator $\widetilde{F}$, as above.

We conclude that by Proposition 8.7.1 and Theorem 8.8.1, we have finished the proof of Theorem 8.1.5. □

Remark 8.8.8. We have replaced the Fredholm operator L by an operator that has the same index... and whose index we know how to compute, because we can describe its kernel and cokernel. It goes without saying that there is no reason for the dimensions of these two subspaces to be those of the kernel or cokernel of L: it is the index that is invariant.

8.9 The Exponential Decay

In this section, we show the decay property that we have already used a number of times, namely the following result.

Theorem 8.9.1. *If Y is a solution of class $\mathcal{C}^2$ of the Floer equation linearized along a solution of finite energy, then:*

- *Either $\int \|Y(s,t)\|^2 \, dt$ tends to infinity when s tends to $\pm\infty$*
- *Or Y satisfies*

$$\|Y(s,t)\| \leq Ce^{-\delta|s|}$$

for certain constants δ and C (and for every t).

Remark 8.9.2. If u is the solution of the Floer equation along which we linearize, then the solution $Y = \partial u / \partial s$ has the exponential decay property and in particular, it is in the space $L^p(\mathbf{R} \times S^1; \mathbf{R}^{2n})$ for every $p > 1$. Indeed, since the energy of u is finite,

$$\int \left\| \frac{\partial u}{\partial s} \right\|^2 dt \text{ does not tend to } +\infty \text{ when } s \longrightarrow \pm\infty,$$

which excludes the first case in the statement of the theorem for this type of solution. Note also that this obviously implies that $\mathcal{M}(x,y) \subset \mathcal{C}^\infty_\searrow(x,y)$, as claimed in Proposition 8.2.3.

We will prove the theorem as a consequence of the following proposition, which asserts an "exponential decay" property.

Proposition 8.9.3. *Let u be a finite energy solution of the Floer equation. If Y is a solution of the Floer equation linearized along u, such that $\int \|Y(s,t)\|^2 \, dt$ does not tend to infinity, then there exist constants $\delta > 0$ (that do not depend on u) and $C > 0$ such that*

$$\int_0^1 \|Y(s,t)\|^2 \, dt \leq Ce^{-\delta|s|}.$$

Proof. The formula

$$f(s) = \frac{1}{2} \int_0^1 \|Y(s,t)\|^2 \, dt = \frac{1}{2} \|Y\|^2_{L^2(S^1)}$$

defines a function $f : \mathbf{R} \to \mathbf{R}$ of class $\mathcal{C}^2$. We are going to show that this function satisfies a differential equation

$$f'' \geq \delta^2 f$$

for some constant δ. Let us therefore compute its derivatives:

$$f'(s) = \int_0^1 \left\langle Y(s,t), \frac{\partial Y}{\partial s}(s,t) \right\rangle dt$$

$$f''(s) = \int_0^1 \left\| \frac{\partial Y}{\partial s}(s,t) \right\|^2 dt + \int_0^1 \left\langle Y(s,t), \frac{\partial^2 Y}{\partial s^2}(s,t) \right\rangle dt.$$

We determine the second term by using the fact that Y is a solution of the linearized equation, that is, satisfies

$$\frac{\partial Y}{\partial s} = -J_0 \frac{\partial Y}{\partial t} - SY.$$

We therefore have

$$\frac{\partial^2 Y}{\partial s^2} = -J_0 \frac{\partial^2 Y}{\partial s\, \partial t} - \frac{\partial S}{\partial s} Y - S \frac{\partial Y}{\partial s}.$$

Hence

$$\int_0^1 \left\langle Y, \frac{\partial^2 Y}{\partial s^2} \right\rangle dt = -\int_0^1 \left\langle Y, J_0 \frac{\partial^2 Y}{\partial s\, \partial t} \right\rangle dt - \int_0^1 \left\langle Y, \frac{\partial S}{\partial s} Y \right\rangle dt$$
$$- \int_0^1 \left\langle Y, S \frac{\partial Y}{\partial s} \right\rangle dt.$$

The first of these integrals can be computed by integration by parts:

$$\int_0^1 \left\langle Y, J_0 \frac{\partial^2 Y}{\partial s\, \partial t} \right\rangle dt = -\int_0^1 \left\langle \frac{\partial Y}{\partial t}, J_0 \frac{\partial Y}{\partial s} \right\rangle dt$$
$$= -\int_0^1 \left\langle J_0 \frac{\partial Y}{\partial s}, J_0 \frac{\partial Y}{\partial s} \right\rangle dt - \int_0^1 \left\langle J_0 SY, J_0 \frac{\partial Y}{\partial s} \right\rangle dt$$
$$= -\int_0^1 \left\| \frac{\partial Y}{\partial s} \right\|^2 dt - \int_0^1 \left\langle SY, \frac{\partial Y}{\partial s} \right\rangle dt.$$

So we have

$$\int_0^1 \left\langle Y, \frac{\partial^2 Y}{\partial s^2} \right\rangle dt = \int_0^1 \left\| \frac{\partial Y}{\partial s} \right\|^2 dt + \int_0^1 \left\langle SY, \frac{\partial Y}{\partial s} \right\rangle dt$$
$$- \int_0^1 \left\langle Y, \frac{\partial S}{\partial s} Y \right\rangle dt - \int_0^1 \left\langle Y, S \frac{\partial Y}{\partial s} \right\rangle dt.$$

The second-order derivative of the function f is therefore

$$f''(s) = \int_0^1 \left\| \frac{\partial Y}{\partial s} \right\|^2 dt - \int_0^1 \left\langle Y, \frac{\partial S}{\partial s} \right\rangle dt + \int_0^1 \left\langle Y, ({}^t S - S) \frac{\partial Y}{\partial s} \right\rangle dt.$$

Using the fact that

$$\lim_{s \to \pm\infty} \sup_t \frac{\partial S}{\partial s}(s,t) = 0$$

(which is proved in Proposition 8.4.4) and the Cauchy–Schwarz inequality, we obtain

$$\int_0^1 \left\langle Y, \frac{\partial S}{\partial s} Y \right\rangle dt \le \left(\int_0^1 \|Y\|^2 \, dt \right)^{1/2} \left(\int_0^1 \left\| \frac{\partial S}{\partial s} Y \right\|^2 dt \right)^{1/2}$$

$$\le \left(\int_0^1 \|Y\|^2 \, dt \right)^{1/2} \varepsilon \left(\int_0^1 \|Y\|^2 \, dt \right)^{1/2}$$

$$\le \varepsilon \int_0^1 \|Y\|^2 \, dt \quad \text{for } |s| \text{ sufficiently large.}$$

Since ${}^tS - S$ tends to 0, we have

$$\left| \int_0^1 \left\langle Y, ({}^tS - S)\frac{\partial Y}{\partial s} \right\rangle dt \right| \le \eta \left(\int_0^1 \|Y\|^2 \, dt \right)^{1/2} \left(\int_0^1 \left\| \frac{\partial Y}{\partial s} \right\|^2 dt \right)^{1/2}$$

for $|s|$ sufficiently large. We therefore obtain the inequality

$$f''(s) \ge \int_0^1 \left\| \frac{\partial Y}{\partial s} \right\|^2 dt - \varepsilon \int_0^1 \|Y\|^2 \, dt$$
$$- \eta \left(\int_0^1 \|Y\|^2 \, dt \right)^{1/2} \left(\int_0^1 \left\| \frac{\partial Y}{\partial s} \right\|^2 dt \right)^{1/2}.$$

Let us now use the fact that

$$\frac{\partial Y}{\partial s} = -J_0 \frac{\partial Y}{\partial t} - SY = AY, \quad \text{with} \quad AY = A_0Y + (S - S^\pm)Y,$$

where A_0 is an operator on L^2 that we have showed (in Lemma 8.7.5) to be invertible and where $S - S^\pm$ tends to 0 when $s \to \pm\infty$. Consequently, A is invertible (from $W^{1,2}(S^1)$ to $L^2(S^1)$) for $|s|$ sufficiently large and we have

$$\|AY\|_{L^2(S^1)} \ge D \|Y\|_{W^{1,2}(S^1)} \ge D \|Y\|_{L^2(S^1)}$$

for some positive constant D. We therefore have

$$f''(s) = \|AY\|_{L^2}^2 - \varepsilon \|Y\|_{L^2}^2 - \eta \|Y\|_{L^2} \|AY\|_{L^2}$$
$$= \|AY\|_{L^2} (\|AY\|_{L^2} - \eta \|Y\|_{L^2}) - \varepsilon \|Y\|_{L^2}^2$$
$$\ge (D(D - \eta) - \varepsilon) \|Y\|_{L^2}^2$$
$$\ge \delta^2 f(s)$$

for $|s|$ sufficiently large and for a constant $\delta > 0$. The function f therefore satisfies a differential equation of the stated type. The end of the proof of the proposition comes from the lemma below (which we state at $+\infty$ but whose analogue at $-\infty$ is obviously also true).

Lemma 8.9.4. *If $f''(s) \geq \delta^2 f(s)$ for $s \geq s_0$, then:*

- *Either $\lim_{s \to +\infty} f(s) = +\infty$*
- *Or $f(s) \leq f(s_0)e^{-\delta(s-s_0)}$ for $s \geq s_0$.*

Proof. Let

$$g(s) = e^{-\delta s}(f'(s) + \delta f(s)),$$

so that

$$g'(s) = e^{-\delta s}(-\delta(f'(s) + \delta f(s)) + f''(s) + \delta f'(s))$$
$$= e^{-\delta s}(f''(s) - \delta^2 f(s))$$
$$\geq 0, \quad \text{by the assumption on } f.$$

In particular, the function g is increasing on $[s_0, +\infty[$.

Let us first suppose that there exists an $s_1 \geq s_0$ with $g(s_1) > 0$. Then $g(s) \geq g(s_1)$ for $s \geq s_1$ and

$$f'(s) + \delta f(s) \geq e^{\delta s}g(s_1)$$

for $s \geq s_1$. Let $h(s) = e^{\delta s}f(s)$, then

$$h'(s) = e^{\delta s}(\delta f + f') \geq e^{2\delta s}g(s_1),$$

hence $h(s) \geq Ae^{2\delta s}$ for $s \geq s_1$ and $f(s) \geq Ae^{\delta s}$ tends to $+\infty$.

If such an s_1 does not exist, then we have $g(s) \leq 0$ for $s \geq s_0$, hence also $f'(s) + \delta f(s) \leq 0$ and $h(s) = e^{\delta s}f(s)$ is decreasing on $[s_0, +\infty[$. Moreover,

$$e^{\delta s}f(s) = h(s) \leq h(s_0) = e^{\delta s_0}f(s_0),$$

that is,

$$f(s) \leq e^{\delta s_0}f(s_0)e^{-\delta s},$$

which concludes the proof of the lemma. $\qquad\square$

And also concludes the proof of Proposition 8.9.3. $\qquad\square$

We have now shown that

$$\forall s \in \mathbf{R}, \quad \|Y\|^2_{L^2(S^1)} \leq e^{-\delta|s|},$$

which is not exactly the statement of the theorem we are working toward. We still need to verify that we have (point by point)

$$\forall (s,t) \in \mathbf{R} \times S^1, \quad |Y(s,t)| \leq Ce^{-\delta|s|}.$$

We will need the following results.

Lemma 8.9.5. *Let* Y *be a solution of class* $\mathcal{C}^2$ *of the linearized Floer equation. There exists a constant* $a > 1$ *such that*

$$\Delta \|Y\|^2 \geq -a \|Y\|^2.$$

Proposition 8.9.6. *Let* $w : \mathbf{R}^2 \to \mathbf{R}$ *be a positive function of class* $\mathcal{C}^2$ *such that* $\Delta w \geq -aw$ *for a constant* $a > 1$. *We then have*

$$\forall (s_0, t_0) \in \mathbf{R}^2, \quad w(s_0, t_0) \leq \frac{8a}{\pi} \int_{B_1(s_0, t_0)} w \, ds \, dt.$$

We now only need to apply the proposition to $w(s,t) = \|Y(s,t)\|^2$.

Proof of Lemma 8.9.5. It is a short computation:

$$\Delta \langle Y, Y \rangle = \frac{\partial^2}{\partial t^2} \langle Y, Y \rangle + \frac{\partial^2}{\partial s^2} \langle Y, Y \rangle$$

$$= 2 \left[\left\| \frac{\partial Y}{\partial s} \right\|^2 + \left\| \frac{\partial Y}{\partial t} \right\|^2 + \langle \Delta Y, Y \rangle \right]$$

and

$$\Delta = \left(\frac{\partial}{\partial s} - J_0 \frac{\partial}{\partial t} \right) \left(\frac{\partial}{\partial s} + J_0 \frac{\partial}{\partial t} \right),$$

so that if Y is a solution of the linearized Floer equation, then

$$\Delta Y = \left(\frac{\partial}{\partial s} - J_0 \frac{\partial}{\partial t} \right) \left(\frac{\partial}{\partial s} + J_0 \frac{\partial}{\partial t} \right) Y$$

$$= \left(\frac{\partial}{\partial s} - J_0 \frac{\partial}{\partial t} \right) (-SY).$$

Hence

$$\langle \Delta Y, Y \rangle = \left\langle -\frac{\partial S}{\partial s} Y, Y \right\rangle - \left\langle S \frac{\partial Y}{\partial s}, Y \right\rangle + \left\langle J_0 \frac{\partial S}{\partial t} Y, Y \right\rangle + \left\langle J_0 S \frac{\partial Y}{\partial t}, Y \right\rangle$$

and

$$\Delta \langle Y, Y \rangle = 2 \left(\left\| \frac{\partial Y}{\partial s} \right\|^2 - \left\langle S \frac{\partial Y}{\partial s}, Y \right\rangle \right) + 2 \left(\left\| \frac{\partial Y}{\partial t} \right\|^2 + \left\langle J_0 S \frac{\partial Y}{\partial t}, Y \right\rangle \right)$$

$$- 2 \left\langle \frac{\partial S}{\partial s} Y, Y \right\rangle + 2 \left\langle J_0 \frac{\partial S}{\partial t} Y, Y \right\rangle.$$

Each term on the right-hand side is bounded from below by some $-c \|Y\|^2$. This is clear for the last two terms (by the Cauchy–Schwarz inequality). We therefore study the first two:

$$\left\|\frac{\partial Y}{\partial s}\right\|^2 - \left\langle Y\frac{\partial S}{\partial s}, Y\right\rangle = \left\|\frac{\partial Y}{\partial s}\right\|^2 - \left\langle \frac{\partial Y}{\partial s}, {}^tSY\right\rangle$$

$$= \left\|\frac{\partial Y}{\partial s} - \frac{1}{2}{}^tSY\right\|^2 - \frac{1}{4}\|{}^tSY\|^2$$

$$\geq -\frac{1}{4}\|{}^tSY\|^2$$

$$\geq -c\|Y\|^2$$

and the same holds for the second term, giving the expected lower bound. □

Proof of Proposition 8.9.6. It begins with a lemma.

Lemma 8.9.7. *Let* $w : B_r(s_0, t_0) \to \mathbf{R}$ *be a positive function of class* $\mathcal{C}^2$ *such that* $\Delta w \geq -b$ *for a constant* $b > 0$. *We then have*

$$w(s_0, t_0) \leq \frac{br^2}{8} + \frac{1}{r^2}\int_{B_r(s_0,t_0)} w.$$

Proof. Consider the function

$$v(s, t) = w(s_0 + s, t_0 + t) + \frac{b}{4}(s^2 + t^2)$$

that satisfies

$$\Delta v(s, t) = \Delta w(s_0 + s, t_0 + t) + b \geq 0.$$

We only need to apply the mean value inequality[12] to v:

$$w(s_0, t_0) = v(0) \leq \frac{1}{\pi r^2}\int_{B_r(0)} v$$

$$= \frac{1}{\pi r^2}\int_{B_r(s_0,t_0)} w + \frac{1}{\pi r^2}\int_{B_r(0)} \frac{b(s^2 + t^2)}{4}\,ds\,dt$$

$$= \frac{1}{\pi r^2}\int_{B_r(s_0,t_0)} w + \frac{br^2}{8},$$

which proves the lemma. □

The next step is called *the Heinz trick* in [51] (which inspired this proof). The trick consists in considering the function

$$f : [0, 1] \longrightarrow \mathbf{R}$$

$$\rho \longmapsto (1 - \rho)^2 \sup_{B_\rho(s_0,t_0)} w$$

---

[12] This variant of the mean value inequality is recalled in Proposition C.5.6.

that satisfies $f(0) = w(s_0, t_0)$ and $f(1) = 0$. There therefore exists $\rho_\star$ in $[0, 1[$ where f reaches its maximum,

$$\max_{\rho \in [0,1]} f = f(\rho_\star).$$

Let

$$c = \sup_{B_{\rho_\star}(s_0,t_0)} w = w(z_\star) \quad \text{for } z_\star \in B_{\rho_\star}(s_0, t_0) \quad \text{and } \eta = \frac{1 - \rho_\star}{2}.$$

Note that $\eta \in \,]0, \frac{1}{2}]$ and that $\rho_\star + \eta \leq 1$, so that

$$B_\eta(z_\star) \subset B_{\rho_\star + \eta}(s_0, t_0) \subset B_1(s_0, t_0).$$

We now have

$$\sup_{B_\eta(z_\star)} w \leq \sup_{B_{\rho_\star + \eta}(s_0,t_0)} w = \frac{f(\rho_\star + \eta)}{(1 - \rho_\star - \eta)^2} = \frac{4f(\rho_\star + \eta)}{(1 - \rho)^2}$$

$$\leq \frac{4f(\rho_\star)}{(1 - \rho_\star)^2} = 4c.$$

Hence on the ball $B_\eta(z_\star)$ we have

$$\Delta w \geq -aw \geq -4ac.$$

Using Lemma 8.9.7 for $r \leq \eta$, we find

$$c = w(z_\star) \leq \frac{4ac}{8} r^2 + \frac{1}{\pi r^2} \int_{B_\eta(z_\star)} w$$

$$\leq \frac{ac}{2} r^2 + \frac{1}{\pi r^2} \int_{B_1(s_0,t_0)} w.$$

To conclude (this is our third and final step), let

$$r = \frac{\eta}{\sqrt{a}} < \eta$$

and use the last inequality to find

$$c \leq \frac{ac\,\eta^2}{2\,a} + \frac{a}{\pi \eta^2} \int_{B_1(s_0,t_0)} w$$

$$\leq \frac{c}{2} + \frac{a}{\pi \eta^2} \int_{B_1(s_0,t_0)} w \quad \text{because } \eta < 1.$$

Hence

$$\frac{c}{2} \leq \frac{a}{\pi \eta^2} \int_{B_1(s_0,t_0)} w \quad \text{or} \quad c\eta^2 \leq \frac{2a}{\pi} \int_{B_1(s_0,t_0)} w.$$

It follows that

$$w(s_0, t_0) = f(0) \leq f(\rho_\star) = (1 - \rho_\star)^2 c$$
$$= 4\eta^2 c \leq \frac{8a}{\pi} \int_{B_1(s_0, t_0)} w,$$

which is the conclusion we were looking for. □

Chapter 9
Floer Homology: Spaces of Trajectories

We now consider a generic (in the sense of Theorem 8.1.1) Hamiltonian H on a symplectic manifold W satisfying Assumptions 6.2.1 and 6.2.2 (for example because $\pi_2(W) = 0$ or because W is the cotangent bundle of a manifold V).

We consider the periodic orbits of fixed Maslov index. Let $C_k(H)$ denote the vector space over $\mathbf{Z}/2$ with basis the periodic orbits of Maslov index k. We know that these orbits are finitely many because the nondegeneracy assumption ensures that they are isolated. We define the differential of the complex using the flow of the gradient of the action functional $\mathcal{A}_H$,

$$\partial : C_k(H) \longrightarrow C_{k-1}(H)$$

with
$$\partial(x) = \sum_{\mathrm{Ind}(y)=k-1} n(x,y)y,$$

where $n(x,y)$ denotes the number (modulo 2) of trajectories of the gradient of $\mathcal{A}_H$ (that is, of solutions of the Floer equation) connecting x to y. The fact that $n(x,y)$ is well defined (and finite) will follow from the fact that under the assumptions we made, the space $\mathcal{L}(x,y)$ of trajectories connecting x to y is a compact manifold of dimension 0 (see Section 8.5).

We then still need to prove that we have defined a complex, that is, that $\partial \circ \partial = 0$. To do this, as in Section 3.2.c, we need to study the space $\mathcal{M}(x,y)$ in more detail when the difference of the indices is 2.

9.1 The Spaces of Trajectories

9.1.a The Space $\mathcal{L}(x,y)$ and Its Topology

Recall that if x and y are critical points of $\mathcal{A}_H$, then $\mathcal{M}(x,y)$ denotes the space of (contractible) solutions (of finite energy) connecting x to y. We have

M. Audin, M. Damian, *Morse Theory and Floer Homology*,
Universitext, DOI 10.1007/978-1-4471-5496-9_9,
© Springer-Verlag London 2014

shown (Theorem 6.5.6) that the space $\mathcal{M}$ of contractible solutions of finite energy of the Floer equation is the union of the spaces $\mathcal{M}(x, y)$.

Let us return to the action of $\mathbf{R}$ on $\mathcal{M}$ used in the previous proofs. Let

$$\mathcal{L}(x, y) = \mathcal{M}(x, y)/\mathbf{R}$$

be the space of trajectories connecting x to y (which we assume to be distinct). It is endowed with the quotient topology. In this topology, a sequence $\tilde{u}_n$ converges to an element $\tilde{u}$ if and only if there exists a sequence s_n of real numbers such that $u_n(s_n + s, \cdot) \to u(s, \cdot)$ in $\mathcal{M}(x, y)$.

Remark 9.1.1. We distinguish between a (parametrized) *solution*, an element of $\mathcal{M}$, and a (nonparametrized) *trajectory*, an element of $\mathcal{L}$.

Proposition 9.1.2. *Let x and y be two distinct critical points of $\mathcal{A}_H$ and let $u_n \in \mathcal{M}(x, y)$, $s_n \in \mathbf{R}$, $\sigma_n \in \mathbf{R}$. Suppose that*

$$\lim u_n(s_n + s, \cdot) = u \in \mathcal{M}(x, z) \quad and \quad \lim u_n(\sigma_n + s, \cdot) = v \in \mathcal{M}(x, w)$$

for two critical points z and w distinct from x. Then $z = w$ and u and v coincide up to the action of $\mathbf{R}$; in other words, there exists an $s_\star$ such that $u(s_\star + s, t) = v(s, t)$.

Corollary 9.1.3. *The quotient topology on $\mathcal{L}(x, y)$ is Hausdorff.*

In fact, Proposition 9.1.2 gives the uniqueness of the limit of a convergent sequence in $\mathcal{L}(x, y)$. □

Proof of Proposition 9.1.2. Since $x \neq y$ and $u_n \in \mathcal{M}(x, y)$, $\mathcal{A}_H(x) > \mathcal{A}_H(y)$ and likewise for z and w. We choose a real number α such that

$$\mathcal{A}_H(x) > \alpha > \sup(\mathcal{A}_H(y), \mathcal{A}_H(z), \mathcal{A}_H(w))$$

and an $\varepsilon > 0$ such that

$$\mathcal{A}_H(x) - \varepsilon > \alpha.$$

We first suppose that the sequence $\sigma_n - s_n$ is not bounded. We may, and do, assume that $s_n = 0$ and that the sequence σ_n is not bounded from above. It then has a subsequence that tends to $+\infty$. At $s = -\infty$, v departs from the critical point x, so there exists an $s_\star$ such that

$$s \leq s_\star \implies \mathcal{A}_H(v(s, t)) > \mathcal{A}_H(x) - \varepsilon.$$

But $u_n(s_\star + \sigma_n, \cdot)$ tends to $v(s_\star, \cdot)$, hence, for n sufficiently large, we also have

$$\mathcal{A}_H(u_n(s_\star + \sigma_n, \cdot)) > \mathcal{A}_H(x) - \varepsilon.$$

The solution u tends to z for $s \to +\infty$, so there exists an s_1 such that

$$s \geq s_1 \implies \mathcal{A}_H(u(s, \cdot)) < \alpha.$$

Since $u_n(s_1, \cdot) \to u(s_1, \cdot)$, we have, for n sufficiently large,

$$\mathcal{A}_H(u_n(s_1, \cdot)) \leq \alpha.$$

It follows that

$$s_\star + \sigma_n < s_1$$

for every n, contradicting the fact that σ_n is not bounded from above.

Consequently, $\sigma_n - s_n$ is bounded and therefore admits a convergent sub-sequence, say $\lim(\sigma_n - s_n) = s_\star$. For s fixed, the sequence $s + \sigma_n - s_n$ remains within a fixed compact set. Hence $u_n(s + \sigma_n, \cdot)$ converges to $v(s, \cdot)$ on the one hand and to $u(s + s_\star)$ on the other. □

Remark 9.1.4. This proof still holds for $u \in \mathcal{M}(x_0, z)$ and $v \in \mathcal{M}(x_0, w)$ for a critical point x_0 of $\mathcal{A}_H$ with $\mathcal{A}_H(x) \geq \mathcal{A}_H(x_0)$.

Remark 9.1.5. In Morse theory, to show that the spaces of trajectories of a pseudo-gradient field are Hausdorff, we studied the intersection with a level set of the function. Here we also have

$$\mathcal{L}(x, y) \cong \mathcal{M}^\alpha(x, y) = \{u \in \mathcal{M}(x, y) \mid \mathcal{A}_H(u(0)) = \alpha\},$$

still using the fact that $\mathcal{A}_H$ is decreasing on the trajectories. Note that to obtain the latter, we need Theorem 8.5.4. We also know that

$$\mathcal{M}^\alpha(x, y) \times \mathbf{R} \longrightarrow \mathcal{M}(x, y)$$
$$(x, \sigma) \longmapsto u(s + \sigma, t)$$

is a diffeomorphism.

Remark 9.1.6. If $x = y$, then $\mathcal{M}(x, y)$ consists of the constant solution (in s) equal to x. If $x \neq y$, then $\mathcal{L}(x, y)$ is a manifold of dimension $\mu(x) - \mu(y) - 1$ (the action of $\mathbf{R}$ is free by the previous remark). If $\mu(x) = \mu(y)$ but $x \neq y$, then $\mathcal{M}(x, y)$ is empty and so is $\mathcal{L}(x, y)$.

9.1.b What We Need to Do to Define the $n(x, y)$ and to Show that $\partial \circ \partial = 0$

Let us consider the case of two critical points with indices whose difference is:

- Equal to 1: then $\mathcal{L}(x, y)$ is a compact (which we still need to prove) manifold of dimension 0 and $n(x, y) = \#\mathcal{L}(x, y)$

- Equal to 2, $\mu(x) = \mu(z) + 2$; then $\mathcal{L}(x, z)$ is a manifold of dimension 1: we consider

$$\overline{\mathcal{L}}(x, z) = \mathcal{L}(x, z) \cup \bigcup_{\mu(y)=\mu(x)+1} \mathcal{L}(x, y) \times \mathcal{L}(y, z)$$

and prove that it is a manifold of dimension 1, whose boundary is the union of the $\mathcal{L}(x, y) \times \mathcal{L}(y, z)$, and that it is compact.

Once we have proved this, since the boundary of a manifold of dimension 1 consists of an even number of points, we have

$$\sum_{\mu(y)=\mu(x)+1} n(x, y)n(y, z) \equiv 0 \mod 2,$$

that is, $\partial \circ \partial = 0$.

We must therefore prove:

- The compactness of the space $\overline{\mathcal{L}}(x, y)$ (Section 9.1.c)
- The fact that $\overline{\mathcal{L}}(x, y)$ is a manifold with boundary when the difference of the indices is 2 (Section 9.2).

9.1.c Broken Trajectories

As we saw in Section 3.2 in the finite-dimensional case, in the closure of the trajectories connecting the critical point x to the critical point y, there are "broken" trajectories, which are unions of trajectories connecting other critical points. The following theorem describes this behavior more precisely.

Theorem 9.1.7. *Let (u_n) be a sequence of elements of $\mathcal{M}(x, y)$. There exist:*

- *A subsequence of (u_n)*
- *Critical points $x_0 = x, x_1, \ldots, x_\ell, x_{\ell+1} = y$*
- *Sequences (s_n^k) (for $0 \leq k \leq \ell$)*
- *And elements $u^k \in \mathcal{M}(x_k, x_{k+1})$*

such that for every $k = 0, \ldots, \ell$,

$$\lim_{n \to \infty} u_n \cdot s_n^k = u^k.$$

Remark 9.1.8. Proposition 9.1.2 also gives the uniqueness of the limit in this setting: one of the critical points, x, was fixed, the other two, z and w, were not.

This theorem defines the convergence of the sequences in $\overline{\mathcal{L}}(x, z)$. Proposition 9.1.2 shows that the limit is unique. We thus define a separated topology on the space $\overline{\mathcal{L}}(x, z)$, for which this space is compact.

Corollary 9.1.9. *The space* $\overline{\mathcal{L}}(x, z)$ *is compact.*

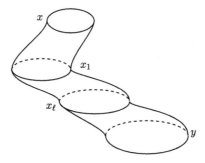

Fig. 9.1

Proof of Theorem 9.1.7. We use the notation of the proof of Theorem 6.5.6. In particular, ε is sufficiently small for the balls with radius ε centered at the critical points of $\mathcal{A}_H$ to be disjoint. For $u \in \mathcal{M}$, we let $u(s) \in \mathcal{L}W$ denote the loop $u(s, t)$.

Seen as a trajectory in $\mathcal{L}W$, u_n must exit $B(x, \varepsilon)$ because it ends up at y. Let $u_n(s_n^1)$ be its first exit point,

$$s_n^1 = \inf \left\{ s \in \mathbf{R} \mid d_\infty(u_n(s), x) > \varepsilon \right\}.$$

By the compactness of $\mathcal{M}$ (and after extracting a subsequence, if necessary), the sequence $(u_n \cdot s_n^1)$ converges to an element u^1 of $\mathcal{M}$. By the definition of s_n^1, we have

$$\begin{cases} d_\infty(u_n(s), x) < \varepsilon & \text{for } s < s_n^1 \\ d_\infty(u_n(s_n^1), x) = \varepsilon, \end{cases}$$

so that, at the limit,

$$u^1(s) \in \overline{B}(x, \varepsilon) \text{ for } s < 0 \quad \text{and} \quad u^1(0) \in \partial B(x, \varepsilon).$$

Hence the limit u^1 is a trajectory starting at x and exiting the ball $B(x, \varepsilon)$. It is therefore also in a $\mathcal{M}(x, x_1)$ for some $x_1 \in \operatorname{Crit} \mathcal{A}_H$ (distinct from x). If $x_1 = y$, then we are done (with $\ell = 0$). Otherwise, we use induction: we assume that we have found sequences $(s_n^0), \ldots, (s_n^k)$ and $u^j \in \mathcal{M}(x_{j-1}, x_j)$ (for certain critical points of $\mathcal{A}_H$) with $x_j \neq y$ and

$$\lim_{n \to \infty} u_n \cdot s_n^j = u^j.$$

The trajectory u^k tends to the critical point x_k when s tends to $+\infty$, and there exists an $s^\star \in \mathbf{R}$ such that

$$\forall s \geq s^\star, \quad u^k(s) \in B(x_k, \varepsilon).$$

Since $u_n \cdot s_n^k(s^*)$ tends to $u^k(s^*)$, we also have, for n sufficiently large,

$$u_n(s_n^k + s^*) \in B(x_k, \varepsilon).$$

Since the trajectory (u_n) tends to y, which we have assumed to be different from x_k, it must exit $B(x_k, \varepsilon)$ for $s > s_n^k + s^*$. Consider the first exit point $u_n(s_n^{k+1})$, where

$$s_n^{k+1} = \sup \left\{ s \geq s_n^k + s^* \mid u_n(\sigma) \in B(x_k, \varepsilon) \text{ for } s_n^k + s^* \leq \sigma \leq s \right\}.$$

Again by the compactness of $\mathcal{M}$ (and after extracting a subsequence, if necessary), the sequence $u_n \cdot s_n^{k+1}$ converges to a limit $u^{k+1} \in \mathcal{M}$. We now want

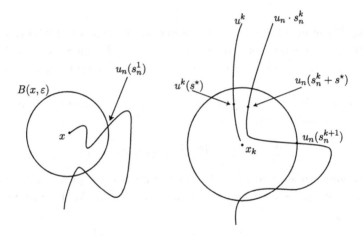

Fig. 9.2

to show that the trajectory u^{k+1} in question is in a space $\mathcal{M}(x_k, x_{k+1})$ for a critical point x_{k+1} distinct from x_k. We first verify that $s_n^{k+1} - s_n^k$ tends to infinity. Indeed, if, on the contrary, we assume that it is bounded, then the interval $[s^*, s_n^{k+1} - s_n^k]$ is contained in a fixed compact interval... on which $u_n \cdot s_n^k$ converges uniformly to u^k. Consequently, for $s \in [s^*, s_n^{k+1} - s_n^k]$, we have $u_n(s_n^k + s) \in B(x_k, \varepsilon)$ and, in particular, $u_n(s_n^{k+1})$ is in this open ball, giving a contradiction (because, by construction, $u_n(s_n^{k+1}) \in \partial B(x_k, \varepsilon)$). Hence $s_n^{k+1} - s_n^k$ indeed tends to $+\infty$.

Let s be a negative real number. For n sufficiently large, we have

$$s_n^k + s^* < s_n^{k+1} + s < s_n^{k+1},$$

so that by the definition of s_n^{k+1}, $u_n(s_n^{k+1} + s) \in B(x_k, \varepsilon)$. Hence, for every $s < 0$, we have

$$u_n \cdot s_n^{k+1} \in B(x_k, \varepsilon)$$

and consequently

$$u^{k+1}(]-\infty, 0[) \subset \overline{B}(x_k, \varepsilon).$$

For $s = 0$, we have $u_n(s_n^{k+1}) \in \partial B(x_k, \varepsilon)$, hence at the limit,

$$u^{k+1}(0) \in \partial B(x_k, \varepsilon),$$

so that u^{k+1} must exit the ball $B(x_k, \varepsilon)$, which is what we wanted to prove.

$\square$

9.2 Broken Trajectories, Gluing: Statements

In Section 9.1.c, we showed that a sequence of solutions of the Floer equation connecting two critical points a and b could converge to a "broken trajectory". The space of broken trajectories appears as a "compactification" of the space of trajectories $\mathcal{L}(a, b)$. Let us study its structure in more detail when the difference of the indices of a and b is 2.

Theorem 9.2.1. *Let (H, J) be a regular pair (with H nondegenerate). Let x and z be two periodic trajectories of H whose indices satisfy*

$$\mu(x) = \mu(z) + 2.$$

Then $\overline{\mathcal{L}}(x, z)$ is a compact manifold of dimension 1 with boundary and

$$\partial \overline{\mathcal{L}}(x, y) = \bigcup_{\mu(x) < \mu(y) < \mu(z)} \mathcal{L}(x, y) \times \mathcal{L}(y, z).$$

Corollary 9.2.2. *Under the same assumptions,*

$$\partial \circ \partial = 0. \qquad \square$$

The remainder of this chapter is devoted to the proof of Theorem 9.2.1. We have already shown, in Section 9.1.c, that the space of trajectories $\overline{\mathcal{L}}(x, z)$ is compact and that $\mathcal{L}(x, z)$ is a manifold of dimension 1. It therefore suffices to study what happens in the neighborhood of the boundary points. This is described in the following so-called "gluing" theorem.

Theorem 9.2.3. *Let x, y and z be three critical points of the action functional $\mathcal{A}_H$ with consecutive indices*

$$\mu(x) = \mu(y) + 1 = \mu(z) + 2$$

and let $(u, v) \in \mathcal{M}(x, y) \times \mathcal{M}(y, z)$ represent trajectories

$$(\widehat{u}, \widehat{v}) \in \mathcal{L}(x, y) \times \mathcal{L}(y, z).$$

We then have:

- *There exists a differentiable map $\psi : [\rho_0, +\infty[\to \mathcal{M}(x, z)$ (for some $\rho_0 > 0$) such that $\pi \circ \psi$ is an embedding*

$$\widehat{\psi} = \pi \circ \psi : [\rho_0, +\infty[\longrightarrow \mathcal{L}(x, z)$$

  satisfying

$$\lim_{\rho \to +\infty} \widehat{\psi}(\rho) = (\widehat{u}, \widehat{v}) \in \overline{\mathcal{L}}(x, z) \supset \mathcal{L}(x, z).$$

- *Moreover, if $\ell_n \in \mathcal{L}(x, z)$ is a sequence that tends to $(\widehat{u}, \widehat{v})$, then $\ell_n \in \operatorname{Im}(\widehat{\psi})$ for n sufficiently large.*

Remark 9.2.4. The last assertion is as essential as its analogue in the Morse case (see Remark 3.2.9).

The proof is considerably more difficult than that of the corresponding result in Morse theory, Proposition 3.2.8. We break it up into three steps:

(1) A "pre-gluing", where we construct an interpolation w_ρ between the solutions u and v of the Floer equation depending on a parameter ρ, which will not exactly be a solution but will be an "approximated" solution in the sense we will give later

(2) The construction of ψ, which we will write as

$$\psi(\rho) = \exp_{w_\rho}(\gamma(\rho))$$

for some

$$\gamma(\rho) \in W^{1,p}(w_\rho^\star TW) = T_{w_\rho}\mathcal{P}(x, z)$$

such that $\psi(\rho)$ is a true solution of the Floer equation; we will obtain it from w_ρ through a variant of Newton's method, due to Picard, which we will call the "Newton–Picard method"

(3) The verification of the three desired properties of $\widehat{\psi} = \pi \circ \psi$, namely:

  - $\lim_{\rho \to +\infty} \widehat{\psi}(\rho) = (\widehat{u}, \widehat{v})$.
  - $\widehat{\psi}$ is an embedding.
  - $\widehat{\psi}$ is unique in the sense of the last assertion of Theorem 9.2.3.

For the proofs we will need estimates of the derivatives of the exponential map and of the Floer operator. Their proofs are not difficult, but they are very long (and some readers may find them "morally obvious"). For this reason, and to ease the reading, we will gather these in Chapter 13. We will point out these technical lemmas as they come up in the text.

9.3 Pre-gluing

We choose, once and for all, two functions of class $\mathcal{C}^\infty$, β^- and $\beta^+ : \mathbf{R} \to [0,1]$ (Figure 9.3), such that

$$\beta^-(s) = \begin{cases} 1 & \text{for } s \leq -1 \\ 0 & \text{for } s \geq -\varepsilon \end{cases} \quad \text{and} \quad \beta^+(s) = \begin{cases} 1 & \text{for } s \geq 1 \\ 0 & \text{for } s \leq \varepsilon. \end{cases}$$

We define the approximate solution w_ρ by setting

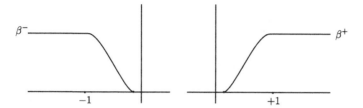

Fig. 9.3

$$w_\rho(s,t) = \begin{cases} u(s+\rho,t) & \text{if } s \leq -1 \\ \exp_{y(t)}\Big(\beta^-(s)\exp_{y(t)}^{-1}(u(s+\rho,t)) \\ \qquad + \beta^+(s)\exp_{y(t)}^{-1}(v(s-\rho,t))\Big) & \text{if } s \in [-1,1] \\ v(s-\rho,t) & \text{if } s \geq 1. \end{cases}$$

This formula indeed defines something if, for $|s| \leq 1$, $u(s+\rho,t)$ and $v(s-\rho,t)$ are in the image of the exponential, or, more precisely, in

$$\Big\{ \exp_{y(t)} Y(t) \mid \sup_{t \in S^1} \|Y(t)\| \leq r_0 \Big\}.$$

Since $\lim_{s \to +\infty} u(s,t) = y(t) = \lim_{s \to -\infty} v(s,t)$, this is true for ρ sufficiently large, let us say for $\rho \geq \rho_0$.

The value of ρ_0, which may increase along the way, does not need to be given explicitly: let us agree[1] that "for $\rho \geq \rho_0$" means "for ρ sufficiently large".

This "interpolation" of u and v has the following properties:

(1) $w_\rho \in \mathcal{C}^\infty(x,z)$.
(2) For $s \in [-\varepsilon,\varepsilon]$, we have $w_\rho(s,t) = y(t)$.

---

[1] A convention that we could also have made in other places.

(3) For $s \leq \rho - 1$, we have $w_\rho(s - \rho, t) = u(s, t)$, in particular

$$\lim_{\rho \to +\infty} w_\rho(s - \rho, t) = u(s, t) \text{ in } \mathcal{C}^\infty_{\text{loc}},$$

and likewise, $w_\rho(s + \rho, t) = v(s, t)$ for $s \geq 1 - \rho$, hence $w_\rho(s + \rho, t)$ tends to $v(s, t)$ in $\mathcal{C}^\infty_{\text{loc}}$.

(4) w_ρ is a differentiable function of ρ.

(5) $w_\rho(s, t)$ tends to $y(t)$ in $\mathcal{C}^\infty_{\text{loc}}$ when ρ tends to $+\infty$.

Figure 9.4 sketches what happens (in the loop space $\mathcal{L}W$).

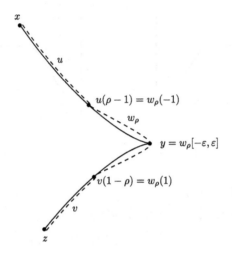

Fig. 9.4

Here is the "linear" version of this construction that we are going to use to apply the Newton–Picard method and construct a true solution from w_ρ. Let $Y \in T_u \mathcal{P}(x, y)$ and let $Z \in T_v \mathcal{P}(y, z)$. We define, in a manner analogous to w_ρ,

$$Y \#_\rho Z \in T_{w_\rho} \mathcal{P}(x, z) = W^{1,p}(w_\rho^\star TW)$$

by setting

$$Y \#_\rho Z(s, t) = \begin{cases} Y(s + \rho, t) \\ T\exp_{y(t)}\Big(\beta^-(s) T_{u(s+\rho,t)} \exp^{-1}_{y(t)}(Y(s + \rho, t)) \\ \qquad\qquad + \beta^+(s) T_{v(s-\rho,t)} \exp^{-1}_{y(t)}(Z(s - \rho, t)) \Big) \\ Z(s - \rho, t) \end{cases}$$

depending on whether s is, respectively, less than or equal to -1, in $[-1, 1]$ or greater than or equal to 1. In order not to lengthen the formula disproportionately, we have not included the point where the tangent to the exponential is taken, namely

$$\beta^-(s)\exp^{-1}_{y(t)}(u(s+\rho,t)) + \beta^+(s)\exp^{-1}_{y(t)}(y(s-\rho,t)).$$

Remark 9.3.1. We can view the construction of w_ρ from u and v as a map

$$\#_\rho : \mathcal{C}^\infty(x,y) \times \mathcal{C}^\infty(y,z) \longrightarrow \mathcal{C}^\infty(x,z).$$

We can also view $Y\#_\rho Z$ as the image of (Y,Z) under the tangent map

$$T_{(u,v)}\#_\rho : T_u\mathcal{P}(x,y) \times T_v\mathcal{P}(y,z) \longrightarrow T_{w_\rho}\mathcal{P}(x,z).$$

The vector field $Y\#_\rho Z$ has properties analogous to those of w_ρ, namely:

(1) As we have said, $Y\#_\rho Z \in T_{w_\rho}\mathcal{P}(x,z)$, and as an element of $W^{1,p}(\mathbf{R} \times S^1; \mathbf{R}^m)$, it is a continuous map.
(2) For $s \in [-\varepsilon, \varepsilon]$, $Y\#_\rho Z = 0$.
(3) We have $\lim_{\rho\to+\infty} Y\#_\rho Z = 0$ in $\mathcal{C}^0_{\mathrm{loc}}$ (and in $\mathcal{C}^\infty_{\mathrm{loc}}$ if Y and Z are of class $\mathcal{C}^\infty$).

Having carried out these constructions, let us proceed with the construction of our parametrization $\widehat{\psi}$.

9.4 Construction of ψ

For every $\rho \geq \rho_0$, we have constructed a w_ρ in $\mathcal{C}^\infty(x,z)$. It is even an element of $\mathcal{C}^\infty_\searrow(x,z)$ because of the exponential decay (Section 8.9). We will now define, for every $\rho \geq \rho_0$, $\psi_\rho \in \mathcal{M}(x,z)$ (a true solution this time), which will be of the form

$$\psi_\rho = \exp_{w_\rho}\gamma(\rho) \quad \text{for a } \gamma(\rho) \in T_{w_\rho}\mathcal{P}(x,z) = W^{1,p}(w_\rho^\star TW).$$

Remark 9.4.1. As before, let $\mathcal{F}$ denote the "Floer" operator

$$\mathcal{F} = \frac{\partial}{\partial s} + J\frac{\partial}{\partial t} + \mathrm{grad}\, H.$$

To verify that ψ_ρ is a solution, it will suffice to verify that $\mathcal{F}(\psi_\rho) = 0$ in the weak sense. Indeed, ψ_ρ will automatically be continuous (since $\gamma(\rho) \in W^{1,p}(w_\rho^\star TW)$ with $p > 2$, $\gamma(\rho)$ is continuous), hence a strong solution and of class $\mathcal{C}^\infty$, again by applying elliptic regularity (Proposition 12.1.4).

Trivializations.

We will describe the equations in coordinates. To do this, we need trivializations of the fiber bundle TW on the maps in question. As in Chapter 7, we begin by choosing disks D_x, D_y and D_z whose boundaries are our contractible loops x, y and z. Next, we fix unitary trivializations:

- $(Z_i^u(s,t))_{i=1,\ldots,2n}$ along $u \cup D_x \cup D_y$ and
- $(Z_i^v(s,t))_{i=1,\ldots,2n}$ along $v \cup D_y \cup D_z$

that coincide along D_y. We still need to define a compatible trivialization along w_ρ. To do this, we of course first define, for $\rho \geq \rho_0$,

$$
Z_i^\rho(s,t) = \begin{cases} Z_i^u(s+\rho,t) & \text{if } s \leq -1 \\ Z_i^v(s-\rho,t) & \text{if } s \geq 1. \end{cases}
$$

We then extend this trivialization for $s \in [-1,1]$ to a unitary trivialization along w_ρ for $\rho \in [\rho_0, +\infty[$ and along $y(t)$ for $\rho = +\infty$ so that, along $y(t) = w_\rho(0,t)$, it coincides with the restrictions of Z_i^u and Z_i^v to y.

In summary, we have constructed a (family of) trivialization(s) $Z_i^\rho(s,t)$ along w_ρ. Each of these coincides with Z_i^u or Z_i^v for $|s|$ sufficiently large. Moreover, they converge (in $\mathcal{C}^\infty_{\text{loc}}$) to a trivialization along y (see Figure 9.5, on which the t-axis has been left out). The family $Z_i^\rho(s,t)$ is a $\mathcal{C}^\infty$ function of ρ.

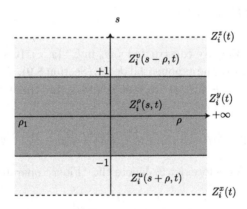

Fig. 9.5

We are not completely done: we need trivializations in the neighborhood of w_ρ. For every ρ, s and t, and for every tangent vector $\xi \in T_{w_\rho(s,t)}W$ of norm less than the injectivity radius, we use parallel transport (see Appendix A.5, if necessary) to construct an orthonormal (but not necessarily unitary) basis of $T_{\exp_{w_\rho(s,t)}(\xi)}W$ that we denote by $(Z_i^{\rho,\xi}(s,t))_{i=1,\dots,2n}$.

Definition of $\mathcal{F}_\rho$.

For every $\rho \geq \rho_0$, we define an operator

$$W^{1,p}(\mathbf{R} \times S^1; \mathbf{R}^{2n}) \xrightarrow{\mathcal{F}_\rho} L^p(\mathbf{R} \times S^1; \mathbf{R}^{2n})$$

$$(y_1,\dots,y_{2n}) \longmapsto \left[\left(\frac{\partial}{\partial s} + J\frac{\partial}{\partial t} + \operatorname{grad} H_t\right)\left(\exp_{w_\rho} \sum y_i Z_i^\rho\right)\right]_{Z_i},$$

a formula in which the result is expanded in the basis $Z_i^{\rho,\sum y_i Z_i^\rho}$ and which, we should note, does not define a *linear* operator. The map $\mathcal{F}_\rho$ is none other than

$$\mathcal{F}_\rho = \mathcal{F} \circ \exp_{w_\rho}$$

written in the bases Z_i.

Remark 9.4.2. The map $\mathcal{F}_\rho$ is well defined on the vectors $(y_1,\dots,y_{2n})$ of the ball

$$B\left(0, r_0/K\right) \subset W^{1,p}(\mathbf{R} \times S^1; \mathbf{R}^{2n}),$$

where r_0 is chosen smaller than the injectivity radius of the metric on W and K is the norm of the injection of $W^{1,p}$ in L^∞ (using the notation of Section 8.2, which we used to define the structure of the Banach manifold on $\mathcal{P}(x,y)$).

We obviously have $\mathcal{F}_\rho(0) = [\mathcal{F}(w_\rho)]_{Z_i^\rho}$. Moreover, since u and v are solutions of the Floer equation, we have

$$\mathcal{F}(w_\rho) = \frac{\partial w_\rho}{\partial s} + J\frac{\partial w_\rho}{\partial t} + \operatorname{grad}_{w_\rho} H_t = 0 \quad \text{for } |s| \geq 1.$$

On $[-1,1]$, $w_\rho(s,t)$ tends uniformly (in the $\mathcal{C}^\infty$ topology) to $y(t)$. Hence, since $\mathcal{F}(y) = 0$, $\mathcal{F}(w_\rho)$ tends to 0 when ρ tends to $+\infty$, both in the $\mathcal{C}^\infty$ topology and in the L^p topology.

The Newton–Picard Method, General Idea.

We are seeking a $\gamma = (\gamma_1,\dots,\gamma_{2n})$ that is a solution of the equation $\mathcal{F}_\rho(\gamma) = 0$. We just noted that even if we do not have $\mathcal{F}_\rho(0) = 0$, the origin 0 is "almost" a solution of the equation. We will use this approximate solution as a starting point for the construction of a true solution using the Newton–Picard method.

In the case of functions $f : \mathbf{R} \to \mathbf{R}$, we know that this allows us to find a zero, α of f from an approximate solution x_0 in the form of the limit of the recursive sequence

$$x_{n+1} = x_n - \frac{f(x_n)}{f'(x_n)}.$$

A variant is to find α as the limit of the sequence

$$x_{n+1} = x_n - \frac{f(x_n)}{f'(x_0)},$$

that has the advantage of using only one value of the derivative and that we will use here for $\mathcal{F}_\rho$. The two methods are represented in Figure 9.6.

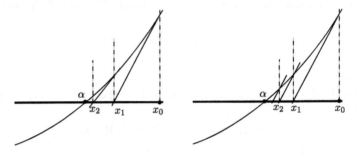

Fig. 9.6

Linearization of $\mathcal{F}_\rho$.

We will now determine what will play the role of the derivative $f'(x_0)$ in the Newton–Picard method. Let L_ρ denote the linearization $(d\mathcal{F}_\rho)_0$ of the operator $\mathcal{F}_\rho$ at 0,

$$L_\rho : W^{1,p}(\mathbf{R} \times S^1; \mathbf{R}^{2n}) \longrightarrow L^p(\mathbf{R} \times S^1; \mathbf{R}^{2n}).$$

Proposition 9.4.3. *The operator L_ρ is a Fredholm operator of index 2.*

Proof. We noted in the previous chapter (Remark 8.4.3) that the differential of $\mathcal{F}$ is of the form

$$(d\mathcal{F})_u = \bar{\partial} + S(s,t)$$

for every u (and not only for the solutions of the Floer equation). In our trivializations, we therefore have

$$L_\rho(Y) = \frac{\partial Y}{\partial s} + J_0 \frac{\partial Y}{\partial t} + S_\rho(s,t)Y$$

for a map

$$S_\rho : \mathbf{R} \times S^1 \longrightarrow M_{2n}(\mathbf{R}).$$

Since we have chosen the trivialization along w_ρ to be compatible with those along u and v, we have

$$S_\rho(s,t) = \begin{cases} S^u(s+\rho, t) & \text{for } s \leq -1 \\ S^v(s-\rho, t) & \text{for } s \geq 1, \end{cases}$$

where S^u and S^v are the matrices corresponding to the linearizations of $\mathcal{F}$ along u and v in the trivializations Z_i^u and Z_i^v, respectively. Therefore, in particular, for ρ tending to infinity, S_ρ tends to the paths of symmetric matrices defined by the critical points x and z:

$$\lim_{s \to -\infty} S_\rho(s,t) = S^x(t) \quad \text{and} \quad \lim_{s \to +\infty} S_\rho(s,t) = S^z(t).$$

We now only need to apply the results of the previous chapter (namely Proposition 8.7.1 and Theorem 8.8.1): L_ρ is a Fredholm operator of index $\mu(x) - \mu(z) = 2$. □

Idea of the Construction of ψ.

In our situation, in the formula defining the recursive sequence used in the Newton–Picard method, the term $1/f'(x_0)$ corresponds to an inverse of the linearized map L_ρ. The fact that this is of index 2 prohibits it from being invertible. We will show that there exists a closed complement $W_\rho^\perp$ of $\operatorname{Ker} L_\rho$ in $W^{1,p}(\mathbf{R} \times S^1; \mathbf{R}^{2n})$ such that $L_\rho|_{W_\rho^\perp}$ is invertible (in other words, there exists a right inverse for L_ρ on $W_\rho^\perp$). We will apply the Newton–Picard method starting out with the approximate solution 0 in order to find a solution of $\mathcal{F}_\rho(\gamma) = 0$.

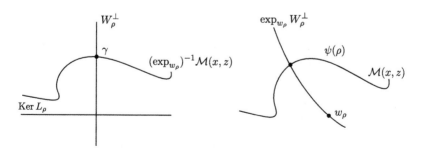

Fig. 9.7

It is not surprising that we need to use such a subspace $W_\rho^\perp$: we know that $\mathcal{M}(x, z)$ is a manifold of dimension 2; therefore for every ρ, we are looking for an element γ of $(\exp_{w_\rho})^{-1}\mathcal{M}(x, z)$, a submanifold of dimension 2 of $T_{w_\rho}\mathcal{P}(x, z)$. It seems natural to determine such a γ by intersecting this submanifold with a subspace of codimension 2, our $W_\rho^\perp$ (we will indeed show that $\dim \operatorname{Ker} L_\rho = 2$). This is sketched in Figure 9.7.

We will therefore obtain the path $\psi(\rho)$ as the intersection in $\mathcal{P}(x, z)$ of $\mathcal{M}(x, z)$ and the space

$$\{\exp_{w_\rho} W_\rho^\perp \mid \rho \geq \rho_0\}.$$

This subspace is of codimension 1; it is the image of the fiber bundle $W^\perp$ consisting of the $W_\rho^\perp$ on w_ρ, a subbundle of $w^\star T\mathcal{P}(x, z)$ of codimension 2. This is sketched in Figure 9.8.

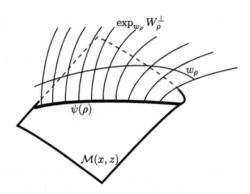

Fig. 9.8

The (Abstract) Newton–Picard Method.

Here is the precise statement we will use.

Lemma 9.4.4. *Let X and Y be two Banach spaces and let $F : X \to Y$ be a continuous map. We write*

$$F(x) = F(0) + L(x) + N(x),$$

where $L(x) = (dF)_0(x)$ and we suppose that there exists a continuous $G : Y \to X$ such that:

(1) $L \circ G = \operatorname{Id}$.
(2) $\|GN(x) - GN(y)\| \leq C(\|x\| + \|y\|)\,\|x - y\|$ *for all* $x, y \in B(0, r)$.
(3) $\|GF(0)\| \leq \varepsilon/2$ *where* $\varepsilon = \min(r, 1/5C)$.

Then there exists a unique $\alpha \in \operatorname{Im}(G) \cap B(0, \varepsilon)$ such that $F(\alpha) = 0$. Moreover, we have $\|\alpha\| \leq 2\,\|GF(0)\|$.

Proof. Keeping the classical Newton–Picard method in mind, we define $\varphi :$ $B(0, \varepsilon) \to \mathrm{Im}(G)$ by setting

$$\varphi(x) = G(L(x) - F(x)) = -G(F(0) + N(x)).$$

Note that

$$L\varphi(x) = L(x) - F(x).$$

Hence if $\varphi(x) = x$, then $F(x) = 0$. Conversely, if $F(x) = 0$ and $x = G(y)$, then

$$\varphi(x) = GL(x) = GLG(y) = G(y) = x.$$

We will therefore show that φ has a unique fixed point in $B(0, \varepsilon)$.

First, φ sends the ball with radius ε into itself: if $\|x\| \leq \varepsilon$, then

$$\begin{aligned}
\|\varphi(x)\| = \|G(F(0) + N(x))\| &\leq \|GF(0)\| + \|GN(x)\| \\
&\leq \frac{\varepsilon}{2} + C\|x\|^2 \\
&\leq \frac{\varepsilon}{2} + C\varepsilon^2 \\
&\leq \frac{\varepsilon}{2} + \frac{\varepsilon}{5} < \varepsilon,
\end{aligned}$$

a sequence of inequalities for which we have used properties (2) and (3) as well as the fact that $N(0) = 0$.

Next, if x and y are two points of the ball $B(0, \varepsilon)$, then

$$\begin{aligned}
\|\varphi(x) - \varphi(y)\| = \|GN(x) - GN(y)\| &\leq C(\|x\| + \|y\|)\|x - y\| \\
&\leq 2C\varepsilon\|x - y\| \\
&\leq \frac{2}{5}\|x - y\| \leq \frac{1}{2}\|x - y\|.
\end{aligned}$$

So the sequence defined by

$$x_0 = 0 \quad \text{and} \quad x_{n+1} = \varphi(x_n)$$

is a Cauchy sequence. It therefore converges to a limit α that is a fixed point of φ and that is the unique fixed point because of the inequality that we have just proved.

To conclude, we prove the inequality stated in the lemma. We have

$$\frac{1}{2}\|\alpha\| = \frac{1}{2}\|\alpha - 0\| \geq \|\varphi(\alpha) - \varphi(0)\| = \|\alpha - \varphi(0)\| \geq \|\alpha\| - \|\varphi(0)\|.$$

It follows that

$$\|\alpha\| \leq 2\|\varphi(0)\| = 2\|GF(0)\|. \qquad \square$$

Application of Lemma 9.4.4.

We are going to apply the lemma to the map

$$\mathcal{F}_\rho : W^{1,p}(\mathbf{R} \times S^1; \mathbf{R}^{2n}) \longrightarrow L^p(\mathbf{R} \times S^1; \mathbf{R}^{2n}).$$

We therefore need to determine a right inverse G_ρ of the differential of L_ρ at 0, and verify that this G_ρ satisfies the conditions of the lemma. As we have said, we will obtain G_ρ using a subspace $W_\rho^\perp$. We therefore begin by defining the latter.

In the trivializations Z_i^u and Z_i^v, we denote the differentials $(d\mathcal{F})_u$ and $(d\mathcal{F})_v$ by L^u and L^v, respectively; *via* these trivializations, we consider

$$\operatorname{Ker} L^u \subset T_u \mathcal{P}(x, y) \quad \text{and} \quad \operatorname{Ker} L^v \subset T_v \mathcal{P}(y, z).$$

We define W_ρ to be the "sum $\#_\rho$" of these subspaces,

$$W_\rho = \{\alpha \#_\rho \beta \mid \alpha \in \operatorname{Ker} L^u, \beta \in \operatorname{Ker} L^v\}.$$

We then define $W_\rho^\perp$ to be its orthogonal, that is,

$$W_\rho^\perp = \Big\{ Y \in W^{1,p}(\mathbf{R} \times S^1; \mathbf{R}^{2n}) \mid$$
$$\int_{\mathbf{R} \times S^1} \langle Y, \alpha \#_\rho \beta \rangle \, ds \, dt = 0 \text{ for all } \alpha \in \operatorname{Ker} L^u, \beta \in \operatorname{Ker} L^v \Big\},$$

(still using the frame $(Z_i^\rho)_{i=1,\dots,2n}$ in order to view $\alpha \#_\rho \beta$ as an element of $W^{1,p}(\mathbf{R} \times S^1; \mathbf{R}^{2n})$).

Remarks 9.4.5.

(1) The two solutions u and v of the Floer equation connect critical points with consecutive indices. Since the pair (H, J) is regular, we therefore know that L^u and L^v are surjective. Since their Fredholm indices are 1, the kernels of L^u and L^v are of dimension 1. By Remark 8.4.7, we can therefore assert that

$$\operatorname{Ker} L^u = \mathbf{R} \cdot \frac{\partial u}{\partial s} \quad \text{and} \quad \operatorname{Ker} L^v = \mathbf{R} \cdot \frac{\partial v}{\partial s}$$

(where the use of the frames (Z_i^u), (Z_i^v) is implied).

(2) Since by the exponential decay (Section 8.9) we have

$$\sup\left(\left|\frac{\partial u}{\partial s}\right|, \left|\frac{\partial v}{\partial s}\right|\right) \leq K e^{-\delta|s|},$$

we know that the vectors $\partial u / \partial s$ and $\partial v / \partial s$ are in L^q for every $q \geq 1$, hence

$$\forall Y \in W^{1,p}(\mathbf{R} \times S^1; \mathbf{R}^{2n}), \ \forall \alpha \in \operatorname{Ker} L^u, \ \forall \beta \in \operatorname{Ker} L^v, \quad \langle Y, \alpha \#_\rho \beta \rangle \in L^1.$$

(3) The space $W^{1,p}(\mathbf{R} \times S^1; \mathbf{R}^{2n})$ is the direct sum of W_ρ and $W_\rho^\perp$. This is a simple and quite general fact that we can state as a lemma.

Lemma 9.4.6. *Let $1/p+1/q = 1$. Let E be a finite-dimensional subspace of $W^{1,p} \cap L^q$. Let*

$$E^\perp = \Big\{ Y \in W^{1,p} \mid \int \langle Y, X \rangle \, ds \, dt = 0 \text{ for every } X \in E \Big\}.$$

Then $W^{1,p} = E \oplus E^\perp$.

Indeed, it is clear that these two subspaces only meet at 0. Next, by Hölder's inequality, since $E \subset L^p \cap L^q$, we have $E \subset L^2$. It now suffices to choose an orthonormal basis $\{e_1, \ldots, e_r\}$ of E. Every element Z of $W^{1,p}$ satisfies

$$Z - \langle e_1, Z \rangle \, e_1 - \cdots - \langle e_r, Z \rangle \, e_r \in E^\perp,$$

giving the expected result. □

Since W_ρ is the image of the two-dimensional space $\operatorname{Ker} L^u \times \operatorname{Ker} L^v$ under the linear map $\#_\rho$, we know that $\dim W_\rho \leq 2$, so that we may apply Lemma 9.4.6.

The proposition below is important. It allows us to define G_ρ and to verify the conditions of the lemma.

Proposition 9.4.7. *There exists a constant $C > 0$ such that for $\rho \geq \rho_0$, we have*

$$\forall Y \in W_\rho^\perp, \quad \|L_\rho(Y)\|_{L^p} \geq C \, \|Y\|_{W^{1,p}}.$$

We begin by giving a list of consequences of this proposition. We assume that $\rho \geq \rho_0$.

(1) First of all, we clearly have $\operatorname{Ker} L_\rho \cap W_\rho^\perp = 0$.
(2) The map L_ρ is surjective and $\dim \operatorname{Ker} L_\rho = \dim W_\rho = 2$. In fact, we always have

$$\dim \operatorname{Ker} L_\rho \geq \operatorname{Ind}(L_\rho) = 2$$

and

$$\operatorname{codim} W_\rho^\perp = \dim W_\rho \leq \dim(\operatorname{Ker} L^u \times \operatorname{Ker} L^v) = 2$$

and the first property transforms these two inequalities into equalities. We therefore have

$$W^{1,p}(\mathbf{R} \times S^1; \mathbf{R}^{2n}) = \operatorname{Ker} L_\rho \oplus W_\rho^\perp.$$

Intuitively, we can say that the kernel of $(d\mathcal{F})_{u \#_\rho v}$ is close to $\operatorname{Ker}(d\mathcal{F})_u \#_\rho \operatorname{Ker}(d\mathcal{F})_v$ when ρ is sufficiently large.

(3) Consequently,

$$L_\rho : W_\rho^\perp \cong W^{1,p}(\mathbf{R} \times S^1; \mathbf{R}^{2n}) / \operatorname{Ker} L_\rho \longrightarrow L^p(\mathbf{R} \times S^1; \mathbf{R}^{2n}) = \operatorname{Im} L_\rho$$

is bijective. We set

$$G_\rho = L_\rho^{-1} : L^p(\mathbf{R} \times S^1; \mathbf{R}^{2n}) \longrightarrow W_\rho^\perp.$$

(4) This map G_ρ is continuous, because the proposition asserts that

$$\|G_\rho(Y)\|_{W^{1,p}} \le \frac{1}{C} \|L_\rho G_\rho(Y)\|_{L^p} = \frac{1}{C} \|Y\|_{L^p}.$$

Conditions (2) and (3) of Lemma 9.4.4 are also consequences of Proposition 9.4.7:

(1) We first verify condition (2) of Lemma 9.4.4 (leaving out the ρ in the notation). We have

$$\|GNx - GNy\| \le C^{-1} \|N(x) - N(y)\| \le C^{-1} \sup_{z \in [x,y]} \|(dN)_z\| \|x - y\|$$

by the mean value theorem. On the segment $[x, y]$, $\|(dN)_z\|$ is bounded by $K \|z\|$, where K is independent of ρ, x and y, by Lemma 9.4.8, one of the technical lemmas proved in Chapter 13 (in Section 13.2):

$$\|(dN)_z\| \le K \|z\|$$

because

$$(dN)_z = (d\mathcal{F})_z - (d\mathcal{F})_0.$$

It follows that

$$\|GNx - GNy\| \le C^{-1} \|N(x) - N(y)\|$$
$$\le C^{-1} K \sup_{z \in [x,y)} \|z\| \|x - y\|$$
$$\le C^{-1} K (\|x\| + \|y\|) \|x - y\|$$

and condition (2) is satisfied.

Lemma 9.4.8. *Let $r_0 > 0$. There exists a constant $K > 0$ such that for every $\rho \ge \rho_0$ and every $Z \in \overline{B}(0, r_0) \subset W^{1,p}(\mathbf{R} \times S^1; \mathbf{R}^{2n})$, we have*

$$\|(d\mathcal{F}_\rho)_Z - (d\mathcal{F}_\rho)_0\|^{\mathrm{op}} \le K \|Z\|_{W^{1,p}}.$$

(2) We finally verify condition (3) of Lemma 9.4.4. We have

$$\|G_\rho \mathcal{F}_\rho(0)\| \le C^{-1} \|\mathcal{F}_\rho(0)\| = C^{-1} \|\mathcal{F}(w_\rho)\|,$$

which tends to 0 when ρ tends to infinity, so that we indeed have $\|G_\rho \mathcal{F}_\rho(0)\| \le \varepsilon/2$ for ρ sufficiently large. We can now apply the Newton–Picard lemma.

Proof of Proposition 9.4.7. We use a reasoning by contradiction. Suppose that there exist a sequence (ρ_n) that tends to infinity and a $Y_n \in W_{\rho_n}^\perp$ such that

$$\lim_{n \to +\infty} \frac{\|L_{\rho_n} Y_n\|_{L^p}}{\|Y_n\|_{W^{1,p}}} = 0.$$

By normalizing, we may, and do, assume that $\|Y_n\| = 1$.

Lemma 9.4.9. *Let* $K = [-a, a] \times S^1 \subset \mathbf{R} \times S^1$. *Then*

$$\lim_{n \to \infty} \|Y_n\|_{W^{1,p}(K)} = 0.$$

Proof. Consider the operator

$$D : W^{1,p}(\mathbf{R} \times S^1; \mathbf{R}^{2n}) \longrightarrow L^p(\mathbf{R} \times S^1; \mathbf{R}^{2n})$$

defined by

$$D(Y) = \frac{\partial Y}{\partial s}(s, t) + J_0 \frac{\partial Y}{\partial t}(s, t) + S^y(t) \cdot Y(s, t),$$

where $t \mapsto S^y(t)$ is the path of symmetric matrices corresponding to the chosen trivialization along the loop y. As we already know,

$$(d\mathcal{F})_{w_\rho}(Y) = \frac{\partial Y}{\partial s} + J \frac{\partial Y}{\partial t} - (dJ)_{w_\rho}(Y) \frac{\partial w_\rho}{\partial t} + d(\mathrm{grad}_{w_\rho} H_t)(Y).$$

Since w_ρ tends to y (in the $\mathcal{C}^\infty_{\mathrm{loc}}$ sense) when ρ tends to infinity, the order 0 part of this operator tends to the order 0 part of $(d\mathcal{F})_y$. Since we have chosen the trivializations in such a way that $Z_i^\rho(s, t)$ tends to $Z_i^y(t)$ (still in the $\mathcal{C}^\infty_{\mathrm{loc}}$ sense), we have

$$\lim_{\rho \to \infty} S_\rho(s, t) = S^y(t) \text{ in the } \mathcal{C}^\infty_{\mathrm{loc}} \text{ sense.}$$

Let $r_n = \rho_n/2$. We choose a plateau function γ with value 1 for $|s| \le 1/2$ and 0 for $|s| \ge 1$ and set $\gamma_n(s) = \gamma(s/r_n)$.

Let us show that $D(\gamma_n Y_n)$ tends to 0 for the L^p norm. We in fact have

$$\|D(\gamma_n Y_n)\|_{L^p} = \left\| \gamma_n D(Y_n) + \frac{1}{r_n} \dot{\gamma} Y_n \right\|_{L^p}$$

$$\le \frac{1}{r_n} \|\dot{\gamma} Y_n\|_{L^p} + \|\gamma_n D(Y_n)\|_{L^p}$$

$$\le \frac{M}{r_n} \|Y_n\|_{L^p} + \|D(Y_n)\|_{L^p([-r_n, r_n] \times S^1)},$$

where M is the upper bound of $|\dot{\gamma}(s)|$ on $\mathbf{R}$. It follows that

$$\|D(\gamma_n Y_n)\|_{L^p} \leq \frac{M}{r_n} \|Y_n\|_{L^p} + \|(D - L_{\rho_n})Y_n\|_{L^p([-r_n, r_n] \times S^1)}$$

$$+ \|L_{\rho_n}(Y_n)\|_{L^p([-r_n, r_n] \times S^1)}$$

$$\leq \frac{M}{r_n} \|Y_n\|_{L^p} + \|(S^y - S_{\rho_n})Y_n\|_{L^p([-r_n, r_n] \times S^1)}$$

$$+ \|L_{\rho_n}(Y_n)\|_{L^p}.$$

Since $\|Y_n\|_{L^p} \leq \|Y_n\|_{W^{1,p}} = 1$ and since $\|L_{\rho_n}(Y_n)\|_{L^p}$ tends to 0, this gives

$$\|D(\gamma_n Y_n)\|_{L^p} \leq \|(S^y - S_{\rho_n})Y_n\|_{L^p} + \tau_n$$

for a $\tau_n \geq 0$ that tends to 0 when n tends to infinity. Next, note that

$$\|(S^y - S_{\rho_n})Y_n\|_{L^p([-r_n, r_n] \times S^1)} \leq \sup_{(s,t) \in [-r_n, r_n] \times S^1} \|S_{\rho_n}(s,t) - S^y(t)\| \|Y_n\|_{L^p}$$

$$\leq \sup_{(s,t) \in [-r_n, r_n] \times S^1} \|S_{\rho_n}(s,t) - S^y(t)\|.$$

For $s \leq -1$, $S_{\rho_n}(s,t) = S^u(s + \rho_n, t)$; hence the supremum of $\|S_{\rho_n}(s,t) - S^y(t)\|$ for $(s,t) \in [-r_n, -1] \times S^1$ equals

$$\sup_{(s,t) \in [-r_n, -1] \times S^1} \|S^u(s + \rho_n, t) - S^y(t)\|,$$

that is,

$$\sup_{(s,t) \in [r_n, \rho_n - 1] \times S^1} \|S^u(s,t) - S^y(t)\|,$$

and this supremum therefore tends to 0. Likewise, for $s \geq 1$, using the fact that $S_{\rho_n}(s,t) = S^v(s - \rho_n, t)$, we can verify that

$$\lim_{n \to +\infty} \sup_{(s,t) \in [1, r_n] \times S^1} \|S_{\rho_n}(s,t) - S^y(t)\| = 0.$$

Finally, we have

$$\lim_{n \to +\infty} \sup_{(s,t) \in [-1,1] \times S^1} \|S_{\rho_n}(s,t) - S^y(t)\| = 0$$

because $S_{\rho_n}(s,t)$ tends to $S^y(t)$ in the $\mathcal{C}^\infty_{\text{loc}}$ sense. We have thus shown that $D(\gamma_n Y_n)$ tends to 0 for the L^p norm, which allows us to conclude the proof of the lemma.

We know (see Proposition 8.7.3 in the proof of the fact that $\mathcal{F}$ is a Fredholm operator) that $D : W^{1,p}(\mathbf{R} \times S^1; \mathbf{R}^{2n}) \to L^p(\mathbf{R} \times S^1; \mathbf{R}^{2n})$ is invertible. From the fact that $\|D(\gamma_n Y_n)\|_{L^p}$ tends to 0, we deduce that $\|\gamma_n Y_n\|_{W^{1,p}}$ tends to 0 and therefore that

$$\lim_{n \to +\infty} \|Y_n\|_{W^{1,p}(K)} = 0,$$

concluding the proof of the lemma. □

Since the $W^{1,p}$ norm of Y_n is 1, this lemma asserts that its support tends to concentrate toward $|s| \to +\infty$.

We will use the relations between L_{ρ_n}, L^u and L^v for $|s|$ sufficiently large.

Lemma 9.4.10. *Let $\beta^{\pm}$ be the two functions used to construct the approximate solution w_ρ. There exist vector fields $Y \in \operatorname{Ker} L^u$ and $Z \in \operatorname{Ker} L^v$ such that after extracting subsequences, if necessary,*

$$\beta^-(s - \rho_n + 1)Y_n(s - \rho_n, t) \text{ tends to } Y \text{ in } W^{1,p}(\mathbf{R} \times S^1; \mathbf{R}^{2n})$$

and

$$\beta^+(s + \rho_n - 1)Y_n(s + \rho_n, t) \text{ tends to } Z \text{ in } W^{1,p}(\mathbf{R} \times S^1; \mathbf{R}^{2n}).$$

Proof. Recall that $\beta^-(s + 1) = 0$ for $s \geq -1$, which means that $\beta^-(s+1)Y_n(s,t)$ has support in $]-\infty, -1] \times S^1$. It follows that

$$
\begin{aligned}
\left\|L^{u(s+\rho_n,t)}(\beta^-(s+1)Y_n(s,t))\right\|_{L^p} &= \left\|L_{\rho_n}(\beta^-(s+1)Y_n(s,t))\right\|_{L^p} \\
&= \left\|\dot{\beta}^-(s+1)Y_n(s,t) + \beta^-(s+1)L_{\rho_n}(Y_n(s,t))\right\|_{L^p} \\
&\leq \sup \dot{\beta}^- \|Y_n\|_{L^p([-1,1]\times S^1)} + \|L_{\rho_n} Y_n\|_{L^p},
\end{aligned}
$$

which tends to 0 by Lemma 9.4.9. Replacing s by $s - \rho_n$ gives

$$\lim_{n \to +\infty} \left\|L^u(\beta^-(s - \rho_n + 1)Y_n(s - \rho_n, t))\right\|_{L^p} = 0.$$

Analogously, we have

$$\lim_{n \to +\infty} \left\|L^v(\beta^+(s + \rho_n - 1)Y_n(s + \rho_n, t))\right\|_{L^p} = 0.$$

The proof of Lemma 9.4.10 is then a direct consequence of the following lemma.

Lemma 9.4.11. *Let $D : E \to F$ be a (linear) Fredholm operator. Let (x_n) be a bounded sequence of elements of E such that the sequence $(D(x_n))$ tends to 0 in F. Then there exists a subsequence of (x_n) that converges to an element x of $\operatorname{Ker} D \subset E$.*

Proof. Since D is a Fredholm operator, we know that there exists an operator D' such that

$$D' \circ D = \operatorname{Id} + K,$$

where K is an operator of finite rank (Proposition C.2.5), which implies that the sequence $(x_n + K(x_n))$ tends to 0. After extracting a subsequence, if necessary, the sequence $(K(x_n))$ is convergent, giving a subsequence of (x_n) that converges. $\square$

This concludes the proof of Lemma 9.4.10. $\square$

And leads us to state another lemma.

Lemma 9.4.12. *The sequences $\beta^-(s+1)Y_n(s,t)$ and $\beta^+(s-1)Y_n(s,t)$ converge to 0 in $W^{1,p}$.*

Proof. Let $Y \in \operatorname{Ker} L^u$ be a vector field given by Lemma 9.4.10. We will now construct $Y \#_\rho 0$, which is an element of W_ρ. Lemma 9.4.10 asserts that $\beta^-(s - \rho_n + 1)Y_n(s - \rho_n, t)$ tends to Y (in $W^{1,p}$), so that

$$\lim_{n\to+\infty} \left\| \beta^-(s+1)Y_n(s,t) - Y(s+\rho_n,t) \right\|_{W^{1,p}} = 0,$$

and, in particular,

$$\lim_{n\to+\infty} \left\| \beta^-(s+1)Y_n(s,t) - Y\#_{\rho_n}0 \right\|_{W^{1,p}(]-\infty,-1]\times S^1)} = 0.$$

Next, $\beta^-(s+1)Y_n(s,t) - Y\#_{\rho_n}0$ has support in $]-\infty,0] \times S^1$ and $Y\#_{\rho_n}0$ tends to 0 in the $\mathcal{C}^\infty_{\mathrm{loc}}$ sense, hence also in the $W^{1,p}([-1,0] \times S^1)$ sense. Note that Y is in the kernel of L^u, hence is $\mathcal{C}^\infty$ (by elliptic regularity), and that Y is a scalar multiple of $\partial u/\partial s$. By also using Lemma 9.4.9, we see that $\|\beta^-(s+1)Y_n(s,t) - Y\#_{\rho_n}0\|_{W^{1,p}}$ tends to 0.

Since Y has exponential decay, it is in L^q for every $q \geq 1$, as is $Y\#_{\rho_n}0$. With $1/p + 1/q = 1$, Hölder's inequality gives

$$\left| \int_{\mathbf{R}\times S^1} \langle \beta^-(s+1)Y_n(s,t) - Y\#_{\rho_n}0(s,t), Y\#_{\rho_n}0(s,t) \rangle \, ds \, dt \right|$$

$$\leq \left\| \beta^-(s+1)Y_n(s,t) - Y\#_{\rho_n}0(s,t) \right\|_{L^p} \left\| Y\#_{\rho_n}0 \right\|_{L^q}.$$

The norm $\|Y\#_{\rho_n}0\|_{L^q}$ is bounded by $\|Y\|_{L^q}$ in $L^q(]-\infty,-1] \times S^1)$ and tends to 0 in $L^q([-1,+\infty[\times S^1)$, so that it is uniformly bounded. We therefore have

$$\lim_{n\to+\infty} \int_{\mathbf{R}\times S^1} \langle \beta^-(s+1)Y_n(s,t) - Y\#_{\rho_n}0(s,t), Y\#_{\rho_n}0(s,t) \rangle \, ds \, dt = 0.$$

Since $Y \#_{\rho_n} 0 \in W_{\rho_n}$ and $Y_n \in W_{\rho_n}^{\perp}$, we have

$$\int_{\mathbf{R} \times S^1} \langle Y_n, Y \#_{\rho_n} 0 \rangle \, ds \, dt = 0.$$

Moreover,

$$\lim_{n \to +\infty} \int_{\mathbf{R} \times S^1} \langle (1 - \beta^-(s+1))Y_n(s,t), Y \#_{\rho_n} 0(s,t) \rangle \, ds \, dt = 0$$

because the term that is integrated has support in $[-1,0] \times S^1$ and, as above, using Hölder's inequality, the absolute value of the integral is bounded from above by

$$\|Y_n\|_{L^p([-1,0] \times S^1)} \cdot \|Y \#_{\rho_n} 0\|_{L^q([-1,0] \times S^1)}.$$

This tends to 0 by Lemma 9.4.9. The two relations above imply that

$$\lim_{n \to +\infty} \int_{\mathbf{R} \times S^1} \langle \beta^-(s+1)Y_n(s,t), Y \#_{\rho_n} 0 \rangle \, ds \, dt = 0$$

and therefore that

$$\lim_{n \to +\infty} \int_{\mathbf{R} \times S^1} \langle Y \#_{\rho_n} 0, Y \#_{\rho_n} 0 \rangle \, ds \, dt = 0.$$

For $s \leq -1$, $Y \#_{\rho_n} 0(s,t) = Y(s + \rho_n, t)$, hence

$$\lim_{n \to +\infty} \int_{S^1} \int_{-\infty}^{-1} \langle Y(s + \rho_n, t), Y(s + \rho_n, t) \rangle \, ds \, dt = 0,$$

or

$$\lim_{n \to +\infty} \int_{S^1} \int_{-\infty}^{-1+\rho_n} \|Y(s,t)\|^2 \, ds \, dt = 0,$$

and finally $Y = 0$ and $\|\beta^-(s+1)Y_n(s,t)\|_{W^{1,p}}$ tends to 0. In an analogous manner, we can show that the same holds for $\|\beta^+(s-1)Y_n(s,t)\|_{W^{1,p}}$. This concludes the proof of Lemma 9.4.12. $\qquad\square$

This will allow us to conclude the proof of Proposition 9.4.7. We have

$$\begin{aligned}
1 &= \|Y_n(s,t)\|_{W^{1,p}} \\
&\leq \|\beta^-(s+1)Y_n(s,t)\|_{W^{1,p}} + \|\beta^+(s-1)Y_n(s,t)\|_{W^{1,p}} \\
&\quad + \|(1 - \beta^-(s+1) - \beta^+(s-1))Y_n(s,t)\|_{W^{1,p}}.
\end{aligned}$$

The first two terms tend to 0 by Lemma 9.4.12 and the last one does also, this time by Lemma 9.4.9. This is the indisputable contradiction we were looking for. $\qquad\square$

We can therefore apply the Newton–Picard method to obtain, for every $\rho \geq \rho_0$, an element $\gamma(\rho)$ of $W_\rho^\perp$ with $\mathcal{F}_\rho(\gamma(\rho)) = 0$. Moreover, this element $\gamma(\rho)$ is unique in $W_\rho^\perp \cap B(0, \varepsilon)$ where, we recall, ε is independent of ρ (by Lemma 9.4.4). We also have the following result.

Lemma 9.4.13.
$$\lim_{\rho \to +\infty} \|\gamma(\rho)\|_{W^{1,p}} = 0.$$

Proof. By the "Newton–Picard" lemma 9.4.4, we have

$$\|\gamma(\rho)\|_{W^{1,p}} \leq 2 \|G_\rho \mathcal{F}_\rho(0)\|_{W^{1,p}} \leq 2C^{-1} \|\mathcal{F}_\rho(0)\|_{L^p} = 2C^{-1} \|\mathcal{F}(w_\rho)\|_{L^p} ,$$

which tends to 0 when ρ tends to infinity. $\qquad\square$

Continuity and Differentiability of γ.

We now apply the implicit function theorem. Let

$$W(\varepsilon)^\perp = \left\{ (\rho, Y) \mid \rho \geq \rho_0, Y \in W_\rho^\perp \text{ and } \|Y\| < \varepsilon \right\}$$

and let $F : W(\varepsilon)^\perp \to L^p(\mathbf{R} \times S^1; \mathbf{R}^{2n})$ be defined by $F(\rho, Y) = \mathcal{F}_\rho(Y)$, so that

$$F(\rho, \gamma(\rho)) = 0 \quad \text{for every } \rho \geq \rho_0.$$

Lemma 9.4.14. *For every sufficiently large ρ (and larger than ρ_0), the derivative*

$$(d_2 F)_{\rho, \gamma(\rho)} = (d\mathcal{F}_\rho)_{\gamma(\rho)}$$

is invertible.

Proof. Fix a ρ. The differential of $\mathcal{F}_\rho$ is a linear map

$$(d\mathcal{F}_\rho)_{\gamma(\rho)} : W_\rho^\perp \longrightarrow L^p(\mathbf{R} \times S^1; \mathbf{R}^{2n}).$$

Consider the inverse G_ρ of $(d\mathcal{F}_\rho)_0$ constructed before,

$$G_\rho : L^p(\mathbf{R} \times S^1; \mathbf{R}^{2n}) \longrightarrow W_\rho^\perp.$$

For the operator norm, we have

$$\begin{aligned}
\left\| G_\rho (d\mathcal{F}_\rho)_{\gamma(\rho)} - \mathrm{Id} \right\| &= \left\| G_\rho (d\mathcal{F}_\rho)_{\gamma(\rho)} - G_\rho (d\mathcal{F}_\rho)_0 \right\| \\
&\leq \|G_\rho\| \left\| (d\mathcal{F}_\rho)_{\gamma(\rho)} - (d\mathcal{F}_\rho)_0 \right\| \\
&\leq C^{-1} K \|\gamma(\rho)\|_{W^{1,p}}
\end{aligned}$$

by Lemma 9.4.8, which we used before. Since we have seen (in Lemma 9.4.13) that the $W^{1,p}$ norm of γ tends to 0, we can conclude that $G_\rho \circ (d\mathcal{F}_\rho)_{\gamma(\rho)}$ is invertible for ρ sufficiently large and therefore that $(d\mathcal{F}_\rho)_{\gamma(\rho)}$ is also invertible.

$\square$

This allows us to apply the implicit function theorem and to conclude that γ is continuous and differentiable for ρ sufficiently large.

Proposition 9.4.15.

$$\lim_{\rho \to +\infty} \left\| \frac{\partial \gamma}{\partial \rho} \right\|_{W^{1,p}} = 0.$$

Proof. Since $F(\rho, \gamma(\rho)) = 0$, we have

$$\frac{\partial F}{\partial \rho}(\rho, \gamma(\rho)) + (d\mathcal{F}_\rho)_{\gamma(\rho)}\left(\frac{\partial \gamma}{\partial \rho} \right) = 0.$$

We have

$$\left\| \frac{\partial \gamma}{\partial \rho} \right\|_{W^{1,p}} \leq \left\| \frac{\partial \gamma}{\partial \rho} - G_\rho (d\mathcal{F}_\rho)_{\gamma(\rho)} \frac{\partial \gamma}{\partial \rho} \right\|_{W^{1,p}} + \left\| G_\rho (d\mathcal{F}_\rho)_{\gamma(\rho)} \frac{\partial \gamma}{\partial \rho} \right\|_{W^{1,p}}$$

$$\leq \left\| G_\rho (d\mathcal{F}_\rho)_{\gamma(\rho)} - \mathrm{Id} \right\| \left\| \frac{\partial \gamma}{\partial \rho} \right\|_{W^{1,p}} + \left\| G_\rho \frac{\partial F}{\partial \rho}(\rho, \gamma(\rho)) \right\|_{W^{1,p}}.$$

Moreover, as in the proof of Lemma 9.4.14,

$$\left\| G_\rho (d\mathcal{F}_\rho)_{\gamma(\rho)} - \mathrm{Id} \right\| \leq C^{-1} K \left\| \gamma(\rho) \right\|_{W^{1,p}}.$$

We now use the following lemma (one of the technical lemmas proved in Chapter 13).

Lemma 9.4.16. *Let $r_0 > 0$. There exists a constant $M > 0$ (independent of ρ) such that for every $\rho \geq \rho_0$ and every $Z \in \overline{B}(0, r_0) \subset W^{1,p}(\mathbf{R} \times S^1; \mathbf{R}^{2n})$, we have*

$$\left\| \frac{\partial F}{\partial \rho}(\rho, Z) - \frac{\partial F}{\partial \rho}(\rho, 0) \right\|_{L^p} \leq M \left\| Z \right\|_{W^{1,p}}.$$

This leads to the estimates

$$\left\| G_\rho \left(\frac{\partial F}{\partial \rho}(\rho, \gamma(\rho)) \right) \right\| \leq C^{-1} \left\| \frac{\partial F}{\partial \rho}(\rho, \gamma(\rho)) \right\|$$

$$\leq C^{-1} \left(\left\| \frac{\partial F}{\partial \rho}(\rho, \gamma(\rho)) - \frac{\partial F}{\partial \rho}(\rho, 0) \right\|_{L^p} + \left\| \frac{\partial F}{\partial \rho}(\rho, 0) \right\|_{L^p} \right)$$

$$\leq C^{-1} \left(M \left\| \gamma(\rho) \right\|_{W^{1,p}} + \left\| \frac{\partial F}{\partial \rho}(\rho, 0) \right\|_{L^p} \right)$$

$$= C^{-1} \left(M \left\| \gamma(\rho) \right\|_{W^{1,p}} + \left\| \frac{\partial}{\partial \rho} \mathcal{F}(w_\rho) \right\|_{L^p} \right).$$

But $\mathcal{F}(w_\rho) = 0$ for $|s| \geq 1$. For $s \in [-1, 1]$, we have

$$w_\rho(s, t) = \exp_{y(t)}\left(\beta^-(s) \exp_{y(t)}^{-1}(u(s+\rho, t)) + \beta^+(s) \exp_{y(t)}^{-1}(v(s-\rho, t))\right)$$

and consequently

$$\frac{\partial w_\rho}{\partial \rho}(s, t) = T \exp_{y(t)}\left(\beta^-(s) T \exp_{y(t)}^{-1} \frac{\partial u}{\partial s}(s+\rho) - \beta^+(s) T \exp_{y(t)}^{-1} \frac{\partial v}{\partial s}(s-\rho)\right).$$

It follows that

$$\lim_{\rho \to +\infty} \frac{\partial w_\rho}{\partial \rho}(s, t) = 0 \quad \text{in } \mathcal{C}^\infty([-1, 1] \times S^1),$$

hence

$$\lim_{\rho \to +\infty} \frac{\partial}{\partial \rho} \mathcal{F}(w_\rho) = \lim_{\rho \to +\infty} (d\mathcal{F})_{w_\rho}\left(\frac{\partial}{\partial \rho} w_\rho\right) = 0.$$

Finally, we have the estimate

$$\left\|\frac{\partial \gamma}{\partial \rho}\right\|_{W^{1,p}} \left(1 - C^{-1} K \|\gamma(\rho)\|_{W^{1,p}}\right) \leq C^{-1}\left(M \|\gamma(\rho)\|_{W^{1,p}} + \left\|\frac{\partial \mathcal{F}(w_\rho)}{\partial \rho}\right\|_{L^p}\right),$$

which implies that

$$\lim_{\rho \to +\infty} \left\|\frac{\partial \gamma}{\partial \rho}\right\|_{W^{1,p}} = 0. \qquad \square$$

Conclusion.

For $\rho \geq \rho_0$, we have constructed

$$\gamma(\rho) \in W_\rho^\perp \subset W^{1,p}(\mathbf{R} \times S^1; \mathbf{R}^{2n}),$$

a continuous and differentiable function of ρ such that $\mathcal{F}_\rho(\gamma(\rho)) = 0$ and

$$\lim_{\rho \to +\infty} \|\gamma(\rho)\|_{W^{1,p}} = \lim_{\rho \to +\infty} \left\|\frac{\partial \gamma}{\partial \rho}\right\|_{W^{1,p}} = 0.$$

Using the trivialization Z_i^ρ, we deduce from $\gamma(\rho)$ a vector field along w_ρ, that is, an element of $T_{w_\rho}\mathcal{P}(x, z)$, which we also denote by $\gamma(\rho)$. We transform this into an element of $\mathcal{M}(x, z)$ using the exponential

$$\psi(\rho) = \exp_{w_\rho} \gamma(\rho) \in \mathcal{M}(x, z),$$

so that the map $\rho \mapsto \psi(\rho)$ is differentiable and that both $\psi(\rho)$ and its derivative tend to 0 in $W^{1,p}$ when ρ tends to infinity.

By projecting ψ onto the space of trajectories $\mathcal{L}(x, z)$, we obtain the desired map

$$\widehat{\psi} = \pi \circ \psi : [\rho_0, +\infty[\longrightarrow \mathcal{L}(x, z).$$

We still need to check that it has the expected properties.

Lemma 9.4.17.

$$\lim_{\rho \to +\infty} \widehat{\psi}(\rho) = (\widehat{u}, \widehat{v}) \in \overline{\mathcal{L}}(x, z).$$

Proof. Consider a sequence (ρ_n) that tends to infinity and let

$$\psi_{\rho_n} = \psi(\rho_n) = \exp_{w_{\rho_n}}(\gamma(\rho_n)).$$

For $s \le -1$, we have

$$\psi_{\rho_n}(s, t) = \exp_{u(s+\rho_n, t)} \gamma_{\rho_n}(s, t).$$

Let K be a compact subset of $\mathbf{R} \times S^1$. For n sufficiently large and $(s, t) \in K$, we have $\psi_{\rho_n}(s - \rho_n, t) = \exp_{u(s,t)} \gamma_{\rho_n}(s - \rho_n, t)$ and

$$\|\gamma_{\rho_n}(s - \rho_n, t)\|_{W^{1,p}(K)} \le \|\gamma_{\rho_n}(s - \rho_n, t)\|_{W^{1,p}} = \|\gamma_{\rho_n}(s, t)\|_{W^{1,p}}.$$

We saw in Lemma 9.4.13 that the latter tends to 0 when n tends to infinity. Since $W^{1,p}(K) \subset \mathcal{C}^0(K)$, we see that γ_{ρ_n} tends to 0 in $\mathcal{C}^0(K)$ and therefore that $\psi_{\rho_n}(s - \rho_n, t)$ tends to u in $\mathcal{C}^0_{\text{loc}}(\mathbf{R} \times S^1; W)$. Since our elements are in $\mathcal{M}$, the convergence in $\mathcal{C}^0_{\text{loc}}$ implies the convergence in $\mathcal{C}^\infty_{\text{loc}}$, by Proposition 6.5.3. Analogously, we can prove that

$$\lim_{n \to +\infty} \psi_{\rho_n}(s + \rho_n, t) = v(s, t)$$

in $\mathcal{C}^\infty_{\text{loc}}$. It follows that $\widehat{\psi}_n$ tends to $(\widehat{u}, \widehat{v})$. $\qquad\square$

We still need to prove that $\widehat{\psi}$ is an injective immersion (at least for ρ_n sufficiently large), which we will do in the next section. Note that Lemma 9.4.17 will imply that this injective immersion is proper and therefore an embedding.

9.5 Properties of $\widehat{\psi}$: $\widehat{\psi}$ Is an Immersion

We want to show that $\widehat{\psi}$ is an immersion. To do this, we must verify that $\partial\psi/\partial\rho$ is not in the kernel of the projection $d\pi$. Here π denotes taking the quotient $\mathcal{M}(x, z) \to \mathcal{L}(x, z)$, so that the kernel of $(d\pi)_\psi$ is generated by $\partial\psi/\partial s$. Supposing that ψ is not an immersion is therefore equivalent to supposing the existence of sequences (ρ_n) and (α_n) with

$$\frac{\partial\psi}{\partial\rho}(\rho_n) = \alpha_n \frac{\partial\psi}{\partial s}(\rho_n).$$

Since $\psi(\rho)$ is close to w_ρ, we will be able deduce the following lemma in Section 13.6.

Lemma 9.5.1. *The sequence (α_n) is bounded and we have*

$$\lim_{n\to+\infty}\left\|\left(\frac{\partial w_\rho}{\partial \rho}-\alpha_n\frac{\partial w_\rho}{\partial s}\right)_{\rho_n}\right\|_{L^p}=0.$$

Then for $s\le -1$, $w_\rho(s,t)=u(s+\rho,t)$, hence

$$\frac{\partial w_\rho}{\partial \rho}=\frac{\partial u}{\partial s}(s+\rho),$$

so that the lemma implies that

$$\lim_{n\to+\infty}\left\|\frac{\partial u}{\partial s}(s+\rho_n,t)-\alpha_n\frac{\partial u}{\partial s}(s+\rho_n,t)\right\|_{L^p(]-\infty,-1]\times S^1)}=0.$$

Consequently, α_n tends to 1. By considering the values for $s\ge 1$ in the same manner, we obtain

$$\lim_{n\to+\infty}\left\|-\frac{\partial v}{\partial s}(s-\rho_n,t)-\alpha_n\frac{\partial v}{\partial s}(s-\rho_n,t)\right\|_{L^p([1,+\infty[\times S^1)}=0,$$

which now implies that α_n tends to -1, giving the desired contradiction.

So $\widehat{\psi}$ is an immersion (for ρ sufficiently large). But it is also injective: its image is contained in a connected component of the manifold $\mathcal{L}(x,z)$ (of dimension 1), which is not compact (since $\lim_{\rho\to+\infty}\widehat{\psi}(\rho)\notin \mathcal{L}(x,z)$). This component is therefore diffeomorphic to an interval. In this case, the immersion $\widehat{\psi}$ is injective (by Rolle's theorem).

9.6 Properties of $\widehat{\psi}$: Uniqueness of the Gluing

We have just shown that the broken trajectory $(\widehat{u},\widehat{v})\in \mathcal{L}(x,y)\times \mathcal{L}(y,z)$ is the endpoint of an interval embedded in $\overline{\mathcal{L}}(x,z)$ whose interior is in a component of $\mathcal{L}(x,z)$. This is not sufficient to conclude that $\overline{\mathcal{L}}(x,z)$ is a manifold of dimension 1 with boundary, as shown in Figure 9.9.

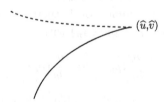

$(\widehat{u},\widehat{v})$

Fig. 9.9

We must still show that the only way to approximate $(\widehat{u}, \widehat{v})$ in $\overline{\mathcal{L}}(x, z)$ (other than with the constant sequence) is by passing through the interval that we just constructed. This is the last assertion of Theorem 9.2.3 (which paraphrases the corresponding statement for the Morse complex, that is, Proposition 3.2.8): if a sequence in $\mathcal{L}(x, z)$ converges to $(\widehat{u}, \widehat{v})$, then it is in the image of $\widehat{\psi}$.

The difficulty comes from the fact that the constructions of the gluing and of the map $\widehat{\psi}$ depend on a number of arbitrary choices. Consider, for example, a function ν of class $\mathcal{C}^\infty$, from $\mathbf{R}_+$ to $\mathbf{R}_+$ and with $\lim_{\rho \to +\infty} \nu(\rho) = +\infty$. We can define a pre-gluing $w_{\nu, \rho}$ by replacing $v(s - \rho)$ by $v(s - \nu(\rho))$ in the formulas that we used:

$$w_{\nu,\rho}(s, t) = \begin{cases} u(s + \rho, t) & \text{if } s \leq -1 \\ \exp_{y(t)} \left(\beta^-(s) \exp_{y(t)}^{-1} u(s + \rho, t) \right. \\ \qquad \left. + \beta^+(s) \exp_{y(t)}^{-1} v(s - \nu(\rho), t) \right) & \text{if } s \in [-1, 1] \\ v(s - \nu(\rho)) & \text{if } s \geq 1. \end{cases}$$

The readers are invited to verify that by taking up the construction of the gluing from $w_{\nu, \rho}$, they obtain a continuous map

$$\psi_\nu : [\rho_\nu, +\infty[\longrightarrow \mathcal{M}(x, z)$$

such that

$$\lim_{\rho \to +\infty} \pi \circ \psi_\nu(\rho) = (\widehat{u}, \widehat{v}).$$

They will then verify that if ν is increasing, then the map $\widehat{\psi}_\nu = \pi \circ \psi_\nu$ is an injective immersion. The case of $\widehat{\psi}$ is the one where $\nu = \text{Id}$.

In order to avoid the situation sketched in Figure 9.9, we need to ensure that the image of the new map $\widehat{\psi}_\nu$ is contained (for ρ sufficiently large) in that of the gluing $\widehat{\psi} = \widehat{\psi}_{\text{Id}}$ constructed before. This will be the first step of our proof, which will consist of four steps:

(1) The first step, which we just described, consists in showing the following result.

   Proposition 9.6.1. Let $\nu : \mathbf{R}_+ \to \mathbf{R}_+$ be an increasing function of class $\mathcal{C}^\infty$ such that $\lim_{\rho \to +\infty} \nu(\rho) = +\infty$. There exists a $\rho_\nu > 0$ such that for $\rho \geq \rho_\nu$, we have $\widehat{\psi}_\nu(\rho) \in \text{Im}(\widehat{\psi})$.

(2) For the second step, consider a sequence $(\ell_n)_{n \in \mathbf{N}}$ that tends to $(\widehat{u}, \widehat{v})$ in $\overline{\mathcal{L}}(x, z)$. As in Theorem 9.2.3, we want to prove that $\ell_n \in \text{Im}(\widehat{\psi})$ for n sufficiently large.

Remark 9.6.2. It suffices to prove that there exists a subsequence $(\ell_{n_k})_{k \in \mathbf{N}}$ such that $\ell_{n_k} \in \operatorname{Im}(\widehat{\psi})$ for k sufficiently large.

Indeed, suppose that the conclusion of Theorem 9.2.3 is false. We would then have a subsequence ℓ_{n_k} that is not in the image of $\widehat{\psi}$ but tends to $(\widehat{u}, \widehat{v})$ in $\overline{\mathcal{L}}(x, z)$. In that case, we can extract a subsequence contained in $\operatorname{Im}(\widehat{\psi})$ from a certain rank on, giving a contradiction.

In the following statements, the conclusions concerning the sequence $(\ell_n)_{n \in \mathbf{N}}$ hold after extracting a subsequence, if necessary. In this second step we prove the following result.

Proposition 9.6.3. *There exist a lift $\widetilde{\ell}_n \in \mathcal{M}(x, z)$ of ℓ_n and an increasing function $\nu : \mathbf{R}_+ \to \mathbf{R}_+$ of class $\mathcal{C}^\infty$ with $\lim_{\rho \to +\infty} \nu(\rho) = +\infty$ such that for every $(s, t) \in \mathbf{R} \times S^1$,*

$$\widetilde{\ell}_n(s, t) = \exp_{w_{\nu, \rho_n}(s, t)} Y_n(s, t),$$

where the sequence (ρ_n) tends to $+\infty$ and $Y_n \in w_{\nu, \rho_n}^\star TW$ satisfies

$$\lim_{n \to +\infty} \|Y_n\|_\infty = 0.$$

The norm $\|Y_n\|_\infty$ is computed by viewing Y_n as a map

$$Y_n : \mathbf{R} \times S^1 \longrightarrow \mathbf{R}^m$$

using the embedding of W in $\mathbf{R}^m$ that we fixed and the Euclidean norm of $\mathbf{R}^m$.

(3) The third step is the most technical one. With the previous notation, we prove the following result.

Proposition 9.6.4. *The vector field Y_n satisfies $Y_n \in W^{1,p}(w_{\nu, \rho_n}^\star TW)$ for every $p > 2$. Moreover, $\lim_{n \to +\infty} \|Y_n\|_{W^{1,p}} = 0$.*

Recall that the first assertion simply says that

$$Y_n \in W^{1,p}(\mathbf{R} \times S^1; \mathbf{R}^m)$$

(see the explanations in Section 8.2).

(4) After steps 2 and 3, we have at our disposal a sequence $\widetilde{\ell}_n$ that is of the same form as a solution produced by the Newton–Picard method with the help of the pre-gluing w_{ν, ρ_n}. Recall that in order to apply the Newton–Picard method (Lemma 9.4.4) starting from w_{ν, ρ_n}, we must first decompose $W^{1,p}(\mathbf{R} \times S^1; \mathbf{R}^{2n})$ as a direct sum $\operatorname{Ker}(L_{\rho_n}) \oplus W_{\rho_n}^\perp$, which now depends on n (the index of the ρ_n in question) and in which the

dimension of $\mathrm{Ker}(L_{\rho_n})$ is 2 (see the consequences of Proposition 9.4.7). Using a contracting map

$$\varphi : W_{\rho_n}^{\perp} \cap B(0, \varepsilon_0) \longrightarrow W_{\rho_n}^{\perp} \cap B(0, \varepsilon_0)$$

(for an $\varepsilon_0 > 0$ that does not depend on n), we find a unique $\gamma_n \in W_{\rho_n}^{\perp} \cap B(0, \varepsilon_0)$ such that $\exp_{w_{\nu,\rho_n}} \gamma_n \in \mathcal{M}(x, z)$: this γ_n is the unique fixed point of the map φ. Attentive readers will have noted that we have identified $W^{1,p}(\mathbf{R} \times S^1; \mathbf{R}^{2n})$ with $w_{\nu,\rho_n}^{\star} TW = T_{w_{\nu,\rho_n}} \mathcal{P}(x, z)$ using the map $i : W^{1,p}(\mathbf{R} \times S^1; \mathbf{R}^{2n}) \to w_{\nu,\rho_n}^{\star} TW$ defined by a fixed unitary trivialization along w_{ν,ρ_n}.
Since $\|Y_n\|_{W^{1,p}}$ tends to 0, Y_n is in the ball $B(0, \varepsilon_0)$ for n sufficiently large. In particular, $Y_n \in h_n + W^{\perp}$ for an $h_n \in B(0, \varepsilon_0) \cap \mathrm{Ker}\, L$ with $\lim_{n \to +\infty} \|h_n\|_{W^{1,p}} = 0$.

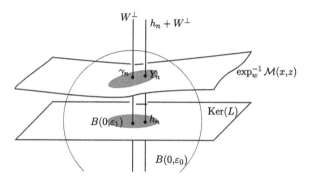

Fig. 9.10

Also note that if $h_n = 0$, then $Y_n = \gamma_n$ (by the uniqueness given in Lemma 9.4.4). In general, in order to have $\|h_n\|_{W^{1,p}} \leq \varepsilon_1$ (for a positive ε_1 that does not depend on n), we will need to generalize the Newton–Picard method (Lemma 9.4.4) and find a contracting map

$$\varphi_n : h_n + W_{\rho_n}^{\perp} \longrightarrow h_n + W_{\rho_n}^{\perp}$$

that gives a unique solution $\exp_{w_{\nu,\rho_n}} \gamma_n(h) \in \mathcal{M}(x, z)$ in $h_n + W_{\rho_n}^{\perp}$. Figure 9.10 repeats Figure 9.7 and gives additional details with this new data.
For n sufficiently large, Y_n will therefore be the unique solution given by the Newton–Picard method in the slice $h_n + W^{\perp}$. By a connectedness argument, this gives the following result.

Proposition 9.6.5. *For n sufficiently large, $\ell_n \in \mathrm{Im}(\widehat{\psi}_\nu)$.*

The first step will then give the following.

Corollary 9.6.6. *For n sufficiently large, $\ell_n \in \mathrm{Im}(\widehat{\psi})$.*

We will therefore have concluded both the fourth step and the proof of Theorem 9.2.3.

Let us now prove all these statements.

9.6.a Step 1: Proof of Proposition 9.6.1

For $\lambda \in [0, 1]$, we set

$$\nu_\lambda(\rho) = (1 - \lambda)\rho + \lambda\nu(\rho).$$

Let $w_{\nu_\lambda,\rho}$ be the corresponding pre-gluing and let us construct the gluing for this $w_{\nu_\lambda,\rho}$.

Proposition 9.6.7. *There exists a continuous map*

$$\psi : [\rho_0, +\infty[\times [0, 1] \longrightarrow \mathcal{M}(x, z)$$

such that for every $\lambda \in [0, 1]$, the map

$$\widehat{\psi}(\cdot, \lambda) = \pi \circ \psi(\cdot, \lambda) : [\rho_0, +\infty[\longrightarrow \mathcal{L}(x, z)$$

is an injective immersion that satisfies

$$\lim_{\rho \to +\infty} \widehat{\psi}(\cdot, \lambda) = (\widehat{u}, \widehat{v}) \ \text{in} \ \overline{\mathcal{L}}(x, z).$$

Proof. We decompose

$$W^{1,p}(\mathbf{R} \times S^1; \mathbf{R}^{2n}) = \mathrm{Ker}\, L_{\rho,\lambda} \oplus W^\perp_{\rho,\lambda}$$

using an analogue of Proposition 9.4.7 (which can be proved in the same manner using the compactness of $[0, 1]$), and then apply the Newton–Picard method (that is, Lemma 9.4.4) in $W^\perp_{\rho,\lambda}$. For $\rho \geq \rho_0$ and $\lambda \in [0, 1]$, we obtain elements

$$\gamma(\rho, \lambda) \in W^\perp_{\rho,\lambda} \quad \text{such that} \quad \exp_{w_{\nu_\lambda,\rho}} \gamma(\rho, \lambda) \in \mathcal{M}(x, z).$$

Moreover, the map $(\rho, \lambda) \mapsto \gamma(\rho, \lambda)$ is continuous and differentiable by the implicit function theorem (as in Lemma 9.4.14). In an analogous manner, we can prove that $\widehat{\psi}(\cdot, \lambda)$ has the desired properties. $\square$

End of the Proof of Proposition 9.6.1. The component of $\mathcal{L}(x, z)$ that contains $\mathrm{Im}(\widehat{\psi})$ is a manifold of dimension 1, without boundary and not compact because

$$\lim_{\rho \to +\infty} \widehat{\psi}(\rho) \notin \mathcal{L}(x, z).$$

Up to a diffeomorphism, we may view this manifold as the interval $]0, 1[$. Consider the image $\widehat{\psi}([\rho_0, +\infty[) \subset]0, 1[$. Since $\widehat{\psi}$ is an injective immersion, we have

$$\operatorname{Im} \widehat{\psi} = [\widehat{\psi}(\rho_0), \lim_{\rho \to +\infty} \widehat{\psi}(\rho)[\subset]0, 1[.$$

But $\lim \widehat{\psi}(\rho) \notin \mathcal{L}(x, z)$, so that

$$\operatorname{Im} \widehat{\psi} =]0, a_0] \quad \text{or} \quad [a_0, 1[.$$

Without loss of generality, we may, and do, assume that this image is $[a_0, 1[$. We apply the same reasoning to

$$\psi(\cdot, \lambda) : [\rho_0, +\infty[\longrightarrow \mathcal{M}(x, z).$$

Since $\widehat{\psi} : [\rho_0, +\infty[\times [0, 1] \to \mathcal{L}(x, z)$ is continuous, the image of $\widehat{\psi}$ is contained in the same component, which we have identified with $]0, 1[$. Since

$$\widehat{\psi}(\cdot, \lambda) : [\rho_0, +\infty[\longrightarrow \mathcal{L}(x, z)$$

is an injective immersion and since

$$\lim \lambda_n = \lambda_\star \text{ and } \lim \rho_n = +\infty \Longrightarrow \lim \widehat{\psi}(\rho_n, \lambda_n) = (\widehat{u}, \widehat{v})$$

(an assertion we leave as an exercise for the readers), we obtain $\operatorname{Im}(\widehat{\psi}(\cdot, \lambda)) = [a_\lambda, 1[$ for every $\lambda \in [0, 1]$ using the connectedness of $[0, 1]$. In particular,

$$\lim_{\rho \to +\infty} \widehat{\psi}_\nu(\rho) = \lim_{\rho \to +\infty} \widehat{\psi}(\rho, 1) = 1.$$

This means that

$$\text{for } \rho \geq \rho_\nu, \quad \widehat{\psi}_\nu(\rho) \in [a_0, 1] = \operatorname{Im}(\widehat{\psi})$$

and Proposition 9.6.1 is proved. $\qquad \square$

9.6.b Step 2

We begin by establishing a number of preliminary results. Let us return to the action functional $\mathcal{A}_H : \mathcal{L}(W) \to \mathbf{R}$, whose critical points are the 1-periodic orbits of the Hamiltonian vector field X_t. We assume, as authorized by Lemma 6.3.5, that $\mathcal{A}_H$ takes on distinct values in distinct critical points. Consider a sequence $\ell_n \in \mathcal{L}(x, z)$ with $\lim_{n\to+\infty} \ell_n = (\widehat{u}, \widehat{v})$, as in the statement of Theorem 9.2.3. We have the following result.

Proposition 9.6.8. *Let $\widetilde{\ell}_n$ be a lift of ℓ_n in $\mathcal{M}(x, z)$. If the sequence $\widetilde{\ell}_n$ converges to a limit λ in $\mathcal{M}$, then*

$$\lambda \in \{x, \widetilde{u}, y, \widetilde{v}, z\},$$

where $\widetilde{u}$ and $\widetilde{v}$ are lifts of $\widehat{u}$ and $\widehat{v}$, respectively, in $\mathcal{M}(x, z)$.

To prove this proposition, we will use the following lemma.

Lemma 9.6.9. *Let s_n be a real sequence that has a limit and let λ_n be a sequence in $\mathcal{M}$. We assume that, in the $\mathcal{C}^\infty_{\mathrm{loc}}$ sense,*

$$\lim_{n\to+\infty} \lambda_n(s, t) = a(s, t) \quad and \quad \lim_{n\to+\infty} \lambda_n(s + s_n, t) = b(s, t)$$

for two trajectories $a \in \mathcal{M}(\alpha, \beta)$, $b \in \mathcal{M}(\gamma, \delta)$ (α, β, γ, δ are critical points of $\mathcal{A}_H$). If $\widehat{a} \neq \widehat{b}$, then the sequence s_n is divergent and we have

$$\mathcal{A}_H(\alpha) \geq \mathcal{A}_H(\beta) \geq \mathcal{A}_H(\gamma) \geq \mathcal{A}_H(\delta) \quad if \lim s_n = +\infty,$$
$$\mathcal{A}_H(\gamma) \geq \mathcal{A}_H(\delta) \geq \mathcal{A}_H(\alpha) \geq \mathcal{A}_H(\beta) \quad if \lim s_n = -\infty.$$

See Figure 9.11, where the configuration on the left corresponds to a sequence s_n that tends to $+\infty$, the middle configuration corresponds to a sequence s_n that tends to $-\infty$ and the configuration on the right is impossible.

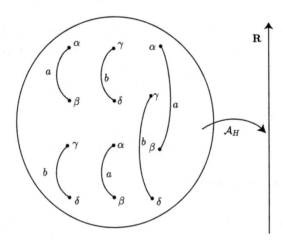

Fig. 9.11

Proof of Lemma 9.6.9. If s_n has a finite limit σ, then we obviously have $a(s + \sigma, t) = b(s, t)$, hence $\widehat{a} = \widehat{b}$. We therefore assume that $\lim s_n = +\infty$

and fix σ, $\tau \in \mathbf{R}$. For n sufficiently large, we have $s_n + \sigma \geq \tau$. Since $\mathcal{A}_H$ is decreasing on the trajectories of $\mathfrak{M}$, we therefore have

$$\mathcal{A}_H(\lambda_n(s_n + \sigma, \cdot)) \leq \mathcal{A}_H(\tau, \cdot)).$$

By letting n tend to infinity, we obtain

$$\mathcal{A}_H(b(\sigma, \cdot)) \leq \mathcal{A}_H(a(\tau, \cdot))$$

for all σ and τ in $\mathbf{R}$. By letting σ tend to $-\infty$ and τ to $+\infty$, we find that

$$\mathcal{A}_H(\beta) \geq \mathcal{A}_H(\gamma),$$

which proves the lemma (the case of a sequence s_n that tends to $-\infty$ is analogous). □

Proof of Proposition 9.6.8. We now apply this lemma to the sequence $\widetilde{\ell}_n$. Since $\widetilde{\ell}_n \in \mathfrak{M}(x, z)$, it is clear that $\lambda = \lim \ell_n$ satisfies

$$\mathcal{A}_H(x) \geq \mathcal{A}_H(\lambda(s, \cdot)) \geq \mathcal{A}_H(z) \quad \text{for all } s \in \mathbf{R}.$$

If $\lambda \notin \{\widehat{u}, \widehat{v}\}$, then since ℓ_n tends to $(\widehat{u}, \widehat{v})$, the previous lemma implies that

$$\mathcal{A}_H(\lambda) \in \{\mathcal{A}_H(x), \mathcal{A}_H(y), \mathcal{A}_H(z)\}.$$

In particular, $\mathcal{A}_H(\lambda(s, \cdot))$ does not depend on s, hence λ is a periodic orbit of X_t. Since we have assumed that the critical values of $\mathcal{A}_H$ are distinct (Lemma 6.3.5), we have now shown that

$$\lambda \in \{x, y, z\}.$$ □

Remark 9.6.10. With the same proof, we can see that more generally, if the sequence $\ell_n \in \mathcal{L}(\alpha, \beta)$ satisfies

$$\lim_{n \to +\infty} \ell_n = (u_1, \ldots, u_k) \in \overline{\mathcal{L}}(\alpha, \beta) \quad \text{with } u_i \in \mathcal{L}(\gamma_{i-1}, \gamma_i), \ \gamma_0 = \alpha, \ \gamma_k = \beta,$$

then, for any lift $\widetilde{\ell}_n$ of ℓ_n, if the sequence $\widetilde{\ell}_n$ is convergent, we have

$$\lim_{n \to +\infty} \widetilde{\ell}_n \in \{\widehat{u}_1, \ldots, \widehat{u}_k, \gamma_0, \ldots, \gamma_k\}.$$

Having taken care of these preliminaries, let us get to the point.

Proof of Proposition 9.6.3. We fix a real number $\varepsilon > 0$. The following lemma, whose proof is obvious, is an immediate consequence of the compactness of the manifold W.

Lemma 9.6.11. *There exist δ and δ' such that $0 < \delta < \delta' < \rho_{\text{inj}}$ and such that for every $a \in W$ and all $p, q \in B(a, \delta')$, we can write*

$$q = \exp_p Y, \quad \text{with } \|Y\| < \varepsilon,$$

and, for every $a \in W$, all $p, q \in B(a, \delta)$ and all $\beta^-, \beta^+ \in [0, 1]$, we have

$$\exp_a(\beta^- \exp_a^{-1}(p) + \beta^+ \exp_a^{-1}(q)) \in B(a, \delta'). \qquad \square$$

We choose a lift $\widetilde{\ell}_n$ of ℓ_n that satisfies $\mathcal{A}_H(\widetilde{\ell}_n(0, \cdot)) = \mathcal{A}_H(y)$. The sequence $\widetilde{\ell}_n$ is convergent in $\mathcal{M}$ (after extracting a subsequence, if necessary) and, by Proposition 9.6.8, has limit y.

Let us show that $\widetilde{\ell}_n$ satisfies the conclusions of Proposition 9.6.3. Here is the idea of the proof. Let w_n denote a pre-gluing of u and v, $w_n = w_{\nu, \rho_n}$ for some function $\nu : \mathbf{R}_+ \to \mathbf{R}_+$ that still needs to be determined. We fix an $\varepsilon > 0$ and let $B(x, \delta)$, $B(y, \delta)$, $B(z, \delta)$ denote the open balls for the $\mathcal{C}^0$ distance on the space of loops[2] $\mathcal{L}W$ (the constant δ is the one given by Lemma 9.6.11 and we may, and do, assume that these balls are disjoint). When s is very small, $\widetilde{\ell}_n(s, \cdot)$ and $w_n(s, \cdot)$ are in $B(x, \delta)$; when s is close to 0, they are in $B(y, \delta)$ and when s is very large, they are in $B(z, \delta)$. In all three cases we can apply Lemma 9.6.11 to conclude the proof. For the other values of s, we use the fact that ℓ_n tends to $(\widehat{u}, \widehat{v})$ in $\overline{\mathcal{L}}(x, z)$, which translates into the existence of sequences σ_n and τ_n and real numbers $\sigma_\star$ and $\tau_\star$ such that

$$\lim \widetilde{\ell}_n(s - \sigma_n, t) = u(s + \sigma_\star, t) \quad \text{and} \quad \lim \widetilde{\ell}_n(s + \tau_n, t) = v(s + \tau_\star, t).$$

The convergence is uniform on the compact subsets of $\mathbf{R} \times S^1$. The first limit tells us that $\widetilde{\ell}_n(s, t)$ is close to $u(s + \sigma_n + \sigma_\star, t)$ on $(K - \sigma_n) \times S^1$, where K is a compact subset of $\mathbf{R}$. We must "cover" the nonshaded part of Figure 9.12 with open sets of this type.

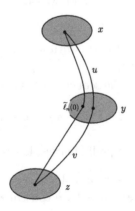

Fig. 9.12

---

[2] Recall that $B(y, \delta) = \{\chi : S^1 \to W \mid d(\chi(t), y(t)) < \delta \; \forall t \in S^1\}$.

The choice of the sequences σ_n and τ_n is therefore very important. This is also what will determine the choice of the pre-gluing $w_n = w_{\nu,\rho_n}$. To simplify the notation, we omit the variable $t \in S^1$ in the following. We have seen that $y = \lim \tilde{\ell}_n$ in $\mathcal{M}$ and in particular that $\lim \tilde{\ell}_n(0) = y$. For $n \geq N_\varepsilon$, we therefore have $\tilde{\ell}_n(0) \in B(y,\delta)$ (still for the $\mathcal{C}^0$ distance on $\mathcal{L}W$). We set

$$\sigma_n = \sup\{s > 0 \mid \tilde{\ell}_n([-s,0]) \subset B(y,\delta)\}$$

and
$$\tau_n = \sup\{s > 0 \mid \tilde{\ell}_n([0,s]) \subset B(y,\delta)\}.$$

Then $\tilde{\ell}_n(-\sigma_n)$ and $\tilde{\ell}_n(\tau_n) \in \partial\overline{B}(y,\delta)$. We have:

(1) The sequences σ_n and τ_n tend to $+\infty$. Indeed, if the sequence σ_n were bounded, then $\tilde{\ell}_n([-\sigma_n,0])$ would tend to y, and we would have $\lim \tilde{\ell}_n(-\sigma_n) = y$, which is absurd. The same reasoning holds for τ_n.

(2) Let $\tilde{\ell}_n^1(s) = \tilde{\ell}_n(s - \sigma_n)$ and let $\tilde{\ell}_n^2(s) = \tilde{\ell}_n(s + \tau_n)$. Then after extracting a subsequence, if necessary,

$$\lim \tilde{\ell}_n^1(s) = u(s + \sigma_\star) \text{ and } \lim \tilde{\ell}_n^2(s) = v(s + \tau_\star) \quad \text{in } \mathcal{M} \text{ for } \sigma_\star, \tau_\star \in \mathbf{R}.$$

Indeed, we have $\tilde{\ell}_n^1(0) = \tilde{\ell}_n(-\sigma_n) \in \partial\overline{B}(y,\delta)$. Hence the sequence $\tilde{\ell}_n^1$ does not tend to y. It does not tend to x either because $\tilde{\ell}_n^1(0) \in \partial\overline{B}(y,\delta)$, so that $\tilde{\ell}_n^1(0)$ is not in $B(x,\delta)$ for any n. Moreover,

$$\mathcal{A}_H(\tilde{\ell}_n^1(0)) = \mathcal{A}_H(\tilde{\ell}_n(-\sigma_n)) > \mathcal{A}_H(\tilde{\ell}_n(0)) = \mathcal{A}_H(y).$$

By Proposition 9.6.8, this implies that

$$\lim \tilde{\ell}_n^1(s) = u(s + \sigma_\star) \text{ in } \mathcal{M} \text{ for a constant } \sigma_\star \in \mathbf{R}.$$

Analogously, we have

$$\lim \tilde{\ell}_n^2(s) = v(s + \tau_\star) \text{ in } \mathcal{M} \text{ for a constant } \tau_\star \in \mathbf{R}.$$

Let us now set

$$\sigma_n' = \inf\{s > 0 \mid \tilde{\ell}_n(]-\infty, -s]) \subset B(x,\delta)\}$$

and
$$\tau_n' = \inf\{s > 0 \mid \tilde{\ell}_n([s, +\infty[) \subset B(z,\delta)\},$$

so that obviously $\tilde{\ell}_n(-\sigma_n') \in \partial\overline{B}(x,\delta)$ and $\tilde{\ell}_n(\tau_n') \in \partial\overline{B}(z,\delta)$. Also note the following:

(1) We have $\sigma'_n \geq \sigma_n$ and $\tau'_n \geq \tau_n$. In particular, the sequences σ'_n and τ'_n tend to $+\infty$. Indeed, suppose that $\sigma_n > \sigma'_n$ and take a σ in $[\sigma'_n, \sigma_n]$. The definitions of σ'_n and σ_n then imply that $\ell_n(-\sigma) \in B(x, \delta) \cap B(y, \delta)$, which is absurd because these two balls were assumed to be disjoint. The same argument holds for τ_n and τ'_n.

(2) After extracting a subsequence, if necessary, we have

$$\lim \widetilde{\ell}_n(s - \sigma'_n) = u(s + \sigma'_\star) \quad \text{and} \quad \lim \widetilde{\ell}_n(s + \tau'_n) = v(s + \tau'_\star)$$

for constants $\sigma'_\star, \tau'_\star \in \mathbf{R}$ (the convergence is in $\mathfrak{M}$, that is, uniform convergence on the compact subsets of $\mathbf{R} \times S^1$). For $\widetilde{\ell}^3_n(s) = \widetilde{\ell}_n(s - \sigma'_n)$, we have

$$\widetilde{\ell}^3_n(0) \in \partial \overline{B}(x, \delta) \quad \text{and} \quad \mathcal{A}_H(\widetilde{\ell}^3_n(0)) \in \,]\mathcal{A}_H(y), \mathcal{A}_H(x)[.$$

Proposition 9.6.8 then implies, as above, that $\widetilde{\ell}^3_n(s)$ converges to $u(s + \sigma'_\star)$. An analogous argument holds for $\widetilde{\ell}^4_n = \widetilde{\ell}_n(s + \tau'_n)$.

We will need a stronger result than this last remark, namely the following.

Lemma 9.6.12. *The sequences $\sigma'_n - \sigma_n$ and $\tau'_n - \tau_n$ are bounded.*

Proof. Suppose, on the contrary, that $\sigma'_n - \sigma_n$ tends to $+\infty$. We will show that this leads to a contradiction. Since σ'_n and σ_n are positive, we have

$$\mathcal{A}_H(\widetilde{\ell}_n(-\sigma_n)) \text{ and } \mathcal{A}_H(\widetilde{\ell}_n(-\sigma'_n)) \in [\mathcal{A}_H(\widetilde{\ell}_n(0)), \mathcal{A}_H(x)] \subset [\mathcal{A}_H(z), \mathcal{A}_H(x)].$$

We will show that $\mathcal{A}_H(\widetilde{\ell}_n(\sigma'_n)) - \mathcal{A}_H(\widetilde{\ell}_n(-\sigma_n))$ tends to $+\infty$. We have

$$\mathcal{A}_H(\widetilde{\ell}_n(-\sigma'_n)) - \mathcal{A}_H(\widetilde{\ell}_n(-\sigma_n)) = \int_{-\sigma_n}^{-\sigma'_n} \frac{\partial}{\partial s} \mathcal{A}_H(\widetilde{\ell}_n(s)) \, ds$$

$$= \int_{-\sigma_n}^{-\sigma'_n} \int_{S^1} \left\| \frac{\partial \widetilde{\ell}_n}{\partial s}(s, t) \right\|^2 dt \, ds$$

(the norm is the one defined by the metric on W). Then there exist $c_n \in [-\sigma'_n, -\sigma_n]$ such that

$$\int_{S^1} \left\| \frac{\partial \widetilde{\ell}_n}{\partial s}(c_n, t) \right\|^2 dt \quad \text{tends to } 0,$$

because otherwise, after extracting a subsequence, if necessary, we would have

$$\int_{S^1} \left\| \frac{\partial \widetilde{\ell}_n}{\partial s}(s, t) \right\|^2 dt \geq \gamma_0 \quad \text{for } s \in [-\sigma'_n, \sigma_n],$$

which implies that

$$\int_{-\sigma'_n}^{-\sigma_n} \int_{S^1} \left\| \frac{\partial \widetilde{\ell}_n}{\partial s}(s,t) \right\|^2 dt\, ds \geq \gamma_0^2 (\sigma'_n - \sigma_n) \quad \text{tends to } +\infty,$$

contradicting the inclusion stated above. Since $\widetilde{\ell}_n$ is a solution of the Floer equation, we can also write this as

$$\int_{S^1} \left\| \frac{\partial \widetilde{\ell}_n}{\partial t}(c_n,t) - X_t(\widetilde{\ell}_n(c_n,t)) \right\|^2 dt \quad \text{tends to } 0.$$

Let $\widetilde{\ell}_n^5(s) = \widetilde{\ell}_n(s+c_n)$. Since $c_n \in [-\sigma'_n, -\sigma_n]$, we have

$$\mathcal{A}_H(\widetilde{\ell}_n^5(0)) = \mathcal{A}_H(\widetilde{\ell}_n(c_n)) \in [\mathcal{A}_H(\widetilde{\ell}_n(-\sigma_n)), \mathcal{A}_H(\widetilde{\ell}_n(-\sigma'_n))].$$

Next, since

$$\lim_{n \to +\infty} \mathcal{A}_H(\widetilde{\ell}_n(-\sigma_n)) = \lim \mathcal{A}_H(\widetilde{\ell}_n^1(0)) = \mathcal{A}_H(u(\sigma_\star))$$

and $$\lim \mathcal{A}_H(\widetilde{\ell}_n(-\sigma'_n)) = \mathcal{A}_H(u(\sigma'_\star)),$$

it follows that

$$\mathcal{A}_H(\widetilde{\ell}_n^5(0)) \in \,]\mathcal{A}_H(y) + \gamma_0, \mathcal{A}_H(x) - \gamma_0[\quad \text{for a } \gamma_0 > 0 \text{ and for every } n.$$

Applying Proposition 9.6.8, we then find that $\widetilde{\ell}_n^5(s)$ tends to $u(s+c_\star)$ in $\mathcal{M}$ and in particular that $\widetilde{\ell}_n(c_n) = \widetilde{\ell}_n^5(0)$ converges uniformly to $u(c_\star)$ for the $\mathcal{C}^\infty$ topology on S^1. Together with the relation given above, this gives

$$\int_{S^1} \left\| \frac{\partial u}{\partial t}(c_\star,t) - X_t(u(c_\star,t)) \right\|^2 dt = 0$$

and therefore

$$\frac{\partial u}{\partial t}(c_\star,t) - X_t(u(c_\star,t)) = 0,$$

which means that $u(c_\star)$ is a critical point of $\mathcal{A}_H$. We call this critical point α. For every $t \in S^1$, we have

$$\frac{\partial u}{\partial s}(c_\star,t) = -J(u(c_\star,t))\left(\frac{\partial u}{\partial t}(c_\star,t) - X_t(u(c_\star,t)) \right)$$

$$= -J(\alpha)\left(\frac{\partial u}{\partial t}(\alpha) - X_t(\alpha) \right) = 0.$$

Consequently, the set $C(u)$ of critical points contains $c_\star \times S^1$, contradicting the fact that by Theorem 8.5.4, this set is discrete.

We conclude that the sequence $\sigma'_n - \sigma_n$ is bounded. We can use the same method to show that $\tau'_n - \tau_n$ is also bounded, concluding the proof of Lemma 9.6.12. $\qquad\qquad\qquad\qquad\qquad\qquad\qquad\qquad\qquad\qquad\qquad\qquad\square$

Let us finish the proof of Proposition 9.6.3. Let A, B and $C \in \mathbf{R}$ be constants such that:

- For $s \leq A$, $u(s) \in B(x, \delta)$ and $v(s) \in B(y, \delta)$.
- For $s \geq B$, $u(s) \in B(y, \delta)$ and $v(s) \in B(z, \delta)$.
- $\sigma'_n - \sigma_n \leq C$ and $\tau'_n - \tau_n \leq C$ $(C > 0)$.

The δ is the one given by Lemma 9.6.11, for an $\varepsilon > 0$ that is still fixed. We also use the constants $\sigma_\star$ and $\tau_\star$ defined in the second remark after the definitions of σ_n and τ_n and consider a compact interval $[E, F]$ such that:

- $E < 0$, $E + \sigma_\star \leq A$, $E + \tau_\star \leq A$.
- $F > 0$, $F + \sigma_\star \geq B$, $F + \tau_\star \geq B$.
- $\sigma'_n - \sigma_n \leq -E$ and $\tau'_n - \tau_n \leq F$ for every $n \in \mathbf{N}$.

We know that $\tilde{\ell}_n(s - \sigma_n)$ converges uniformly to $u(s + \sigma_\star)$ on the compact subsets of $\mathbf{R} \times S^1$. For a fixed $\varepsilon > 0$, there then exists an N_ε such that for $n \geq N_\varepsilon$, $t \in S^1$ and $s \in [E, F]$, we have

$$\tilde{\ell}_n(s - \sigma_n, t) = \exp_{u(s + \sigma_\star, t)} Y^1_n(s, t) \quad \text{with} \quad \left\| Y^1_n(s, t) \right\| \leq \varepsilon$$

(for the Euclidean norm). By replacing s by $s + \sigma_n$, we find that for $n \geq N_\varepsilon$,

$$\tilde{\ell}_n(s, t) = \exp_{u(s + \sigma_n + \sigma_\star, t)} Y_n(s, t)$$

with

$$\|Y_n(s, t)\| \leq \varepsilon \quad \text{for every } (s, t) \in [E - \sigma_n, F - \sigma_n] \times S^1.$$

In the same manner, for $n \geq N_\varepsilon$, we have

$$\tilde{\ell}_n(s, t) = \exp_{v(s + \tau_\star - \tau_n, t)} Y_n(s, t)$$

with

$$\|Y_n(s, t)\| \leq \varepsilon \quad \text{for every } (s, t) \in [E + \tau_n, F + \tau_n] \times S^1.$$

Recall that the intervals $[E - \sigma_n, F - \sigma_n]$ and $[E + \tau_n, F + \tau_n]$ are disjoint for n sufficiently large... there is therefore no confusion between the two Y_n defined by these two relations.

We define a pre-gluing $w_n(s,t)$ by

$$
w_n(s,t) = \begin{cases}
u(s + \sigma_\star + \sigma_n, t) & \text{if } s \leq -1, \\[2mm]
\exp_{y(t)}\Big(\beta^-(s)\exp^{-1}_{y(t)} u(s + \sigma_\star + \sigma_n, t) & \\[1mm]
\qquad + \beta^+(s)\exp^{-1}_{y(t)} v(s + \tau_\star - \tau_n, t)\Big) & \text{if } s \in [-1,1], \\[2mm]
v(s + \tau_\star - \tau_n, t) & \text{if } s \geq 1.
\end{cases}
$$

Let us show that for every $n \geq N_\varepsilon$ and $(s,t) \in \mathbf{R} \times S^1$, we have

$$
\widetilde{\ell}_n(s,t) = \exp_{w_n(s,t)} Y_n(s,t), \quad \text{with } \|Y_n(s,t)\| \leq \varepsilon.
$$

To do this, we cut $\mathbf{R}$ up into several intervals:

(1) For $s < E - \sigma_n \leq -\sigma'_n$, we have $\widetilde{\ell}_n(s,t) \in B(x(t), \delta)$ (by the definition of σ'_n) and

$$
w_n(s,t) = u(s + \sigma_\star + \sigma_n, t) \in B(x(t), \delta)
$$

because

$$
s + \sigma_\star + \sigma_n \leq E + \sigma_\star \leq A.
$$

We obtain the desired relation by applying the first assertion of Lemma 9.6.11.

(2) For $s \in [E - \sigma_n, F - \sigma_n]$, we have the result by using the definition of Y_n.

(3) For $s \in [F - \sigma_n, E + \tau_n]$, $\widetilde{\ell}_n(s) \in B(y, \delta)$ by the definitions of σ_n and τ_n (using the inequalities $F > 0$ and $E < 0$). Next, $u(s + \sigma_\star + \sigma_n) \in B(y, \delta)$ because $s + \sigma_\star + \sigma_n \geq B$ and likewise $v(s + \tau_\star - \tau_n) \in B(y, \delta)$ because $s + \tau_\star - \tau_n \leq E + \tau_\star \leq A$. The second assertion of Lemma 9.6.11 gives $w_n(s,t) \in B(y(t), \delta')$; we can therefore once again apply its first assertion to obtain the desired relation.

(4) The case where $s \in [E + \tau_n, F + \tau_n]$ is analogous to the one where $s \in [E - \sigma_n, F - \sigma_n]$.

(5) For $s \geq F + \tau_n \geq \tau'_n$, we have $\widetilde{\ell}_n(s) \in B(z, \delta)$ by the definition of τ'_n and $w_n(s,t) \in B(z(t), \delta)$ because $w_n(s,t) = v(s + \tau_\star - \tau_n, t)$ and $s + \tau_\star - \tau_n \geq F + \tau_\star \geq B$.

We have thus obtained the desired relation for every $s \in \mathbf{R}$. Note that we may assume that $\|Y_n(s,t)\|_W < \rho_{\mathrm{inj}}$ (norm of Y_n for the metric on W) for every $n \geq N_\varepsilon$, $(s,t) \in \mathbf{R} \times S^1$ if we choose ε sufficiently small, and therefore

$$
Y_n(s,t) = \exp^{-1}_{w_n(s,t)} \widetilde{\ell}_n(s,t) \quad \text{is of class } \mathcal{C}^\infty.
$$

The proof of Proposition 9.6.3 is almost finished. Let $\rho_n = \sigma_n + \sigma_\star$ and let ν be a function of class $\mathcal{C}^\infty$ that satisfies $\nu(\rho_n) = \tau_n - \tau_\star$. We may, and do, choose ν to be an increasing function (after once more extracting subsequences of ρ_n and τ_n, if necessary) that tends to $+\infty$ when ρ tends to $+\infty$. It follows that for $n \geq N_\varepsilon$ and $(s,t) \in \mathbf{R} \times S^1$, we have

$$\widetilde{\ell}_n(s,t) = \exp_{w_{\nu,\rho_n}(s,t)} Y_n(s,t) \quad \text{with } \|Y_n(s,t)\| \leq \varepsilon,$$

and this time, the proof of the proposition is truly finished.   □

9.6.c Step 3: Proof of Proposition 9.6.4

We will now show that the Y_n given by Proposition 9.6.3 is in $W^{1,p}(\mathbf{R} \times S^1; \mathbf{R}^m)$ for $p > 2$. To do this, we will use the exponential decay of the solutions of the Floer equation (Section 8.9), that is, the fact that if $\ell \in \mathcal{M}$, then there exists a constant $C > 0$ such that for every $(s,t) \in \mathbf{R} \times S^1$, we have

$$\left\| \frac{\partial \ell}{\partial s}(s,t) \right\| \leq C e^{-\delta|s|}$$

(with either the norm of the metric of W or the Euclidean norm in $\mathbf{R}^m$; we choose the latter). The previous step gives us the relation

$$\widetilde{\ell}_n(s,t) = \exp_{w_n(s,t)} Y_n(s,t) \text{ or } Y_n(s,t) = \exp^{-1}_{w_n(s,t)} \widetilde{\ell}_n(s,t).$$

The maps w_n and $\widetilde{\ell}_n$ both have exponential decay (w_n is a solution of the Floer equation for $|s| \geq 1$), which will be useful when we prove the following.

Lemma 9.6.13. *There exists a constant $K > 0$ (depending on n in general) such that for every $(s,t) \in \mathbf{R} \times S^1$, we have*

$$\max\left(\left\| \frac{\partial Y_n}{\partial s}(s,t) \right\|, \|Y_n(s,t)\|, \left\| \frac{\partial Y_n}{\partial t}(s,t) \right\| \right) \leq K e^{-\delta|s|}.$$

It is clear that this lemma immediately implies the first assertion of Proposition 9.6.4. Let us therefore prove it.

Proof of Lemma 9.6.13. Consider the open subset Ω of $W \times W$ defined by

$$\Omega = \{(a,b) \in W \times W \mid d(a,b) < \rho_{\mathrm{inj}}\}.$$

Let $\Phi : \Omega \to \mathbf{R}^m$ be defined by

$$\Phi(a,b) = \exp^{-1}_a(b) \in T_a W \subset \mathbf{R}^m.$$

Let $\Omega_0 \subset \Omega$ be defined by

$$\Omega_0 = \{(a,b) \in W \times W \mid d(a,b) \leq \rho_{\text{inj}}/2\};$$

this is a compact subset of $W \times W$. We choose a constant $A < 0$ such that for every $s \leq A$ and every $t \in S^1$, we have

$$(w_n(s,t), \widetilde{\ell}_n(s,t)) \in \Omega_0$$

(we can check that for $s \leq A$, $d(w_n(s,\cdot),x) \leq \rho_{\text{inj}}/6$ and $d(\widetilde{\ell}_n(s,\cdot),x) \leq \rho_{\text{inj}}/6$). We therefore have

$$Y_n(s,t) = \Phi(w_n(s,t), \widetilde{\ell}_n(s,t)) \quad \text{for } (s,t) \in]-\infty, A] \times S^1.$$

By the compactness of Ω_0, there exists an $M > 0$ such that

$$\left\|D_{(a,b)}\Phi\right\| \leq M \quad \forall (a,b) \in \Omega_0.$$

Therefore for every $s \leq A$ and every $t \in S^1$, we have

$$\left\|\frac{\partial Y_n}{\partial s}(s,t)\right\| = \left\|\frac{\partial}{\partial s}\Phi(w_n(s,t), \widetilde{\ell}_n(s,t))\right\|$$

$$\leq \left\|D_1\Phi_{(w_n(s,t),\widetilde{\ell}_n(s,t))}\frac{\partial w_n}{\partial s}(s,t)\right\| + \left\|D_2\Phi_{(w_n(s,t),\widetilde{\ell}_n(s,t))}\frac{\partial \widetilde{\ell}_n}{\partial s}(s,t)\right\|$$

$$\leq M\left\|\frac{\partial w_n}{\partial s}(s,t)\right\| + M\left\|\frac{\partial \widetilde{\ell}_n}{\partial s}(s,t)\right\|$$

$$\leq 2MCe^{\delta s}$$

(because of the exponential decay). Likewise, we can prove that for $s \geq B$,

$$\left\|\frac{\partial Y_n}{\partial s}(s,t)\right\| \leq 2MCe^{-\delta s},$$

which gives the "for $\partial Y_n/\partial s$" part of the lemma. Let us now prove it for Y_n itself. Let $A < 0$ as before. For $s_1 \leq s_2 \leq A < 0$ and $t \in S^1$, we have

$$\|Y_n(s_2,t) - Y_n(s_1,t)\| = \left\|\int_{s_1}^{s_2} \frac{\partial Y_n}{\partial s}(s,t)\,ds\right\| \leq \int_{s_1}^{s_2}\left\|\frac{\partial Y_n}{\partial s}(s,t)\right\|\,ds$$

$$\leq \int_{s_1}^{s_2} Ke^{\delta s}\,ds = K(e^{\delta s_2} - e^{\delta s_1}).$$

We let s_1 tend to $-\infty$ in this inequality and use the expression of Y_n as a function of $\widetilde{\ell}_n$ to obtain

$$\lim_{s \to -\infty} Y_n(s,t) = \lim_{s \to -\infty} \Phi(w_n(s,t), \widetilde{\ell}_n(s,t))$$
$$= \Phi(x(t), x(t)) = \exp_{x(t)}^{-1} x(t) = 0.$$

We therefore have

$$\|Y_n(s_2, t)\| \le K e^{\delta s_2}.$$

Proceeding analogously for the $s \ge B$ gives the desired result for Y_n. To conclude the proof of Lemma 9.6.13, we still need to prove an inequality of the same type for $\partial Y_n / \partial t$.

Starting out from the expression of Y_n as a function of $\widetilde{\ell}_n$, we find

$$\frac{\partial Y_n}{\partial t}(s,t) = D_1 \Phi_{(w_n(s,t), \widetilde{\ell}_n(s,t))} \frac{\partial w_n}{\partial t}(s,t) + D_2 \Phi_{(w_n(s,t), \widetilde{\ell}_n(s,t))} \frac{\partial \widetilde{\ell}_n}{\partial t}(s,t).$$

The negative constant A chosen above is assumed to be less than -1. For $s \le A \le -1$, w_n is a solution of the Floer equation. At every point (s,t), we can therefore write

$$\frac{\partial Y_n}{\partial t} = D_1 \Phi_{(w_n, \widetilde{\ell}_n)} \left(X_t(w_n) - J(w_n) \cdot \frac{\partial w_n}{\partial s} \right)$$
$$+ D_2 \Phi_{(w_n, \widetilde{\ell}_n)} \left(X_t(\widetilde{\ell}_n) - J(\widetilde{\ell}_n) \cdot \frac{\partial \widetilde{\ell}_n}{\partial s} \right)$$

(where we leave out the point (s,t) to simplify the notation) and for every point $(s,t) \in \,]-\infty, A] \times S^1$, we can write

$$\left\| \frac{\partial Y_n}{\partial t} \right\| \le \left\| D_1 \Phi_{(w_n, \widetilde{\ell}_n)} J(w_n) \frac{\partial w_n}{\partial s} \right\| + \left\| D_2 \Phi_{(w_n, \widetilde{\ell}_n)} J(\widetilde{\ell}_n) \frac{\partial \widetilde{\ell}_n}{\partial s} \right\|$$
$$+ \left\| D_1 \Phi_{(w_n, \widetilde{\ell}_n)} X_t(w_n) + D_2 \Phi_{(w_n, \widetilde{\ell}_n)} X_t(\widetilde{\ell}_n) \right\|,$$

so that

$$\left\| \frac{\partial Y_n}{\partial t} \right\| \le K e^{\delta s} + \left\| D_1 \Phi_{(w_n, \widetilde{\ell}_n)} X_t(w_n) + D_2 \Phi_{(w_n, \widetilde{\ell}_n)} X_t(\widetilde{\ell}_n) \right\|.$$

For the last inequality, we used the fact that the norms $\|D\Phi\|$ and $\|J\|$ are uniformly bounded on Ω_0 and on W, respectively, as well as the exponential decay of w_n and $\widetilde{\ell}_n$. To give an upper bound for the last term, consider the map $\Gamma : \Omega \to \mathbf{R}^m$ defined by

$$\Gamma(a, b) = D_1 \Phi(a, b) X_t(a) + D_2 \Phi_{(a,b)} X_t(b),$$

so that the term we want to bound is $\|\Gamma(w_n(s,t), \widetilde{\ell}_n(s,t))\|$. As above, by compactness, there exists an $M > 0$ such that we have $\|D\Gamma_{(a,b)}\| \le M$ for every $(a, b) \in \Omega_0$. Therefore, for $s_1 \leq s_2 \leq A$ and $t \in S^1$, we have

$$\left\| \Gamma(w_n(s_2, t), \widetilde{\ell}_n(s_2, t)) - \Gamma(w_n(s, t), \widetilde{\ell}_n(s, t)) \right\|$$

$$\leq \left\| \int_{s_1}^{s_2} \frac{\partial}{\partial s} \Gamma(w_n(s, t), \widetilde{\ell}_n(s, t)) \, ds \right\|$$

$$\leq \int_{s_1}^{s_2} \left\| \frac{\partial}{\partial s} \Gamma(w_n(s, t), \widetilde{\ell}_n(s, t)) \right\| \, ds$$

$$= \int_{s_1}^{s_2} \left\| D_1 \Gamma_{(w_n, \widetilde{\ell}_n)} \frac{\partial w_n}{\partial s} + D_2 \Gamma_{(w_n, \widetilde{\ell}_n)} \frac{\partial \widetilde{\ell}_n}{\partial s} \right\| \, ds$$

$$\leq \int_{s_1}^{s_2} M \left(\left\| \frac{\partial w_n}{\partial s} \right\| + \left\| \frac{\partial \widetilde{\ell}_n}{\partial s} \right\| \right) \, ds$$

$$\leq MC \int_{s_1}^{s_2} e^{\delta s} \, ds = MC(e^{\delta s_2} - e^{\delta s_1}),$$

still using the exponential decay. Let s_1 tend to $-\infty$. We have

$$\lim_{s \to -\infty} \Gamma(w_n(s, t), \widetilde{\ell}_n(s, t)) = \Gamma(x(t), x(t))$$

$$= D_1 \Phi_{(x(t), x(t))} X_t(x(t)) + D_2 \Phi_{(x(t), x(t))} X_t(x(t))$$

$$= D_1 \Phi_{(x(t), x(t))} x'(t) + D_2 \Phi_{(x(t), x(t))} x'(t)$$

because $x(t)$ is an orbit of the vector field X_t. We find

$$\lim_{s \to -\infty} \Gamma(w_n(s, t), \widetilde{\ell}_n(s, t)) = \frac{\partial}{\partial t} \Phi(x(t), x(t)) = \frac{\partial}{\partial t} 0 = 0.$$

It therefore follows that for $s_2 \leq A$ and $t \in S^1$,

$$\left\| \Gamma(w_n(s_2, t), \widetilde{\ell}_n(s_2, t)) \right\| \leq K e^{\delta s_2}.$$

We conclude the proof of Lemma 9.6.13 by proceeding in the same manner for $s \geq B$. $\qquad\square$

As we have already noted, the fact that our Y_n is in $W^{1,p}(\mathbf{R} \times S^1; \mathbf{R}^m)$ for every $p > 2$ immediately follows. To conclude the proof of Proposition 9.6.4, we still need to prove that Y_n tends to 0 for the $W^{1,p}$ norm. We therefore consider a unitary trivialization $(Z_i^n)_i$ along the pre-gluing w_n, chosen as in Section 9.4 (see Figure 9.5). Using the frame Z_i, we write $Y_n = i(\zeta_n)$ where $\zeta_n \in W^{1,p}(\mathbf{R} \times S^1; \mathbf{R}^{2n})$. Here $\mathcal{F}$ denotes the Floer operator

$$\mathcal{F} = \frac{\partial}{\partial s} + J \frac{\partial}{\partial t} + \mathrm{grad}(H_t).$$

The operator $F : W^{1,p}(\mathbf{R} \times S^1; \mathbf{R}^{2n}) \to L^p(\mathbf{R} \times S^1; \mathbf{R}^{2n})$ is defined by

$$F(\zeta) = p(i(\zeta), \widetilde{\mathcal{F}}(i(\zeta))),$$

where

$$\widetilde{\mathcal{F}} : W^{1,p}(\mathbf{R} \times S^1; \mathbf{R}^m) \longrightarrow L^p(\mathbf{R} \times S^1; \mathbf{R}^m)$$

is given by

$$\widetilde{\mathcal{F}}(X) = \mathcal{F}(\exp_{w_n}(X)).$$

Let L denote the differential DF_0. The maps F, p, i, $\widetilde{\mathcal{F}}$ and L above depend on w_n and on the trivialization Z_i^n, hence in particular on n. We will leave this dependence out so as not to complicate the notation. As in Section 9.4, we consider the subspace

$$W_n = \{\alpha \#_{w_n} \beta \mid \alpha \in \operatorname{Ker} L^u,\ \beta \in \operatorname{Ker} L^v\}$$

and its orthogonal

$$W_n^\perp = \left\{ Y \in W^{1,p}(\mathbf{R} \times S^1; \mathbf{R}^{2n}) \mid \right.$$
$$\left. \int_{\mathbf{R} \times S^1} \langle Y, v \rangle \, ds \, dt = 0 \text{ for every } v \in W_n \right\}.$$

We have already noted (in Remarks 9.4.5 and Proposition 9.4.7) that W_n and $W_n^\perp$ are in direct sum in $W^{1,p}(\mathbf{R} \times S^1; \mathbf{R}^{2n})$ and that W_n has dimension 2. In fact, W_n is generated by $(\partial u/\partial s)\#_{w_n} 0$ and $0 \#_{w_n}(\partial v/\partial s)$. We decompose ζ_n in this direct sum:

$$\zeta_n = \chi_n + \omega_n \quad \text{with } \chi_n \in W_n \text{ and } \omega_n \in W_n^\perp.$$

Lemma 9.6.14.
$$\lim_{n \to +\infty} \|\chi_n\|_{W^{1,p}} = 0.$$

The proof of this lemma (by simple estimates) will be given in Section 13.7. We use it to find an upper bound for $\|Y_n\|_{W^{1,p}}$ that will allow us to conclude that its limit is zero. This is done in the following lemma, whose proof can be found in Section 13.7.

Lemma 9.6.15. *There exist positive constants K_1 and K_2 such that for every $n \in \mathbf{N}$,*

$$\|Y_n\|_{W^{1,p}} \le K_1 \frac{\|\chi_n\|_{W^{1,p}} + \|Y_n\|_{L^\infty} + \|\widetilde{\mathcal{F}}(0)\|_{L^p}}{1 - K_2 \|Y_n\|_{L^\infty}}.$$

Let us show that the right-hand side tends to 0. We know that $\lim \|Y_n\|_{L^\infty} = 0$ (by Proposition 9.6.3) and that $\lim \|\chi_n\|_{W^{1,p}} = 0$ (by Lemma 9.6.14). Moreover, since $\widetilde{\mathcal{F}}(0) = \mathcal{F}(w_n)$ is zero for $s \notin [-1, 1]$, we have

$$\|\widetilde{\mathcal{F}}(0)\|_{L^p} = \|\mathcal{F}(w_n)\|_{L^p([-1,1] \times S^1; \mathbf{R}^m)}.$$

Since $\lim w_n = y$ uniformly on the compact subsets of $\mathbf{R} \times S^1$ and $\mathcal{F}(y) = 0$, we have $\lim_{n \to +\infty} \|\widetilde{\mathcal{F}}(0)\|_{L^p} = 0$, which shows that the right-hand side of our inequality indeed tends to 0 and concludes the proof of Proposition 9.6.4.

9.6.d Step 4 (Last Step)

We begin with a more general version of the Newton–Picard method, a generalization of Lemma 9.4.4, whose notation we keep.

Lemma 9.6.16. *Let X and Y be two Banach spaces and let $F : X \to Y$ be a continuous map. We write*

$$F(x) = F(0) + L(x) + N(x),$$

where $L(x) = (dF)_0(x)$, and we suppose that there exists a continuous $G : Y \to X$ such that:

(1) $L \circ G = \mathrm{Id}$.
(2) $\|GN(x) - GN(y)\| \leq C(\|x\| + \|y\|)\,\|x - y\|$ *for all $x, y \in B(0, r)$.*
(3) $\|GF(0)\| \leq \varepsilon_0/2$ *where $\varepsilon_0 = \min(r, 1/5C)$.*

Let $h \in \operatorname{Ker} L$ satisfy $\|h\| < \varepsilon_0/5$. Then there exists a unique $\gamma_h \in (h + \operatorname{Im} G) \cap B(0, \varepsilon_0)$ such that $F(\gamma_h) = 0$. Moreover,

$$\|\gamma_h\| \leq \|GF(0)\| + \|h\|.$$

Proof. It is similar to that of the original, Lemma 9.4.4. We consider the map $\varphi : B(0, \varepsilon_0) \to \operatorname{Im} G$ defined by

$$\varphi(x) = G(L(x) - F(x)) = -G(F(0) + N(x)),$$

which therefore satisfies $L(\varphi(x)) = L(x) - F(x)$. We then define the sequence

$$x_0 = h, \quad x_{n+1} = \varphi(x_n) + h.$$

As in the proof of Lemma 9.4.4, for $x \in B(0, \varepsilon_0)$, we have

$$\|\varphi(x) + h\| \leq \|\varphi(x)\| + \|h\| \leq \frac{\varepsilon_0}{2} + \frac{\varepsilon_0}{5} + \frac{\varepsilon_0}{5} < \varepsilon_0,$$

which shows that $x_n \in B(0, \varepsilon_0)$ for every n. Still following the proof of Lemma 9.4.4, we then have

$$\|x_{n+1} - x_n\| = \|\varphi(x_n) - \varphi(x_{n-1})\| \leq \frac{1}{2}\|x_n - x_{n-1}\|$$

(hence φ is a contracting map), whence

$$\lim x_n = \gamma_h \in B(0, \varepsilon_0) \cap \{h + \operatorname{Im} G\}$$

and $\varphi(\gamma_h) + h = \gamma_h$. We therefore have

$$L(\gamma_h) = L(\varphi(\gamma_h) + h) = L\varphi(\gamma_h) = L(\gamma_h) - F(\gamma_h),$$

which implies that $F(\gamma_h) = 0$.

Let us show the uniqueness: if $\gamma \in h + \operatorname{Im} G \cap B(0, \varepsilon_0)$ satisfies $F(\gamma) = 0$, then we set $\gamma = h + G(y)$ and obtain

$$\varphi(\gamma) = GL(\gamma) = GL(h + G(y)) = GLG(y) = G(y) = \gamma - h,$$

hence $\gamma = \varphi(\gamma) + h$. But this equation admits a unique solution because φ is a contraction, as we just saw.   □

We apply Lemma 9.6.16 to the operator

$$F : W^{1,p}(\mathbf{R} \times S^1; \mathbf{R}^{2n}) \longrightarrow L^p(\mathbf{R} \times S^1; \mathbf{R}^{2n})$$

(which we defined using the unitary trivialization Z_i along w_n). If n is sufficiently large for the conditions of Lemma 9.6.16 to be satisfied and to have $h \in \operatorname{Ker} L = \operatorname{Ker}(DF)_0$ with $\|h\| \le \varepsilon_0/5$, then we obtain elements $\gamma_n(h) \in W^{1,p}(\mathbf{R} \times S^1; \mathbf{R}^{2n})$ such that

$$\exp_{w_n}(i(\gamma_n(h))) \in \mathcal{M}(x, z).$$

We need the continuity of these solutions with respect to h.

Lemma 9.6.17. *There exists a real number $\varepsilon_1 > 0$ that does not depend on n, satisfies $\varepsilon_1 < \varepsilon_0/5$ and is such that for $\|h\| \le \varepsilon_1$, the map $h \mapsto \gamma_n(h)$ is continuous.*

Proof. This follows from the implicit function theorem. Recall the decomposition into a direct sum:

$$W^{1,p}(\mathbf{R} \times S^1; \mathbf{R}^{2n}) = \operatorname{Ker} L \oplus W^{\perp}$$

(this depends on the pre-gluing w_n in question) and the fact that $\gamma_n(h) \in h + W^{\perp}$. For n fixed, define

$$\overline{F} : \operatorname{Ker} L \oplus W^{\perp} \longrightarrow L^p(\mathbf{R} \times S^1; \mathbf{R}^{2n})$$

by setting $\overline{F}(h, \omega) = F(h + \omega)$, so that $\overline{F}(h, \gamma_n(h) - h) = 0$. Let us show that

$$(D_2\overline{F})_{(h, \gamma_n(h) - h)} = (dF)_{(\gamma_n(h))} : W^{\perp} \longrightarrow L^p(\mathbf{R} \times S^1; \mathbf{R}^{2n})$$

is invertible. We proceed as in the proof of Lemma 9.4.14:

$$\left\|G(dF)_{\gamma_n(h)} - \mathrm{Id}\right\| = \left\|G(dF)_{\gamma_n(h)} - G(dF)_0\right\|$$
$$\le C\left\|(dF)_{\gamma_n(h)} - (dF)_0\right\|$$
$$\le CK\left\|\gamma_n(h)\right\|_{W^{1,p}}$$

by Proposition 9.4.7 and Lemma 9.4.4. By Lemma 9.6.16, this leads to

$$\left\|G(dF)_{\gamma_n(h)} - \mathrm{Id}\right\| \le CK\left(\|h\|_{W^{1,p}} + \|GF(0)\|_{W^{1,p}}\right)$$
$$= CK\left(\|h\|_{W^{1,p}} + \|G\mathcal{F}(w_n)\|_{W^{1,p}}\right)$$
$$\le CK\left(\|h\|_{W^{1,p}} + C\|\mathcal{F}(w_n)\|_{L^p}\right).$$

We have already noted that $\lim\|\mathcal{F}(w_n)\|_{L^p} = 0$. The constants C and K do not depend on n. For an ε_1 that does not depend on n, with $0 < \varepsilon_1 < \varepsilon_0/5$, and for n sufficiently large, the inequality above shows that $d(dF)_{\gamma_n(h)}$ is invertible for $\|h\|_{W^{1,p}} \le \varepsilon_1$ (G is invertible by Proposition 9.4.7). Hence $D_2\overline{F}$ is invertible. We can therefore apply the implicit function theorem to conclude that $h \mapsto \gamma_n(h) - h$ is continuous and therefore that $h \mapsto \gamma_n(h)$ is also continuous. $\qquad\square$

We will now prove Proposition 9.6.5.

Proof of Proposition 9.6.5. By Propositions 9.6.3 and 9.6.4, we know that

$$\widetilde{\ell}_n = \exp_{w_n} Y_n \quad \text{with} \quad \lim_{n\to+\infty} \|Y_n\|_{W^{1,p}} = 0.$$

As in step 3, we write $Y_n = i(\zeta_n)$ for

$$i : W^{1,p}(\mathbf{R} \times S^1; \mathbf{R}^{2n}) \longrightarrow W^{1,p}(\mathbf{R} \times S^1; \mathbf{R}^m).$$

We therefore have $\lim\|\zeta_n\|_{W^{1,p}} = 0$. We have the decomposition

$$\zeta_n = h_n + w'_n \in \mathrm{Ker}\, L \oplus W^\perp$$

(where $w'_n = GL(\zeta_n)$ and $h_n = \zeta_n - GL(\zeta_n)$). Recall that $W^\perp$, G and L also depend on n. We know that the operator norms of G and L are bounded from above by constants that do not depend on n: for G by Proposition 9.4.7 and for L by Lemma 13.5.1 (another technical lemma proved in Chapter 13). Therefore the $W^{1,p}$ norm of h_n, which is bounded from above by

$$\|\zeta_n\|_{W^{1,p}} + \|G\|^{\mathrm{op}}\,\|L\|^{\mathrm{op}}\,\|\zeta_n\|_{W^{1,p}},$$

tends to 0 when n tends to infinity. In particular, for n sufficiently large, $\|h_n\|_{W^{1,p}} < \varepsilon_1$, where ε_1 is given by Lemma 9.6.17. By the uniqueness given in Lemma 9.6.16, we then have $\zeta_n = \gamma_n(h_n)$ and therefore $\widetilde{\ell}_n = \exp_{w_n} i(\gamma_n(h_n))$

is a solution obtained using the Newton–Picard method. Let us show that its projection on $\mathcal{L}(x, z)$ is in the image of $\psi_\nu : [\rho_\nu, +\infty[\to \mathcal{L}(x, z)$.

Note that since $w_n = w_{\nu, \rho_n}$ and since, by the construction of ψ_ν, $\psi_\nu(\rho_n) = \exp_{w_n}(\gamma_n(0))$, the conclusion holds if $h_n = 0$. In the general case, we use a connectedness argument that depends on the continuity of $h \mapsto \gamma_n(h)$ that we just established (Lemma 9.6.17). As in the proof of Proposition 9.6.1, we identify the component of $\mathcal{L}(x, z)$ that contains $\operatorname{Im} \widehat{\psi}_\nu$ with $]0, 1[$ and the image of $\widehat{\psi}_\nu$ with $[a, 1[$. Let $\overline{\rho}_\nu > \rho_\nu$ satisfy

$$\widehat{\psi}_\nu([\overline{\rho}_\nu, +\infty[) = [c, 1[\quad \text{with } c > a.$$

For $0 \le \varepsilon \le \varepsilon_1$, consider the set $U_\varepsilon \subset \mathcal{M}(x, z)$ defined by

$$U_\varepsilon = \psi_\nu[\overline{\rho}_\nu, +\infty[\cup \bigcup_{\rho_n > \overline{\rho}_\nu} \{\exp_{w_n}(i(\gamma_n(h))) \mid \|h\| \le \varepsilon\}.$$

By the above, $\widetilde{\ell}_n \in U_\varepsilon$ for n sufficiently large. More generally, for every fixed ε ($\varepsilon \le \varepsilon_1$), then $\widetilde{\ell}_n \in U_\varepsilon$ for $n \ge N_\varepsilon$, by Propositions 9.6.3 and 9.6.4 as well as the uniqueness in Lemma 9.6.16. Moreover, U_ε is pathwise connected, hence its projection $I_\varepsilon \subset \mathcal{L}(x, z)$ is an interval.

Lemma 9.6.18. *There exists an ε_2 such that $0 < \varepsilon_2 < \varepsilon_1$ and*

$$I_{\varepsilon_2} \subset [a, 1[= \widehat{\psi}_\nu([\rho_\nu, +\infty[).$$

Proof. By construction, $I_0 = [c, 1[$ with $c > a$. If the conclusion of the lemma were false, then we would have a sequence ε_k that decreases toward 0 and satisfies $I_{\varepsilon_k} \supset [a, 1[$ with $I_{\varepsilon_k} \ne [a, 1[$ (because for every ε, I_ε is an interval that contains $I_0 = [c, 1[$). In particular, we would have trajectories $\lambda_k \in U_{\varepsilon_k}$ such that

$$\widehat{\lambda}_k \in [a - \delta_1, a - \delta_2] \subset \mathcal{L}(x, z) \quad \text{for small } \delta_1, \delta_2.$$

Moreover, $\lambda_k \notin \psi_\nu([\overline{\rho}_\nu, +\infty[) = [c, 1[$. Let

$$\lambda_k = \exp_{w_{n_k}}(i(\gamma_{n_k}(h_k))) \quad \text{with } \|h_k\| < \varepsilon_k.$$

We distinguish between two cases:

(1) If n_k tends to infinity, then

$$\lim_{k \to +\infty} \|\gamma_{n_k}(h_k)\|_{W^{1,p}} = 0.$$

Indeed, by Lemma 9.6.16,

$$\|\gamma_{n_k}(h_k)\|_{W^{1,p}} \le \|h_k\|_{W^{1,p}} + C \left\|\widetilde{\mathcal{F}}(0)\right\|_{L^p} \le \varepsilon_k + C \|\mathcal{F}(w_{n_k})\|_{L^p}$$

and the right-hand side tends to 0 when k tends to infinity. As in Lemma 9.4.16, we therefore have

$$\lim_{k \to +\infty} \widehat{\lambda}_k = (u, v) \quad \text{in } \overline{\mathcal{L}}(x, z),$$

which is impossible because $\widehat{\lambda}_k \in [a - \delta_1, a - \delta_2] \subset \mathcal{L}(x, z)$. We have used the fact that the topology of $\overline{\mathcal{L}}(x, z)$ is separated, as we proved in Section 9.1.

(2) If, on the other hand, the sequence n_k is bounded, then it admits a constant subsequence (n_0). Restricting ourselves to this subsequence, we therefore have

$$\lambda_k = \exp_{w_{n_0}}(i(\gamma_{n_0}(h_k))) \quad \text{for every } k.$$

Since $\|h_k\| \leq \varepsilon_k$, we have $\lim h_k = 0$. Since $h \mapsto \gamma_n(h)$ is continuous, we have

$$\lim_{k \to +\infty} \lambda_k = \exp_{w_{n_0}}(i(\gamma_{n_0}(0))) = \psi_\nu(\rho_{n_0}) \in \psi_\nu([\overline{\rho}_\nu, +\infty[).$$

It follows that $\lim \widehat{\lambda}_k \in \widehat{\psi}_\nu([\overline{\rho}_\nu, +\infty[) = [c, 1[$, which is impossible because

$$\widehat{\lambda}_k \in [a - \delta_1, a - \delta_2] \quad \text{and} \quad c > a.$$

This concludes the proof of the lemma. $\qquad \square$

And also that of Proposition 9.6.5: for n sufficiently large, $\widetilde{\ell}_n \in U_{\varepsilon_2}$ (ε_2 is the one from Lemma 9.6.18), hence $\ell_n \in I_{\varepsilon_2} \subset \widehat{\psi}_\nu([\rho_\nu, +\infty[)$. $\qquad \square$

Corollary 9.6.6 immediately follows because Proposition 9.6.1 gives $\widehat{\psi}_\nu([\rho_\nu, +\infty[) \subset \text{Im } \widehat{\psi}$, hence $\ell_n \in \text{Im } \widehat{\psi}$ for n sufficiently large. $\qquad \square$

This also finally concludes the proof of Theorem 9.2.3.

Chapter 10
From Floer to Morse

In this chapter, we prove that in the case of a nondegenerate Hamiltonian that does not depend on time and is sufficiently small (in the sense of the $\mathcal{C}^2$ topology), when we are able to define the Morse complex and the Floer complex; the two coincide.

10.1 The Results

For the sake of simplicity and to alleviate the writing, we have used more or less the same notation for the Morse complex (in Chapter 3) and for the Floer complex (in Chapter 9). At this point, we need to distinguish between the two (in order to show that they coincide). From now on, let $CF_\star(H, J)$ denote the Floer complex associated with the Hamiltonian H and the almost complex structure J (which was called $(C_\star, \partial)$ in Chapter 9), and let $CM_\star(H, J)$ denote the Morse complex associated with the Morse function H and the vector field $\operatorname{grad} H$, the gradient of H for the metric defined by J (and ω) (which was called $(C_\star(H), \partial_{\operatorname{grad}_H})$ in Chapter 3).

We want to prove the following.

Theorem 10.1.1. *There exists a nondegenerate, sufficiently small (for the $\mathcal{C}^2$ topology) Hamiltonian H for which*

$$CF_\star(H, J) = CM_{\star+n}(H, J).$$

This statement of course also contains the fact that the two complexes in question are well defined. Starting with a nondegenerate Hamiltonian H_0, we construct H as $H = H_0/k$ for a sufficiently large k.

M. Audin, M. Damian, *Morse Theory and Floer Homology*, Universitext, DOI 10.1007/978-1-4471-5496-9_10, © Springer-Verlag London 2014

Since H is sufficiently small, its periodic trajectories are constant (Proposition 6.1.5), hence $\mathrm{Crit}(\mathcal{A}_H) = \mathrm{Crit}(H)$. On the other hand, Proposition 5.4.5, which compares the two notions of nondegeneracy (of the critical points of the function H and of the periodic trajectories of the Hamiltonian H), implies that H is a Morse function and that $\mathrm{Crit}(\mathcal{A}_H) = \mathrm{Crit}(H)$.

By Remark 5.4.6, we know that the Hessian of H has no eigenvalues in $2\pi\mathbf{Z}$, so that Proposition 7.2.1 allows us to compare the (Morse) index of a critical point of H to the (Maslov) index of the corresponding constant trajectory:

$$\mathrm{Ind}_H(x) = \mu(x) + n.$$

This implies that the vector spaces that occur in the definitions of the two complexes are the same up to a shift in the indices.

Next, we need to consider the two differentials. More exactly, we must:

- Be able to define the differentials of the two complexes
- Show that they coincide.

To define the differential of the Morse complex, we need a vector field X adapted to the Morse function H, which satisfies the Smale condition. On the other hand, we want a relation between the trajectories of this vector field and the solutions of the Floer equation, that is, between the solutions of

$$\frac{du}{ds} + X(u) = 0 \quad \text{and} \quad \frac{\partial u}{\partial s} + J(u)\frac{\partial u}{\partial t} + \mathrm{grad}\, H(u) = 0.$$

We therefore want X to be the gradient of the function H for the metric defined by an almost complex structure J calibrated by ω. We will therefore prove the following result.

Theorem 10.1.2. *Let H be a Morse function on the symplectic manifold (W, ω). There exists a dense subset $\mathcal{J}_{\mathrm{reg}}(H)$ consisting of almost complex structures J calibrated by ω such that the pair $(H, -JX_H)$ is Morse–Smale.*

We will carry out the proof in two steps. The first will be devoted to a general Morse function f and an adapted vector field X. We will linearize the equation

$$\frac{du}{ds} + X(u) = 0$$

of the flow of the vector field $-X$ along one of its solutions in $L_u Y = 0$, and then show the following result.

Theorem 10.1.3. *When f is a Morse function and u is a trajectory connecting two critical points x and y, L_u is a Fredholm operator whose index is the difference of the Morse indices of the two critical points.*

Because of the relation between the Morse and Maslov indices mentioned earlier, this immediately implies the following corollary.

Corollary 10.1.4. *For a nondegenerate Hamiltonian H and a trajectory u of $-JX_H$, the Fredholm operators $(d\mathcal{F})_u$ and L_u have the same index.*

We will also show the following result.

Theorem 10.1.5. *The vector field X is Smale if and only if the operators L_u are surjective.*

In the second step, we will consider the specific case of the Hamiltonian H and prove Theorem 10.1.2, a transversality result analogous to the ones we established in Section 8.5.

Having chosen the almost complex structure and therefore the Smale vector field, we will then compare the solutions of the Floer equation and the trajectories of the vector field.

Remark 10.1.6. It is clear that the solutions of the Floer equation that do not depend on t are exactly the trajectories of the vector field $X = -\operatorname{grad} H$.

We want to prove the following proposition.

Proposition 10.1.7. *If H is sufficiently small (in the $\mathcal{C}^2$ sense), then*

$$\operatorname{Ker}(d\mathcal{F})_u = \operatorname{Ker} L_u.$$

We will prove this later. The elements of the kernel of $(d\mathcal{F})_u$ therefore do not depend on t. Using the identity of the indices (Corollary 10.1.4 and the characterization of the Smale vector fields, in Theorem 10.1.5), this implies the following result.

Corollary 10.1.8. *The Fredholm operator $(d\mathcal{F})_u$ is surjective along every trajectory of the gradient of H.*

On the other hand, we will show that, after replacing H by $H_k = H/k$ (which has the same critical points with the same indices) for k sufficiently large, if necessary, all solutions of the Floer equation that interest us are independent of t.

Proposition 10.1.9. *If k is sufficiently large, then the solutions of the Floer equation for H_k connecting critical points x and y with*

$$\operatorname{Ind}_{H_k}(x) - \operatorname{Ind}_{H_k}(y) \le 2$$

are all independent of t.

Let $H_k = H/k$ with k sufficiently large, and let $J \in \mathcal{J}_{\text{reg}}$ (the dense subset given by Theorem 10.1.2). The conclusion is that when $\text{Ind}(x) - \text{Ind}(y) \leq 2$, the trajectories of the Floer equation associated with (H, J) that connect the two critical points x and y (critical points both for H and for $\mathcal{A}_H$ since the two sets of critical points coincide) are exactly the trajectories of the Smale vector field $X = -JX_H$ (by Proposition 10.1.9). Moreover, the Floer operator linearized along these trajectories is surjective (by Corollary 10.1.8). Such a regularity condition implies that $\mathcal{M}^{(H,J)}(x, y)$ is a manifold, which allows us to define the Floer complex (see Theorem 8.1.2).

We establish this regularity property only for $\text{Ind}(x) - \text{Ind}(y) \leq 2$ (and not in general, as in Chapter 8 (see Theorem 8.1.1)), but this case suffices to construct the Floer complex $CF_\star(H, J)$. We have seen that it coincides with the Morse complex $CM_{\star+n}(H, J)$, which proves Theorem 10.1.1. We still need to show the intermediate results (Theorems 10.1.2, 10.1.3, 10.1.5 and Proposition 10.1.7).

10.2 The Linearization of the Flow of a Pseudo-Gradient Field, Proof of Theorem 10.1.3

We consider a Morse function f on a manifold V and an adapted pseudo-gradient field X. The trajectories of this vector field are the solutions of

$$\frac{du}{ds} + X(u(s)) = 0.$$

To simplify, assume that the manifold V is embedded in a space $\mathbf{R}^m$ (m sufficiently large) so that we can view $u \mapsto X(u)$ as a map with values in $\mathbf{R}^m$. We fix a metric g on V so that X is the gradient of f for g.

The space

$$\mathcal{M} = \left\{ u : \mathbf{R} \to V \mid \frac{\partial u}{\partial s} + \text{grad} f = 0 \text{ and } \int_{\mathbf{R}} \left\| \frac{\partial u}{\partial s} \right\|^2 ds < +\infty \right\}$$

of solutions of finite energy is compact[1] and we have

$$\mathcal{M} = \bigcup_{x,y \in \text{Crit}(f)} \mathcal{M}(x, y).$$

---

[1] Recall that if V is compact, then all trajectories are of finite energy.

10.2.a Linearization of the Equation

We fix a solution u that connects a critical point x to a critical point y and fix a trivialization $(Z_1, \ldots, Z_n)$ (that is orthonormal for the metric g) of TV in the neighborhood of the image of u. Using Morse charts, we choose the Z_i in such a way that $Z_i(s)$ does not depend on s in the neighborhood of the critical points x and y. For $Y = (y_1, \ldots, y_n) \in \mathbf{R}^n$, we set

$$\widetilde{Y}(s) = \sum_{i=1}^{n} y_i(s) Z_i(u(s)).$$

Linearizing the equation of the flow along the solution u gives a linear differential equation

$$\frac{d\widetilde{Y}}{ds} + (dX)_{u(s)}(\widetilde{Y}) = 0 \quad \text{or} \quad \widetilde{L}_u \widetilde{Y} = 0$$

whose unknown function $s \mapsto \widetilde{Y}(s)$ is a vector tangent to V along the solution u. In the given trivialization, we can write

$$\widetilde{L}_u(\widetilde{Y}) = \frac{d}{ds}\left(\sum y_i Z_i\right) + S_u(s)\left(\sum y_i Z_i\right)$$

$$= \sum_{i=1}^{n}\left(\frac{dy_i}{ds} + \sum_{j=1}^{n}(a_{ji} + S_{ji})y_j\right) Z_i,$$

where $S_u(s) = (dX)_{u(s)}$ and the matrices a_{ij} and S_{ij} are defined by

$$\frac{dZ_i}{ds} = \sum a_{ij} Z_j \quad \text{and} \quad S_u(s) \cdot Z_i = \sum S_{ij} Z_j.$$

Let $A_{ij} = a_{ij} + S_{ij}$ and let L_u be the linear operator

$$L_u : W^{1,2}(\mathbf{R}; \mathbf{R}^n) \longrightarrow L^2(\mathbf{R}; \mathbf{R}^n)$$

$$Y \longmapsto \frac{dY}{ds} + A(s)Y.$$

For the vector $Y(s) \in \mathbf{R}^n$, we now have the differential equation

$$L_u Y = \frac{dY}{ds} + AY = 0.$$

By our assumption on the Z_i, $a_{ij}(s)$ is zero for $s \to \pm\infty$ and when $s \to \pm\infty$, A tends to the Hessian of f at the critical point x or y, which is a symmetric matrix:

$$\lim_{s \to -\infty} A(s) = \text{Hess}_x(f) \quad \text{and} \quad \lim_{s \to +\infty} A(s) = \text{Hess}_y(f).$$

Remark 10.2.1. The space of solutions can be viewed as the tangent space to the space of trajectories $\mathcal{M}(x, y)$ at the point u.

10.2.b The Exponential Decay of the Solutions

First note that if Y is a solution of $L_u Y = 0$ in $W^{1,2}(\mathbf{R}; \mathbf{R}^n)$, then it is continuous, hence since it satisfies the differential equation, it is of class $\mathcal{C}^1$, and so on, so that the solutions in $W^{1,2}$ are $\mathcal{C}^\infty$ (elementary bootstrapping). In particular, the solutions form a finite-dimensional vector space.

Let us study the behavior at infinity that the inclusion in $W^{1,2}$ imposes on the solutions. In the neighborhood of a critical point, say x, we use a Morse chart of V. We can choose the trivialization of TV in a standard way in this chart, and the differential equation $L_u Y = 0$ can simply be written as

$$\frac{dY}{ds} = -AY,$$

where A is a constant matrix that we may, and do, assume to be diagonal, so that the system is

$$\frac{dy_i}{ds} = -\lambda_i y_i, \quad 1 \le i \le n$$

and its solutions are of the form

$$y_i(s) = y_i e^{-\lambda_i s}.$$

It is clear that for such a vector to be in $W^{1,2}(\mathbf{R}; \mathbf{R}^n)$, it must tend to 0 when $s \to -\infty$, which it can only do exponentially (and likewise at $+\infty$).

Let us give an interpretation in terms of the operator L_u of the properties of the function f and the vector field X that we have used to construct the Morse complex.

10.2.c The Fredholm Property

More precisely, we will prove the following.

Proposition 10.2.2. *If u is a trajectory of the gradient connecting two nondegenerate critical points x and y, then the operator L_u is a Fredholm operator.*

We need to prove that the image of L_u is a closed subspace of $L^2(\mathbf{R}; \mathbf{R}^n)$, and that its kernel and cokernel are finite-dimensional. As in Section 8.7.c, we want to use Proposition 8.7.4, for which we first need the following result.

Proposition 10.2.3. *For $T > 0$ sufficiently large, there exists a constant C such that for every solution of $L_u Y = 0$,*

$$\|Y\|_{W^{1,2}} \leq C\big(\|L_u Y\|_{L^2} + \|Y\|_{L^2([-T,T])}\big).$$

This will give exactly the condition of Proposition 8.7.4, because the composition

$$W^{1,2}(\mathbf{R}; \mathbf{R}^n) \subset L^2(\mathbf{R}; \mathbf{R}^n) \longrightarrow L^2([-T,T]; \mathbf{R}^n)$$

is compact. The proof of this proposition depends on the following two lemmas.

Lemma 10.2.4. *Let B be an invertible symmetric matrix. There exists a constant $C_1 > 0$ such that every $Y \in W^{1,2}(\mathbf{R}; \mathbf{R}^n)$ satisfies the inequality*

$$\|Y\|_{W^{1,2}} \leq C_1 \left\|\frac{dY}{ds} + BY\right\|_{L^2}.$$

This lemma is the analogue, in Morse theory, of Proposition 8.7.3. We apply it by using one of the symmetric matrices $\mathrm{Hess}_x(f)$, $\mathrm{Hess}_y(f)$ for B. These are invertible because the critical points x and y are nondegenerate. Since the property is clearly stable under small perturbations, we find that if $Y(s) = 0$ for $-M \leq s \leq M$ and M is sufficiently large, then

$$\|Y\|_{W^{1,2}} = \int_{-\infty}^{+\infty} \left(\|Y\|^2 + \left\|\frac{dY}{ds}\right\|^2\right) ds \leq C_2 \int_{-\infty}^{+\infty} \left\|\frac{dY}{ds} + AY\right\|^2 ds.$$

These integrals are computed over $]-\infty, -M] \cup [M, +\infty[$. As in Subsection 8.7.c, M is chosen such that $A(s)$ is close to $\mathrm{Hess}_x(f)$ for $s \leq -M$ and to $\mathrm{Hess}_y(f)$ for $s \geq M$. In particular it does not depend on Y. In the second lemma we therefore study what happens on the bounded interval $[-M, M]$.

Lemma 10.2.5. *There exists a constant $C_3 > 0$ such that*

$$\int_{-M}^{M} \left(\|Y\|^2 + \left\|\frac{dY}{ds}\right\|^2\right) ds \leq C_3 \int_{-M}^{M} \left(\|Y\|^2 + \left\|\frac{dY}{ds} + AY\right\|^2\right) ds.$$

Next, we choose a function β (still as in Section 8.7.c) with value 1 on $[-M, M]$ and 0 outside of $[-M - 1, M + 1]$. To simplify the notation, we set $T = M + 1$. From $Y = \beta Y + (1 - \beta)Y$, we deduce that

$$\|Y\|_{W^{1,2}} \leq \|\beta Y\|_{W^{1,2}} + \|(1 - \beta)Y\|_{W^{1,2}}.$$

Next, note that for every function α,

$$L_u(\alpha Y) = \frac{d\alpha}{ds} Y + \alpha L_u Y.$$

We therefore have:

- The function $(1 - \beta)Y$ is zero on $[-M, M]$, hence satisfies

$$\|(1 - \beta)Y\|_{W^{1,2}} \leq C_2 \|L_u(1 - \beta)Y\|_{L^2}$$
$$\leq C_2 \left(\left\| \frac{d(1 - \beta)}{ds} Y \right\|_{L^2} + \|(1 - \beta)L_u Y\|_{L^2} \right).$$

- To βY, which is zero outside of $[-T, T]$, we apply the inequality of Lemma 10.2.5, giving

$$\|\beta Y\|_{W^{1,2}} \leq C_3 \left(\|\beta Y\|_{L^2} + \|L_u(\beta Y)\|_{L^2} \right)$$
$$\leq C_3 \left(\|\beta Y\|_{L^2} + \left\| \frac{d\beta}{ds} Y \right\|_{L^2} + \|\beta L_u Y\|_{L^2} \right),$$

and therefore

$$\|Y\|_{W^{1,2}} \leq C_4 \left(\|\beta Y\|_{L^2} + 2 \left\| \frac{d\beta}{ds} Y \right\|_{L^2} + \|\beta L_u Y\|_{L^2} + \|(1 - \beta)L_u Y\|_{L^2} \right).$$

We now use the fact that β and $d\beta/ds$ are zero outside of $[-T, T]$, giving

$$\|\beta Y\|_{L^2} + 2 \left\| \frac{d\beta}{ds} Y \right\|_{L^2} \leq K \|Y\|_{L^2[-T,T]}$$

and likewise

$$\|\beta L_u Y\|_{L^2} + \|(1 - \beta)L_u Y\|_{L^2}$$
$$\leq \left(\int_{-\infty}^{-M} \|L_u Y\|^2 \, ds \right)^{1/2} + \left(\int_{-T}^{T} \|L_u Y\|^2 \, ds \right)^{1/2} + \left(\int_{M}^{+\infty} \|L_u Y\|^2 \, ds \right)^{1/2}$$
$$\leq 3 \left(\int_{-\infty}^{+\infty} \|L_u Y\|^2 \, ds \right)^{1/2}.$$

Summarizing, we have found that for T sufficiently large, there exists a constant C_5 such that

$$\|Y\|_{W^{1,2}} \leq C_5 \left(\|Y\|_{L^2[-T,T]} + \|L_u Y\|_{L^2} \right),$$

which we wanted to prove, since it is the statement of Proposition 10.2.3, up to the proofs of Lemmas 10.2.4 and 10.2.5, which follow.

Proof of Lemma 10.2.4. We set

$$Z = \frac{dY}{ds} + BY.$$

We want to show that

$$\|Y\|_{W^{1,2}} \leq C_1 \|Z\|_{L^2}$$

for some constant C_1. We therefore want to compare

$$\|Y\|^2_{W^{1,2}} = \int_{-\infty}^{+\infty} \left(\|Y\|^2 + \left\| \frac{dY}{ds} \right\|^2 \right) ds$$

and

$$\left\| \frac{dY}{ds} + BY \right\|^2_{L^2} = \int_{-\infty}^{+\infty} \left\| \frac{dY}{ds} + BY \right\|^2 ds$$

under the assumption that the matrix B is invertible and symmetric. We use the Fourier transformation

$$\widehat{Y}(v) = \frac{1}{\sqrt{2\pi}} \int_{-\infty}^{+\infty} e^{-ivs} Y(s) \, ds.$$

For every $v \in \mathbf{R}$,

$$\widehat{Z}(v) = (iv \cdot \mathrm{Id} + B) \cdot \widehat{Y}(v).$$

Using Plancherel's formula we have

$$\|Z\|_{L^2} = \left\| \widehat{Z} \right\|_{L^2} = \left\| (iv \cdot \mathrm{Id} + B) \cdot \widehat{Y}(v) \right\|_{L^2}.$$

Recall that B is symmetric and invertible. Let $V \in \mathbf{R}^n$. We decompose V as a sum of eigenvectors of B to get

$$|\langle (iv \cdot \mathrm{Id} + B) \cdot V, V \rangle| \geq \sqrt{v^2 + C_0^2} \, \|V\|^2,$$

where $C_0 > 0$ is the minimum of the absolute values of the eigenvalues of B. Using the Cauchy–Schwarz inequality, this implies

$$\|(iv \cdot \mathrm{Id} + B) \cdot V\| \geq \sqrt{C_0^2 + v^2} \, \|V\| \geq \sqrt{\frac{1}{C_1}(1 + v^2)} \, \|V\|,$$

where $C_1 = \max(1, 1/C_0^2)$. Setting $V = \widehat{Y}(v)$ and integrating the square of the left-hand side we obtain

$$\|Z\|^2_{L^2} = \left\| \widehat{Z} \right\|^2_{L^2} \geq \frac{1}{C_1} \int_{\mathbf{R}} \left(\left\| \widehat{Y}(v) \right\|^2 + v^2 \left\| \widehat{Y}(v) \right\|^2 \right) dv$$

$$= \frac{1}{C_1} \int_{\mathbf{R}} \left(\|Y(s)\|^2 + \left\| \frac{\partial Y}{\partial s} \right\|^2 \right) ds = \frac{1}{C_1} \|Y\|_{W^{1,2}},$$

again by Plancherel's formula. □

Proof of Lemma 10.2.5. Let us determine a lower bound for the integral

$$\int_{-M}^{M} \|L_u Y\|^2 \, ds.$$

Expanding $\|u + 2v\|^2 \geq 0$ gives the inequality

$$\|u + v\|^2 \geq \frac{1}{2} \|u\|^2 - \|v\|^2$$

and the lower bound

$$\int_{-M}^{M} \|L_u Y\|^2 \, ds = \int_{-M}^{M} \left\| \frac{dY}{ds} + AY \right\|^2 \, ds \geq \int_{-M}^{M} \left(\frac{1}{2} \left\| \frac{dY}{ds} \right\|^2 - \|AY\|^2 \right) ds$$

$$\geq \frac{1}{2} \int_{-M}^{M} \left\| \frac{dY}{ds} \right\|^2 \, ds - C \int_{-M}^{M} \|Y\|^2 \, ds,$$

and finally

$$\frac{1}{2} \int_{-M}^{M} \left\| \frac{dY}{ds} \right\|^2 \, ds \leq C \int_{-M}^{M} \|Y\|^2 \, ds + \int_{-M}^{M} \|L_u Y\|^2 \, ds,$$

which gives the desired upper bound.   □

We now know (by Proposition 8.7.4) that L_u has a finite-dimensional kernel and a closed image. In order to finish the proof that L_u is a Fredholm operator, we need to determine its cokernel.

Lemma 10.2.6. *The cokernel of u is the kernel of the operator*

$$L_u^\star : W^{1,2}(\mathbf{R}; \mathbf{R}^n) \longrightarrow L^2(\mathbf{R}; \mathbf{R}^n)$$

defined by

$$L_u^\star Z = -\frac{dZ}{ds} + A^\star Z$$

(where $A^\star$ is the transpose of A).

Proof. The cokernel of L_u is

$$\left\{ Z \in L^2(\mathbf{R}; \mathbf{R}^n) \mid \int_{-\infty}^{+\infty} \langle L_u Y, Z \rangle \, ds = 0 \text{ for every } Y \in W^{1,2}(\mathbf{R}; \mathbf{R}^n) \right\}.$$

Let $L_u^\star$ be the operator defined in the lemma. We have

$$\int_{-\infty}^{+\infty} \langle L_u(Y), Z \rangle \, ds = \int_{-\infty}^{+\infty} \left\langle \frac{dY}{ds}, Z \right\rangle \, ds + \int_{-\infty}^{+\infty} \langle AY, Z \rangle \, ds$$

$$= -\int_{-\infty}^{+\infty} \left\langle \frac{dZ}{ds}, Y \right\rangle \, ds + \int_{-\infty}^{+\infty} \langle A^\star Z, Y \rangle \, ds.$$

If $Z \in \operatorname{Coker} L_u$, then $L_u^\star Z = 0$ in the sense of distributions, hence by the definition of $L_u^\star$, dZ/ds is in L^2 and therefore $Z \in W^{1,2}$ and $Z \in \operatorname{Ker} L_u^\star$. Consequently, $\operatorname{Coker} L_u = \operatorname{Ker} L_u^\star$ (the opposite inclusion is clear). □

The kernel of $L_u^\star$ is finite-dimensional, as is that of L_u, by the same theorem on linear differential equations. The same therefore holds for the cokernel of L_u. This concludes the proof that L_u is a Fredholm operator when L_u connects two nondegenerate critical points, that is, the proof of Proposition 10.2.2.

Corollary 10.2.7. *If f is a Morse function, then for every trajectory u, the operator L_u is a Fredholm operator.* □

10.2.d Computation of the Index

Let us now compute the index of this operator.

Proposition 10.2.8. *The index of the Fredholm operator L_u is*

$$\operatorname{Ind}(x) - \operatorname{Ind}(y).$$

Proof. We have already noted that the solutions of $L_u Y = 0$ in $W^{1,2}$ tend to 0 exponentially when $s \to \pm\infty$. If σ and s are two real numbers, then let

$$\Phi_{(\sigma,s)} : T_{u(\sigma)} V \longrightarrow T_{u(s)} V$$

be the resolvent of the linear differential equation, that is, the map that sends a vector $\widetilde{Y} \in T_{u(\sigma)} V$ to the value in s of the unique solution with value $\widetilde{Y}$ at σ. Let

$$E^u(\sigma) = \{\widetilde{Y} \in T_{u(\sigma)} V \mid \lim_{s \to -\infty} \Phi_{(\sigma,s)} \widetilde{Y} = 0\}$$

and likewise

$$E^s(\sigma) = \{\widetilde{Y} \in T_{u(\sigma)} V \mid \lim_{s \to +\infty} \Phi_{(\sigma,s)} \widetilde{Y} = 0\}.$$

These spaces are the tangent spaces at $u(\sigma)$ of the unstable and stable manifolds of x and y, respectively,

$$E^u(\sigma) = T_{u(\sigma)} W^u(x) \quad \text{and} \quad E^s(\sigma) = T_{u(\sigma)} W^s(y).$$

If $\widetilde{Y} \in E^u(\sigma) \cap E^s(\sigma)$, then the solution $Y(s)$ with value $\widetilde{Y}$ at σ is in $W^{1,2}(\mathbf{R}; \mathbf{R}^n)$ and conversely, so that

$$\forall \sigma \in \mathbf{R}, \quad \operatorname{Ker} L_u \cong E^u(\sigma) \cap E^s(\sigma).$$

We thus have

$$\operatorname{Ker} L_u \cong T_{u(\sigma)} W^u(x) \cap T_{u(\sigma)} W^s(y).$$

We still need to determine the kernel of $L_u^\star$. Let

$$\Psi_{(\sigma,s)} = \Phi_{(s,\sigma)}^\star : T_{u(\sigma)} V \longrightarrow T_{u(s)} V.$$

Let us show that this map is the resolvent of $L_u^\star$. We choose a $Z_0 \in \mathbf{R}^n$ and set $Z_0(s) = \Psi_{(\sigma,s)} Z_0$. Note that since $\Psi_{(\sigma,\sigma)} = \operatorname{Id}$, we have $Z_0(\sigma) = Z_0$. We also choose a $Y_0 \in \mathbf{R}^n$. By the definition of $\Psi_{(\sigma,s)}$,

$$\langle \Psi_{(\sigma,s)} Z_0, \Phi_{(\sigma,s)} Y_0 \rangle = \langle Z_0, Y_0 \rangle.$$

Differentiating this identity with respect to s gives

$$0 = \left\langle \frac{dZ_0}{ds}, \Phi_{(\sigma,s)} Y_0 \right\rangle + \left\langle \Psi_{(\sigma,s)} Z_0, \frac{dY_0}{ds} \right\rangle.$$

Since the vector field $Y_0(s) = \Phi_{(\sigma,s)} Y_0$ is a solution of $L_u Y_0 = 0$, and therefore $Y_0(s)/ds = -A Y_0(s)$, this equality becomes

$$\left\langle \frac{dZ_0}{ds}, Y_0(s) \right\rangle - \langle Z_0(s), A Y_0(s) \rangle = 0,$$

that is,

$$\left\langle \frac{dZ_0}{ds} - A^\star Z_0(s), Y_0(s) \right\rangle = 0.$$

Since we can take any tangent vector for Y_0, we have shown that $Z_0(\sigma) = Z_0$ and $L_u^\star Z_0 = 0$, in other words, that $\Psi_{(\sigma,s)}$ is the resolvent of $L_u^\star$.

This computation also shows that if $Z(s)$ is a solution of $L_u^\star Z = 0$, then $\lim_{s \to -\infty} Z(s) = 0$ if and only if $Z(\sigma) \perp E^u(\sigma)$ and likewise $\lim_{s \to +\infty} Z(s) = 0$ if and only if $Z(\sigma) \perp E^s(\sigma)$. We have therefore shown that

$$\operatorname{Ker} L_u^\star = (T_{u(\sigma)} W^u(x) + T_{u(\sigma)} W^s(y))^\perp.$$

Since $\dim T_{u(\sigma)} W^u(x) = \operatorname{Ind}(x)$, $\dim T_{u(\sigma)} W^s(y) = n - \operatorname{Ind}(y)$, we obtain

$$\begin{aligned}
\dim \operatorname{Ker} L_u &= \dim T_{u(\sigma)} W^u(x) \cap T_{u(\sigma)} W^s(y) \\
&= \dim W^u(x) + \dim W^s(y) - \dim(T_{u(\sigma)} W^u(x) + T_{u(\sigma)} W^s(y)), \\
\dim \operatorname{Ker} L_u^\star &= \dim(T_{u(\sigma)} W^u(x) + T_{u(\sigma)} W^s(y))^\perp \\
&= n - \dim(T_{u(\sigma)} W^u(x) + T_{u(\sigma)} W^s(y)), \\
\operatorname{Ind}(L_u) &= \dim W^u(x) + \dim W^s(y) - n \\
&= \operatorname{Ind}(x) + n - \operatorname{Ind}(y) - n \\
&= \operatorname{Ind}(x) - \operatorname{Ind}(y),
\end{aligned}$$

which we wanted to prove.   □

Another way to compute the index of this operator can be found in Exercise 46.

10.2.e The Smale Condition

We will now prove that the vector field X satisfies the Smale condition if and only if all L_u are surjective, in other words, Theorem 10.1.5.

Remark 10.2.9. If X is the gradient of f for a metric g, then this condition of course concerns that metric.

Proof of Theorem 10.1.5. This is a consequence of the computation given above. Saying that L_u is surjective is saying that its cokernel is reduced to 0, in other words, that L_u^* is injective, or that

$$T_{u(\sigma)}W^u(x) + T_{u(\sigma)}W^s(y) = T_{u(\sigma)}V.$$

The latter is the transversality condition of the stable and unstable manifolds, which we want for all critical points x and y.									□

We could also have worked out the theory of the Morse complex in this setting (see [65, 68]).

10.3 Proof of Theorem 10.1.2 (Regularity)

The Hamiltonian H is now fixed and we consider two critical points x and y. Let $\mathcal{Z}(x, y, H)$ be defined as

$$\{(u, J) \mid J \in \mathcal{J}_c(\omega) \text{ and } u \text{ is a trajectory of } -JX_H \text{ connecting } x \text{ to } y\}.$$

10.3.a Infinitesimal Variations of the Almost Complex Structure

The space $\mathcal{J}_c(\omega)$ of almost complex structures calibrated by ω is a subset of the vector space of sections of the fiber bundle of endomorphisms of TW. We have already noted (Proposition 5.5.7) that the tangent space is

$$T_J\mathcal{J}_c(\omega) = \{S \in \text{End}(TW) \mid JS + SJ = 0 \text{ and } \omega(S\xi, \eta) + \omega(\xi, S\eta) = 0\}.$$

We fix such an S and set $J_t = J \exp(-tJS)$.

Lemma 10.3.1. *For t sufficiently small, the endomorphism J_t is an almost complex structure calibrated by ω.*

Proof. First of all, J_t is an almost complex structure: since J is "anticommutative" with S, $J_t = \exp(tJS)J$ and therefore

$$J_t^2 = \exp(tJS)JJ\exp(-tJS) = J^2 = -\mathrm{Id}.$$

Next, J_t is an isometry of ω because

$$
\begin{aligned}
\frac{d}{dt}\omega(J_t\xi, J_t\eta) &= \frac{d}{dt}\omega(\exp(-tJS)\xi, \exp(-tJS)\eta)\\
&= \omega(-JS\exp(-tJS)\xi, \exp(-tJS)\eta)\\
&\quad + \omega(\exp(-tJS)\xi, -JS\exp(-tJS)\eta)\\
&= \omega(SJ\exp(-tJS)\xi, \exp(-tJS)\eta)\\
&\quad + \omega(\exp(-tJS)\xi, SJ\exp(-tJS)\eta)\\
&= \omega(SJ\Xi, H) + \omega(\Xi, SJH) = 0
\end{aligned}
$$

(where we have set $\Xi = \exp(-tJS)\xi$ and $H = \exp(-tJS)\eta$ (uppercase η)), hence $\omega(J_t\xi, J_t\eta)$ is constant and equal to $\omega(J\xi, J\eta) = \omega(\xi, \eta)$. This computation also gives

$$\omega(J_t\xi, \eta) = \omega(J_t^2\xi, J_t\eta) = -\omega(\xi, J_t\eta) = \omega(J_t\eta, \xi),$$

so that $\omega(\cdot, J_t\cdot)$ is a symmetric bilinear form. Next, we have

$$\omega(\xi, J_t\eta) = \omega(\xi, J\eta) + O(t),$$

so that $\omega(\cdot, J_t\cdot)$ is indeed a Riemannian metric, at least for t sufficiently small. $\square$

10.3.b Proof of Theorem 10.1.2

As in Section 8.3, we use the $\mathcal{C}_\varepsilon^\infty$ norm on this space of perturbations of J,

$$\|S\|_\varepsilon = \sum_{k=0}^\infty \varepsilon_k \|S\|_{\mathcal{C}^k}$$

(for a sufficiently decreasing sequence $\varepsilon = (\varepsilon_k)$). As in Section 8.3, we have the following result.

Proposition 10.3.2. *For a well-chosen sequence ε, the space $\mathcal{C}_\varepsilon^\infty(J)$ of sections of $\mathrm{End}(TW)$ such that*

$$
\begin{cases}
JS + SJ = 0\\
\omega(S\xi, \eta) + \omega(\xi, S\eta) = 0
\end{cases}
\qquad \text{and} \quad \|S\|_\varepsilon < +\infty
$$

is a separable Banach space that is dense in the space of L^2 sections of the fiber bundle $T\mathcal{J}_c(\omega)$. □

We fix an almost complex structure $J_0 \in \mathcal{J}_c(\omega)$ and a real number $\delta > 0$. We define the image of the unit ball:

$$\mathcal{J}_0(\delta) = \{J_0 \exp(-J_0 S) \mid S \in \mathcal{C}_\varepsilon^\infty(J_0) \text{ and } \|S\|_\varepsilon < \delta\}$$

and

$$\mathcal{Z}_0(x, y) = \{(u, J) \in \mathcal{Z}(x, y, H) \mid J \in \mathcal{J}_0(\delta)\}$$

(this space depends on the choice of the radius δ, which we have left out to simplify the notation).

Proposition 10.3.3. *The subspace $\mathcal{Z}_0(x, y)$ is a Banach manifold.*

The remainder of this section is devoted to the proof of this proposition. As in Section 8.5, we will show that $\mathcal{Z}_0$ is a set of zeros of a section of a fiber bundle. The analysis is easier here because we only have one variable and can stay in L^2 and $W^{1,2}$. We therefore consider

$$\mathcal{P}^{1,2}(x, y) = \{u \in W^{1,2}(\mathbf{R}; W) \mid \lim_{s \to -\infty} u(s) = x \text{ and } \lim_{s \to +\infty} u(s) = y\}$$

(the limit has a sense because the elements of $W^{1,2}$ are continuous maps) and

$$\mathcal{E} = \{(u, J, Y) \mid u \in \mathcal{P}^{1,2}(x, y), J \in \mathcal{J}_0(\delta), Y \text{ is a vector field } L^2 \text{ along } u\},$$

a fiber bundle on $\mathcal{P}^{1,2}(x, y) \times \mathcal{J}_0(\delta)$ whose fiber at (u, J) is the space of L^2 vector fields along u. Using a trivialization Z_i of TW (like the one we fixed in Chapter 8), we see that this space is none other than $L^2(\mathbf{R}; \mathbf{R}^{2n})$. The map

$$\mathcal{G} : \mathcal{P}^{1,2}(x, y) \times \mathcal{J}_0(\delta) \longrightarrow \mathcal{E}$$
$$(u, J) \longmapsto \left(u, \frac{du}{ds} + \operatorname{grad}_u H\right) = \left(u, \frac{du}{ds} - JX_H\right)$$

is a section of $\mathcal{E}$ that is zero along $\mathcal{Z}_0(x, y)$. Let us show that it is transversal to the zero section. We need to compute its differential

$$(d\mathcal{G})_{(u, J_0)} : W^{1,2}(\mathbf{R}; \mathbf{R}^{2n}) \times \mathcal{J}_0(\delta) \longrightarrow L^2(\mathbf{R}; \mathbf{R}^{2n}).$$

We have already linearized $\mathcal{G}$ with a constant metric (hence with a constant J) in Section 10.2.a and $\mathcal{F}$ (with the additional variable t) in Section 8.4. After taking the composition with the projection onto the fiber, the same computation gives

$$\Gamma = \pi \circ (d\mathcal{G})_{(u,J_0)}(Y,S) = \left(\frac{dY}{ds} - J_0[(X_H)_u, Y] \right) - S(X_H)_u$$
$$= L_u(Y) - S(X_H)_u,$$

where $L_u : W^{1,2}(\mathbf{R}; \mathbf{R}^{2n}) \to L^2(\mathbf{R}; \mathbf{R}^{2n})$ is the operator defined in Section 10.2.a. We have said that L_u is a Fredholm operator (because H is a Morse function), hence its image is closed and its codimension is finite. The same reasoning as in the proof of Lemma 8.5.1 tells us that the image of Γ is a finite-dimensional closed subspace. To show the surjectivity of Γ at the points of $\mathcal{Z}_0$, it suffices to show the following result (the dual of L^2 is L^2).

Lemma 10.3.4. *The orthogonal of the image of Γ in $L^2(\mathbf{R}; \mathbf{R}^{2n})$ is reduced to 0.*

Proof. Let Z be an element of the orthogonal, that is, such that for all Y and S, we have

$$\int_{-\infty}^{+\infty} \langle Z(s), \Gamma(Y,S) \rangle \, ds = 0,$$

or equivalently

$$\int_{-\infty}^{+\infty} \left\langle Z(s), \frac{dY}{ds} - J_0[X_H, Y] \right\rangle ds - \int_{-\infty}^{+\infty} \langle Z(s), S(X_H) \rangle \, ds = 0$$

for every Y and S; that is,

$$\int_{-\infty}^{+\infty} \left\langle Z(s), \frac{dY}{ds} - J_0[X_H, Y] \right\rangle ds = 0 \quad \text{for every field } Y \text{ along } u$$

and

$$\int_{-\infty}^{+\infty} \langle Z(s), S(X_H) \rangle \, ds = 0 \quad \text{for every section } S.$$

The first of these equalities, $\langle Z, L_u(Y) \rangle = 0$, reduces to $\langle L_u^\star Z, Y \rangle = 0$ for every Y, that is, $L_u^\star Z = 0$, a differential equation of the form

$$-\frac{dZ}{ds} + B(s)Z = 0.$$

This guarantees that the solution Z, which we initially assume to be only in L^2, is in $W^{1,2}$ and is therefore $\mathcal{C}^\infty$.

The second equality is

$$\langle Z, S(X_H) \rangle = \left\langle Z, -SJ\frac{du}{ds} \right\rangle = -\left\langle SZ, J\frac{du}{ds} \right\rangle$$

because S is symmetric. We want to show that Z is zero. We suppose that this is not the case and choose an s_0 such that $Z(s_0) \neq 0$. We use a unitary trivialization in the neighborhood of $x_0 = u(s_0) \in W$ in which J_0 is standard. Then S is simply a symmetric matrix (that depends on the chosen point) such that $S = J_0 S J_0$. We consider the vector $J_0(du/ds)(s_0)$ and construct a matrix S_0 such that

$$\left\langle Z(s_0), S_0 J_0 \frac{du}{ds}(s_0) \right\rangle \neq 0.$$

For the existence of S_0, we use the following easy result from linear algebra.

Lemma 10.3.5. *Let U and V be two nonzero vectors in $\mathbf{C}^n = \mathbf{R}^{2n}$. There exists a real symmetric matrix S, that is anti-$\mathbf{C}$-linear and such that the Euclidean inner product $\langle U, SV \rangle$ is nonzero.*

Admitting this lemma, there exists a $\mathcal{C}_\varepsilon^\infty$ map with support in the neighborhood of x_0 that takes on the value S_0 at x_0. This gives the desired contradiction. $\square$

For the sake of completeness, here is a proof of Lemma 10.3.5. The complex vector subspace generated by the two vectors U and V is of dimension (at most) 2, it therefore suffices to prove this lemma in $\mathbf{C}^2$. Since U is nonzero, we may, and do, assume that it is the first vector of a basis that we will now use. The matrix S must be of the form

$$S = \begin{pmatrix} A & B \\ -B & A \end{pmatrix}, \quad \text{where } A \text{ is symmetric and } B \text{ is antisymmetric.}$$

There are therefore no constraints on the first column of S, for which we can choose the vector V. But then $S(U) = V$ and

$$\langle U, SV \rangle = \langle SU, V \rangle = \langle V, V \rangle = \|V\|^2 \neq 0,$$

which we wanted to prove. $\square$

This implies Proposition 10.3.3 since Γ admits a continuous right inverse according to Lemma 8.5.6.

To conclude the proof of Theorem 10.1.2, we consider the projection

$$\pi : \mathcal{Z}_0(x, y) \longrightarrow \mathcal{J}_0(\delta)$$

defined by $\pi(u, J) = J$. It is easy to check that π is a Fredholm map (as in Subsection 8.5.c). The Sard–Smale theorem (Theorem 8.5.7) states the existence of a dense open subset $\mathcal{J}_{\text{reg}} \subset \mathcal{J}_0(\delta)$ consisting of regular values of π.

Lemma 10.3.6. *If $J \in \mathcal{J}_{\mathrm{reg}}$, then for every trajectory u of the vector field $-JX_H$ connecting x to y, the linearized operator L_u is surjective.*

Proof. If $L_u : W^{1,2}(\mathbf{R}; \mathbf{R}^{2n}) \to L^2(\mathbf{R}; \mathbf{R}^{2n})$ is not surjective, then there exists a nonzero $Z \in L^2(\mathbf{R}; \mathbf{R}^{2n})$ that is orthogonal to the image of L_u. On the other hand, the assumption ensures that $(d\pi)_{(u,J)}$ is surjective. The proof of Proposition 10.3.2 gives a description of the tangent space $T_{(u,J)}\mathcal{Z}_0(x,y)$ as the kernel of Γ; that is,

$$T_{(u,J)}\mathcal{Z}_0(x,y)$$
$$= \left\{ (Y,S) \in W^{1,2}(\mathbf{R}; \mathbf{R}^{2n}) \times T_J\mathcal{J}_0(\delta) \mid L_u(Y) - S(X_H)_u = 0 \right\}.$$

Since $\langle L_u Y, Z \rangle = 0$ for every $Y \in W^{1,2}(\mathbf{R}; \mathbf{R}^{2n})$, the surjectivity of $(d\pi)_{(u,J)}$ implies that

$$\text{for every } S \in T_J\mathcal{J}_0(\delta), \quad \langle S(X_H)_u, Z \rangle = 0.$$

In the proof of Lemma 10.3.4, we saw that this implies that $Z = 0$, which both contradicts the assumption and proves the lemma. $\square$

By taking the intersection of the different sets $\mathcal{J}_{\mathrm{reg}}$ obtained for the different pairs of critical points of H, we obtain the set $\mathcal{J}_{\mathrm{reg}}(H)$ announced in the statement of Theorem 10.1.2 (we also use Theorem 10.1.5). $\square$

10.4 The Morse and Floer Trajectories Coincide

10.4.a The Trajectories that Do Not Depend on t Are Regular

We will now show Proposition 10.1.7 (and Corollary 10.1.8). We clearly have $\operatorname{Ker} L_u \subset \operatorname{Ker}(d\mathcal{F})_u$: if $Y(s)$ satisfies

$$\frac{dY}{ds} + S(s)Y = 0,$$

then it also satisfies

$$\frac{\partial Y}{\partial s} + J\frac{\partial Y}{\partial t} + S(s)Y = 0.$$

Let us show the opposite inclusion. We set $L = (d\mathcal{F})_u$ and $L_0 = L_u$. Let $Y \in \operatorname{Ker} L$. We have

$$\int_0^1 J\frac{\partial Y}{\partial t}\, dt = 0, \quad \text{hence} \quad \int_0^1 Y(s,t)\, dt \in \operatorname{Ker} L_0.$$

We may, and do, therefore assume that $\int_0^1 Y(s,t)\, dt = 0$. We use an elementary lemma on functions in real variables (whose proof is given later).

Lemma 10.4.1. *Let f be a differentiable map on $[0,1]$ with mean value zero on this interval. Then for every $p \geq 1$, we have*

$$\int_0^1 \|f(t)\|^p \, dt \leq \int_0^1 \|f'(t)\|^p \, dt.$$

We apply this to $f(t) = Y(s,t)$ and $p = 2$. We then integrate with respect to s:

$$\int_{-\infty}^{+\infty} \int_0^1 \|Y(s,t)\|^2 \, dt \, ds \leq \int_{-\infty}^{+\infty} \int_0^1 \left\|\frac{\partial Y}{\partial t}(s,t)\right\|^2 \, dt \, ds.$$

For the L^2 norm, we have

$$\begin{aligned}
\left\|\frac{\partial Y}{\partial s}\right\|_{L^2}^2 + \left\|\frac{\partial Y}{\partial t}\right\|_{L^2}^2 &= \left\langle \frac{\partial Y}{\partial s}, \frac{\partial Y}{\partial s} \right\rangle + \left\langle \frac{\partial Y}{\partial t}, \frac{\partial Y}{\partial t} \right\rangle \\
&= -\langle Y, \Delta Y \rangle \\
&= -\left\langle Y, \left(\frac{\partial}{\partial s} - J\frac{\partial}{\partial t}\right)\left(\frac{\partial}{\partial s} + J\frac{\partial}{\partial t}\right)Y \right\rangle \\
&= \left\|\frac{\partial Y}{\partial s} + J\frac{\partial Y}{\partial t}\right\|_{L^2}^2 \\
&= \|S(s)Y\|_{L^2}^2 \\
&\leq \sup_s \|S(s)\|^2 \, \|Y\|_{L^2}^2
\end{aligned}$$

(using the operator norm of $S(s)$). Consequently, by our lemma, we find

$$\|Y\|_{L^2}^2 \leq \|\operatorname{grad} Y\|_{L^2}^2 \leq \sup_s \|S(s)\|^2 \, \|Y\|_{L^2}^2 .$$

The fact that H is "$\mathcal{C}^2$-small" implies that $\sup_s \|S(s)\|$ is sufficiently small, and therefore that $Y = 0$. $\qquad\square$

Proof of Lemma 10.4.1. For $t, t_1 \in [0,1]$, we write

$$f(t_1) - f(t) = \int_t^{t_1} f'(\tau) \, d\tau.$$

We then integrate this relation with respect to t between 0 and 1,

$$f(t_1) = \int_0^1 \left(\int_t^{t_1} f'(\tau) \, d\tau\right) dt,$$

from which we deduce that

$$\int_0^1 \|f(t_1)\|^p \, dt_1 \leq \int_0^1 \left(\int_0^1 \int_t^{t_1} \|f'(\tau)\|^p \, d\tau \, dt\right) dt_1 \leq \int_0^1 \|f'(\tau)\|^p \, d\tau,$$

which we wanted to prove. $\qquad\square$

10.4.b The Trajectories Are Independent of t

We will now show that the trajectories of H/k that count for the Floer complex are exactly those that count for the Morse complex, in other words, Proposition 10.1.9.

Proof of Proposition 10.1.9. We assume that it is not true. This means that there exist a sequence (n_k) that tends to infinity and a solution u_{n_k} (that effectively depends on t) that we can assume to connect the critical points x and y, of the Floer equation

$$\frac{\partial u}{\partial s} + J \frac{\partial u}{\partial t} + \frac{1}{n_k} \operatorname{grad} H = 0.$$

Let

$$v_{n_k}(s, t) = u_{n_k}(n_k s, n_k t).$$

This is a solution of the Floer equation for the original Hamiltonian H, which is periodic of period $1/n_k$. We may therefore consider it of period 1, so that $v_{n_k} \in \mathcal{M}(x, y, H)$.

First consider the case where the difference of the indices is 1,

$$\operatorname{Ind}(x) - \operatorname{Ind}(y) = 1 = \mu(x) - \mu(y).$$

By the convergence theorem toward broken trajectories (Theorem 9.1.7), after extracting a subsequence, if necessary, we may, and do, assume that the sequence (v_{n_k}) tends to a limit $v \in \mathcal{M}(x, y, H)$. If we show that v does not depend on t, then since $(d\mathcal{F})_v$ is surjective (by Corollary 10.1.8), v must be in a component of $\mathcal{M}(x, y, H)$ of dimension 1, that is, must be an isolated point of $\mathcal{L}(x, y)$. For k sufficiently large, we would then have

$$v_{n_k}(s, t) = v(s + \sigma_k, t) = v(s + \sigma_k),$$

and v_{n_k} would not depend on t, a contradiction with the assumption we made.

It therefore suffices to prove that the limit v does not depend on t. We use the fact that v is the limit of a sequence whose period tends to 0. Let $r \in \mathbf{R}$. We fix an $s \in \mathbf{R}$ and a $t \in [0, 1]$. Since v_{n_k} is periodic of period $1/n_k$, we have

$$v_{n_k}(s, t) = v_{n_k}\left(s, t + \frac{[rn_k]}{n_k}\right)$$

(where $[rn_k]$ denotes the integral part of rn_k). When k tends to infinity, $[rn_k]/n_k$ tends to r, so that the left-hand side tends to $v(s, t)$ while the right-hand side tends to $v(s, t + r)$. Consequently, for every r,

$$v(s, t) = v(s, t + r),$$

which we wanted to prove.

We now assume that the difference of the indices is 2,

$$\text{Ind}(x) - \text{Ind}(y) = 2 = \mu(x) - \mu(y).$$

In this case, Theorem 9.1.7 states that a subsequence of $(v_{n_k}(s + s_k, t))$ tends either to a limit $v \in \mathcal{M}(x, y, H)$ or to a broken trajectory

$$(v, w) \in \mathcal{M}(x, z) \times \mathcal{M}(z, y).$$

In the first case, we prove as above that v is independent of t. Once again, $(d\mathcal{F})_v$ is surjective by Corollary 10.1.8. As in the proof of Lemma 8.5.9, we therefore find that $\mathcal{M}(x, y, H)$ is a submanifold of $\mathcal{Z}(x, y, J)$ of dimension 2 in a neighborhood of (v, H) (we use the notation

$$\mathcal{Z}(x, y, J) = \{(v, H + h) \mid h \in \mathcal{C}_\varepsilon^\infty(H), \, v \in \mathcal{M}(x, y, J, H + h)\}$$

of Chapter 8). Moreover, since the gradient $-JX_H$ of H has the Smale property, its trajectories that connect x to y form a manifold of dimension 2. But these trajectories are also in $\mathcal{M}(x, y, H)$, so that we obtain a parametrization of this submanifold in the neighborhood of v, by trajectories that do not depend on t. Next, since $v_{n_k}(s + s_k, t) \in \mathcal{M}(x, y, H)$, and since this sequence tends to v, it follows that $v_{n_k}(s + s_k, t)$ is independent of t for k sufficiently large, a contradiction.

We are left with the case where $\lim v_{n_k} = (v, w)$, that is, where there exist sequences (s_k^1) and (s_k^2) such that

$$\lim_{k \to +\infty} v_{n_k}(s + s_k^1, t) = v(s, t) \quad \text{and} \quad \lim_{k \to +\infty} v_{n_k}(s + s_k^2, t) = w(s, t).$$

As above, we prove that v and w do not depend on t. By Corollary 10.1.8, the two operators $(d\mathcal{F})_v$ and $(d\mathcal{F})_w$ are surjective. We can then apply the gluing theorem (Theorem 9.2.3). From this we deduce the existence of an embedding

$$\widehat{\psi} : [\rho_0, +\infty[\longrightarrow \mathcal{L}(x, y)$$

such that

$$\lim_{\rho \to +\infty} \widehat{\psi}(\rho) = (\widehat{v}, \widehat{w}) \in \mathcal{L}(x, z) \times \mathcal{L}(z, y).$$

On the other hand, v and w are also (Morse) trajectories of the Smale field $-JX_H$. In this setting, the gluing theorem (that is, Theorem 3.2.7) states that the broken trajectory $(\widehat{u}, \widehat{v})$ is a boundary point of a manifold of dimension 1 consisting of Morse trajectories that connect x to y. But these are also Floer trajectories, so that we have a map

$$\varphi : [\rho_0, +\infty[\longrightarrow \mathcal{M}(x, y, H)$$

such that

$$\widehat{\varphi} : [\rho_0, +\infty[\longrightarrow \mathcal{L}(x, y)$$

is an embedding. In addition, when ρ tends to $+\infty$, $\widehat{\varphi}(\rho)$ tends to $(\widehat{v}, \widehat{w})$ in the sense of the convergence toward broken orbits in Morse theory (which is defined in Section 3.2.a). In particular, this means that

$$\lim_{\rho \to +\infty} \varphi(\rho)(s_\rho^+) = v(s^+),$$

where s_{ρ^+} and s^+ denote the points where the trajectories $\varphi(\rho)$ and v, respectively, exit a (fixed) Morse neighborhood of x. This implies that for the $\mathcal{C}_{\text{loc}}^\infty$ topology,

$$\lim_{\rho \to +\infty} \varphi(\rho)(s + s_\rho^+) = v(s + s^+)$$

(to see this, it suffices to write

$$\varphi(\rho)(s + s_\rho^+) = \Phi_s(\varphi(\rho)(s_\rho^+)) \quad \text{and} \quad v(s + s^+) = \Phi_s(v(s^+)),$$

where Φ_s is the flow of $-JX_H$).

The same reasoning applies to w. We have thus obtained that

$$\lim_{\rho \to +\infty} \widehat{\varphi}(\rho) = (\widehat{v}, \widehat{w})$$

in the sense of the convergence toward broken orbits in Floer theory (which is defined by Theorem 9.1.7).

In summary, we have three convergences toward $(\widehat{v}, \widehat{w})$ (see Figure 10.1):

- The convergence of (v_{n_k}) we assumed for k tending to infinity
- The convergence of $\widehat{\psi}(\rho)$ for $\rho \to +\infty$ given by the "Floer" gluing
- The convergence of $\widehat{\varphi}(\rho)$ for $\rho \to +\infty$ given by the "Morse" gluing.

We now apply the "uniqueness" part of the gluing theorem (Theorem 9.2.3). It implies that for k sufficiently large, (v_{n_k}) is in the image of $\widehat{\psi}$. The same uniqueness argument also implies that for ρ sufficiently large, say $\rho \geq \rho_1$, $\widehat{\varphi}(\rho) \in \operatorname{Im} \widehat{\psi}$. Moreover, $\widehat{\varphi}([\rho_1, +\infty[)$ is an interval in the manifold $\mathcal{L}(x, y)$,

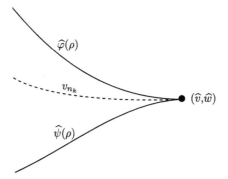

Fig. 10.1

which is of dimension 1. Since

$$\lim_{\rho \to +\infty} \widehat{\varphi}(\rho) = \lim_{\rho \to +\infty} \widehat{\psi}(\rho) = (\widehat{v}, \widehat{w}) \notin \mathcal{L}(x, y),$$

this means that $\widehat{\psi}(\rho) \in \operatorname{Im} \widehat{\varphi}$ for ρ sufficiently large. In particular, $\widehat{v}_{n_k} \in \operatorname{Im} \widehat{\varphi}$ for k sufficiently large, which contradicts the fact that v_{n_k} does not depend on t. □

We have now shown that all Floer solutions connecting two consecutive critical points are Morse trajectories and that $(d\mathcal{F})_v$ is surjective along these trajectories. We therefore have the desired equality of the complexes.

Chapter 11
Floer Homology: Invariance

We have just defined the Floer homology $HF_\star(H, J)$ as the homology of the complex $CF_\star(H, J)$. The object of this chapter is to show that the homology $HF_\star(H, J)$ does not depend on the chosen regular pair $(H, J) \in (\mathcal{H} \times \mathcal{J})_{\mathrm{reg}}$ (in the sense of Section 8.1).

To prove this we will use a method analogous to the one that allowed us to show the invariance of Morse homology in Section 3.4. We will proceed as follows: let (H^a, J^a) and (H^b, J^b) be two pairs in $(\mathcal{H} \times \mathcal{J})_{\mathrm{reg}}$. We consider a smooth homotopy $\Gamma = (H, J)$ that connects (H^a, J^a) to (H^b, J^b); more precisely,

$$H : \mathbf{R} \times S^1 \times W \longrightarrow \mathbf{R} \quad \text{and} \quad J : \mathbf{R} \longrightarrow \mathrm{End}(TW)$$

with $J(s) \in \mathcal{J}$ for every s and

$$\begin{cases} H(s, \cdot, \cdot) = H^a & \text{if } s \leq -R \\ H(s, \cdot, \cdot) = H^b & \text{if } s \geq R, \end{cases} \quad \text{and} \quad \begin{cases} J(s) = J^a & \text{if } s \leq -R \\ J(s) = J^b & \text{if } s \geq R. \end{cases}$$

Here R is a constant (that will not necessarily be the same for all homotopies). The existence of such homotopies follows from the fact that $\mathcal{J}$ is contractible (Proposition 5.5.6).

The proof is carried out in two steps:

(1) Starting from a homotopy Γ, we define (in Sections 11.1 and 11.2) a morphism of complexes

$$\Phi^\Gamma : CF_\star(H^a, J^a) \longrightarrow CF_\star(H^b, J^b)$$

and we verify that for the stationary homotopy Γ connecting (H^a, J^a) to itself, this morphism Φ^Γ is the identity (Proposition 11.1.14).

M. Audin, M. Damian, *Morse Theory and Floer Homology*, Universitext, DOI 10.1007/978-1-4471-5496-9_11, © Springer-Verlag London 2014

(2) If (H^a, J^a), (H^b, J^b) and (H^c, J^c) are pairs in $(\mathcal{H} \times \mathcal{J})_{\mathrm{reg}}$ and if Γ, Γ' and Γ'' are homotopies connecting (H^a, J^a) to (H^c, J^c), (H^a, J^a) to (H^b, J^b) and (H^b, J^b) to (H^c, J^c), respectively, then we prove that the morphisms

$$\Phi^{\Gamma''} \circ \Phi^{\Gamma'} \quad \text{and} \quad \Phi^{\Gamma} : CF_\star(H^a, J^a) \longrightarrow CF_\star(H^c, J^c)$$

are homotopic and in particular induce the same morphism at the homology level. This second step in turn has two substeps:

(a) We first prove that two homotopies Γ_1 and Γ_2 define homotopic morphisms Φ^{Γ_1} and Φ^{Γ_2} (Proposition 11.2.8, proved in Sections 11.3 and 11.4).

(b) We then prove the existence of a homotopy Γ for which the morphisms of complexes $\Phi^{\Gamma''} \circ \Phi^{\Gamma'}$ and Φ^{Γ} coincide (Proposition 11.2.9, proved in Section 11.5).

As in Section 3.4, we then deduce the invariance of the Floer homology by considering the special case where $(H^a, J^a) = (H^c, J^c)$ and $\Gamma = \mathrm{Id}$. It is clear that $\Phi^{\Gamma'}$ and $\Phi^{\Gamma''}$ then induce isomorphisms that are each other's inverses at the homology level.

11.1 The Morphism Φ^{Γ}

11.1.a The Floer Equation with Parameters

Let $\Gamma(s) = (H_{s,t}, J_s)$ and consider the equation

$$\frac{\partial u}{\partial s} + J_s(u)\frac{\partial u}{\partial t} + \mathrm{grad}_u H_{s,t} = 0$$

that can also be written as

$$\frac{\partial u}{\partial s} + J_s(u)\left(\frac{\partial u}{\partial t} - X_{s,t}(u)\right) = 0,$$

where $X_{s,t}$ is the symplectic dual of $dH_{s,t}$. If u is a solution, then we define its energy to be

$$E(u) = \int_{-\infty}^{+\infty} \int_{S^1} \left\|\frac{\partial u}{\partial s}\right\|^2 dt\, ds.$$

The norm we use is the one associated with the metric $\omega(\cdot, J_s \cdot)$—it therefore depends on s.

Consider the space

$$\mathcal{M}^\Gamma = \{u : \mathbf{R} \times S^1 \to W \mid u \text{ is a contractible solution and } E(u) < +\infty\}.$$

Recall that the homotopy Γ has been defined to be stationary for $|s| \geq R$. This allows us to give proofs that are more or less analogous to the following versions of the statements of Chapter 6 with parameters.

We first give a version of Theorem 6.5.6 with parameters.

Theorem 11.1.1. *Let X^a and X^b be the symplectic duals of the forms dH^a and dH^b, respectively. Suppose that all 1-periodic trajectories of X^a and X^b are nondegenerate. Then for every $u \in \mathcal{M}^\Gamma$, there exist a critical point x of $\mathcal{A}_{H^a}$ and a critical point y of $\mathcal{A}_{H^b}$ such that*

$$\lim_{s \to -\infty} u(s, \cdot) = x(\cdot) \quad and \quad \lim_{s \to +\infty} u(s, \cdot) = y(\cdot).$$

Let

$$\mathcal{M}^\Gamma(x, y) = \{u \in \mathcal{M}^\Gamma \mid \lim_{s \to -\infty} u(s) = x \text{ and } \lim_{s \to +\infty} u(s) = y\}.$$

An element of $\mathcal{M}^\Gamma(x, y)$ is therefore a trajectory that departs from x along a trajectory of the gradient of $\mathcal{A}_{H^a}$ for $s \leq -R$ and that arrives at y along a trajectory of the gradient of $\mathcal{A}_{H^b}$ for $s \geq R$. Every solution of finite energy therefore connects two critical points of $\mathcal{A}_{H^a}$ and $\mathcal{A}_{H^b}$, respectively.

For $s \leq -R$ or $s \geq R$, our equation coincides with the Floer equation (without parameters) for (H^a, J^a) or (H^b, J^b), respectively. Consequently, Theorem 11.1.1 can be proved in a manner similar to Theorem 6.5.6: we first copy the proof of Proposition 6.5.7 to show that for every $u \in \mathcal{M}^\Gamma$, there exist two critical points $x \in \mathrm{Crit}(\mathcal{A}_{H^a})$ and $y \in \mathrm{Crit}(\mathcal{A}_{H^b})$ such that

$$\lim_{s \to -\infty} \mathcal{A}_{H^a}(u(s)) = \mathcal{A}_{H^a}(x) \quad and \quad \lim_{s \to +\infty} \mathcal{A}_{H^b}(u(s)) = \mathcal{A}_{H^b}(y).$$

We then prove the following result.

Proposition 11.1.2. *There exists a constant k such that for every $u \in \mathcal{M}^\Gamma$ satisfying the conditions above for critical points $x \in \mathrm{Crit}(\mathcal{A}_{H^a})$ and $y \in \mathrm{Crit}(\mathcal{A}_{H^b})$, we have*

$$E(u) \leq \mathcal{A}_{H^a}(x) - \mathcal{A}_{H^b}(y) + k.$$

Proof. We have

$$
\begin{aligned}
E(u) &= \int_{\mathbf{R} \times S^1} \left\| \frac{\partial u}{\partial s} \right\|^2 ds\, dt \\
&= \int_{\mathbf{R} \times S^1} \left\langle \frac{\partial u}{\partial s}, \frac{\partial u}{\partial s} \right\rangle ds\, dt \\
&= \int_{\mathbf{R} \times S^1} \omega\left(\frac{\partial u}{\partial s}, J_s \frac{\partial u}{\partial s} \right) ds\, dt \\
&= \int_{\mathbf{R} \times S^1} \omega\left(\frac{\partial u}{\partial s}, \frac{\partial u}{\partial t} - X_{t,s} \right) ds\, dt \\
&= \int_{\mathbf{R} \times S^1} u^\star \omega - dH_{t,s}\left(\frac{\partial u}{\partial s} \right) ds\, dt.
\end{aligned}
$$

Because of the contractibility of x, we can now choose an extension of u, that is, a map

$$
\tilde{u} : \mathbf{R} \times D^2 \longrightarrow W \quad \text{such that } \tilde{u}|_{\partial D^2} = u.
$$

We determine the energy of u using this extension:

$$
\begin{aligned}
E(u) &= \lim_{\sigma \to +\infty} \int_{[-\sigma,\sigma] \times S^1} u^\star \omega - dH_{s,t}\left(\frac{\partial u}{\partial s} \right) ds\, dt \\
&= \lim_{\sigma \to +\infty} \left(\int_{[-\sigma,\sigma] \times S^1} u^\star \omega + \int_{[-\sigma,\sigma] \times S^1} -\frac{\partial}{\partial s} H_{s,t}(u) + \frac{\partial H}{\partial s}(u)\, ds\, dt \right) \\
&= \lim_{\sigma \to +\infty} \left(\int_{D^2} \tilde{u}_\sigma^\star \omega - \int_{D^2} \tilde{u}_{-\sigma}^\star \omega - \int_{S^1} H_t^b(u_\sigma)\, dt + \int_{S^1} H_t^a(u_{-\sigma})\, dt \right) \\
&\quad + \int_{[-R,R] \times S^1} \frac{\partial H}{\partial s}(u)\, ds\, dt,
\end{aligned}
$$

where

$$
u_{\pm \sigma}(t) = u(\pm \sigma, t) \text{ for } t \in S^1 \quad \text{and} \quad \tilde{u}_{\pm \sigma}(z) = \tilde{u}(\pm \sigma, z) \text{ for } z \in D^2.
$$

We have used the fact that the homotopy $H_{s,t}$ is stationary for $|s| \geq R$. It follows that

$$
\begin{aligned}
E(u) &= \lim_{\sigma \to +\infty} (\mathcal{A}_{H^a}(u_{-\sigma}) - \mathcal{A}_{H^b}(u_\sigma)) + \int_{[-R,R] \times S^1} \frac{\partial H}{\partial s}(u)\, ds\, dt \\
&= \mathcal{A}_{H^a}(x) - \mathcal{A}_{H^b}(y) + \int_{[-R,R] \times S^1} \frac{\partial H}{\partial s}(u)\, ds\, dt
\end{aligned}
$$

using the assumptions. We set

$$k = \sup_{\substack{s \in [-R,R] \\ t \in S^1 \\ z \in W}} \frac{\partial H}{\partial s}(s,t,z)$$

to obtain

$$E(u) \leq \mathcal{A}_{H^a}(x) - \mathcal{A}_{H^b}(y) + k$$

and conclude the proof of the proposition. $\qquad\square$

The finiteness of the number of critical points of $\mathcal{A}_{H^a}$ and $\mathcal{A}_{H^b}$ leads to the following corollary (analogous to Corollary 6.5.9).

Corollary 11.1.3. *There exists a real number $C > 0$ such that for every $u \in \mathcal{M}^\Gamma$, $E(u) \leq C$.*

This result allows us to prove a compactness property analogous to Theorem 6.5.4.

Theorem 11.1.4. *The space of trajectories $\mathcal{M}^\Gamma$ is compact for the $\mathcal{C}^\infty_{\text{loc}}(\mathbf{R} \times S^1, W)$ topology.*

The proof is similar in all details to that of Theorem 6.5.4; it relies on the following proposition (which is analogous to Proposition 6.6.2):

Proposition 11.1.5. *There exists a constant $A > 0$ such that*

$$\forall u \in \mathcal{M}^\Gamma, \ \forall (s,t) \in \mathbf{R} \times S^1, \quad \left\| \text{grad}_{(s,t)} \, u \right\| \leq A.$$

Remark. The proof, like that of Proposition 6.6.2, uses Corollary 11.1.3 (which is analogous to Corollary 6.5.9) and is done by contradiction. If the conclusion were false, then we could deduce the existence of a map $v : \mathbf{R}^2 \to W$ such that

$$\frac{\partial v}{\partial s} + J(s)\frac{\partial v}{\partial t} = 0.$$

This is not exactly a holomorphic curve as in the proof of Proposition 6.6.2 because J depends on s, but the proof can be carried out in an analogous manner using the metrics

$$g_s(\cdot,\cdot) = \omega(\cdot, J(s)\cdot).$$

In particular, to compute the area of $v(\mathbf{R}^2)$ and the length of $v(\partial B(0, r_k))$, as in the proof of Lemma 6.6.5, we must use the metric g defined by

$$g_{v(s,t)}(\cdot,\cdot) = \omega_{v(s,t)}(\cdot, J(s)\cdot).$$

Using Theorem 11.1.4, we can conclude the proof of Theorem 11.1.1 in the same manner as that of Theorem 6.5.6. To do this, we need a result analogous to Lemma 6.5.13, which can be proved, in a similar way, using Lemma 11.1.12 below.

11.1.b The Transversality

We return to the results of Chapter 8 and adapt them to the Floer equation with parameters. The dependence on s will simplify some of the proofs, as we will see: a larger source space will make the surjectivity easier to show. As before, let $\Gamma = (H, J)$ be a homotopy that connects (H^a, J^a) and (H^b, J^b). We introduce the space $\mathcal{C}_\varepsilon^\infty$ of functions (perturbations)

$$h : \mathbf{R} \times S^1 \times W \longrightarrow \mathbf{R}$$

with compact support such that $\|h\|_\varepsilon < +\infty$. Since h has compact support (in s), the Floer trajectories of the perturbed homotopy near the critical points are the same as those of the nonperturbed homotopy.

Let us now give versions of Theorem 8.1.1 and 8.1.2 with parameters.

Theorem 11.1.6. *There exist a neighborhood of 0 in $\mathcal{C}_\varepsilon^\infty$ and a countable intersection of dense open subsets of $\mathcal{H}_{\mathrm{reg}}$ in this neighborhood such that if $h \in \mathcal{H}_{\mathrm{reg}}$, then setting $\Gamma(h) = (H + h, J)$ for every $x \in \mathrm{Crit}\,\mathcal{A}_{H^a}$ and every $y \in \mathrm{Crit}\,\mathcal{A}_{H^b}$, the space of trajectories $\mathcal{M}^{\Gamma(h)}(x, y)$ is a manifold of dimension $\mu(x) - \mu(y)$. Moreover, for every $u \in \mathcal{M}^\Gamma(x, y)$, the differential*

$$(d\mathcal{F}^\Gamma)_u : W^{1,p}(u^\star TW) \longrightarrow L^p(u^\star TW)$$

is surjective.

For the sake of simplicity, we left out in the notation the fact that the Maslov indices $\mu(x)$ and $\mu(y)$ are computed using the flows of X^a and X^b, respectively.

The proof of Theorem 11.1.6 is more or less analogous to that of Theorem 8.1.2. Let

$$\mathcal{F}^\Gamma : W^{1,p}(\mathbf{R} \times S^1, u^\star TW) \longrightarrow L^p(\mathbf{R} \times S^1, u^\star TW)$$

be defined by

$$\mathcal{F}^\Gamma(u) = \frac{\partial u}{\partial s} + J_s\left(\frac{\partial u}{\partial t} - X_{s,t}\right).$$

The main ingredient of the proof of Theorem 11.1.6 is Theorem 11.1.7, the analogue of Theorem 8.1.5.

Theorem 11.1.7. *For every $u \in \mathcal{M}^\Gamma(x,y)$, the linearization of $\mathcal{F}^\Gamma$ is a Fredholm operator of index $\mu(x) - \mu(y)$.*

The proof is identical to that of Theorem 8.1.5 because since Γ is stationary for $|s| \geq R$, the linearized operator $(d\mathcal{F}^\Gamma)_u$, written in a unitary basis along u, is of the same form,

$$(d\mathcal{F}^\Gamma)_u(Y) = \bar{\partial}Y + SY,$$

as the linearized operator $(d\mathcal{F})_u$, where $S(s,t)$ is a matrix that tends to a symmetric matrix when $s \to \pm\infty$.

Following the example of Chapter 8 and more precisely the outline sketched on p. 224, Theorem 11.1.7 serves to prove the version of Proposition 8.1.3 with parameters, which is an immediate consequence of the following analogue of Proposition 8.1.4 via the implicit function theorem.

Proposition 11.1.8. *Let $\Gamma = (H_0, J_0)$ be a homotopy between (H^a, J^a) and (H^b, J^b). If $u \in \mathcal{M}^\Gamma(x,y)$, then the map*

$$\Phi : W^{1,p}(u^\star W) \times \mathcal{C}_\varepsilon^\infty(H_0) \longrightarrow L^p(u^\star W)$$
$$(Y, h) \longmapsto (d\mathcal{F}^\Gamma)_u(Y) + \operatorname{grad}_u h$$

is surjective and has a right inverse.

Proof. The dependence on s of the Hamiltonians of $\mathcal{C}_\varepsilon^\infty(H_0)$ considerably simplifies the proof of the surjectivity compared to the proof of Proposition 8.1.4: the source space is larger. We no longer need the regularity (that is, Theorem 8.5.4) nor Section 8.6, which explains this notion. Here are the details.

As in Section 8.5, we begin by proving, in a manner analogous to Lemma 8.5.1, that if Φ is not surjective, then there exists a *nonzero* vector field $Z \in L^q(u^\star TW)$ (q is such that $1/p + 1/q = 1$), of class $\mathcal{C}^\infty$, and such that for every $h \in \mathcal{C}_\varepsilon^\infty(H_0)$ and every $Y \in W^{1,p}(u^\star TW)$, we have

$$\langle Z, (d\mathcal{F}^\Gamma)_u(Y)\rangle = 0 \quad \text{and} \quad \langle Z, \operatorname{grad}_u(h)\rangle = 0.$$

Next, we replace Lemma 8.5.3 by the following stronger result.

Lemma 11.1.9. *If $Z \in L^q(u^\star TW) \cap \mathcal{C}^\infty(\mathbf{R} \times S^1; TW)$ satisfies*

$$\langle Z, \operatorname{grad}_u h\rangle = 0 \text{ for every } h \in \mathcal{C}_\varepsilon^\infty(H_0),$$

then Z is identically zero.

Since this lemma contradicts what precedes it, we deduce that Φ is surjective. It has a right inverse, once again by Lemma 8.5.6. Proposition 11.1.8 is proved. $\qquad\square$

Proof of Lemma 11.1.9. The relation that is the assumption of the lemma can be rewritten as

$$\int_{\mathbf{R} \times S^1} dh(Z) \, ds \, dt = 0 \quad \text{for every } h \in \mathcal{C}^\infty_\varepsilon(H_0).$$

Consider the map

$$\tilde{u} : \mathbf{R} \times S^1 \longrightarrow W \times \mathbf{R} \times S^1$$
$$(s, t) \longmapsto (u(s, t), s, t).$$

It is easily shown that $\tilde{u}$ is an embedding. We view Z as a vector field along $\tilde{u}$ on $W \times \mathbf{R} \times S^1$, which does not have any components in the directions $\partial/\partial t \in TS^1$ and $\partial/\partial s \in T\mathbf{R}$. In particular, Z is not in the plane tangent to $\tilde{u}$ at the points where it is nonzero.

We assume, in order to get a contradiction, that there does exist such a point $(s_0, t_0) \in \mathbf{R} \times S^1$. We proceed exactly as in the proof of Lemma 8.5.3: we consider a small neighborhood C_δ of (s_0, t_0) in $\mathbf{R} \times S^1$ such that $Z(s, t)$ is nonzero (and therefore transversal to $\tilde{u}$ for (s, t) in this neighborhood). We take a function

$$\beta : \mathbf{R} \times S^1 \longrightarrow \mathbf{R}$$

with support in this neighborhood and define $h \in \mathcal{C}^\infty_\varepsilon(H_0)$ with support in a tubular neighborhood B of $\tilde{u}(C_\delta)$ in such a way that if $\gamma_{(s,t)}(\sigma)$ is the integral curve of Z passing through $\tilde{u}(s, t)$ for $\sigma = 0$, then we have

$$h_{s,t}(\gamma_{(s,t)}(\sigma)) = \beta(s, t) \cdot \sigma \quad \text{for } |\sigma| \le \eta$$

(where $\eta > 0$ is sufficiently small). Since Z is transversal to $\tilde{u}(C_\delta)$, the function h is well defined. We also assume that

$$B \cap \mathrm{Im}(\tilde{u}) = \tilde{u}(C_\delta),$$

which in particular means that

$$\mathrm{Supp}(h) \cap \mathrm{Im}(\tilde{u}) = \tilde{u}(C_\delta)$$

(see Figure 11.1).

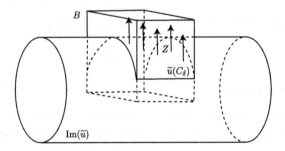

Fig. 11.1

We then obtain

$$
\int_{\mathbf{R} \times S^1} dh(Z(s,t)) \, ds \, dt = \int_{C_\delta} dh_{s,t}(Z(s,t)) \, ds \, dt
$$

$$
= \int_{C_\delta} dh_{s,t} \left(\frac{\partial \gamma_{s,t}(\sigma)}{\partial \sigma} \Big|_{\sigma=0} \right) ds \, dt
$$

$$
= \int_{C_\delta} \frac{\partial}{\partial \sigma} \Big|_{\sigma=0} h_{s,t}(\gamma_{(s,t)}(\sigma)) \, ds \, dt
$$

$$
= \int_{C_\delta} \beta(s,t) \, ds \, dt.
$$

It suffices to choose β in such a manner that this integral is not zero to arrive at a contradiction, which shows that $Z(s,t) = 0$ for every $(s,t) \in \mathbf{R} \times S^1$. This concludes the proof of the lemma. □

The end of the proof of Theorem 11.1.6 is analogous to those of Theorems 8.1.1 and 8.1.2.

We will call a homotopy satisfying the conclusion of Theorem 11.1.6 a *regular homotopy*.

Remark. Since the perturbation h has compact support, the homotopy $\Gamma(h)$ connects (H^a, J^a) and (H^b, J^b) and is stationary for $|s| \geq R$ (for a sufficiently large R).

11.1.c The Compactness

Let Γ be a regular homotopy connecting (H^a, J^a) to (H^b, J^b). The morphism

$$
\Phi^\Gamma : CF_*(H^a, J^a) \longrightarrow CF_*(H^b, J^b)
$$

that we have our eye on is defined as follows. For a critical point x of $\mathcal{A}_{H^a}$ of index $\mu(x) = k$, we set

$$
\Phi_k^\Gamma(x) = \sum_{\substack{y \in \mathrm{Crit}\, \mathcal{A}_{H^b} \\ \mu(y)=k}} n^\Gamma(x,y) y,
$$

where $n^\Gamma(x,y)$ denotes the number (modulo 2) of elements of $\mathcal{M}^\Gamma(x,y)$... whose finiteness we will need to show in order for Φ^Γ to be well defined. We will also need to verify that this Φ^Γ is a morphism of complexes, that is, that

$$
\Phi^\Gamma \circ \partial_{(H^a, J^a)} = \partial_{(H^b, J^b)} \circ \Phi^\Gamma.
$$

To do this we will need the compactness result announced in the following theorem, which is a version of Theorem 9.1.7 with parameters.

Theorem 11.1.10. *Let* (u_n) *be a sequence of elements of* $\mathcal{M}^\Gamma(x,y)$. *There exist:*

- *A subsequence of* (u_n)
- *Critical points* $x = x_0, x_1, \ldots, x_k$ *of* $\mathcal{A}_{H^a}$
- *Critical points* $y_0, y_1, \ldots, y_\ell = y$ *of* $\mathcal{A}_{H^b}$
- *Real sequences* (s_n^i) *for* $0 \le i \le k-1$ *that tend to* $-\infty$, *and* (s'^j_n) *for* $0 \le j \le \ell - 1$ *that tend to* $+\infty$
- *Elements* $u^i \in \mathcal{M}_{(H^a,J^a)}(x_i, x_{i+1})$ *for* $0 \le i \le k-1$ *and elements* $v^j \in \mathcal{M}_{(H^b,J^b)}(y_j, y_{j+1})$ *for* $0 \le j \le \ell - 1$
- *An element* $w \in \mathcal{M}^\Gamma(x_k, y_0)$

such that for $0 \le i \le k-1$ *and* $0 \le j \le \ell - 1$,

$$\lim_{n \to +\infty} u_n \cdot s_n^i = u^i, \qquad \lim_{n \to +\infty} u_n \cdot s'^j_n = v^j$$

and such that

$$\lim_{n \to +\infty} u_n = w.$$

This theorem asserts that after extracting subsequences, if necessary, the sequences of trajectories in $\mathcal{M}^\Gamma$ have limits that are concatenations of (at most) one broken trajectory corresponding to the pair (H^a, J^a), exactly one trajectory of $\mathcal{M}^\Gamma$ and (at most) one broken trajectory corresponding to the pair (H^b, J^b).

Before giving a proof of Theorem 11.1.10, we first state an immediate consequence (an upper bound for the number of breaks).

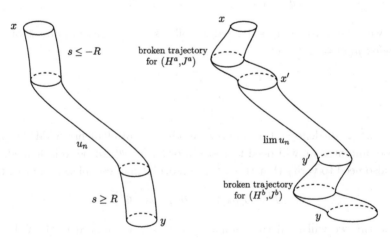

Fig. 11.2

Corollary 11.1.11. *Under the assumptions of Theorem 11.1.10,*

$$\mu(x) - \mu(y) \geq k + \ell.$$

Proof. By Theorem 8.1.2 (and Section 9.1.a), we know that

$$\begin{cases} \mathcal{M}_{(H^a, J^a)}(x_i, x_{i+1}) = \varnothing & \text{if } \mu(x_i) - \mu(x_{i+1}) < 1 \\ \mathcal{M}_{(H^b, J^b)}(y_j, y_{j+1}) = \varnothing & \text{if } \mu(y_j) - \mu(y_{j+1}) < 1, \end{cases}$$

hence, for $0 \leq i \leq k - 1$ and $0 \leq j \leq \ell - 1$, we have

$$\mu(x_i) - \mu(x_{i+1}) \geq 1 \quad \text{and} \quad \mu(y_j) - \mu(y_{j+1}) \geq 1.$$

By Theorem 11.1.6, $\mathcal{M}^\Gamma(x_k, y_0) \neq \varnothing$ implies that $\mu(x_k) \geq \mu(y_0)$. By taking the sum of all these inequalities, we find the desired inequality (recall that $x_0 = x$ and $y_\ell = y$). $\qquad\square$

Proof of Theorem 11.1.10. It begins with a lemma.

Lemma 11.1.12. *Let (u_n) be a sequence in $\mathcal{M}^\Gamma(x, y)$ and let (s_n) be a sequence of real numbers such that $\lim s_n = +\infty$. Then there exist a subsequence of (u_n) (also denoted by (u_n)) and an element $v \in \mathcal{M}_{(H^b, J^b)}$ such that $\lim u_n \cdot s_n = v$. Likewise, if $\lim s_n = -\infty$, then there exists a $u \in \mathcal{M}_{(H^a, J^a)}$ such that (after extracting a subsequence, if necessary) $\lim u_n \cdot s_n = u$.*

Proof. As before, we will leave out the variable t in the notation $u_n = u_n(s, t)$. It of course suffices to consider the case of a sequence (s_n) that tends to $+\infty$. Since $u_n \in \mathcal{M}^\Gamma$, the conclusion of Proposition 11.1.5, namely the fact that $\|\text{grad}_{(s,t)} u\| \leq A$, is true for u_n and therefore also for $u_n \cdot s_n$, so that the family $(u_n \cdot s_n)$ is equicontinuous and so that by the Arzelà–Ascoli theorem (see Appendix C.1, if necessary), there exists a subsequence of $(u_n \cdot s_n)$ that converges to a continuous limit v for the $\mathcal{C}^0_{\text{loc}}$ topology.

But $v_n = u_n \cdot s_n$ is a solution of the Floer-type equation

$$\frac{\partial v_n}{\partial s} + J_{s+s_n}\left(\frac{\partial v_n}{\partial t} - X_{s+s_n,t}\right) = 0.$$

Elliptic regularity (Proposition 6.5.3, again) then implies that v is of class $\mathcal{C}^\infty$ and that (v_n) converges to v in $\mathcal{C}^\infty_{\text{loc}}$.

We still need to verify that $v \in \mathcal{M}_{(H^b, J^b)}$. Consider a closed interval $[-r, r] \subset \mathbf{R}$ and the compact subset $K = [-r, r] \times S^1$ of $\mathbf{R} \times S^1$. For n sufficiently large, $s_n > R + r$, so that for $(s, t) \in K$ and n sufficiently large, we have $s + s_n > R$ and therefore

$$\frac{\partial v_n}{\partial s} + J^b\left(\frac{\partial v_n}{\partial t} - X^b_t(v_n)\right) = 0.$$

By letting n go to infinity in this equation, we indeed find that the limit v is in $\mathcal{M}_{(H^b, J^b)}$. □

We can now prove Theorem 11.1.10. As in the proof of Theorem 6.5.6, we choose $\varepsilon > 0$ sufficiently small for the open balls

$$B(z, \varepsilon) = \{\gamma \in \mathcal{L}W \mid d_\infty(z, \gamma) < \varepsilon\}$$

to be disjoint for $z \in \operatorname{Crit} \mathcal{A}_{H^a}$ (the same property is true for $z \in \operatorname{Crit} \mathcal{A}_{H^b}$).

From now on, and to simplify the notation, we leave out the necessary extractions of subsequences. Since $\mathcal{M}^\Gamma$ is compact (Theorem 11.1.4), we have $w = \lim u_n \in \mathcal{M}^\Gamma$. By Theorem 11.1.1, there exist critical points x' of $\mathcal{A}_{H^a}$ and y' of $\mathcal{A}_{H^b}$ such that $w \in \mathcal{M}(x', y')$. We take up the argument of the proof of Corollary 9.1.9. There exists an $s^\star \in \mathbf{R}$ such that $w(s) \in B(y', \varepsilon)$ for $s \geq s^\star$. Since $w = \lim u_n$, we also have

$$u_n(s^\star) \in B(y', \varepsilon) \quad \text{for } n \text{ sufficiently large.}$$

If $y' \neq y$ (otherwise there is nothing to prove), this trajectory must exit the ball $B(y', \varepsilon)$ for an $s \geq s^\star$. Let s_n be its first exit point:

$$s_n = \sup\left\{s \geq s^\star \mid u_n(\sigma) \in B(y', \varepsilon) \text{ for } \sigma \in [s^\star, s]\right\}.$$

We will now show that the sequence (s_n) tends to $+\infty$. We assume that it is bounded and therefore that after extracting a subsequence, if necessary, it tends to an $s_\bullet \in \mathbf{R}$. Since the convergence of (u_n) to w takes place in $\mathcal{C}^\infty_{\text{loc}}$ and since $s_\bullet \geq s^\star$,

$$\lim_{n \to +\infty} u_n(s_n) = w(s_\bullet) \in B(y', \varepsilon).$$

However, by the definition of s_n, we know that $u_n(s_n) \in \partial B(y', \varepsilon)$ for every n, which contradicts the previous statement.

We have thus proved that $\lim s_n = +\infty$, hence (by Lemma 11.1.12)

$$\lim_{n \to +\infty} u_n \cdot s_n = v^0 \in \mathcal{M}_{(H^b, J^b)}.$$

Let $s < 0$. For n sufficiently large, $s^\star < s + s_n < s_n$, so that by the definition of s_n,

$$u_n(s + s_n) \in B(y', \varepsilon) \quad \text{for } n \text{ sufficiently large,}$$

which implies that $v^0(s) \in B(y', \varepsilon)$. Consequently

$$v^0 \in \mathcal{M}_{(H^b, J^b)}(y', y_1) \quad \text{for some } y_1 \in \operatorname{Crit} \mathcal{A}_{H^b}.$$

The proof then continues (and concludes) in a manner completely analogous to that of Corollary 9.1.9; it leads to a limit that is a broken trajectory $(v^0, v^1, \ldots, v^\ell)$ with $v^j \in \mathcal{M}_{(H^b, J^b)}(y_j, y_{j+1})$ ($y_0 = y'$ and $y_\ell = y$).

We now assume that $x' \neq x$. An analogous reasoning using an $s_\star$ such that $w(s) \in B(x', \varepsilon)$ for $s < s_\star$, and then the last entry point $s'_n < s_\star$ of $u_n(s)$ in $B(x', \varepsilon)$, produces a sequence s'_n that tends to $-\infty$ and for which $\lim u_n \cdot s'_n = u^\bullet \in \mathcal{M}(x_1, x')$. As in the proof of Corollary 9.1.9, the limit is a broken trajectory $(u^0, u^1, \ldots, u^k)$ with $u^i \in \mathcal{M}_{(H^a, J^a)}(x_i, x_{i+1})$ ($x_0 = x$, $x_k = x'$). The theorem has now been proved. □

Corollary 11.1.13. *If $\mu(x) = \mu(y)$, then the space $\mathcal{M}^\Gamma(x, y)$ is compact.*

Proof. Corollary 11.1.11 shows that a sequence (u_n) in $\mathcal{M}^\Gamma(x, y)$ cannot tend to a broken trajectory. □

The map

$$\Phi_k^\Gamma : CF_k(H^a, J^a) \longrightarrow CF_k(H^b, J^b)$$

is therefore well defined by the formula

$$\Phi_k^\Gamma(x) = \sum_{\substack{y \in \mathrm{Crit}\, \mathcal{A}_{H^b} \\ \mu(y)=k}} n^\Gamma(x, y) y.$$

We will also verify the following result.

Proposition 11.1.14. *If $(H^a, J^a) = (H^b, J^b)$ and $\Gamma = \mathrm{Id}$, then Φ_k^Γ is the identity for every k.*

Proof. Under the assumption, $\mathcal{M}^\Gamma(x, y) = \mathcal{M}_{(H^a, J^a)}(x, y)$. If, moreover, $\mu(x) = \mu(y)$, then we know (see Remark 9.1.6) that

$$\mathcal{M}_{(H^a, J^a)}(x, y) = \begin{cases} \varnothing & \text{if } x \neq y \\ \{x\} & \text{if } x = y. \end{cases}$$

Consequently, $\Phi_k^\Gamma = \mathrm{Id}$. □

To finish realizing the objectives that we fixed for this section, we need to prove that Φ^Γ is a morphism of complexes, that is, that

$$\Phi^\Gamma \circ \partial_{(H^a, J^a)} = \partial_{(H^b, J^b)} \circ \Phi^\Gamma.$$

We must show that if $x \in \mathrm{Crit}\, \mathcal{A}_{H^a}$, then for every $z \in \mathrm{Crit}\, \mathcal{A}_{H^b}$ such that $\mu(x) - \mu(z) = 1$, the following equality holds (modulo 2);

$$\sum_{\substack{y' \in \mathrm{Crit}\, \mathcal{A}_{H^a} \\ \mu(x)-\mu(y')=1}} n^a(x, y') n^\Gamma(y', z) = \sum_{\substack{y \in \mathrm{Crit}\, \mathcal{A}_{H^b} \\ \mu(x)=\mu(y)}} n^\Gamma(x, y) n^b(y, z)$$

(it goes without saying that n^a and n^b are the coefficients that occur in the differentials $\partial_{(H^a,J^a)}$ and $\partial_{(H^b,J^b)}$, respectively). It suffices to verify that the number of points of the compact manifold of dimension 0,

$$\Pi^\Gamma(x,z) = \bigcup_{\substack{y'\in \operatorname{Crit}\mathcal{A}_{H^a} \\ \mu(x)-\mu(y')=1}} \mathcal{L}_{(H^a,J^a)}(x,y') \times \mathcal{M}^\Gamma(y',z)$$

$$\cup \bigcup_{\substack{y\in\operatorname{Crit}\mathcal{A}_{H^b} \\ \mu(x)=\mu(y)}} \mathcal{M}^\Gamma(x,y) \times \mathcal{L}_{(H^b,J^b)}(y,z),$$

is even. This will be a consequence of the following theorem.

Theorem 11.1.15. *For $x \in \operatorname{Crit}\mathcal{A}_{H^a}$ and $z \in \operatorname{Crit}\mathcal{A}_{H^b}$ with $\mu(x)-\mu(z) = 1$, the space $\mathcal{M}^\Gamma(x,z) \cup \Pi^\Gamma(x,z)$ is a compact manifold of dimension 1 with boundary, and its boundary is $\Pi^\Gamma(x,z)$.*

We know (by Theorem 11.1.6) that $\mathcal{M}^\Gamma(x,z)$ is a manifold (without boundary) of dimension 1. Using the convergence toward broken trajectories described in Theorem 11.1.10, we define a topology on $\mathcal{M}^\Gamma(x,z) \cup \Pi^\Gamma(x,z)$ that is compatible with that of $\mathcal{M}^\Gamma(x,z)$ (that is, the topology of the $\mathcal{C}^\infty_{\mathrm{loc}}$ convergence). As in Proposition 9.1.2, this topology is Hausdorff and Theorem 11.1.10 therefore ensures that this space is compact. We still need to prove the "manifold with boundary" part of the theorem, that is, to study the structure of $\mathcal{M}^\Gamma(x,z) \cup \Pi^\Gamma(x,z)$ near the points of $\Pi^\Gamma(x,z)$. We will do so now.

11.1.d The Gluing

For $\mu(x) - \mu(z) = 1$, the elements of $\Pi^\Gamma(x,z)$ are broken trajectories (u,v). One of these trajectories is a solution of the Floer equation with parameters and the other is a solution of the Floer equation without parameters associated with (H^a, J^a) or (H^b, J^b). To prove Theorem 11.1.15, it will suffice to glue the trajectories u and v as in Section 9.2. We will prove the following theorem, which is analogous to the gluing theorem 9.2.3.

Theorem 11.1.16. *Let x be a critical point of $\mathcal{A}_{H^a}$ and let y, z be critical points of $\mathcal{A}_{H^b}$ such that*

$$\mu(x) = \mu(y) = \mu(z) + 1.$$

Let $u \in \mathcal{M}^\Gamma(x,y)$ and let $\widehat{v} \in \mathcal{L}_{(H^b,J^b)}(y,z)$. Then:

- *There exists an embedding*

$$\psi : [\rho_0, +\infty[\longrightarrow \mathcal{M}^\Gamma(x,z)$$

(for some $\rho_0 > 0$) such that

$$\lim_{\rho \to +\infty} \psi(\rho) = (u, \widehat{v}).$$

- *Moreover, if (ℓ_n) is a sequence of elements of $\mathcal{M}^\Gamma(x, z)$ that tends to $(u, \widehat{v})$, then $\ell_n \in \mathrm{Im}\,\psi$ for n sufficiently large.*

Remarks.

- The indices $\mu(y)$ and $\mu(z)$ correspond to H^b while $\mu(x)$ corresponds to H^a, a dependence that we have left out of the notation.
- The convergence of $\psi(\rho)$ toward $(u, \widehat{v})$ asserted in this statement should be viewed in the sense of Theorem 11.1.10.
- To prove Theorem 11.1.15, we also need to glue trajectories

$$\widehat{u}' \in \mathcal{L}_{(H^a, J^a)}(x, y') \quad \text{and} \quad v' \in \mathcal{M}^\Gamma(y', z)$$

(for $\mu(y') = \mu(z) = \mu(x) - 1$). Such a gluing is done in a manner analogous to that described by Theorem 11.1.16 and we can thus show that in the neighborhood of the points of $\Pi^\Gamma(x, z)$, the space $\mathcal{M}^\Gamma(x, z) \cup \Pi^\Gamma(x, z)$ is a manifold of dimension 1. This concludes the proof of Theorem 11.1.15.

We will devote the next section to the proof of Theorem 11.1.16.

11.2 Proof of Theorem 11.1.16

To prove Theorem 11.1.16, we fix a lift $v \in \mathcal{M}_{(H^b, J^b)}(y, z)$ of $\widehat{v}$. For $\rho \geq \rho_0$, we want to define a map

$$\psi_\rho : \mathbf{R} \times S^1 \longrightarrow W$$

that is a solution of the Floer equation with parameters

$$\frac{\partial \psi_\rho}{\partial s} + J_s \frac{\partial \psi_\rho}{\partial t} + \mathrm{grad}_{\psi_\rho} H_{s,t} = 0$$

for every ρ. Once we prove that

$$\lim_{\rho \to +\infty} \psi_\rho(s, t) = u(s, t) \quad \text{and} \quad \lim_{\rho \to +\infty} \psi_\rho(s + 2\rho, t) = v(s, t)$$

uniformly on all compacts, the convergence toward $(u, \widehat{v})$ for $\rho \to +\infty$ will follow. In order to proceed as in the proof of Theorem 9.2.3, we need to use the substitution

$$\varphi_\rho(s, t) = \psi_\rho(s + \rho, t).$$

So $\varphi_\rho \in \mathcal{C}^\infty(x, z)$ will be a solution of

$$\frac{\partial \varphi_\rho}{\partial s} + J_{s+\rho} \frac{\partial \varphi_\rho}{\partial t} + \operatorname{grad}_{\varphi_\rho} H_{s+\rho,t} = 0$$

and will satisfy the conditions

$$\lim_{\rho \to +\infty} \varphi_\rho(s - \rho, t) = u(s, t) \quad \text{and} \quad \lim_{\rho \to +\infty} \varphi_\rho(s + \rho, t) = v(s, t)$$

(that is, the desired convergence property for ψ_ρ).

As in the proof of 9.2.3, we will proceed in three steps:

(1) Pre-gluing, in Section 11.2.a
(2) Construction of φ (and therefore of ψ), in Section 11.2.b
(3) Verification of the properties of ψ, in Section 11.2.c.

11.2.a Pre-gluing

Let $\rho_0 \geq 0$ be such that the homotopy $\Gamma(s, t) = (H_{s,t}, J_s)$ is stationary and equal to (H_t^b, J^b) for $s \geq \rho_0$. Using the same notation as in Section 9.3, we define the pre-gluing w_ρ of u and v for $\rho \geq \rho_0$ using the (same) formula[1]

$$w_\rho(s, t) = \begin{cases} u(s + \rho, t) & \text{if } s \leq -1 \\ \exp_{y(t)}\Big(\beta^-(s) \exp_{y(t)}^{-1}(u(s + \rho, t)) \\ \qquad + \beta^+(s) \exp_{y(t)}^{-1}(v(s - \rho, t))\Big) & \text{if } s \in [-1, 1] \\ v(s - \rho, t) & \text{if } s \geq 1 \end{cases}$$

(we have assumed that ρ_0 is sufficiently large for w_ρ to be well defined). In the same manner, we can then define, for $Y \in T_u \mathcal{P}(x, y)$ and $Z \in T_v \mathcal{P}(y, z)$, the pre-gluing

$$Y \#_\rho Z \in T_{w_\rho} \mathcal{P}(x, z)$$

by the same formula as in Section 9.3. Since they use the same formulas, these constructions bring forth objects having all the properties stated in Section 9.3. Also note that if $\mathcal{F}_\rho^\Gamma$ is the operator

$$\mathcal{F}_\rho^\Gamma = \frac{\partial}{\partial s} + J_{s+\rho} \frac{\partial}{\partial t} + \operatorname{grad} H_{s+\rho,t},$$

then we have

$$\mathcal{F}_\rho^\Gamma(w_\rho)(s, t) = 0 \quad \text{for } |s| \geq 1:$$

---

[1] Recall the convention we made concerning the notation $\rho \geq \rho_0$, stated on p. 313, which stands for "ρ sufficiently large".

- For $s \leq -1$, this is because u is a solution of the Floer equation with parameters.

- For $s \geq 1$, we note that

$$\mathcal{F}_\rho^\Gamma = \frac{\partial}{\partial s} + J^b \frac{\partial}{\partial t} + \operatorname{grad} H^b \quad \text{for } \rho \geq \rho_0$$

and $v(s - \rho, t)$ is a solution of the Floer equation associated with the pair (H^b, J^b).

The last argument also tells us that

$$\lim_{\rho \to +\infty} \mathcal{F}_\rho^\Gamma (w_\rho(s,t)) = 0 \quad \text{in } \mathcal{C}^\infty_{\text{loc}}$$

because $\lim_{\rho \to +\infty} w_\rho(s,t) = y(t)$.

11.2.b Construction of φ

We want to construct a $\varphi(\rho)$ satisfying $\mathcal{F}_\rho^\Gamma (\varphi(\rho)) = 0$ from the pre-gluing w_ρ. To do this, we use the Newton–Picard method, as in Section 9.4.

The Operator $\mathcal{F}_\rho^\Gamma$.

As in Section 9.4, we start out with unitary trivializations $(Z_i^u(s,t))_{i=1,\ldots,2n}$ and $(Z_i^v(s,t))_{i=1,\ldots,2n}$ of the tangent bundle TW along u and v, respectively. This leads to a unitary trivialization $(Z_i^\rho(s,t))_{i=1,\ldots,2n}$ along w_ρ, which we extend by parallel transport (see Appendix A.5) and to an orthonormal triv-ialization of TW in a neighborhood of $w_\rho(s,t)$ (for every (s,t)). The latter trivialization is denoted by $(Z_i^{\rho,\xi}(s,t))_{i=1,\ldots,2n}$, with

$$Z_i^{\rho,\xi}(s,t) \in T_{\exp_{w_\rho}(s,t)\xi} W, \quad \text{where } \xi \in T_{w_\rho(s,t)} W$$

(and the norm of ξ is less than the injectivity radius of the metric on W). Using these trivializations, we define a (nonlinear) operator

$$F_\rho^\Gamma : B(0,r) \subset W^{1,p}(\mathbf{R} \times S^1; \mathbf{R}^{2n}) \longrightarrow L^p(\mathbf{R} \times S^1; \mathbf{R}^{2n})$$

for a well-chosen r ($r = r_0/K$, where r_0 is the injectivity radius of the metric and K is the norm of the injection $W^{1,p} \subset L^\infty$, satisfies the requirements).

By definition, if ξ is written as

$$\xi = \sum y_i Z_i^\rho \quad \text{in the basis } (Z_i^\rho),$$

then written in the basis $(Z_i^{\rho,\xi})$, $F_\rho^\Gamma(y_1,\ldots,y_{2n})$ is $\mathcal{F}_\rho^\Gamma(\exp_{w_\rho}(\xi))$.

The Properties of F_ρ^Γ.

The construction of F_ρ^Γ is analogous to that of F_ρ in Section 9.4. The Floer operator that defines it depends on Γ but once we have written F_ρ^Γ in coordinates, this dependence is no longer visible. In other words, the operators F_ρ^Γ and F_ρ are of the same form and have the same properties. To simplify the notation and alleviate the writing, we will, from now on, omit the dependence on Γ. Let us summarize the properties of F_ρ:

(1) $F_\rho(0) = [\mathcal{F}_\rho^\Gamma(w_\rho)]_{Z_i^\rho}$, in particular,

$$F_\rho(0) = 0 \text{ for } |s| \geq 1 \quad \text{and} \quad \lim_{\rho \to +\infty} F_\rho(0) = 0 \text{ in } \mathcal{C}_{\text{loc}}^\infty.$$

(2) Consider the operators

$$F_u, F_v : B(0,r) \subset W^{1,p}(\mathbf{R} \times S^1; \mathbf{R}^{2n}) \longrightarrow L^p(\mathbf{R} \times S^1; \mathbf{R}^{2n})$$

defined in an analogous manner from the Floer operators $\mathcal{F}^\Gamma$ and $\mathcal{F}$ using the trivializations Z_i^u and Z_i^v. Let

$$L^u = (dF^u)_0, \quad L^v = (dF^v)_0 \quad \text{and} \quad L_\rho = (dF_\rho)_0.$$

The same computation as in Section 9.4 gives

$$L^u(Y) = \frac{\partial Y}{\partial s} + J_0 \frac{\partial Y}{\partial t} + S^u(Y)$$

$$L^v(Y) = \frac{\partial Y}{\partial s} + J_0 \frac{\partial Y}{\partial t} + S^v(Y)$$

$$L_\rho(Y) = \frac{\partial Y}{\partial s} + J_0 \frac{\partial Y}{\partial t} + S_\rho^\Gamma(Y),$$

where J_0 denotes the standard complex structure on $\mathbf{R}^{2n}$ and the operators

$$S^u, S^v, S_\rho^\Gamma : \mathbf{R} \times S^1 \longrightarrow \text{End}(\mathbf{R}^{2n})$$

satisfy

$$\lim_{s \to -\infty} S^u(s,t) = S^x(t), \quad \lim_{s \to +\infty} S^u(s,t) = S^y(t)$$

$$\lim_{s \to -\infty} S^v(s,t) = S^y(t), \quad \lim_{s \to +\infty} S^v(s,t) = S^z(t)$$

(where S^x, S^y and S^z are the loops of symmetric matrices defined by the critical points x, y and z), as well as

$$S_\rho^\Gamma(s,t) = S^u(s+\rho,t) \quad \text{for } s \leq -1$$

$$S_\rho^\Gamma(s,t) = S^v(s-\rho,t) \quad \text{for } s \geq 1 \text{ and } \rho \geq R$$

$$\lim_{\rho \to +\infty} S_\rho^\Gamma(s,t) = S^y(t).$$

The last relation needs a small proof, which we now give. We fix a compact subset $K \subset \mathbf{R} \times S^1$. For $\rho \geq \rho_0$, the restriction of $\mathcal{F}_\rho^\Gamma$ to $W^{1,p}(K; TW)$ is the Floer operator associated with (H^b, J^b). Written in the trivialization $(Z_i^\rho)_i$, its differential $(d\mathcal{F}_\rho^\Gamma)_{w_\rho}$ is $(dF_\rho)_0$, which we have denoted by L_ρ. Since $\lim_{\rho \to +\infty} w_\rho = y$ in $\mathcal{C}_{\mathrm{loc}}^\infty$, the order 0 part of $L_\rho = (dF_\rho)_0$ (restricted to $W^{1,p}(K; \mathbf{R}^{2n})$) tends to the order 0 part of $(d\mathcal{F}^b)_y$ written in the basis Z_i^y, that is, to S^y.

(3) By Theorem 8.1.5, we know that L^u, L^v and L_ρ^Γ are Fredholm operators with respective indices

$$\mathrm{Ind}(L^u) = \mu(x) - \mu(y) = 0$$
$$\mathrm{Ind}(L^v) = \mu(y) - \mu(z) = 1$$
$$\mathrm{Ind}(L_\rho) = \mu(x) - \mu(z) = 1.$$

Furthermore, the homotopy Γ and the pair (H^b, J^b) are regular, so that by Theorem 8.1.1 and Theorem 11.1.6, the operators L^u and L^v are surjective and in particular

$$\mathrm{Ker}\, L^u = 0 \quad \text{and} \quad \mathrm{Ker}\, L^v = \{\alpha \partial v / \partial s \mid \alpha \in \mathbf{R}\}.$$

Next, we consider the subspaces

$$W_\rho = \{0 \#_\rho \beta \mid \beta \in \mathrm{Ker}\, L^v\}$$

and

$$W_\rho^\perp = \left\{ Y \in W^{1,p}(\mathbf{R} \times S^1; \mathbf{R}^{2n}) \mid \int_{\mathbf{R} \times S^1} \langle Y, Z \rangle \, ds \, dt = 0 \quad \forall Z \in W_\rho \right\}.$$

Copying the proof of Proposition 9.4.7 gives the analogous result.

Proposition 11.2.1. *There exists a constant $C > 0$ such that for every $\rho \geq \rho_0$, we have*

$$\forall Y \in W_\rho^\perp, \quad \|L_\rho(Y)\|_{L^p} \geq C \, \|Y\|_{W^{1,p}}.$$

As in Section 9.4, it follows that L_ρ is surjective and that it admits a right inverse

$$G_\rho : L^p(\mathbf{R} \times S^1; \mathbf{R}^{2n}) \longrightarrow W_\rho^\perp \subset W^{1,p}(\mathbf{R} \times S^1; \mathbf{R}^{2n}).$$

We can therefore apply the Newton–Picard method, more precisely Lemma 9.4.4. Using the same arguments as in Section 9.4, we can show the following result.

Theorem 11.2.2. *There exists a $\rho_0 > 0$ such that for every $\rho \geq \rho_0$, there exists a*

$$\gamma(\rho) \in W_\rho^\perp \subset W^{1,p}(\mathbf{R} \times S^1; \mathbf{R}^{2n})$$

with $F_\rho(\gamma(\rho)) = 0$. Such a γ is unique in $B(0, \varepsilon) \cap W_\rho^\perp$ for an $\varepsilon > 0$ that is independent of ρ. Moreover, it has the following properties:

(1) $\lim_{\rho \to +\infty} \|\gamma(\rho)\|_{W^{1,p}} = 0$.
(2) *The map $\rho \mapsto \gamma(\rho)$ is differentiable.*
(3) $\lim_{\rho \to +\infty} \|\partial\gamma/\partial\rho\|_{W^{1,p}} = 0$.

Proof. In order to prove the theorem, we need to verify that $F_\rho = F_\rho^\Gamma$ satisfies the properties that we gather in Chapter 13. The difference between the situations studied here and in that chapter comes from the fact that the Floer operator is now $\mathcal{F}_\rho^\Gamma$. Let us explain it below.

Since Γ is stationary for $|s| \geq R$, we obtain the same estimates in an analogous manner (and without much trouble): it suffices to rewrite Lemma 13.2.3 for maps

$$A : \mathbf{R} \times W \times \mathbf{R}^m \times \mathbf{R}^m \longrightarrow \mathbf{R}^m \quad \text{and} \quad B : \mathbf{R} \times W \times \mathbf{R}^m \times \mathbf{R}^m \times \mathbf{R}^m \longrightarrow \mathbf{R}^m$$

that are constant (with respect to the first variable $s \in \mathbf{R}$) when $|s| \geq R$ (with a completely analogous proof).

As to the statement analogous to that of Lemma 9.4.16, its proof requires a more serious modification: we must now take into account the dependence of H and J on the parameter ρ. The proof of this variant is given in Section 13.8. $\square$

We can now define the desired maps φ_ρ and ψ_ρ: we set

$$\varphi_\rho = \exp_{w_\rho} \gamma(\rho) \quad \text{and} \quad \psi_\rho(s, t) = \varphi_\rho(s - \rho, t).$$

By definition, φ_ρ is a solution of

$$\frac{\partial\varphi_\rho}{\partial s} + J_{s+\rho}\frac{\partial\varphi_\rho}{\partial t} + \operatorname{grad} H_{s+\rho,t}(\varphi_\rho) = 0$$

and satisfies

$$\lim_{s \to -\infty} \varphi_\rho(s, t) = x(t) \quad \text{and} \quad \lim_{s \to +\infty} \varphi_\rho(s, t) = z(t),$$

so that $\psi_\rho \in \mathcal{M}^\Gamma(x, z)$ for every $\rho \geq \rho_0$.

11.2.c The Properties of ψ_ρ

We will now verify that ψ_ρ has the desired properties:

(1) It tends to $(u, \widehat{v})$. We use the properties of the pre-gluing w_ρ and those of $\gamma(\rho)$ (stated in Theorem 11.2.2) to obtain, as in Section 9.4, that

$$\lim_{\rho \to +\infty} \varphi_\rho(s - \rho, t) = u(s, t) \quad \text{and} \quad \lim_{\rho \to +\infty} \varphi_\rho(s + \rho, t) = v(s, t),$$

in other words, that

$$\lim_{\rho \to +\infty} \psi_\rho(s, t) = u(s, t) \quad \text{and} \quad \lim_{\rho \to +\infty} \psi_\rho(s + 2\rho, t) = v(s, t),$$

so that we have

$$\lim_{\rho \to +\infty} \psi_\rho = (u, \widehat{v}) \in \mathcal{M}^\Gamma(x, y) \times \mathcal{L}_{(H^b, J^b)}(y, z).$$

(2) It is an immersion. Let us show that $\psi'(\rho) \neq 0$. Otherwise,

$$\frac{\partial \varphi}{\partial \rho}(\rho, s - \rho, t) - \frac{\partial \varphi}{\partial s}(\rho, s - \rho, t) = 0,$$

hence $\partial \varphi / \partial \rho = \partial \varphi / \partial s$. The same proof as in Section 9.5 (where α_n is replaced by 1) leads to a contradiction.

(3) It is injective. Indeed, its image is contained in a component of the manifold $\mathcal{M}^\Gamma(x, z)$ whose dimension is 1. This component is not compact because

$$\lim_{\rho \to +\infty} \psi(\rho) \notin \mathcal{M}^\Gamma(x, z).$$

It is therefore an interval in $\mathbf{R}$ and the injectivity of ψ follows from the fact that it is immersive (and from Rolle's theorem...).

We still need to prove the uniqueness of the manner of tending to the limit (see Figure 9.9), namely the last assertion of Theorem 11.1.16. As in that statement, we consider a sequence $(\ell_n)_n$ that tends to $(u, \widehat{v})$ and show that for n sufficiently large, $\ell_n \in \operatorname{Im} \psi$. As in Remark 9.6.2, it suffices to prove this for a subsequence of (ℓ_n) (and the following statements are all "after extracting a subsequence, if necessary"). As in Section 9.6 (and as usual), we proceed in several steps (but we will not need the first step of Section 9.6):

(1) We prove a proposition that is a simplified analogue of Proposition 9.6.3.

Proposition 11.2.3. *There exist a real sequence (ρ_n) tending to $+\infty$ and for every n, a vector $Y_n \in w_{\rho_n}^\star TW$ such that, for every $(s, t) \in \mathbf{R} \times S^1$,* *we have*

$$\ell_n(s + \rho_n, t) = \exp_{w_{\rho_n}(s,t)} Y_n(s, t).$$

Moreover, $\lim_{n \to +\infty} \|Y_n\|_\infty = 0.$

(2) We prove an analogue of Proposition 9.6.4.

Proposition 11.2.4. *The vector field Y_n is in $W^{1,p}(w_{\rho_n}^\star TW)$. Moreover,* $\lim_{n \to +\infty} \|Y_n\|_{W^{1,p}} = 0.$

(3) Finally, we finish the proof.

Proof of Proposition 11.2.3. Recall that R denotes a real positive number such that for $s \geq R$, the homotopy $\Gamma(s)$ is stationary, equal to (H^b, J^b). To simplify the notation, we will, in this proof, leave out the variable $t \in S^1$ in the expressions of the maps defined on $\mathbf{R} \times S^1$.

We begin the proof with an analogue of Lemma 9.6.9.

Lemma 11.2.5. *Let (λ_n) be a sequence in $\mathcal{M}^\Gamma(x, z)$ and let (s_n), (σ_n) be two real sequences tending to $+\infty$. Suppose that*

$$\lim_{n \to +\infty} \lambda_n(s + s_n) = a(s) \quad and \quad \lim_{n \to +\infty} \lambda_n(s + \sigma_n) = b(s)$$

for

$$a \in \mathcal{M}_{(H^b, J^b)}(\alpha, \beta), \quad b \in \mathcal{M}_{(H^b, J^b)}(\gamma, \delta)$$

(α, β, γ and δ are critical points of $\mathcal{A}_{H^b}$). Then we have:

- *If $\lim_{n \to +\infty}(s_n - \sigma_n) = -\infty$, then*

$$\mathcal{A}_{H^b}(\alpha) \geq \mathcal{A}_{H^b}(\beta) \geq \mathcal{A}_{H^b}(\gamma) \geq \mathcal{A}_{H^b}(\delta).$$

- *If $\lim_{n \to +\infty}(s_n - \sigma_n) = +\infty$, then*

$$\mathcal{A}_{H^b}(\gamma) \geq \mathcal{A}_{H^b}(\delta) \geq \mathcal{A}_{H^b}(\alpha) \geq \mathcal{A}_{H^b}(\beta).$$

Proof. The two assertions can be proved in completely analogous manners. Let us therefore show only the second one. We assume that

$$\lim(s_n - \sigma_n) = +\infty.$$

For $s \geq R$, $\lambda_n(s)$ is a solution of the Floer equation for (H^b, J^b), so that, in particular, $s \mapsto \mathcal{A}_{H^b}(\ell_n(s))$ is a decreasing function on $[R, +\infty[$. We fix σ and $\tau \in \mathbf{R}$ and choose n sufficiently large to have

$$s_n + \tau > \sigma_n + \sigma \geq R.$$

We then have

$$\mathcal{A}_{H^b}(\lambda_n(s_n + \tau)) < \mathcal{A}_{H^b}(\lambda_n(\sigma_n + \tau)).$$

Letting n tend to infinity, we obtain

$$\mathcal{A}_{H^b}(a(\tau)) \leq \mathcal{A}_{H^b}(b(\sigma)),$$

an inequality that holds for every τ and every σ. It suffices to let σ tend to $+\infty$ and τ to $-\infty$ to conclude the proof of this lemma. □

We can use this lemma to prove the following.

Lemma 11.2.6. *Let (ℓ_n) be a sequence in $\mathcal{M}^\Gamma(x, z)$ that tends to $(u, \widehat{v}) \in \mathcal{M}^\Gamma(x, y) \times \mathcal{L}_{(H^b, J^b)}(y, z)$. Then:*

(1) There exists a real sequence (s_n) with $s_n \geq R$ tending to $+\infty$, such that
$$\mathcal{A}_{H^b}(\ell_n(s_n)) = \mathcal{A}_{H^b}(y).$$
(2) Moreover, $\lim_{n \to +\infty} \ell_n(s + s_n) = y$.

Proof. As in the proof of the previous lemma, the function $s \mapsto \mathcal{A}_{H^b}(\ell_n(s))$ is decreasing for $s \geq R$. Since $u \in \mathcal{M}^\Gamma(x, y)$, the same holds for $s \mapsto \mathcal{A}_{H^b}(u(s))$. We fix an $s \geq R$. Since $\lim \ell_n(s) = u(s)$, we have

$$\lim_{n \to +\infty} \mathcal{A}_{H^b}(\ell_n(s)) = \mathcal{A}_{H^b}(u(s)) > \mathcal{A}_{H^b}(y).$$

In particular, $\mathcal{A}_{H^b}(\ell_n(s)) > \mathcal{A}_{H^b}(y)$ for n sufficiently large.

We have fixed a lift $v \in \mathcal{M}_{(H^b, J^b)}(y, z)$ of $\widehat{v}$. The convergence of (ℓ_n) implies the existence of a sequence (σ_n) that tends to $+\infty$ and satisfies

$$\lim_{n \to +\infty} \ell_n(s + \sigma_n) = v(s).$$

In particular, for the s fixed above, we have

$$\lim_{n \to +\infty} \mathcal{A}_{H^b}(\ell_n(s + \sigma_n)) = \mathcal{A}_{H^b}(v(s)) < \mathcal{A}_{H^b}(y),$$

which implies that

$$\mathcal{A}_{H^b}(\ell_n(s + \sigma_n)) < \mathcal{A}_{H^b}(y)$$

for n sufficiently large. From this we deduce the existence, for n sufficiently large, of an $s_n \in]s, s + \sigma_n[$ with $\mathcal{A}_{H^b}(\ell_n(s_n)) = \mathcal{A}_{H^b}(y)$.

Suppose that the sequence (s_n) is bounded. After extracting a subsequence, if necessary, we may, and do, assume that it tends to a limit $s^\star \geq R$. Then

$$\lim_{n \to +\infty} \ell_n(s + s_n) = u(s + s^\star) \quad \text{in } \mathcal{C}^\infty_{\text{loc}}.$$

In particular, $\lim \ell_n(s_n) = u(s^\star)$, hence

$$\lim_{n \to +\infty} \mathcal{A}_{H^b}(\ell_n(s_n)) = \mathcal{A}_{H^b}(u(s^\star)) > \mathcal{A}_{H^b}(y),$$

which gives a contradiction because the sequence on the left-hand side is constant and equal to $\mathcal{A}_{H^b}(y)$. Consequently (always after extracting a subsequence, if necessary), $\lim s_n = +\infty$.

We have now proved the first assertion of the lemma. The second one is a consequence of this. We use Lemma 11.1.12 to show that

$$\lim_{n \to +\infty} \ell_n(s + s_n) = a \in \mathcal{M}_{(H^b, J^b)}(\alpha, \beta) \quad \text{for } \alpha, \beta \in \mathrm{Crit}(\mathcal{A}_{H^b}).$$

Note that

$$\mathcal{A}_{H^b}(a(0)) = \lim_{n \to +\infty} \mathcal{A}_{H^b}(\ell_n(s_n)) = \mathcal{A}_{H^b}(y)$$

(and recall that $\lim \ell_n(s + \sigma_n) = v$). Suppose that $\sigma_n - s_n$ is bounded, hence (after extracting a subsequence, if necessary) converges to $s^\bullet$. Then $v(s) = a(s + s^\bullet)$ and, in particular,

$$\mathcal{A}_{H^b}(v(-s^\bullet)) = \mathcal{A}_{H^b}(a(0)) = \mathcal{A}_{H^b}(y),$$

which is impossible because $v \in \mathcal{M}_{(H^b, J^b)}(y, z)$. This means that $\sigma_n - s_n$ is not bounded. The previous lemma then implies that

$$\mathcal{A}_{H^b}(a(s)) = \mathcal{A}_{H^b}(y) \quad \text{for every } s.$$

Hence a does not depend on s, and is therefore a critical point of $\mathcal{A}_{H^b}$. Since the critical values of $\mathcal{A}_{H^b}$ are distinct (see Lemma 6.3.5, if necessary), we therefore have $a = y$, concluding the proof of the lemma. $\qquad\square$

We once more take up the notation of Proposition 9.6.3. We fix an $\varepsilon > 0$ and choose a $\delta > 0$ that satisfies Lemma 9.6.11. Consider the open balls (for the $\mathcal{C}^0$ distance) $B(x, \delta)$, $B(y, \delta)$ and $B(z, \delta)$ in the loop space $\mathcal{L}W$. After decreasing δ, if necessary, we may, and do assume that these balls are mutually disjoint and that $u(0) \notin B(x, \delta) \cup B(y, \delta)$. By the previous lemma, we know that $\ell_n(s + s_n)$ tends to y, hence for n sufficiently large, $\ell_n(s_n) \in B(y, \delta)$. We define the following numbers:

$$\begin{aligned}
\sigma'_n &= \sup \{s \mid \ell_n(]-\infty, s]) \subset B(x, \delta)\} \\
\sigma_n &= \inf \{s < s_n \mid \ell_n([s, s_n]) \subset B(y, \delta)\} \\
\tau_n &= \sup \{s > s_n \mid \ell_n([s_n, s]) \subset B(y, \delta)\} \\
\tau'_n &= \inf \{s \mid \ell_n([s, +\infty[) \subset B(z, \delta)\}.
\end{aligned}$$

Note that

$$\ell_n(\sigma'_n) \in \partial B(x,\delta), \quad \ell_n(\sigma_n) \text{ and } \ell_n(\tau_n) \in \partial B(y,\delta) \text{ and } \ell_n(\tau'_n) \in \partial B(z,\delta).$$

Since these three balls are disjoint, we have

$$\sigma'_n \le \sigma_n \le \tau_n \le \tau'_n.$$

Moreover, since $\lim_{n \to +\infty} \ell_n(s) = u(s)$, for n sufficiently large, we have

$$\ell_n(0) \notin B(x,\delta) \cup B(y,\delta),$$

hence

$$\sigma'_n \le 0 \le \sigma_n.$$

Let us now prove the following result.

Lemma 11.2.7. *The sequences* (σ'_n), (σ_n) *and* $(\tau'_n - \tau_n)$ *are bounded. Moreover, there exists a* $\tau^* \in \mathbf{R}$ *such that*

$$\lim_{n \to +\infty} \ell_n(s + \tau_n) = v(s + \tau^*).$$

Proof. Assume that (σ'_n) is not bounded, so that after extracting a subsequence, if necessary, $\lim_{n \to +\infty} \sigma'_n = -\infty$. Let

$$\lambda_n(s) = \ell_n(s + \sigma'_n).$$

Lemma 11.1.12 ensures the existence of a $w \in \mathcal{M}_{(H^a, J^a)}$ such that

$$\lim_{n \to +\infty} \lambda_n(s) = w(s).$$

Since $\lambda_n(s) \in B(x,\delta)$ for every $s < 0$, $w \in \mathcal{M}_{(H^a, J^a)}(x, x')$ for some x', and $x \ne x'$ because

$$w(0) = \lim_{n \to +\infty} \lambda_n(0) = \lim_{n \to +\infty} \ell_n(\sigma'_n) \in \partial B(x,\delta).$$

Let us show that this is absurd. We know that for $s < -R$, ℓ_n and u are solutions of the Floer equation associated with (H^a, J^a). In particular, the functions

$$s \longmapsto \mathcal{A}_{H^a}(\ell_n(s)) \quad \text{and} \quad s \longmapsto \mathcal{A}_{H^a}(u(s))$$

are decreasing for $s < -R$. The same holds for the function $s \mapsto \mathcal{A}_{H^a}(w(s))$. We therefore choose s_1 and $s_2 < -R$ with $\mathcal{A}_{H^a}(u(s_1)) > \mathcal{A}_{H^a}(w(s_2))$, that is, with

$$\lim_{n \to +\infty} \mathcal{A}_{H^a}(\ell_n(s_1)) > \lim_{n \to +\infty} \mathcal{A}_{H^a}(\ell_n(s_2 + \sigma'_n)).$$

For n sufficiently large, the assumption we made on σ'_n implies that we must have $s_2 + \sigma'_n < s_1 < -R$ and therefore that

$$\mathcal{A}_{H^a}(\ell_n(s_1)) < \mathcal{A}_{H^a}(\ell_n(s_2 + \sigma'_n)),$$

which is the desired contradiction. Consequently, (σ'_n) is bounded.

We now turn to (σ_n) and show that this sequence is also bounded. Assume that it is not, and therefore (always after extracting a subsequence, if necessary) that it tends to $+\infty$. As before, we find that

$$\lim_{n \to +\infty} \ell_n(s + \sigma_n) = w' \in \mathcal{M}_{(H^b, J^b)}$$

with

$$w'(0) = \lim_{n \to +\infty} \ell_n(\sigma_n) \in \partial B(y, \delta).$$

In particular, the sequence $(s_n - \sigma_n)$ tends to $+\infty$ because if we were to assume that it is bounded, then since $\lim_{n \to +\infty} \ell_n(s + s_n) = y$, we would deduce that

$$\lim_{n \to +\infty} \ell_n(s + \sigma_n) = y$$

and therefore that $w' = y$, which is absurd. Consequently, every $s > 0$ satisfies $s + \sigma_n \in \,]\sigma_n, s_n]$ for n sufficiently large and therefore $\ell_n(s + \sigma_n) \in B(y, \delta)$. So

$$w'(s) = \lim_{n \to +\infty} \ell_n(s + \sigma_n) \in \overline{B}(y, \delta),$$

in particular $w' \in \mathcal{M}_{(H^b, J^b)}(y', y)$ for some critical point $y' \neq y$ of $\mathcal{A}_{H^b}$. A contradiction can be revealed as before by taking $s_1, s_2 > R$ with

$$\mathcal{A}_{H^b}(u(s_1)) < \mathcal{A}_{H^b}(w'(s_2)).$$

Let us now turn to the sequence $(\tau'_n - \tau_n)$. For n sufficiently large, we have $s_n > R$ (by Lemma 11.2.6), hence $\tau'_n \geq \tau_n \geq s_n > R$. In particular,

$$\mathcal{A}_{H^b}(\ell_n(s_n)) > \mathcal{A}_{H^b}(\ell_n(\tau_n)) > \mathcal{A}_{H^b}(\ell_n(\tau'_n)) > \mathcal{A}_{H^b}(z).$$

Lemma 11.2.6 tells us that $\mathcal{A}_{H^b}(\ell_n(s_n)) = \mathcal{A}_{H^b}(y)$, hence

$$\mathcal{A}_{H^b}(\ell_n(\tau_n)) \quad \text{and} \quad \mathcal{A}_{H^b}(\ell_n(\tau'_n)) \in \,]\mathcal{A}_{H^b}(z), \mathcal{A}_{H^b}(y)[$$

and the restriction of ℓ_n to the interval $[\tau_n, \tau'_n]$ is a solution of the Floer equation associated with (H^b, J^b). The same arguments as in the proof of Lemma 9.6.12 then show that $(\tau_n - \tau'_n)$ is bounded.

Let us finally prove the last assertion. We again use Lemma 11.1.12, which asserts that

$$\lim_{n \to +\infty} \ell_n(s + \tau_n) = w'' \in \mathcal{M}_{(H^b, J^b)}$$

with, as above, $w'' \in \mathcal{M}_{(H^b, J^b)}(y, y'')$ for a $y'' \neq y$ (using the fact that $(\tau_n - s_n)$ tends to $+\infty$, which is also proved as for $(s_n - \sigma_n)$). The assumption on ℓ_n moreover implies the existence of a sequence (ρ_n) that tends to $+\infty$ and for which $\lim_{n \to +\infty} \ell_n(s + \rho_n) = v$. Lemma 11.2.5 then implies that the sequence $(\tau_n - \rho_n)$ is bounded and therefore (after extracting a subsequence, if necessary) convergent, to a limit that we denote by τ^*. But then

$$\lim_{n \to +\infty} \ell_n(s + \tau_n) = v(s + \tau^*)$$

and the lemma is proved.   □

Let us now finish the proof of Proposition 11.2.3. Let

$$\rho_n = \frac{\tau_n - \tau^*}{2}$$

(it is τ^* whose existence we have just proved) and let us show that (ρ_n) satisfies the properties we announced. Consider the pre-gluing w_{ρ_n}, which, recall, is defined by

$$w_{\rho_n}(s) = \begin{cases} u(s + \rho_n) & \text{if } s \leq -1 \\ \exp_y\Big(\beta^-(s) \exp_y^{-1}(u(s + \rho_n)) \\ \qquad + \beta^+(s) \exp_y^{-1}(v(s - \rho_n))\Big) & \text{if } s \in [-1, 1] \\ v(s - \rho_n) & \text{if } s \geq 1. \end{cases}$$

We will show that

$$\ell_n(s + \rho_n) = \exp_{w_{\rho_n}(s)} X(s), \quad \text{with } \|X\|_\infty < \varepsilon.$$

Choose A and $B \in \mathbf{R}$ such that:

- $A - \tau^* < 0$, $B - \tau^* > \tau'_n - \tau_n$ and $[\sigma_n, \sigma'_n] \subset [A, B]$.
- For $s \leq A$, $u(s) \in B(x, \delta)$ and $v(s) \in B(y, \delta)$.
- For $s \geq B$, $u(s) \in B(y, \delta)$ and $v(s) \in B(z, \delta)$.

We will prove the desired relation for every $s \in \mathbf{R}$ by cutting up $\mathbf{R}$ into several intervals (in a manner similar to what we did to prove Proposition 9.6.3):

(1) On $]-\infty, A - \rho_n]$. Since $s + \rho_n < A$,

$$w_{\rho_n}(s) = u(s + \rho_n) \in B(x, \delta),$$

and since $s + \rho_n < A < \sigma'_n$,

$$\ell_n(s + \rho_n) \in B(x, \delta).$$

In this case, the relation follows from Lemma 9.6.11.

(2) On $[A - \rho_n, B - \rho_n]$. This time, $s + \rho_n \in [A, B]$ and we have $w_{\rho_n}(s) = u(s + \rho_n)$. Moreover, $\ell_n(s)$ tends to $u(s)$ uniformly on $[A, B]$, hence for n sufficiently large and $s \in [A, B]$,

$$\ell_n(s) = \exp_{u(s)} Y(s), \quad \text{with } \|Y\|_\infty < \varepsilon.$$

We therefore set $X(s) = Y(s + \rho_n)$, so that we obviously have $\|X\|_\infty < \varepsilon$ and

$$\ell_n(s + \rho_n) = \exp_{u(s + \rho_n)} Y(s + \rho_n) = \exp_{w_{\rho_n}(s)} X(s).$$

(3) On $[B - \rho_n, A + \rho_n]$. Here

$$s + \rho_n \in [B, A + 2\rho_n] = [B, A + \tau_n - \tau^\star] \quad \text{and} \quad s - \rho_n \in [B - 2\rho_n, A],$$

which implies that

$$u(s + \rho_n) \in B(y, \delta) \quad \text{and} \quad v(s - \rho_n) \in B(y, \delta).$$

And, since $B > \sigma_n$ and $A + \tau_n - \tau^\star < \tau_n$,

$$\ell_n(s + \rho_n) \in B(y, \delta).$$

The desired relation then follows from Lemma 9.6.11.

(4) On $[A + \rho_n, B + \rho_n]$. This time,

$$s + \rho_n \in [A + 2\rho_n, B + 2\rho_n] = [A + \tau_n - \tau^\star, B + \tau_n - \tau^\star], \quad s - \rho_n \in [A, B]$$

and $w_{\rho_n}(s) = v(s - \rho_n)$. On the compact set $[A - \tau^\star, B - \tau^\star]$, the sequence $\ell_n(s + \tau_n)$ converges uniformly to $v(s + \tau^\star)$ by Lemma 11.2.7. In particular, if n is sufficiently large and if $s \in [A - \tau^\star, B - \tau^\star]$, then

$$\ell_n(s + \tau_n) = \exp_{v(s + \tau^\star)} Y(s), \quad \text{with } \|Y\|_\infty < \varepsilon.$$

We replace s by $s - \tau^\star - \rho_n$ in this equality to find that

for $s \in [A + \rho_n, B + \rho_n], \quad \ell_n(s + \tau_n - \tau^\star - \rho_n) = \exp_{v(s - \rho_n)} Y(s - \tau^\star - \rho_n),$

which can also be written as $\ell_n(s + \rho_n) = \exp_{w_{\rho_n}(s)} X(s)$ for s in the desired interval, where $X(s) = Y(s - \tau^\star - \rho_n)$ satisfies $\|X\|_\infty < \varepsilon$ on this interval.

(5) On $[B + \rho_n, +\infty[$. Here

$$s + \rho_n \in [B + 2\rho_n, +\infty[= [B + \tau_n - \tau^\star, +\infty[, \quad s - \rho_n \in [B, +\infty[$$

and $w_{\rho_n}(s) = v(s - \rho_n)$. Hence, since $B + \tau_n - \tau^\star > \tau'_n$,

$$w_{\rho_n}(s) \in B(z, \delta) \quad \text{and} \quad \ell_n(s + \rho_n) \in B(z, \delta),$$

so that, once again, the desired relation follows from Lemma 9.6.11.

Proposition 11.2.3 is now proved. $\qquad\qquad\qquad\qquad\qquad\qquad\qquad\qquad\qquad\qquad\qquad$ □

Proof of Proposition 11.2.4. It is analogous to that of Proposition 9.6.4 in Section 9.6.c using Lemmas 9.6.13, 9.6.14 and 13.7.1. These three lemmas still hold in the present context:

- For Lemma 9.6.13, the proof is identical, based on the fact that ℓ_n, a solution of a Floer equation, has an exponential decay property.
- The proof of Lemma 9.6.14 is simplified by the fact that W_ρ is now of dimension 1.
- Finally, the analogue of Lemma 13.7.1 can be proved in an identical manner because the Floer operators $\mathcal{F}^\Gamma_\rho$ and $\mathcal{F}_\rho$ have the same properties. □

End of the Proof of the Uniqueness. This too is completely analogous to the proof of the corresponding property (Proposition 9.6.5), this time in Section 9.6.d. By applying Lemmas 9.6.16 and 9.6.17 to the operator

$$F^\Gamma_{\rho_n} : W^{1,p}(\mathbf{R} \times S^1; \mathbf{R}^{2n}) \longrightarrow L^p(\mathbf{R} \times S^1; \mathbf{R}^{2n}),$$

we obtain the existence of an $\varepsilon_1 > 0$ that is independent of n and of a continuous map

$$\gamma_n : \operatorname{Ker}(L^\Gamma_{\rho_n}) \cap B(0, \varepsilon_1) \longrightarrow W^{1,p}(\mathbf{R} \times S^1; \mathbf{R}^{2n})$$

such that for every h, $F^\Gamma_{\rho_n}(\gamma_n(h)) = 0$ and that $\gamma_n(h)$ is the unique element of $h + W^\perp_u \cap B(0, \varepsilon_1)$ with this property. Using Propositions 11.2.3 and 11.2.4, we obtain, for n sufficiently large, the existence of

$$h_n \in B(0, \varepsilon_1) \subset W^{1,p}(\mathbf{R} \times S^1; \mathbf{R}^{2n})$$

with

$$\ell_n(s + \rho_n) = \exp_{w_{\rho_n}(s)} \left(i_{\rho_n}(\gamma_n(h_n(s))) \right)$$

(that is, such that $\ell_n(s + \rho_n)$ is a solution obtained by the Newton–Picard method). On the other hand, the formula

$$h \longmapsto \left(\exp_{w_{\rho_n}}\left(i_{\rho_n}(\gamma_n(h_n))\right)\right)(s - \rho_n, t)$$

defines a continuous map from $B(0, \varepsilon_1) \cap \mathrm{Ker}(L^{\Gamma}_{\rho_n})$ to the space of solutions $\mathcal{M}^{\Gamma}(x, z)$, which is of dimension 1.

Let $\overline{\rho}_0$ be a real number greater than ρ_0 given by the first part of Theorem 11.1.16. For $\varepsilon \in [0, \varepsilon_1]$, let I_ε be the interval contained in $\mathcal{M}^{\Gamma}(x, z)$ and defined by

$$I_\varepsilon = \psi([\overline{\rho}_0, +\infty[) \cup \bigcup_{\rho_n > \overline{\rho}_0} \left\{\exp_{\rho_n}(i_{\rho_n}(\gamma_n(h))) \mid \|h\| \leq \varepsilon\right\}.$$

For every $\varepsilon > 0$, by the above, $\ell_n \in I_\varepsilon$ for n sufficiently large. The analogue of Lemma 9.6.18 (which can be proved in the same manner) shows that there exists an $\varepsilon_2 > 0$ such that

$$I_{\varepsilon_2} \subset \psi([\rho_0, +\infty[).$$

This concludes the proof of Theorem 11.1.16. $\square$

Consequently, Theorem 11.1.15 is also completely proved. With this proof, we have finished the first part of the outline established at the beginning of this chapter, namely the definition of the morphism of complexes

$$\Phi^{\Gamma} : CF_*(H^a, J^a) \longrightarrow CF_*(H^b, J^b).$$

The aim of the second and last step of this outline is to prove that this morphism induces an isomorphism at the homology level. This is in turn divided into two steps corresponding to the following two statements.

Proposition 11.2.8. *At the homology level, the morphism Φ^{Γ} induces a morphism that is independent of the choice of the regular homotopy Γ between (H^a, J^a) and (H^b, J^b).*

Proposition 11.2.9. *Let (H^a, J^a), (H^b, J^b) and $(H^c, J^c) \in (\mathcal{H} \times \mathcal{J})_{\mathrm{reg}}$ and let Γ' and Γ'' be two regular homotopies connecting (H^a, J^a) to (H^b, J^b) and (H^b, J^b) to (H^c, J^c), respectively. There exists a regular homotopy Γ connecting (H^a, J^a) to (H^c, J^c) such that*

$$\Phi^{\Gamma''} \circ \Phi^{\Gamma'} \quad \text{and} \quad \Phi^{\Gamma} : CF_*(H^a, J^a) \longrightarrow CF_*(H^c, J^c)$$

induce the same homomorphism at the homology level.

These two propositions imply the relation

$$\Phi^{\Gamma''} \circ \Phi^{\Gamma'} = \Phi^{\Gamma} \text{ at the homology level,}$$

regardless of the choices of the regular homotopies Γ'', Γ' and Γ, as above. This is step 2 of the outline of this chapter, as stated at its beginning. From this, we deduce that $\Phi^{\Gamma'}$ is an isomorphism at the homology level by taking $(H^a, J^a) = (H^c, J^c)$, $\Gamma = \mathrm{Id}$, and using the fact that $\Phi^{\mathrm{Id}} = \mathrm{Id}$.

The following sections contain the proofs of these two propositions.

11.3 Invariance of Φ^{Γ}: Proof of Proposition 11.2.8

Consider two regular homotopies Γ_0 and Γ_1 connecting (H^a, J^a) to (H^b, J^b). We want to prove that $\Phi^{\Gamma_0} = \Phi^{\Gamma_1}$ at the homotopy level. To do this, we will construct a homotopy

$$S : CF_\star(H^a, J^a) \longrightarrow CF_{\star+1}(H^b, J^b)$$

between Φ^{Γ_0} and Φ^{Γ_1}, in other words, an S satisfying the relation

$$\Phi^{\Gamma_1} - \Phi^{\Gamma_0} = S \circ \partial_{(H^a, J^a)} + \partial_{(H^b, J^b)} \circ S$$

(which implies the desired equality).

We therefore consider a "homotopy of homotopies" $\Gamma = (\Gamma_\lambda)_{\lambda \in [0,1]}$ that connects Γ_0 and Γ_1, which we assume to be stationary near $\lambda = 0$ and $\lambda = 1$. It can be chosen in such a way that there exists an $R > 0$ with the property that for every $\lambda \in [0,1]$,

$$\Gamma_\lambda(s) = \begin{cases} (H^a, J^a), & s \leq -R \\ (H^b, J^b), & s \geq R. \end{cases}$$

See Figure 11.3. We use the contractibility of $\mathcal{J}$ (more exactly, the fact that it is simply connected).

We view Γ as a map (H, J), where

$$H : [0,1] \times \mathbf{R} \times S^1 \times W \longrightarrow \mathbf{R},$$
$$J : [0,1] \times \mathbf{R} \longrightarrow \mathrm{End}(TW),$$

with $J_s^\lambda \in \mathcal{J}$ for every $(\lambda, s) \in [0,1] \times \mathbf{R}$. We may, and do, assume that H and J are of class $\mathcal{C}^\infty$. For every $\lambda \in [0,1]$, these data define a Floer equation with parameters. Using these equations, we prove Proposition 11.2.8 by more or less following the same plan as in Section 11.1.

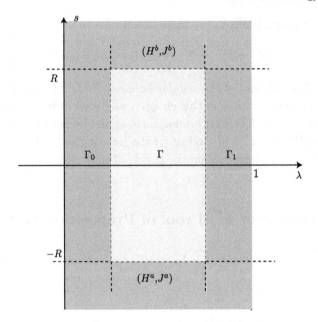

Fig. 11.3

11.3.a The Floer Equations

For $\Gamma_\lambda(s) = (H_{s,t}^\lambda, J_s^\lambda)$ with $\lambda \in [0,1]$ fixed, consider the equation

$$\frac{\partial u}{\partial s} + J_s^\lambda(u)\frac{\partial u}{\partial t} + \mathrm{grad}_u\, H_{s,t}^\lambda = 0$$

and the corresponding space of solutions

$$\mathcal{M}^{\Gamma_\lambda} = \left\{u : \mathbf{R} \times S^1 \to W \mid u \text{ is contractible, with } E(u) < +\infty\right\}.$$

By Theorem 11.1.1, we know that

$$\mathcal{M}^{\Gamma_\lambda} = \bigcup_{\substack{x \in \mathrm{Crit}\,\mathcal{A}_{H^a} \\ y \in \mathrm{Crit}\,\mathcal{A}_{H^b}}} \mathcal{M}^{\Gamma_\lambda}(x,y).$$

For $x \in \mathrm{Crit}\,\mathcal{A}_{H^a}$ and $y \in \mathrm{Crit}\,\mathcal{A}_{H^b}$, we define the space

$$\mathcal{M}^\Gamma(x,y) = \left\{(\lambda, u) \mid \lambda \in [0,1], u \in \mathcal{M}^{\Gamma_\lambda}(x,y)\right\}.$$

Remark 11.3.1. We can view $\mathcal{M}^\Gamma(x,y)$ as a cobordism between the manifolds $\mathcal{M}^{\Gamma_0}(x,y)$ and $\mathcal{M}^{\Gamma_1}(x,y)$. Indeed, if

$$\pi : \mathcal{M}^\Gamma(x,y) \longrightarrow [0,1]$$

denotes the projection (on the space of λ's), then we have

$$\pi^{-1}(\lambda) = \mathcal{M}^{\Gamma_\lambda}(x, y).$$

We will also need to prove that $\mathcal{M}^{\Gamma}(x, y)$ is a manifold. We will do so in the next section.

11.3.b The Transversality

We will use the space $\mathcal{C}_\varepsilon^\infty$ (of perturbations) consisting of the maps

$$h : [0, 1] \times \mathbf{R} \times S^1 \times W \longrightarrow \mathbf{R}$$

with compact support in $]0, 1[\times \mathbf{R} \times W$ such that $\|h\|_\varepsilon < +\infty$. Let

$$h_{s,t}^\lambda(z) = h(\lambda, s, t, z),$$

and let $\Gamma = (H, J)$. We have the following result.

Theorem 11.3.2. *There exist a neighborhood of 0 in $\mathcal{C}_\varepsilon^\infty$ and a countable intersection of dense open subsets $\mathcal{H}_{\mathrm{reg}}$ in this neighborhood such that if $h \in \mathcal{H}_{\mathrm{reg}}$, then for $\Gamma(h) = (H + h, J)$ and for every $x \in \mathrm{Crit}\, \mathcal{A}_{H^a}$ and every $y \in \mathrm{Crit}\, \mathcal{A}_{H^b}$, the space $\mathcal{M}^{\Gamma(h)}(x, y)$ is a manifold with boundary, of dimension $\mu(x) - \mu(y) + 1$, and its boundary is*

$$\partial\mathcal{M}^{\Gamma(h)}(x, y) = \left(\{0\} \times \mathcal{M}^{\Gamma_0}(x, y)\right) \cup \left(\{1\} \times \mathcal{M}^{\Gamma_1}(x, y)\right).$$

In this statement, we use the topology on $\mathcal{M}^{\Gamma(h)}(x, y)$ induced by that of $\mathbf{R} \times \mathcal{C}_{\mathrm{loc}}^\infty(\mathbf{R} \times S^1; W)$.

Let us begin by taking a look at what happens near the boundary. Let $x \in \mathrm{Crit}\, \mathcal{A}_{H^a}$ and let $y \in \mathrm{Crit}\, \mathcal{A}_{H^b}$. For a fixed arbitrary $h \in \mathcal{C}_\varepsilon^\infty$, we analyze the structure of $\mathcal{M}^{\Gamma(h)}(x, y)$ close to its points (λ, u) with $\lambda \in \{0, 1\}$.

Let $\delta > 0$ be sufficiently small such that

$$\mathrm{Supp}(h) \subset [\delta, 1 - \delta] \times \mathbf{R} \times S^1 \times W$$

and for the isotopy $\Gamma = (H, J)$ to be stationary for $\lambda \leq \delta$ and for $\lambda \geq 1 - \delta$. We therefore have $\Gamma(h) = \Gamma_0$ for $\lambda \leq \delta$ and $\Gamma(h) = \Gamma_1$ for $\lambda \geq 1 - \delta$. It is then clear that

$$\mathcal{M}^{\Gamma(h)}(x, y) \cap \{\lambda < \delta\} = [0, \delta[\times \mathcal{M}^{\Gamma_0}(x, y)$$

and $$\mathcal{M}^{\Gamma(h)}(x, y) \cap \{\lambda > 1 - \delta\} =]1 - \delta, 1] \times \mathcal{M}^{\Gamma_1}(x, y).$$

This shows that in the neighborhood of the points of

$$\{0\} \times \mathcal{M}^{\Gamma_0}(x, y) \cup \{1\} \times \mathcal{M}^{\Gamma_1}(x, y),$$

the space $\mathcal{M}^{\Gamma(h)}$ has the structure of a manifold with boundary, as stated in the theorem.

Next, we follow the same plan as in Chapter 8 (see the outline at the end of Section 8.1). Our starting point is an analogue of Theorem 8.1.5, namely a version of Theorem 11.1.7 that holds for the homotopies Γ_λ for a fixed λ in $[0, 1]$ with the same proof.

Theorem 11.3.3. *For every fixed $\lambda \in {]}0, 1[$, all critical points $x \in \mathrm{Crit}\, \mathcal{A}_{H^a}$, $y \in \mathrm{Crit}\, \mathcal{A}_{H^b}$ and every $u \in \mathcal{M}^{\Gamma_\lambda}(x, y)$, the operator $(d\mathcal{F}^{\Gamma_\lambda})_u$ is a Fredholm operator of index $\mu(x) - \mu(y)$.*

Using this theorem, we can establish a statement analogous to Proposition 8.1.3. To do this, we fix $J = (J^\lambda)_{\lambda \in [0,1]}$ and, as in Section 8.5, consider the fiber bundle

$$\mathcal{E} \longrightarrow \mathcal{P}^{1,p}(x, y) \times \mathcal{C}_\varepsilon^\infty,$$

where

$$\mathcal{E} = \left\{ (u, h, Y) \mid (u, h) \in \mathcal{P}^{1,p}(x, y) \times \mathcal{C}_\varepsilon^\infty, Y \in L^p(u^\star TW) \right\}.$$

We define a family of sections $(\sigma_\lambda)_{\lambda \in [0,1]}$ by setting

$$\sigma_\lambda(u, h) = \frac{\partial u}{\partial s} + J^\lambda(u)\frac{\partial u}{\partial t} + \mathrm{grad}_u(H^\lambda + h^\lambda).$$

Exactly as in Section 11.1 (using the analogue of Proposition 11.1.8), we prove that for every $\lambda \in {]}0, 1[$, the map σ_λ is transversal to the zero section of the fiber bundle $\mathcal{E}$ defined above. It follows that the same property holds for the $\mathcal{C}^\infty$ map

$$\sigma : {]}0, 1[\times \mathcal{P}^{1,p}(x, y) \times \mathcal{C}_\varepsilon^\infty \longrightarrow \mathcal{E}$$
$$(\lambda, u, h) \longmapsto \sigma_\lambda(u, h),$$

which, by the implicit function theorem, implies the analogue of Proposition 8.1.3.

Proposition 11.3.4. *For $x \in \mathrm{Crit}\, \mathcal{A}_{H^a}$ and $y \in \mathrm{Crit}\, \mathcal{A}_{H^b}$, the space $\mathcal{Z}(x, y, J)$ defined as*

$$\left\{ (\lambda, u, H + h) \mid \lambda \in {]}0, 1[, h \in \mathcal{C}_\varepsilon^\infty, u \in \mathcal{M}^{\Gamma_\lambda}(x, y, (H + h)^\lambda, J^\lambda) \right\}$$

is a Banach manifold.

The presence of the parameter λ forces us to modify (with respect to Section 8.5.c) the expression of the tangent space of $\mathcal{Z}(x, y, J)$ at a point $(\lambda, u, H + h_0)$. In our new setting, this space, which is the kernel of $(d\sigma)_{(\lambda, u, H + h_0)}$, consists of all $(a, Y, h) \in \mathbf{R} \times W^{1,p} \times \mathcal{C}_\varepsilon^\infty$ that satisfy the equation

$$a \frac{\partial J^\lambda}{\partial \lambda}(u) \frac{\partial u}{\partial t} + a \operatorname{grad}_u \frac{\partial (H + h_0)^\lambda}{\partial \lambda} + (d\mathcal{F}^{\Gamma_\lambda})_u(Y) + \operatorname{grad}_u(h^\lambda) = 0.$$

To prove Theorem 11.3.3, we use the following result.

Proposition 11.3.5. *Let* $\pi : \mathcal{Z}(x, y, J) \to \mathcal{C}_\varepsilon^\infty$ *be the projection. The set of regular values of* π *in a neighborhood of* 0 *in* $\mathcal{C}_\varepsilon^\infty$ *is a dense open subset of this neighborhood.*

Proof. The statement is a direct application of the Sard–Smale theorem (Theorem 8.5.7), provided that we first prove that π is a Fredholm map. Let us therefore show that for every $(\lambda, u, H + h_0) \in \mathcal{Z}(x, y, J)$, the operator

$$(d\pi)_{(\lambda, u, H + h_0)} : T_{(\lambda, u, H + h_0)} \mathcal{Z}(x, y, J) \longrightarrow T_{h_0} \mathcal{C}_\varepsilon^\infty,$$

which is of the form $(a, Y, h) \mapsto h$, is a Fredholm operator. Let V denote the vector field

$$V = \frac{\partial J^\lambda}{\partial \lambda}(u) \frac{\partial u}{\partial t} + \operatorname{grad}_u \frac{\partial (H^\lambda + h_0^\lambda)}{\partial \lambda} \in L^p(u^\star TW).$$

By the expression of the tangent space of $\mathcal{Z}(x, y, J)$, we see that the kernel of $(d\pi)_{(\lambda, u, H + h_0)}$ is the space

$$\left\{ (a, Y, 0) \mid (a, Y) \in \mathbf{R} \times W^{1,p}(u^\star TW) \text{ and } aV + (d\mathcal{F}^{\Gamma_\lambda})_u(Y) = 0 \right\}.$$

Let us therefore show that this space is finite-dimensional. We distinguish between two cases:

(1) $V \notin \operatorname{Im}((d\mathcal{F}^{\Gamma_\lambda})_u)$. In this case, we find

$$\operatorname{Ker}(d\pi)_{(\lambda, u, H + h_0)} = \left\{ (0, Y, 0) \mid Y \in \operatorname{Ker}(d\mathcal{F}_u^{\Gamma_\lambda}) \right\},$$

which is finite-dimensional by Theorem 11.3.3.

(2) $V \in \operatorname{Im}((d\mathcal{F}^{\Gamma_\lambda})_u)$. We choose a $Y_0 \in W^{1,p}(u^\star TW)$ such that $(d\mathcal{F}^{\Gamma_\lambda})_u(Y_0) = V$. It follows that

$$\operatorname{Ker}(d\pi)_{(\lambda, u, H + h_0)} = \left\{ (a, Y, 0) \mid a(d\mathcal{F}^{\Gamma_\lambda})_u(Y_0) + (d\mathcal{F}^{\Gamma_\lambda})_u(Y) = 0 \right\}.$$

This space is isomorphic to $\mathbf{R}Y_0 + \operatorname{Ker}(d\mathcal{F}^{\Gamma_\lambda})_u$, which is also finite-dimensional.

Next, the image of $(d\pi)_{(\lambda, u, H + h_0)}$ is closed and has a finite codimension, still by Theorem 11.3.3. Indeed, it is the inverse image of the finite-codimensional closed subspace

$$\mathbf{R}V + \mathrm{Im}((d\mathcal{F}_u^{\Gamma_\lambda})) \subset L^p(u^\star TW)$$

under the linear map $h \mapsto \mathrm{grad}_u\, h$ viewed as a map

$$\mathcal{C}_\varepsilon^\infty \longrightarrow L^p(u^\star TW).$$

Consequently, π is indeed a Fredholm map, which proves Proposition 11.3.5 (by the Sard–Smale theorem). $\qquad\square$

Let $\mathcal{H}_{\mathrm{reg}} \subset \mathcal{C}_\varepsilon^\infty$ denote the neighborhood given by this proposition. We have just proved that for $h \in \mathcal{H}_{\mathrm{reg}}$, the homotopy $\Gamma(h)$ has the property that for all critical points $x \in \mathrm{Crit}\,\mathcal{A}_{H^a}$ and $y \in \mathrm{Crit}\,\mathcal{A}_{H^b}$, the set

$$\pi^{-1}(h) = \mathcal{M}^{\Gamma(h)}(x,y) \cap \{\lambda \in \,]0,1[\}$$

is a manifold (with the $\mathcal{C}_{\mathrm{loc}}^\infty$ topology; see Remark 8.5.10). Using the same argument as at the beginning of the proof of Theorem 11.3.2, we deduce that $\mathcal{M}^{\Gamma(h)}(x,y)$ is a manifold with boundary.

To conclude the proof of Theorem 11.3.2, let us determine the dimension of this manifold. It equals the dimension of the kernel of $(d\pi)_{(\lambda,u,H+h_0)}$ for some $h_0 \in \mathcal{H}_{\mathrm{reg}}$. We described this vector space in the proof of Proposition 11.3.5. To determine its dimension, we use the following lemma.

Lemma 11.3.6. *Let $h_0 \in \mathcal{H}_{\mathrm{reg}}$ and let $(\lambda,u) \in \mathcal{M}^{\Gamma(h_0)}(x,y)$. The operator*

$$\mathcal{Y} : \mathbf{R} \times W^{1,p}(u^\star TW) \longrightarrow L^p(u^\star TW)$$

defined by $\mathcal{Y}(a,Y) = aV + (d\mathcal{F}^{\Gamma_\lambda(H+h_0)})_u(Y)$ is surjective.

In this statement, V still denotes the vector field defined and used in the proof of Proposition 11.3.5.

Proof. First note that $\mathrm{Ker}\,\mathcal{Y} = \mathrm{Ker}(d\pi)_{(\lambda,u,H+h_0)}$ is finite-dimensional and that $\mathrm{Im}\,\mathcal{Y} = \mathbf{R}V + \mathrm{Im}(d\mathcal{F}^{\Gamma_\lambda})_u$ is closed and finite-codimensional in $L^p(u^\star TW)$. In other words, $\mathcal{Y}$ is a Fredholm operator. Suppose that it is not surjective. Then, as in Lemma 8.5.1, there exists a nonzero vector field $Z \in L^q(u^\star TW)$ (here $1/p + 1/q = 1$) such that $\langle Z, \mathrm{Im}\,\mathcal{Y}\rangle = 0$, which is equivalent to

$$\langle Z, V\rangle = 0 \quad \text{and} \quad \langle Z, \mathrm{Im}(d\mathcal{F}^{\Gamma_\lambda})_u\rangle = 0.$$

The second condition implies that Z is of class $\mathcal{C}^\infty$, by elliptic regularity, as in the proof of Lemma 8.5.1. We now use the assumption that $h_0 \in \mathcal{H}_{\mathrm{reg}}$. It implies that $(d\pi)_{(\lambda,u,H+h_0)}$ is surjective, which means that for every $h \in \mathcal{C}_\varepsilon^\infty$, there exists an $(a, Y) \in \mathbf{R} \times W^{1,p}(u^\star TW)$ such that

$$aV + (d\mathcal{F}^{\Gamma_\lambda})_u(Y) + \operatorname{grad}_u h = 0$$

(in other words, $(a, Y, h) \in T_{(\lambda, u, H + h_0)} \mathcal{Z}(x, y, J)$). It follows that

$$\langle Z, \operatorname{grad}_u h \rangle = 0 \quad \text{for every } h \in \mathcal{C}_\varepsilon^\infty,$$

which gives a contradiction because of Lemma 11.1.9. This concludes the proof of the lemma.   □

With the notation of the previous lemma, we then find that

$$\dim \mathcal{M}^{\Gamma(h)}(x, y) = \dim \operatorname{Ker}(d\pi)_{(\lambda, u, H + h_0)} = \dim \operatorname{Ker} \mathcal{Y} = \operatorname{Ind} \mathcal{Y}.$$

To compute the Fredholm index of $\mathcal{Y}$, we consider the path of operators $(\mathcal{Y}_\sigma)_{\sigma \in [0,1]}$:

$$\mathcal{Y}_\sigma : \mathbf{R} \times W^{1,p}(u^\star TW) \longrightarrow L^p(u^\star TW)$$
$$(a, Y) \longmapsto a\sigma V + (d\mathcal{F}^{\Gamma_\lambda(H + h)})_u(Y).$$

These are Fredholm operators because they are of the same form as $\mathcal{Y}$. In particular, their index does not depend on σ (by C.2.11), it is therefore equal to that of $\mathcal{Y}_0$, but

$$\mathcal{Y}_0(a, Y) = (d\mathcal{F}^{\Gamma_\lambda})_u(Y),$$

hence

$$\operatorname{Ind} \mathcal{Y} = \operatorname{Ind} \mathcal{Y}_0 = \operatorname{Ind}(d\mathcal{F}^{\Gamma_\lambda})_u + 1 = \mu(x) - \mu(y) + 1$$

by Theorem 11.3.3. This concludes the proof of Theorem 11.3.2.   □

From now on, we will assume that the homotopies $\Gamma = (H, J)$ are regular, which implies that the spaces $\mathcal{M}^\Gamma(x, y)$ are manifolds of dimension $\mu(x) - \mu(y) + 1$, as in the conclusion of Theorem 11.3.2. We will moreover assume that the operator $\mathcal{Y}$ defined in Lemma 11.3.6 is surjective, as authorized by Theorem 11.3.2, after taking a perturbation of H by an $h \in \mathcal{C}_\varepsilon^\infty$, if necessary.

11.3.c Compactness, Broken Orbits

Let $\Gamma = (H, J)$ be as above. Let

$$\mathcal{M}^\Gamma = \bigcup_{\substack{x \in \operatorname{Crit} \mathcal{A}_{H^a} \\ y \in \operatorname{Crit} \mathcal{A}_{H^b}}} \mathcal{M}^\Gamma(x, y) = \bigcup_{\lambda \in [0,1]} \{\lambda\} \times \mathcal{M}^{\Gamma_\lambda}.$$

We will prove the following.

Theorem 11.3.7. *There exists a constant $C > 0$ such that $E(u) \le C$ for every $(\lambda, u) \in \mathcal{M}^\Gamma$. The space $\mathcal{M}^\Gamma$ is compact for the $\mathcal{C}^\infty_{\mathrm{loc}}$ topology.*

In this statement, the energy $E(u)$ is computed using the norm associated with the metric $\omega(\cdot, J^\lambda_s)$.

Proof of Theorem 11.3.7. We first show that the energy is bounded. Let $(\lambda, u) \in \mathcal{M}^\Gamma$. There exist two critical points x and y (of H^a and H^b, respectively) such that $u \in \mathcal{M}^{\Gamma_\lambda}(x, y)$. Proposition 11.1.2 then asserts that

$$E(u) \le \mathcal{A}_{H^a} - \mathcal{A}_{H^b} + k,$$

where k is the maximum of $\partial H^\lambda / \partial s(s, t, z)$ on $[-R, R] \times S^1 \times W$. It suffices to define K as the maximum of this same function when λ also varies,

$$K = \sup \left\{ \frac{\partial H^\lambda}{\partial s}(s, t, z) \mid (\lambda, s, t, z) \in [0, 1] \times [-R, R] \times S^1 \times W \right\},$$

and to set

$$C = \max_{\substack{x \in \operatorname{Crit} \mathcal{A}_{H^a} \\ y \in \operatorname{Crit} H^b}} \mathcal{A}_{H^a} - \mathcal{A}_{H^b} + K$$

to have $E(u) \le C$.

We will now show the compactness statement. Let $(\lambda_n, u_n)_{n \in \mathbf{N}}$ be a sequence in $\mathcal{M}^\Gamma$. After extracting a subsequence, if necessary, (λ_n) converges to a number $\lambda \in [0, 1]$. Using the fact that the energy is bounded, we prove the following result in the same way as Proposition 11.1.5.

Proposition 11.3.8. *There exists a constant $A > 0$ such that*

$$\forall (u, \lambda) \in \mathcal{M}^{\Gamma_\lambda}, \ \forall (s, t) \in \mathbf{R} \times S^1, \ \ \left\| \operatorname{grad}_{(s,t)} u \right\| \le A.$$

This statement implies that the family (u_n) is equicontinuous, whence we can conclude using the Arzelà–Ascoli theorem and the elliptic regularity (Lemma 12.1.1) that the sequence (u_n) tends to a limit u in the $\mathcal{C}^\infty_{\mathrm{loc}}$ topology. This limit u is a solution of

$$\frac{\partial u}{\partial s} + J^\lambda_s \frac{\partial u}{\partial t} + \operatorname{grad}_u H^\lambda_{s,t}(u) = 0.$$

It satisfies $E(u) \le C$, hence $u \in \mathcal{M}^{\Gamma_\lambda}$ and consequently $(\lambda, u) \in \mathcal{M}^\Gamma$. Theorem 11.3.7 is now proved. $\square$

Let us now analyze the behavior of the sequences (λ_n, u_n) of elements of $\mathcal{M}^\Gamma(x, y)$. We begin with an analogue of Lemma 11.1.12.

Lemma 11.3.9. *Let* $x \in \text{Crit}\,\mathcal{A}_{H^a}$, *let* $y \in \text{Crit}\,\mathcal{A}_{H^b}$ *and let* (λ_n, u_n) *be a sequence in* $\mathcal{M}^\Gamma(x, y)$. *Let* (s_n) *be a sequence of real numbers that tends to* $+\infty$. *Then there exist a subsequence (also denoted by* (λ_n, u_n)*) and an element* $(\lambda_\star, v) \in [0, 1] \times \mathcal{M}^{(H^b, J^b)}$ *such that*

$$\lim \lambda_n = \lambda_\star \quad and \quad \lim u_n \cdot s_n = v.$$

Likewise, if $\lim s_n = -\infty$, *then there exist a subsequence and an element* $(\lambda_\star, u) \in [0, 1] \times \mathcal{M}^{(H^a, J^a)}$ *such that*

$$\lim \lambda_n = \lambda_\star \quad and \quad \lim u_n \cdot s_n = u.$$

Proof. After extracting a subsequence, if necessary, we may, and do, assume that the sequence of the λ_n converges, to a number $\lambda_\star \in [0, 1]$. Next, $v_n = u_n \cdot s_n$ is a solution of the Floer equation

$$\frac{\partial v_n}{\partial s} + J^{\lambda_n}_{s+s_n} \frac{\partial v_n}{\partial t} + \text{grad}_{v_n} H^{\lambda_n}_{s+s_n} = 0.$$

Applying Proposition 11.3.8, and using the Arzelà–Ascoli theorem and elliptic regularity (Lemma 12.1.1), we show that $u_n \cdot s_n$ converges, for the $\mathcal{C}^\infty_{\text{loc}}$ topology, to a limit $v \in \mathcal{C}^\infty(\mathbf{R} \times S^1; W)$. By letting n tend to $+\infty$ in the Floer equation, we find that v is indeed a solution of

$$\frac{\partial v}{\partial s} + J^b \frac{\partial v}{\partial t} + \text{grad}_v H^b = 0$$

(because $\Gamma = (H^b, J^b)$ for s sufficiently large); in other words, $v \in \mathcal{M}^{(H^b, J^b)}$. The case where (s_n) tends to infinity is analogous. $\qquad\square$

We will use this lemma to prove a theorem on the convergence toward broken orbits, which is analogous to Theorem 11.1.10.

Theorem 11.3.10. *Let* (λ_n, u_n) *be a sequence of elements of* $\mathcal{M}^\Gamma(x, y)$. *Then there exist:*

- *A subsequence of* (λ_n, u_n)
- *Critical points* $x = x_0, x_1, \ldots, x_k$ *of* $\mathcal{A}_{H^a}$
- *Critical points* $y_0, y_1, \ldots, y_\ell = y$ *of* $\mathcal{A}_{H^b}$
- *Real sequences* (s^i_n) *for* $0 \leq i \leq k - 1$ *(that tend to* $-\infty$*) and* (s'^j_n) *for* $0 \leq j \leq \ell - 1$ *(that tend to* $+\infty$*)*
- *Elements* $u^i \in \mathcal{M}^{(H^a, J^a)}(x_i, x_{i+1})$ *for* $0 \leq i \leq k - 1$ *and elements* $v^j \in \mathcal{M}^{(H^b, J^b)}(y_j, y_{j+1})$ *for* $0 \leq j \leq \ell - 1$
- *An element* $(\lambda_\star, w) \in \mathcal{M}^\Gamma(x_k, y_0)$

such that for $0 \le i \le k-1$ and $0 \le j \le \ell - 1$, we have

$$\lim u_n \cdot s_n^i = u^i \quad \text{and} \quad \lim u_n \cdot s_n^j = v^j$$

and

$$\lim(\lambda_n, u_n) = (\lambda_*, w).$$

Moreover, we have the inequality

$$\mu(x) - \mu(y) + 1 \ge k + \ell.$$

Proof. The proof of the existence is similar in all details to that of the analogous statement (Theorem 11.1.10). It depends on the compactness assertion of Theorem 11.3.7 and on Lemma 11.3.9. The final inequality can be proved in the same manner as Corollary 11.1.11.   □

Here is a consequence of Theorem 11.3.10:

Theorem 11.3.11. (i) *Let x and y be critical points of H^a and H^b, respectively, and let $\Gamma = (H, J)$ be a regular homotopy. If $\mu(x) - \mu(y) + 1 = 0$, then $\mathcal{M}^\Gamma(x, y)$ is a compact manifold of dimension 0 (that is, a finite number of points).*

(ii) *Let x and z be critical points of H^a and H^b, respectively, and let $\Gamma = (H, J)$ be a regular homotopy. If $\mu(x) = \mu(z)$, and if $\Pi^\Gamma(x, z)$ denotes*

$$\Pi^\Gamma(x, z) = \left(\bigcup_{\substack{y' \in \mathrm{Crit}\, \mathcal{A}_{H^a} \\ \mu(x) - \mu(y') = 1}} \mathcal{L}_{(H^a, J^a)}(x, y') \times \mathcal{M}^\Gamma(y', z) \right)$$
$$\cup \left(\bigcup_{\substack{y \in \mathrm{Crit}\, \mathcal{A}_{H^b} \\ \mu(y) - \mu(z) = 1}} \mathcal{M}^\Gamma(x, y) \times \mathcal{L}_{(H^b, J^b)}(y, z) \right),$$

then $\mathcal{M}^\Gamma(x, z) \cup \Pi^\Gamma(x, z)$ is a compact manifold of dimension 1 with boundary, and its boundary is

$$\Pi^\Gamma(x, z) \cup (\{0\} \times \mathcal{M}^{\Gamma_0}(x, z)) \cup (\{1\} \times \mathcal{M}^{\Gamma_1}(x, z)).$$

Let us, for the moment, admit this theorem. We can then achieve the goal of this section, namely the proof of Proposition 11.2.8.

Proof of Proposition 11.2.8. We define the homotopy

$$S : CF_*(H^a, J^a) \longrightarrow CF_{*+1}(H^b, J^b).$$

If x is a critical point of $\mathcal{A}_{H^a}$ of index $\mu(x) = k$, then we set

$$S_k(x) = \sum_{\substack{y \in \mathrm{Crit}\, \mathcal{A}_{H^a} \\ \mu(y) = k+1}} m^\Gamma(x, y) \cdot y,$$

where $m^\Gamma(x, y)$ is, of course, the number of elements of $\mathcal{M}^\Gamma(x, y)$ counted modulo 2. We want to show that

$$\Phi^{\Gamma_1} - \Phi^{\Gamma_0} = S \circ \partial_{(H^a, J^a)} + \partial_{(H^b, J^b)} \circ S.$$

We first determine the right-hand side for an $x \in \mathrm{Crit}\, \mathcal{A}_{H^a}$ with $\mu(x) = k$. We have

$$S \circ \partial_{(H^a, J^a)}(x) + \partial_{(H^b, J^b)} \circ S(x)$$

$$= S_{k-1} \sum_{\substack{y' \in \mathrm{Crit}\, \mathcal{A}_{H^a} \\ \mu(y') = k-1}} n^a(x, y') y' + \partial_{(H^b, J^b)} \sum_{\substack{y \in \mathrm{Crit}\, \mathcal{A}_{H^b} \\ \mu(y) = k+1}} m^\Gamma(x, y) y$$

$$= \sum_{\substack{z \in \mathrm{Crit}\, \mathcal{A}_{H^b} \\ \mu(z) = k}} \sum_{\substack{y' \in \mathrm{Crit}\, \mathcal{A}_{H^a} \\ \mu(y') = k-1}} n^a(x, y') m^\Gamma(y', z) z$$

$$+ \sum_{\substack{z \in \mathrm{Crit}\, \mathcal{A}_{H^b} \\ \mu(z) = k}} \sum_{\substack{y \in \mathrm{Crit}\, \mathcal{A}_{H^b} \\ \mu(y) = k+1}} m^\Gamma(x, y) n^b(y, z) z$$

$$= \sum_{\substack{z \in \mathrm{Crit}\, \mathcal{A}_{H^b} \\ \mu(z) = k}} (\# \Pi^\Gamma(x, z)) z.$$

On the other hand,

$$\Phi^{\Gamma_0}(x) + \Phi^{\Gamma_1}(x) = \sum_{\substack{z \in \mathrm{Crit}\, \mathcal{A}_{H^b} \\ \mu(z) = k}} (\# \mathcal{M}^{\Gamma_0}(x, z)) z + \sum_{\substack{z \in \mathrm{Crit}\, \mathcal{A}_{H^b} \\ \mu(z) = k}} (\# \mathcal{M}^{\Gamma_1}(x, z)) z.$$

By Theorem 11.3.11, the boundary of the manifold $\mathcal{M}^\Gamma(x, z) \cup \Pi^\Gamma(x, z)$ (which is compact of dimension 1) is the union

$$\Pi^\Gamma(x, z) \cup (\{0\} \times \mathcal{M}^{\Gamma_0}(x, z)) \cup (\{1\} \times \mathcal{M}^{\Gamma_1}(x, z)),$$

hence the total number of points of this union is even, so that

$$S \circ \partial_{(H^a, J^a)}(x) + \partial_{(H^b, J^b)} \circ S(x) = (\Phi^{\Gamma_0} + \Phi^{\Gamma_1})(x),$$

which modulo 2 is indeed the equality

$$S \circ \partial_{(H^a, J^a)} + \partial_{(H^b, J^b)} \circ S = \Phi^{\Gamma_1} - \Phi^{\Gamma_0}.$$

We have now proved Proposition 11.2.8. □

We have one more proof to carry out, namely that of Theorem 11.3.11.

Proof of Theorem 11.3.11.

(i) The homotopy Γ is regular, hence $\mathcal{M}^\Gamma$ is a manifold of dimension 0. The compactness of $\mathcal{M}^\Gamma(x, y)$ follows from Theorem 11.3.10.

Remark 11.3.12. Under the assumptions of Theorem 11.3.11, let $(\lambda_1, u_1), \dots, (\lambda_k, u_k)$ denote the elements of $\mathcal{M}^\Gamma(x, y)$. Then the corresponding homotopies Γ_i that connect (H^a, J^a) to (H^b, J^b) cannot be regular. Indeed, if, for example, Γ_1 were regular, then $\mathcal{M}^{\Gamma_1}(x, y)$ would be empty (since its dimension $\mu(x) - \mu(y) = -1$ would be negative). This would give a contradiction with the fact that $u_1 \in \mathcal{M}^{\Gamma_1}(x, y)$.

Let us return to the proof of Theorem 11.3.11 and prove part (ii). The compactness of $\mathcal{M}^\Gamma(x, y) \cup \Pi^\Gamma(x, z)$ is also an immediate consequence of Theorem 11.3.10. Next, since Γ is regular, $\mathcal{M}^\Gamma(x, z)$ is a manifold of dimension 1 with boundary, and its boundary is

$$\left(\{0\} \times \mathcal{M}^{\Gamma_0}(x, z)\right) \cup \left(\{1\} \times \mathcal{M}^{\Gamma_1}(x, z)\right).$$

To conclude the proof, we need to study the structure of $\mathcal{M}^\Gamma(x, z) \cup \Pi^\Gamma(x, z)$ near the points of the (compact) manifold (of dimension 0) $\Pi^\Gamma(x, z)$. We will do this in the next section, using a "gluing"-type method. Before that, let us highlight a particular case where studying this structure is unnecessary because $\Pi^\Gamma(x, z)$ is empty.   □

Remark 11.3.13. If the homotopies Γ_λ that the homotopy of homotopies Γ passes through are all regular, then $\mathcal{M}^\Gamma(x, z)$ is compact: it is a compact cobordism between $\mathcal{M}^{\Gamma_0}(x, z)$ and $\mathcal{M}^{\Gamma_1}(x, z)$ (see Remark 11.3.1 and Figures 11.4 and 11.5). Consequently, the numbers of elements of $\mathcal{M}^{\Gamma_0}(x, z)$ and

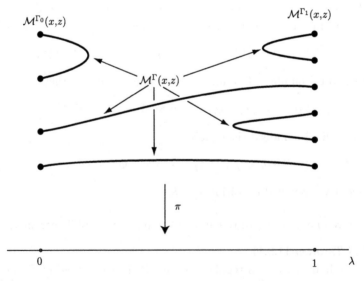

Fig. 11.4

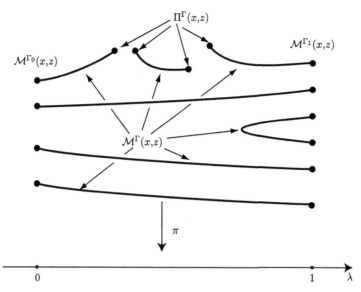

Fig. 11.5

$\mathcal{M}^{\Gamma_1}(x, z)$ have the same parity and in particular the two morphisms

$$\Phi^{\Gamma_0}, \Phi^{\Gamma_1} : CF_\star(H^a, J^a) \longrightarrow CF_\star(H^b, J^b)$$

coincide.

This remark is an easy consequence of Remark 11.3.12. If all the homotopies Γ_λ are regular, then $\Pi^\Gamma(x, z)$ is empty because the spaces $\mathcal{M}^\Gamma(y', z)$ and $\mathcal{M}^\Gamma(x, y)$ that occur in its definition are empty. Hence the cobordism $\mathcal{M}^\Gamma(x, z)$ is compact.

Figure 11.4 represents the case where Γ_λ is regular for every $\lambda \in [0, 1]$, in which case $\Pi^\Gamma(x, z)$ is empty. Figure 11.5 represents the general case where Γ is regular but not all Γ_λ are.

11.3.d The Gluing

When $\mu(x) = \mu(z)$, a point of $\Pi^\Gamma(x, z)$ is a broken orbit, which can be:

- Of the form $[\widehat{u}', (\lambda', v')] \in \mathcal{L}_{(H^a, J^a)}(x, y') \times \mathcal{M}^\Gamma(y', z)$
- Or of the form $[(\lambda, u), \widehat{v}] \in \mathcal{M}^\Gamma(x, y) \times \mathcal{L}_{(H^b, J^b)}(y, z)$

for a $y' \in \mathrm{Crit}(\mathcal{A}_{H^a})$ that satisfies $\mu(x) - \mu(y') = 1$ or for a $y \in \mathrm{Crit}(\mathcal{A}_{H^b})$ that satisfies $\mu(y) - \mu(z) = 1$.

To conclude the proof of Theorem 11.3.11 (ii), we use a gluing process analogous to that of Section 11.1.d to construct, for every point of $\Pi^\Gamma(x, z)$, an embedding $\rho \mapsto \psi(\rho)$ in $\mathcal{M}^\Gamma(x, z)$, which will give a parametrization of the manifold with boundary $\mathcal{M}^\Gamma(x, z) \cup \Pi^\Gamma(x, z)$ near the point of $\Pi^\Gamma(x, z)$ in question.

We will content ourselves with doing this only for the points of the form $[(\lambda, u), \widehat{v}]$, since the proof for the other points is analogous. The precise statement is as follows.

Theorem 11.3.14. *Let x be a critical point of $\mathcal{A}_{H^a}$, and let y, z be critical points of $\mathcal{A}_{H^b}$ such that*

$$\mu(x) = \mu(z) = \mu(y) - 1.$$

Let $(\lambda_\star, u) \in \mathcal{M}^\Gamma(x, y)$ and let $\widehat{v} \in \mathcal{L}_{(H^b, J^b)}(y, z)$. Then:

- *There exists an embedding $\psi : [\rho_0, +\infty[\to \mathcal{M}^\Gamma(x, z)$ (for some ρ_0) such that $\lim_{\rho \to +\infty} \psi(\rho) = [(\lambda_\star, u), \widehat{v}]$.*
- *If $[\lambda_n, \ell_n]$ is a sequence of elements of $\mathcal{M}^\Gamma(x, z)$ that tends to $[(\lambda_\star, u), \widehat{v}]$, then $[\lambda_n, \ell_n] \in \operatorname{Im} \psi$ for n sufficiently large.*

The convergence in this theorem is the one defined in Theorem 11.3.10. The proof is given in the following section.

11.4 Proof of Theorem 11.3.14

We take up the proof of Theorem 11.1.16 (given in Section 11.2), emphasizing the necessary modifications.

First note that the $\lambda_\star$ of the statement is in the open interval $]0, 1[$. Indeed, the manifold $\mathcal{M}^\Gamma(x, y)$ (of dimension 0) consists of the pairs (λ, u) for which the homotopies Γ_λ are not regular (Remark 11.3.12). This excludes the values $\lambda_\star = 0$ and 1. Our objective is to define, for $\rho \geq \rho_0$, a map

$$\psi_\rho : \mathbf{R} \times S^1 \longrightarrow W$$

and a constant λ_ρ such that ψ_ρ is a solution of the Floer equation with parameters

$$\frac{\partial \psi_\rho}{\partial s} + J_s^{\lambda_\rho} \frac{\partial \psi_\rho}{\partial t} + \operatorname{grad}_{\psi_\rho} H_{s,t}^{\lambda_\rho} = 0,$$

with conditions

$$\lim_{s \to -\infty} \psi_\rho(s, \bullet) = x, \qquad \lim_{s \to +\infty} \psi(s, \bullet) = z.$$

Remark 11.4.1. A naive solution would be to take $\lambda_\rho = \lambda_\star$ and to try to define ψ_ρ as in Section 11.2, starting from the pre-gluing of u and a lift

$v \in \mathcal{M}_{(H^b, J^b)}(y, z)$ of $\hat{v}$. This method is destined to fail because the homotopy Γ_{λ_*} is not regular (Remark 11.3.12), so that we cannot deduce that the linearized operator $L_u = (d\mathcal{F}^{\Gamma_\lambda})_u$ is surjective. We therefore cannot construct the inverse operator G_ρ, which is essential for the Newton–Picard method of Sections 9.4 and 11.2. Here Coker L_u is of dimension 1. It is the variation of λ that will provide the missing dimension.

Still following Section 9.4, we carry out the substitution

$$\varphi_\rho(s, t) = \psi_\rho(s + \rho, t).$$

The map φ_ρ will need to satisfy the equation

$$\frac{\partial \varphi_\rho}{\partial s} + J^{\lambda_\rho}_{s+\rho} \frac{\partial \varphi_\rho}{\partial t} + \text{grad}_{\varphi_\rho} H^{\lambda_\rho}_{s+\rho,t} = 0.$$

We keep the same plan as in Sections 9.4 and 11.2, that is:

(1) Pre-gluing
(2) Construction of φ (and therefore of ψ, *via* the substitution given above)
(3) Properties of ψ.

11.4.a Pre-gluing

We fix a lift $v \in \mathcal{M}_{(H^b, J^b)}(y, z)$ of $\hat{v}$. The pre-gluing formula $w_\rho = u \#_\rho v$ remains the same:

$$w_\rho(s, t) = \begin{cases} u(s + \rho, t) & \text{if } s \le -1 \\ \exp_{y(t)}\Big(\beta^-(s) \exp^{-1}_{y(t)}(u(s + \rho, t)) \\ \qquad\qquad + \beta^+(s) \exp^{-1}_{y(t)}(v(s - \rho, t))\Big) & \text{if } s \in [-1, 1] \\ v(s - \rho, t) & \text{if } s \ge 1, \end{cases}$$

and its properties are analogous to those given in Section 9.3.

Likewise, the linear version of the pre-gluing

$$Y \#_\rho Z, \quad \text{for } Y \in T\mathcal{P}_u(x, y) \text{ and } Z \in T\mathcal{P}_v(y, z),$$

is defined by the same formula and has the same properties as its analogue in Section 9.3.

11.4.b Construction of φ

As in Sections 9.4 and 11.2.b, we once again use the Newton–Picard method. Taking inspiration from Remark 11.4.1, we copy the beginning of Section 11.2.b for $\lambda = \lambda_*$. We define the (nonlinear) operators

$$F_u, F_v, F^{\Gamma_{\lambda_*}}_\rho : B(0, r) \subset W^{1,p}(\mathbf{R} \times S^1; \mathbf{R}^{2n}) \longrightarrow L^p(\mathbf{R} \times S^1; \mathbf{R}^{2n})$$

and their respective linearizations (differentials at 0)

$$L^u, L^v, L_\rho^{\Gamma_{\lambda_*}} : W^{1,p}(\mathbf{R} \times S^1; \mathbf{R}^{2n}) \longrightarrow L^p(\mathbf{R} \times S^1; \mathbf{R}^{2n}).$$

As in Section 11.2.b, these are Fredholm operators. On the other hand, their indices are modified as follows:

$$\operatorname{Ind} L^u = \mu(x) - \mu(y) = -1$$
$$\operatorname{Ind} L^v = \mu(y) - \mu(z) = 1$$
$$\operatorname{Ind} L_\rho^{\Gamma_{\lambda_*}} = \mu(x) - \mu(z) = 0.$$

We noted (Remark 11.4.1) that we could not construct φ while keeping λ constant and equal to λ_*. We therefore consider, for $\lambda \in \,]0,1[$, the Floer operator $\mathcal{F}_\rho^{\Gamma_\lambda}$ defined by

$$\mathcal{F}_\rho^{\Gamma_\lambda} = \frac{\partial}{\partial s} + J_{s+\rho}^\lambda \frac{\partial}{\partial t} + \operatorname{grad} H_{s+\rho,t}^\lambda.$$

Using the trivializations of Section 11.2.b, $\mathcal{F}_\rho^{\Gamma_\lambda}$ defines a (nonlinear) operator

$$F_\rho^{\Gamma_\lambda} : B(0,r) \subset W^{1,p}(\mathbf{R} \times S^1; \mathbf{R}^{2n}) \longrightarrow L^p(\mathbf{R} \times S^1; \mathbf{R}^{2n}).$$

Still using the same trivializations, this defines a (nonlinear) operator

$$F_\rho^\Gamma : \,]0,1[\,\times W^{1,p}(\mathbf{R} \times S^1; \mathbf{R}^{2n}) \longrightarrow L^p(\mathbf{R} \times S^1; \mathbf{R}^{2n})$$

through the formula

$$F_\rho^\Gamma(\lambda, Y) = F_\rho^{\Gamma_\lambda}(Y).$$

Note that if (λ_ρ, Y_ρ) is a zero of F_ρ^Γ, then $\mathcal{F}_\rho^{\Gamma_\lambda}(\exp_{w_\rho} Y_\rho) = 0$, which means that $\varphi_\rho = \exp_{w_\rho}(Y_\rho)$ satisfies the desired Floer equation.

Our aim is therefore to find such a zero... using the Newton–Picard method. To do this, we first determine the linearized operator $L_\rho^\Gamma = (dF_\rho^\Gamma)_{(\lambda_*,0)}$. Note that $L_\rho^\Gamma(0, \bullet)$ is, by definition, the operator $L_\rho^{\Gamma_{\lambda_*}} = (d\mathcal{F}_\rho^{\Gamma_{\lambda_*}})_0$. Next,

$$L_\rho^\Gamma(a,0) = \frac{\partial}{\partial \lambda}\Big|_{\lambda=0} \big(\mathcal{F}_\rho^{\Gamma_{\lambda_*+a\lambda}} \exp_{w_\rho}(0)\big)_{(Z_i^\rho)_{i=1,\dots,2n}}$$

$$= \frac{\partial}{\partial \lambda}\Big|_{\lambda=0} \Big(\frac{\partial w_\rho}{\partial s} + J_{s+\rho}^{\lambda_*+a\lambda} \frac{\partial w}{\partial t} + \operatorname{grad}_{w_\rho} H_{s+\rho,t}^{\lambda_*+a\lambda}\Big)_{(Z_i^\rho)_{i=1,\dots,2n}}$$

$$= a\Big(\frac{\partial J}{\partial \lambda}(\lambda_*, s+\rho)\frac{\partial w_\rho}{\partial t} + \operatorname{grad}_{w_\rho}\frac{\partial H}{\partial \lambda}(\lambda_*, s+\rho, t)\Big)_{(Z_i^\rho)_{i=1,\dots,2n}}$$

$$= a(V_\rho)_{(Z_i^\rho)_{i=1,\dots,2n}},$$

where the formula defines V_ρ, a vector field along w_ρ. Its form greatly resembles that of the vector field V along $u \in \mathcal{M}^\Gamma(x,y)$ (here $\Gamma = \Gamma_{\lambda_*}$) defined in the proof of Proposition 11.3.5. From now on, we will no longer mention the frame $(Z_i^\rho)_{i=1,\ldots,2n}$ when writing the formula for L_ρ^Γ.

These two vector fields satisfy the relation

$$V_\rho(s,t) = V(s+\rho,t) \quad \text{if } s \le -1.$$

Also note that since $\Gamma = (H^b, J^b)$ for $s \ge R$ and $\lambda \in [0,1]$, we have

$$V_\rho(s,t) = 0 \quad \text{if } s + \rho \ge R,$$

which includes the case $s \ge 1$ and $\rho \ge R$. Summarizing, we have obtained

$$L_\rho^\Gamma = a(V_\rho) + L_\rho^{\Gamma_{\lambda^*}}(Y).$$

By reasoning as in the proof of Proposition 11.3.5, we find that L_ρ is a Fredholm operator, whose index we compute using the path of Fredholm operators

$$L_{\rho,\sigma}(a, Y) = a\sigma V_\rho + L_\rho^{\Gamma_{\lambda^*}}(Y) \quad \text{for } \sigma \in [0,1].$$

We find that

$$\operatorname{Ind} L_\rho^\Gamma = \operatorname{Ind} L_{\rho,0}^\Gamma = \operatorname{Ind} L_\rho^{\Gamma_{\lambda^*}} + 1 = 1.$$

Recall that by Lemma 11.3.6, the operator

$$\mathcal{Y}^u : \mathbf{R} \times W^{1,p}(\mathbf{R} \times S^1; \mathbf{R}^{2n}) \longrightarrow L^p(\mathbf{R} \times S^1; \mathbf{R}^{2n})$$

defined by

$$\mathcal{Y}(a, Y) = aV + L^u(Y)$$

is a Fredholm operator and has index

$$\operatorname{Ind} \mathcal{Y}^u = 1 + \operatorname{Ind} L^u = 0$$

(computed as above). Moreover, since the homotopy Γ is regular, Lemma 11.3.6 asserts that $\mathcal{Y}^u$ is surjective, hence $\operatorname{Ker} \mathcal{Y}^u = 0$ and $\mathcal{Y}^u$ is bijective.

On the other hand, the homotopy (H^b, J^b) is also regular, hence L^v is surjective. Consequently, its kernel is of dimension 1 and we have

$$\operatorname{Ker} L^v = \left\{ \alpha \left(\frac{\partial v}{\partial s} \right)_{(Z_i^v)} \mid \alpha \in \mathbf{R} \right\}.$$

Still following Subsection 11.2.b, we define, for $\rho \ge \rho_0$, the spaces

$$W_\rho = \{ 0 \#_\rho \beta \mid \beta \in \operatorname{Ker} L^v \}$$

and

$$W_\rho^\perp = \left\{ Y \in W^{1,p}(\mathbf{R} \times S^1; \mathbf{R}^{2n}) \mid \int_{\mathbf{R} \times S^1} \langle Y, Z \rangle = 0 \text{ for every } Z \in W_\rho \right\}.$$

Here we view W_ρ as contained in $L^q(\mathbf{R} \times S^1; \mathbf{R}^{2n})$ (with $1/p + 1/q = 1$), using the frame (Z_i^ρ) and the exponential decay (of Section 8.9, more precisely Remark 8.9.2), as in Section 9.4.

In order to apply the Newton–Picard method (Lemma 9.4.4), we need to define a right inverse for the operator L_ρ^Γ. To do this, we need an analogue of Proposition 9.4.7.

Proposition 11.4.2. *There exist a real number $\rho_0 > 0$ and a constant $C > 0$ such that, for $\rho \geq \rho_0$,*

$$\forall Y \in W_\rho^\perp, \ \forall a \in \mathbf{R}, \quad \left\| L_\rho^\Gamma(a, Y) \right\|_{L^p} \geq C \left(\|Y\|_{W^{1,p}} + |a| \right).$$

For the meaning of $\rho \geq \rho_0$, we keep the convention of p. 313 (in other words, we do not need to make ρ_0 more precise).

Proof of Proposition 11.4.2. Assume the result is false (as at the beginning of the proof of Proposition 9.4.7). There then exist sequences

$$\rho_n \longrightarrow +\infty \text{ and } (a_n, Y_n) \in \mathbf{R} \times W^{1,p}(\mathbf{R} \times S^1; \mathbf{R}^{2n})$$

such that

$$|a_n| + \|Y_n\|_{W^{1,p}} = 1 \quad \text{and} \quad \lim_{n \to +\infty} \left\| L_{\rho_n}^\Gamma(a_n, Y_n) \right\|_{L^p} = 0.$$

Let $r_n = \rho_n/2$. We have

$$V_{\rho_n}(s, t) = 0 \quad \text{for } (s, t) \in [-r_n, r_n] \times S^1 \text{ and } n \text{ sufficiently large}$$

(in general, we have seen that $V_\rho(s, t) = 0$ for $s + \rho > R$, where R is the constant starting from which Γ_s is stationary). We therefore have, for n sufficiently large,

$$\left\| L_{\rho_n}^\Gamma(a_n, Y_n) \right\|_{L^p([-r_n, r_n] \times S^1)} = \left\| L_{\rho_n}^{\Gamma_{\lambda_*}} Y_n \right\|_{L^p([-r_n, r_n] \times S^1)}.$$

In particular, this last term tends to 0 when n tends to infinity. We can then use the same argument as in Lemma 9.4.9 to prove the following lemma.

Lemma 11.4.3. *For every compact subset K of $\mathbf{R} \times S^1$, we have*

$$\lim_{n \to +\infty} \|Y_n\|_{W^{1,p}(K)} = 0. \qquad \square$$

Next, this time following the proof of Lemma 9.4.10, we consider the real function β^- used to construct the pre-gluing w_ρ: it has support in $]-\infty, 0]$ and has value 1 on $]-\infty, -1]$. As in Lemma 9.4.10, we use

$$\left\|L^\Gamma_{\rho_n}(a_n, \beta^-(s+1)Y_n(s,t))\right\|_{L^p}$$
$$= \left\|\dot\beta^- Y_n(s+1,t) + \beta^-(s+1)L^\Gamma_{\rho_n}(a_n, Y_n(s,t))\right\|_{L^p}$$
$$\leq (\sup \dot\beta^-)\|Y_n\|_{L^p([-1,1]\times S^1)} + \left\|L^\Gamma_{\rho_n}(a_n, Y_n)\right\|_{L^p},$$

so that

$$\lim_{n\to+\infty}\left\|L^\Gamma_{\rho_n}(a_n, \beta^-(s+1)Y_n(s,t))\right\|_{L^p} = 0,$$

which is equivalent to

$$\lim_{n\to+\infty}\left\|\mathcal{Y}^{u(s+\rho_n,t)}(a_n, \beta^-(s+1)Y_n(s,t))\right\|_{L^p} = 0,$$

that is, to

$$\lim_{n\to+\infty}\left\|\mathcal{Y}^u(a_n, \beta^-(s-\rho_n+1)Y_n(s-\rho_n,t))\right\|_{L^p} = 0.$$

But we have already said that $\mathcal{Y}^u$ is a bijective Fredholm operator. In other words:

- We have $\lim a_n = 0$ (which implies that

$$\lim_{n\to+\infty}\|Y_n\|_{W^{1,p}} = 1$$

because the sum of the two is 1).
- In $W^{1,p}(\mathbf{R} \times S^1; \mathbf{R}^{2n})$, we have

$$\lim_{n\to+\infty}\beta^-(s-\rho_n+1)Y_n(s-\rho_n,t) = 0,$$

which is the first part of the result of Lemma 9.4.10.

The second part of this result and the end of the proof of Proposition 11.4.2 can be obtained as in Section 9.4. □

Corollary 11.4.4. *For $\rho \geq \rho_0$, L^Γ_ρ is surjective and admits a right inverse*

$$G_\rho : L^p(\mathbf{R} \times S^1; \mathbf{R}^{2n}) \longrightarrow \mathbf{R} \times W^{1,p}(\mathbf{R} \times S^1; \mathbf{R}^{2n}).$$

Proof. We have seen that the dimension of W_ρ is 1 and it is clear that

$$W_\rho \oplus W_\rho^\perp = W^{1,p}(\mathbf{R} \times S^1; \mathbf{R}^{2n}).$$

On the other hand, Proposition 11.4.2 implies that

$$\operatorname{Ker} L_\rho^\Gamma \cap (\mathbf{R} \times W_\rho^\perp) = \{0\},$$

hence $\dim \operatorname{Ker} L_\rho^\Gamma \le 1$ and therefore, since L_ρ^Γ is of index 1, this operator must be surjective and its kernel must be of dimension 1. It follows that

$$\operatorname{Ker} L_\rho^\Gamma \oplus (\mathbf{R} \times W_\rho^\perp) = \mathbf{R} \times W^{1,p}(\mathbf{R} \times S^1; \mathbf{R}^{2n}),$$

which allows us to define the right inverse G_ρ, which by Proposition 11.4.2 is continuous and of norm less than a constant that is independent of ρ.   □

We now apply the Newton–Picard method, that is, Lemma 9.4.4, to the operator

$$\overline{F}_\rho : \mathbf{R} \times W^{1,p}(\mathbf{R} \times S^1; \mathbf{R}^{2n}) \longrightarrow L^p(\mathbf{R} \times S^1; \mathbf{R}^{2n})$$

defined by

$$\overline{F}_\rho(\lambda, Y) = F_\rho^{\Gamma_{\lambda+\lambda_\star}}(Y).$$

We have

$$\overline{F}_\rho(\lambda, Y) = \begin{cases} F_\rho^{\Gamma_0}(Y) & \text{if } \lambda + \lambda_\star < 0 \\[2mm] F_\rho^{\Gamma_1}(Y) & \text{if } \lambda + \lambda_\star > 1, \end{cases}$$

while our operator L_ρ^Γ is exactly the differential of $\overline{F}_\rho$ at 0 (this is why we modified F_ρ^Γ using the translation of $\lambda_\star$).

Let us now verify that the conditions of Lemma 9.4.4 are satisfied. Condition (1) is the conclusion of Corollary 11.4.4.

Next, we verify condition (3). With the constant C given by Proposition 11.4.2, we first have

$$\left\| G_\rho(\overline{F}_\rho(0,0)) \right\|_{W^{1,p}} \le C^{-1} \left\| \overline{F}_\rho(0,0) \right\|_{L^p},$$

and then

$$\left\| \overline{F}_\rho(0,0) \right\|_{L^p} = \left\| F_\rho^{\Gamma_{\lambda_\star}}(0) \right\|_{L^p} = \left\| (\mathcal{F}_\rho^{\Gamma_{\lambda_\star}}(w_\rho))_{(Z_i^\rho)} \right\|_{L^p},$$

where $\mathcal{F}_\rho^{\Gamma_{\lambda_\star}}$ is the Floer operator

$$\mathcal{F}_\rho^{\Gamma_{\lambda_\star}} = \frac{\partial}{\partial s} + J_{s+\rho}^{\Gamma_{\lambda_\star}} \frac{\partial}{\partial t} + \operatorname{grad} H_{s+\rho,t}^{\lambda_\star}.$$

Now $\mathcal{F}_\rho^{\Gamma_{\lambda_\star}}(w_\rho)(s,t) = 0$ for $|s| \ge 1$ and $\mathcal{F}_\rho^{\Gamma_{\lambda_\star}}(w_\rho)$ tends to 0 uniformly on $[-1,1] \times S^1$, which implies that

$$\lim_{\rho \to 0} \left\| \mathcal{F}_\rho^{\Gamma_{\lambda_\star}}(w_\rho) \right\|_{L^p} = 0 \text{ and therefore that } \lim_{\rho \to 0} \left\| \overline{F}_\rho(0,0) \right\|_{L^p} = 0.$$

This in turn implies that condition (3) of Lemma 9.4.4 is satisfied.

Condition (2) is verified as in Section 9.4 (when we verified condition (2) of the lemma on p. 324), using Proposition 11.4.2, with the exception that we need to adapt Lemma 9.4.8 as follows.

Lemma 11.4.5. *Let $r_0 > 0$. There exists a constant $K > 0$ such that for every $\rho \geq \rho_0$ and every $(\lambda, Z) \in \mathbf{R} \times W^{1,p}(\mathbf{R} \times S^1; \mathbf{R}^{2n})$ (with $\|Z\| \leq r_0$), we have*

$$\left\|(d\overline{F}_\rho)_{(\lambda,Z)} - (d\overline{F}_\rho)_{(0,0)}\right\|^{\mathrm{op}} \leq K(\|Z\|_{W^{1,p}} + |\lambda|).$$

The proof of this version can be found in Section 13.8.

The Newton–Picard method (Lemma 9.4.4) then gives us a pair $(\overline{\lambda}_\rho, \gamma_\rho)$ such that

$$\overline{F}_\rho(\overline{\lambda}_\rho, \gamma_\rho) = 0,$$

which, by the definition of $\overline{F}_\rho$, is equivalent to

$$F_\rho^\Gamma(\overline{\lambda}_\rho + \lambda_\star, \gamma_\rho) = 0.$$

Hence $\varphi_\rho = \exp_{w_\rho} \gamma_\rho$ is a solution of the equation

$$\mathcal{F}_\rho^{\Gamma_{\lambda_\rho}}(\cdot) = 0 \quad (\text{with } \lambda_\rho = \overline{\lambda}_\rho + \lambda_\star).$$

With respect to the three parts in which we cut up the proof of Theorem 11.3.14 (p. 427), the construction of this φ brings us to the end of the second part. We set

$$\psi_\rho(s,t) = \varphi_\rho(s - \rho, t)$$

and find that

$$\frac{\partial \psi_\rho}{\partial s} + J_s^{\lambda_\rho} \frac{\partial \psi_\rho}{\partial t} + \mathrm{grad}_{\psi_\rho} H_{s,t}^{\lambda_\rho} = 0,$$

that is, that $(\lambda_\rho, \psi_\rho) \in \mathcal{M}^\Gamma(x, z)$. We set

$$\psi : [\rho_0, +\infty[\longrightarrow \mathcal{M}^\Gamma(x, z)$$
$$\rho \longmapsto (\lambda_\rho, \psi_\rho).$$

For the third and last part of the proof of Theorem 11.3.14 according to the plan established on p. 427, we now need to establish the desired properties of ψ.

11.4.c The Properties of ψ

As in Lemma 9.4.13, we have

$$\lim_{\rho \to +\infty} \overline{\lambda}_\rho = 0 \quad \text{and} \quad \lim_{\rho \to +\infty} \|\gamma_\rho\|_{W^{1,p}} = 0.$$

The first equality implies that $\lim_{\rho \to +\infty} \lambda_\rho = \lambda_\star$. Using the second equality, we follow the reasoning of Sections 9.4 and 11.2.c to show that

$$\lim_{\rho \to +\infty} \varphi_\rho(s - \rho, t) = u(s, t) \quad \text{and} \quad \lim_{\rho \to +\infty} \varphi_\rho(s + \rho, t) = v(s, t)$$

in the $\mathcal{C}^\infty_{\mathrm{loc}}$ topology. It follows that

$$\lim_{\rho \to +\infty} \psi(\rho) = [(\lambda_\star, u), \widehat{v}]$$

for the convergence defined by Theorem 11.3.10.

Let us now show that the map ψ is (continuous and) differentiable. To do this, we need to prove these properties for the map $\rho \mapsto (\lambda_\rho, \gamma_\rho)$. We use the implicit function theorem, as in Section 9.4. We must show that for ρ sufficiently large, the operator $(d\overline{F}_\rho)_{(\overline{\lambda}_\rho, \gamma_\rho)}$ is invertible, which we do exactly as in the proof of Lemma 9.4.14, using Lemma 11.4.5.

Let us now show that ψ is an embedding. We will need the result stated below, which is an analogue of Proposition 9.4.15 and of Theorem 11.2.2 (3).

Proposition 11.4.6.

$$\lim_{\rho \to +\infty} \left\| \frac{\partial \gamma}{\partial \rho} \right\|_{W^{1,p}} = 0 \quad \text{and} \quad \lim_{\rho \to +\infty} \frac{\partial \lambda_\rho}{\partial \rho} = 0.$$

Proof. Since $\lambda_\rho = \lambda_\star + \overline{\lambda}_\rho$, the second relation is equivalent to $\partial \overline{\lambda}_\rho / \partial \rho = 0$. Let

$$\widetilde{F}(\rho, \lambda, Y) = \overline{F}_\rho(\lambda, Y),$$

so that

$$\widetilde{F}(\rho, \overline{\lambda}_\rho, \gamma_\rho) = 0.$$

Differentiating this identity with respect to ρ, we obtain

$$\frac{\partial \overline{F}_\rho}{\partial \rho}(\overline{\lambda}_\rho, \gamma_\rho) + (d\overline{F}_\rho)_{(\overline{\lambda}_\rho, \gamma_\rho)} \left(\frac{\partial \overline{\lambda}_\rho}{\partial \rho}, \frac{\partial \gamma_\rho}{\partial \rho} \right) = 0.$$

As in the proof of Proposition 9.4.15, this relation implies that

$$\left\| \left(\frac{\partial \overline{\lambda}_\rho}{\partial \rho}, \frac{\partial \gamma_\rho}{\partial \rho} \right) \right\|_{\mathbf{R} \times W^{1,p}} \leq k_1 \left\| (\overline{\lambda}_\rho, \gamma_\rho) \right\|_{\mathbf{R} \times W^{1,p}} \left\| \left(\frac{\overline{\lambda}_\rho}{\partial \rho}, \frac{\partial \gamma_\rho}{\partial \rho} \right) \right\|_{\mathbf{R} \times W^{1,p}}$$
$$+ k_2 \left\| \frac{\partial \overline{F}_\rho}{\partial \rho}(\overline{\lambda}_\rho, \gamma_\rho) \right\|_{L^p}$$

for positive constants k_1 and k_2 that do not depend on ρ. We will use the following result.

Lemma 11.4.7. *There exists a constant $C > 0$ that does not depend on ρ, such that for $\rho \geq \rho_0$, we have*

$$\left\| \frac{\partial \overline{F}_\rho}{\partial \rho}(\overline{\lambda}_\rho, \gamma_\rho) - \frac{\partial \overline{F}_\rho}{\partial \rho}(0,0) \right\|_{L^p} \leq C \left\| (\overline{\lambda}_\rho, \gamma_\rho) \right\|_{\mathbf{R} \times W^{1,p}} .$$

The proof of this lemma can be found in Section 13.8, together with those of the lemmas similar to it.

Using Lemma 11.4.7 in the inequality just above it, we obtain

$$\left\| \left(\frac{\partial \overline{\lambda}_\rho}{\partial \rho}, \frac{\partial \gamma_\rho}{\partial \rho} \right) \right\|_{\mathbf{R} \times W^{1,p}} \left(1 - k_1 \left\| (\overline{\lambda}_\rho, \gamma_\rho) \right\|_{\mathbf{R} \times W^{1,p}} \right)$$

$$\leq k_2 C \left\| (\overline{\lambda}_\rho, \gamma_\rho) \right\|_{\mathbf{R} \times W^{1,p}} + \left\| \frac{\partial \overline{F}}{\partial \rho}(0,0) \right\|_{L^p} .$$

The last term is

$$\left\| \frac{\partial \overline{F}}{\partial \rho}(0,0) \right\|_{L^p} = \left\| \left(\frac{\partial \mathcal{F}_\rho^{\Gamma_{\lambda_*}}}{\partial \rho}(w_\rho) \right)_{Z_i^\rho} \right\|_{L^p}$$

and tends to 0 when ρ tends to $+\infty$, exactly as in the proof of Proposition 9.4.15. Using the fact that $\lim_{\rho \to +\infty} \left\| (\overline{\lambda}_\rho, \gamma_\rho) \right\|_{\mathbf{R} \times W^{1,p}} = 0$, our inequality then implies the equality

$$\lim_{\rho \to +\infty} \left\| \left(\frac{\partial \overline{\lambda}_\rho}{\partial \rho}, \frac{\partial \gamma_\rho}{\partial \rho} \right) \right\|_{\mathbf{R} \times W^{1,p}} = 0.$$

This concludes the proof of Proposition 11.4.6. $\qquad\square$

To finish proving that the desired properties of ψ hold, we still need to show that it is an embedding. To do this, it suffices to prove that it is an immersion (by an argument we have already used in Subsection 11.2.c). But if $\psi'_\rho = 0$, then as in Section 11.2.c, we must have

$$\frac{\partial \varphi_\rho}{\partial \rho} = \frac{\partial \varphi_\rho}{\partial s}$$

(because $\psi_\rho(s,t) = \varphi_\rho(s - \rho, t)$). The desired contradiction follows using the method of Section 9.5 (for $\alpha_n = 1$) with Proposition 11.4.6.

We still need to prove the last part of Theorem 11.3.14, the "uniqueness", namely the fact that a sequence $[\lambda_n, \ell_n]$ of elements of $\mathcal{M}^\Gamma(x, z)$ that tends to $[(\lambda_*, u), \widetilde{v}]$ is contained in the image of ψ for n sufficiently large.

To do this, we need results analogous to those given in Propositions 11.2.3 and 11.2.4.

Proposition 11.4.8. *There exist a real sequence* (ρ_n) *that tends to* $+\infty$ *and, for every* u, *a vector* $Y_n \in w^\star_{\rho_n} TW$ *such that for every* $(s,t) \in \mathbf{R} \times S^1$,

$$\ell_n(s + \rho_n, t) = \exp_{w_{\rho_n}(s,t)} Y_n(s,t).$$

Moreover, $\lim_{n \to +\infty} \|Y_n\|_{L^\infty} = 0$.

Proposition 11.4.9. *The vector field* Y_n *is in* $W^{1,p}(w^\star_{\rho_n} TW)$ *and*

$$\lim_{n \to +\infty} \|Y_n\|_{W^{1,p}} = 0.$$

The proof of Proposition 11.4.8 is analogous in every detail to that of Proposition 11.2.3. It uses the fact that ℓ_n is in the space of solutions $\mathcal{M}^{\Gamma_{\lambda_n}}(x,z)$ for a homotopy $\Gamma_{\lambda_n} = (H^{\lambda_n}_{s,t}, J^{\lambda_n}_s)$ that is stationary for $s \le -R$ and for $s \ge R$, as well as the convergence of ℓ_n to $(u, \widehat{v})$ (in the sense of Theorem 11.1.10), which follows from the convergence of $[\lambda_n, \ell_n]$ to $[\lambda_\star, (u, \widehat{v})]$.

The proof of Proposition 11.4.9 follows that of Proposition 11.2.4, with the exception that in this new setting, the Taylor formula used in the proof (p. 505) becomes

$$\widetilde{\mathcal{F}}^{\Gamma_{\lambda_\star}}(Y_n) = \widetilde{\mathcal{F}}^{\Gamma_{\lambda_\star}}(0) + (d\widetilde{\mathcal{F}}^{\Gamma_{\lambda_\star}})_0(Y_n) + \mathcal{N}(Y_n).$$

The left-hand side is not zero because

$$\ell_n = \exp_{w_{\rho_n}}(Y_n) \in \mathcal{M}^{\Gamma_{\lambda_n}}(x,z)$$

(in other words, we have the equality $\widetilde{\mathcal{F}}^{\Gamma_{\lambda_n}}(Y_n) = 0$ for λ_n and not for $\lambda_\star$). To complete the proof, we need the following upper bound.

Lemma 11.4.10. *There exist positive constants* C *and* k *that do not depend on* n, *such that*

$$\left\|\widetilde{\mathcal{F}}^{\Gamma_{\lambda_\star}}(Y_n)\right\|_{L^p} \le C\,|\lambda_n - \lambda_\star|\,\|Y_n\|_{W^{1,p}} + k\,|\lambda_n - \lambda_\star|.$$

Proof. We have

$$\left\|\widetilde{\mathcal{F}}^{\Gamma_{\lambda_\star}}(Y_n)\right\|_{L^p} = \left\|\widetilde{\mathcal{F}}^{\Gamma_{\lambda_\star}}(Y_n) - \widetilde{\mathcal{F}}^{\Gamma_{\lambda_n}}(Y_n)\right\|_{L^p}$$

$$\le |\lambda_n - \lambda_\star| \left\|\sup_\lambda \frac{\partial \widetilde{\mathcal{F}}}{\partial \lambda}(\lambda, Y_n)\right\|_{L^p}$$

$$= |\lambda_n - \lambda_\star| \left\|\sup_\lambda \widetilde{V}_{\rho_n}(\lambda, Y_n)\right\|_{L^p}.$$

Next, by Lemma 13.8.1,

$$\left\|\sup_\lambda \widetilde{V}_{\rho_n}(\lambda, Y_n)\right\|_{L^p} \le C\,\|Y_n\|_{W^{1,p}} + \left\|\sup_\lambda \widetilde{V}_{\rho_n}(\lambda, 0)\right\|_{L^p}.$$

Since, by definition,

$$\widetilde{V}_{\rho_n}(\lambda, 0) = \frac{\partial J}{\partial \lambda}(\lambda, s + \rho_n)\frac{\partial w_{\rho_n}}{\partial t} + \frac{\partial H}{\partial \lambda}(\lambda, s + \rho_n, t),$$

$\widetilde{V}_{\rho_n}(\lambda, 0)$ is bounded for the L^∞ norm. Its support is $[-R - \rho_n, R - \rho_n] \times S^1$. It follows that

$$\|\widetilde{V}_{\rho_n}(\lambda, 0)\|_{L^p} \leq k,$$

proving the lemma. □

Using this lemma and the analogue of Lemma 13.7.1 for $\widetilde{\mathcal{F}}^{\Gamma_{\lambda_\star}}$, Proposition 11.4.9 can be proved as in Section 11.2, using the fact that $\lim \lambda_n = \lambda_\star$.

The proof of the uniqueness can be concluded by applying Lemmas 9.6.16 and 9.6.17 to the operator

$$\overline{F}_\rho : \mathbf{R} \times W^{1,p}(\mathbf{R} \times S^1; \mathbf{R}^{2n}) \longrightarrow L^p(\mathbf{R} \times S^1; \mathbf{R}^{2n})$$

and proceeding exactly as in Section 11.2.c.

This concludes the proof of Theorem 11.3.14. □

And that of Proposition 11.2.8. □

11.5 Conclusion of the Proof of the Invariance of the Floer Homology: Proof of Proposition 11.2.9

Let $\Gamma' = (H', J')$ and $\Gamma'' = (H'', J'')$ be two regular homotopies connecting (H^a, J^a) to (H^b, J^b) and (H^b, J^b) to (H^c, J^c), respectively. As in the previous sections of this chapter, these homotopies are chosen to be stationary for $|s| \geq R$, where $R > 0$ is a constant that is not yet fixed (it may increase during the proof).

The concatenation of Γ' and Γ'' defines a homotopy $\Gamma_\rho = (H_\rho, J_\rho)$ through the formulas

$$H_\rho(s, t, p) = \begin{cases} H'(s + \rho, t, p) & \text{if } s \leq 0 \\ H''(s - \rho, t, p) & \text{if } s \geq 0 \end{cases}$$

$$J_\rho(s, p) = \begin{cases} J'(s + \rho, p) & \text{if } s \leq 0 \\ J''(s - \rho, p) & \text{if } s \geq 0. \end{cases}$$

The homotopy Γ_ρ is defined for ρ sufficiently large ($\rho > R$) and connects (H^a, J^a) to (H^c, J^c). It is stationary for $|s| \geq R + \rho$. Note that *a priori*, it might not be regular. We will show the following result.

Lemma 11.5.1. *After taking a small perturbation of Γ' and Γ'' (within regular homotopies), we may assume that Γ_ρ is regular for arbitrarily large values of ρ.*

There therefore exists a sequence ρ_n that tends to infinity and is such that Γ_{ρ_n} is regular for every n.

For these values of ρ, we can define the morphism of complexes

$$\Phi^{\Gamma_\rho} : CF_\star(H^a, J^a) \longrightarrow CF_\star(H^c, J^c)$$

of Section 11.1.

Note that by Proposition 11.2.8, the perturbations of Γ', Γ'' in Lemma 11.5.1 define the same morphisms as $\Phi^{\Gamma'}$ and $\Phi^{\Gamma''}$, respectively, at the homology level. We will therefore keep the same notation Γ', Γ'' for these homotopies.

Proposition 11.2.9 is obviously a consequence of the following.

Proposition 11.5.2. *There exists a ρ such that Γ_ρ is regular and the morphisms of complexes $\Phi^{\Gamma''} \circ \Phi^{\Gamma''}$ and Φ^{Γ_ρ} coincide.*

Proof of Lemma 11.5.1. Consider the space $\mathcal{C}_\varepsilon^\infty$ defined in Section 11.1.b. Let $\mathcal{C}_{\varepsilon,0}^\infty$ be the subspace of the functions

$$h : \mathbf{R} \times S^1 \times W \longrightarrow \mathbf{R}$$

with $h(s, t, p) = 0$ for $|s| < \delta$, where δ is an arbitrary positive number. We fix a ρ_1 that is sufficiently large for Γ_{ρ_1} to be defined. Given a function $h \in \mathcal{C}_{\varepsilon,0}^\infty$, we associate with it two functions h' and $h'' \in \mathcal{C}_\varepsilon^\infty$ defined by the formulas

$$h'(s, t, p) = \begin{cases} h(s - \rho_1, t, p) & \text{if } s \leq \rho_1 \\ 0 & \text{if } s \geq \rho_1 \end{cases}$$

$$h''(s, t, p) = \begin{cases} 0 & \text{if } s \leq -\rho_1 \\ h(s + \rho_1, t, p) & \text{if } s \geq -\rho_1, \end{cases}$$

so that the homotopy Γ_{ρ_1} defined by $(H' + h', J')$ and $(H'' + h'', J'')$ is exactly $(H_{\rho_1} + h, J_{\rho_1})$. Consequently, to make Γ_{ρ_1} regular, it suffices to repeat the proof of the transversality given in Section 11.1.b for the (smaller) space of perturbations $\mathcal{C}_{\varepsilon,0}^\infty$. The only small modification occurs in the proof of the lemma analogous to Lemma 11.1.9. If the vector field Z is not zero, then there exists a point $(s_0, t_0) \in (\mathbf{R} - \{0\}) \times S^1$ such that $Z(s_0, t_0) \neq 0$. The remainder of the proof is the same.

We can then repeat this proof for a $\rho_2 > \rho_1$, choosing perturbations h' and h'' sufficiently small for Γ_{ρ_1} to stay regular; then Γ_{ρ_1} and Γ_{ρ_2} will both be regular. Continuing in an analogous manner, we construct a sequence ρ_n that tends to infinity and for which Γ_{ρ_n} is regular for every n. □

Proof of Proposition 11.5.2. Let $x \in \mathrm{Crit}(\mathcal{A}_{H^a})$. With the notation of Section 11.1.c, we have

$$\Phi^{\Gamma''} \circ \Phi^{\Gamma'}(x) = \Phi^{\Gamma''}\left(\sum_{\substack{y \in \mathrm{Crit}(\mathcal{A}_{H^b}) \\ \mu(y) = \mu(x)}} n^{\Gamma'}(x, y) \cdot y \right)$$

$$= \sum_{\substack{z \in \mathrm{Crit}(\mathcal{A}_{H^c}) \\ \mu(z) = \mu(x)}} \sum_{\substack{y \in \mathrm{Crit}(\mathcal{A}_{H^b}) \\ \mu(y) = \mu(x)}} n^{\Gamma'}(x, y)\, n^{\Gamma''}(y, z) \cdot z.$$

As in Section 11.1, $n^{\Gamma'}(x, y)$ and $n^{\Gamma''}(y, z)$ are the numbers (modulo 2) of elements in $\mathcal{M}^{\Gamma'}(x, y)$ and $\mathcal{M}^{\Gamma''}(y, z)$, respectively. It is clear that Proposition 11.5.2 is a consequence of the following. □

Proposition 11.5.3. *Let* $x \in \mathrm{Crit}(\mathcal{A}_{H^a})$ *and* $z \in \mathrm{Crit}(\mathcal{A}_{H^c})$ *be such that* $\mu(x) = \mu(z)$. *For every sufficiently large* ρ, *the sets*

$$\bigcup_{\substack{y \in \mathrm{Crit}(\mathcal{A}_{H^b}) \\ \mu(y) = \mu(x)}} \mathcal{M}^{\Gamma'}(x, y) \times \mathcal{M}^{\Gamma''}(y, z) \quad and \quad \mathcal{M}^{\Gamma_\rho}(x, z)$$

are in bijection.

We now prove this proposition. Here are the ideas of the proof. It comes down to (which is not surprising):

(1) Defining, for ρ sufficiently large, a map

$$\chi_\rho : \bigcup_{\substack{y \in \mathrm{Crit}(\mathcal{A}_{H^b}) \\ \mu(y) = \mu(x)}} \mathcal{M}^{\Gamma'}(x, y) \times \mathcal{M}^{\Gamma''}(y, z) \longrightarrow \mathcal{M}^{\Gamma_\rho}(x, z)$$

(2) Showing that it is injective for ρ sufficiently large
(3) Showing that it is surjective for ρ sufficiently large.

To define $\chi_\rho(u, v)$ for a pair $(u, v) \in \mathcal{M}^{\Gamma'}(x, y) \times \mathcal{M}^{\Gamma''}(y, z)$, we use a gluing process, as in Sections 9.4 and 11.3.d: from the pre-gluing $w_\rho = u \#_\rho v$, we construct a solution $\varphi(\rho) \in \mathcal{M}^{\Gamma_\rho}$ using the Newton–Picard method.

As for the other Floer solutions obtained using this method, we will find that φ_ρ tends to (u, v) (in the sense of the convergence toward broken orbits) when ρ tends to infinity; see Subsection 11.1.c.

To prove the injectivity of φ, we use a contradiction. If χ_ρ were not injective from some value of ρ, then there would exist a sequence ρ_n tending to infinity and pairs $(u_n, v_n) \neq (u'_n, v'_n)$ such that $\chi_{\rho_n}(u_n, v_n) = \chi_{\rho_n}(u'_n, v'_n)$. Since the sequences (u_n, v_n) take on their values in a finite set, after extracting subsequences, if necessary, we may, and do, assume that they are constant, say equal to (u, v) and (u', v'), respectively. By letting n tend to infinity in the equality

$$\chi_{\rho_n}(u, v) = \chi_{\rho_n}(u', v'),$$

we obtain $(u, v) = (u', v')$, a contradiction.

For the surjectivity of χ_ρ, the reasoning is similar. If, for a sequence ρ_n that tends to infinity, there exists an ℓ_n that is not in the image of χ_{ρ_n}, then we first show that $\lim \ell_n = (u, v)$ for some pair $(u, v) \in \mathcal{M}^{\Gamma'}(x, y) \times \mathcal{M}^{\Gamma''}(y, z)$ ($y \in \mathrm{Crit}\, \mathcal{A}_{H^b}$, $\mu(y) = \mu(x)$). Next we apply a uniqueness property of the gluing (like that of Section 9.6) to show that $\ell_n \in \mathrm{Im}\, \chi_n$ for large n and arrive at a contradiction.

Here are the details of this proof.

11.5.a Definition of χ

Let $y \in \mathrm{Crit}\, \mathcal{A}_{H^b}$ be such that $\mu(y) = \mu(x)$. Consider a pair (u, v) in $\mathcal{M}^{\Gamma'}(x, y) \times \mathcal{M}^{\Gamma''}(y, z)$. The pre-gluing w_ρ of u and v is defined by the same formula as in Section 9.3. Since $w_\rho(s, t) = u(s + \rho, t)$ for $s \leq -1$ and $w_\rho(s, t) = v(s - \rho, t)$ for $s \geq 1$, the definition of $\Gamma_\rho = (H_\rho, J_\rho)$ implies that

$$\left(\frac{\partial w_\rho}{\partial s} + J_\rho \frac{\partial w_\rho}{\partial t} + \mathrm{grad}_{w_\rho} H_\rho \right)(s, t) = 0 \quad \text{for } |s| \geq 1.$$

This expression tends to 0 for the $\mathcal{C}^\infty_{\mathrm{loc}}$ norm (and therefore also for the L^p norm) when ρ tends to $+\infty$. Indeed,

$$\lim_{\rho \to +\infty} w_\rho(s, t) = y(t) \quad \text{and} \quad \lim_{\rho \to +\infty} (H_\rho, J_\rho) = (H^b, J^b)$$

(for the $\mathcal{C}^\infty_{\mathrm{loc}}$ norm in both cases).

The solution $\varphi(\rho) \in \mathcal{M}^{\Gamma_\rho}(x, z)$ will be obtained from an approximate solution w_ρ using a formula of the type

$$\varphi(\rho) = \exp_{w_\rho}(\gamma_\rho).$$

This is therefore a zero of

$$Y \xrightarrow{\ \mathcal{F}_\rho\ } \left(\frac{\partial}{\partial s} + J_\rho \frac{\partial}{\partial t} + \mathrm{grad}\, H_\rho \right)(\exp_{w_\rho} Y).$$

Using frames (Z_i^ρ) (at the source and target of $\mathcal{F}_\rho$) constructed exactly as in Section 9.4, we may, and do, view $\mathcal{F}_\rho$ as a map

$$\mathcal{F}_\rho : W^{1,p}(\mathbf{R} \times S^1; \mathbf{R}^{2n}) \longrightarrow L^p(\mathbf{R} \times S^1; \mathbf{R}^{2n}).$$

The linearized operator $L_\rho = (d\mathcal{F}_\rho)_0$ is of the form

$$Y \longmapsto \frac{\partial Y}{\partial s} + J_0 \frac{\partial Y}{\partial t} + S_\rho \cdot Y,$$

where S_ρ is a map from $\mathbf{R} \times S^1$ to $M_{2n}(\mathbf{R})$. It is a Fredholm operator of index 0 because $\mu(x) = \mu(z)$.

The analogue of Proposition 11.2.1, which can be proved in an identical manner, then implies that L_ρ is bijective, with inverse

$$G_\rho : L^p(\mathbf{R} \times S^1; \mathbf{R}^{2n}) \longrightarrow W^{1,p}(\mathbf{R} \times S^1; \mathbf{R}^{2n})$$

whose norm is bounded by a constant that does not depend on ρ. The conditions under which we can apply the Newton–Picard method (Lemma 9.4.4) are satisfied: the estimate analogous to the one in Lemma 9.4.8, which allows us to verify condition (2) of 9.4.4, can also be proved in an identical manner.

We thus obtain a $\gamma_\rho \in W^{1,p}(\mathbf{R} \times S^1; \mathbf{R}^{2n})$ with

$$\varphi(\rho) = \exp_{w_\rho} \gamma_\rho \in \mathcal{M}^{\Gamma_\rho}(x, z).$$

We can therefore set $\chi_\rho(u, v) = \varphi(\rho)$. As in Lemma 9.4.13, we obtain

$$\lim_{\rho \to +\infty} \|\gamma_\rho\|_{W^{1,p}} = 0.$$

Exactly as in Section 9.4, this implies the following result.

Proposition 11.5.4. *The element $\varphi(\rho)$ satisfies*

$$\lim_{\rho \to +\infty} \varphi(\rho)(s - \rho, t) = u(s, t), \qquad \lim_{\rho \to +\infty} \varphi(\rho)(s + \rho, t) = v(s, t)$$

in $\mathcal{C}^\infty_{\mathrm{loc}}$. □

11.5.b The Injectivity of χ

We assume that χ is not injective, that is, that there exist arbitrarily large ρ for which χ_ρ is not injective. Consider three sequences ρ_n, (u_n, v_n) and (u'_n, v'_n), with

$$(u_n, v_n) \text{ and } (u'_n, v'_n) \in \bigcup_{\substack{y \in \mathrm{Crit}(\mathcal{A}_{H^b}) \\ \mu(y) = \mu(x)}} \mathcal{M}^{\Gamma'}(x, y) \times \mathcal{M}^{\Gamma''}(y, z)$$

and $\lim_{n \to +\infty} \rho_n = +\infty$, $(u_n, v_n) \neq (u'_n, v'_n)$, $\chi_{\rho_n}(u_n, v_n) = \chi_{\rho_n}(u'_n, v'_n)$.

The sequences (u_n, v_n) and (u'_n, v'_n) take on values in a finite set. After extracting subsequences, if necessary, we may, and do, therefore assume that they are constant, say equal to (u, v), and (u', v'), respectively, with

$$(u, v) \neq (u', v') \quad \text{and} \quad \chi_{\rho_n}(u, v) = \chi_{\rho_n}(u', v').$$

By Proposition 11.5.4, we now have

$$
\begin{aligned}
u(s, t) &= \lim_{n \to +\infty} (\chi_{\rho_n}(u, v))(s - \rho_n, t) \\
&= \lim_{n \to +\infty} (\chi_{\rho_n}(u', v'))(s - \rho_n, t) \\
&= u'(s, t)
\end{aligned}
$$

and likewise $v(s, t) = v'(s, t)$. The injectivity of χ_ρ follows.

11.5.c The Surjectivity of χ

We assume (once more in order to obtain a contradiction) that for arbitrarily large values of ρ, χ_ρ is not surjective. Consider a sequence (ρ_n) that tends to infinity and a sequence of elements $\ell_n \in \mathcal{M}^{\Gamma_{\rho_n}}(x, z)$ with $\ell_n \notin \operatorname{Im}(\chi_{\rho_n})$ (for every n). We will prove the following proposition.

Proposition 11.5.5. *There exist a point $y \in \operatorname{Crit} A_{H^b}$ with $\mu(y) = \mu(x)$ and a pair*

$$(u, v) \in \mathcal{M}^{\Gamma'}(x, y) \times \mathcal{M}^{\Gamma''}(y, z)$$

such that, after extracting a subsequence, if necessary,

$$\lim_{n \to +\infty} \ell_n(s - \rho_n, t) = u(s, t) \quad \text{and} \quad \lim_{n \to +\infty} \ell_n(s + \rho_n, t) = v(s, t)$$

for the $\mathcal{C}_{\text{loc}}^\infty$ topology.

For the proof, we will need the following result.

Proposition 11.5.6.

(1) *Let (s_n) be a sequence of real numbers. Then the sequence $\ell_n(s + s_n, t)$ admits a convergent subsequence for the $\mathcal{C}_{\text{loc}}^\infty$ topology.*
(2) *Let ℓ be the limit of such a subsequence. There exists a constant $s_\star$ such that $\ell(s + s_\star, t)$ is a solution of the Floer equation corresponding to one of the pairs (H^a, J^a), (H', J'), (H^b, J^b), (H'', J''), (H^c, J^c).*

Proof of Proposition 11.5.6. Let us first prove point (2), admitting point (1). The map $(s, t) \mapsto \ell_n(s + s_n, t)$ is a solution of the Floer equation corresponding to the pair

$$(H_n, J_n) = (H_{\rho_n}(s + s_n, t, p), J_{\rho_n}(s + s_n, p)).$$

Recall that, by definition, H_n and J_n are given by

$$H_n(s,t,p) = \begin{cases} H'(s + \rho_n + s_n, t, p) & \text{if } s \leq -s_n \\ H''(s - \rho_n + s_n, t, p) & \text{if } s \geq -s_n \end{cases}$$

$$J_n(s,p) = \begin{cases} J'(s + \rho_n + s_n, p) & \text{if } s \leq -s_n \\ J''(s - \rho_n + s_n, p) & \text{if } s \geq -s_n. \end{cases}$$

Let us study the different possible limits of (H_n, J_n) (for the $\mathcal{C}^\infty_{\text{loc}}$ topology) in terms of the behavior of the sequence (s_n).

In the special case where $s_n = -\rho_n$, it is obvious that (H_n, J_n) tends to (H', J'). Likewise, when $s_n = \rho_n$, (H_n, J_n) tends to (H'', J''). The limit ℓ will therefore be a solution of the Floer equation corresponding to $\Gamma' = (H', J')$ in the first case and to $\Gamma'' = (H'', J'')$ in the second case.

Since the statement of (2) allows us to add a convergent sequence to (s_n), we only need to study the case where the sequences $(s_n \pm \rho_n)$ are divergent:

- If $\lim(s_n + \rho_n) = -\infty$, that is, if $s_n \ll -\rho_n$, then we easily obtain

$$\lim_{n \to +\infty} (H_n, J_n) = (H^a, J^a).$$

- If $\lim_{n \to +\infty}(s_n + \rho_n) = +\infty$ and $\lim_{n \to +\infty}(s_n - \rho_n) = -\infty$, in other words, if $-\rho_n \ll s_n \ll \rho_n$, then by analyzing separately the cases where (s_n) tends to $-\infty$, is convergent or tends to $+\infty$, we find that

$$\lim_{n \to +\infty} (H_n, J_n) = (H^b, J^b).$$

- If $\lim(s_n - \rho_n) = +\infty$, that is, if $s_n \gg \rho_n$, then we have

$$\lim_{n \to +\infty} (H_n, J_n) = (H^c, J^c).$$

We have thus proved point (2); let us now move on to point (1). We first copy the proof of Proposition 6.6.2 (a bound on the gradient in the proof of the compactness theorem) to prove that there exists a constant $A > 0$ such that

$$\forall \rho, \ \forall \ell \in \mathcal{M}^{\Gamma_\rho}(x, z), \ \forall (s,t) \in \mathbf{R} \times S^1, \quad \|\text{grad}_{(s,t)}\ell\| \leq A$$

(here $\|\cdot\|$ denotes an arbitrary norm on TW—they are all equivalent because W is compact—for example the norm coming from $\mathbf{R}^m$).

If such a constant did not exist, then as in the proof of Proposition 6.6.2, we would obtain a J-holomorphic curve v, which would lead to a contradiction as in Lemma 6.6.4. The structure J in question is the limit (for the $\mathcal{C}^\infty_{\text{loc}}$ topology) of a sequence J_{ρ_n}. It is therefore either equal to $J_{\rho_\star}$ for a $\rho_\star > 0$

(and in this case depends on s), or equal to J^b. The inequality above is therefore satisfied by ℓ_n for every n and also by the elements of the sequence $(\ell_n(s + s_n, t))$. The latter form an equicontinuous family, which allows us to apply the Arzelà–Ascoli theorem and to find a subsequence that converges to a limit ℓ for the $\mathcal{C}^0_{\text{loc}}$ topology.

Point (2) then shows that there exists a constant $s_\star \in \mathbf{R}$ such that $\ell(s+s_\star)$ is a solution, in the weak sense, of one of the Floer equations stated in the proposition. Elliptic regularity (Lemma 12.1.1) then implies that ℓ is of class $\mathcal{C}^\infty$ and that the convergence of $\ell_n(s + s_n, t)$ to ℓ indeed holds in the $\mathcal{C}^\infty_{\text{loc}}$ sense.

This concludes the proof of Proposition 11.5.6.   □

To conclude the proof of Proposition 11.5.5, we will use an argument of convergence to a broken trajectory analogous to the one we used in Section 9.1.c. More precisely, a proof analogous to that of Theorem 9.1.7 gives the existence of sequences (s_n^k) for $0 \le k \le m$ such that (after extracting a subsequence, if necessary) for every k, the sequence $\ell_n(s + s_n^k, t)$ converges to a limit $\ell \in \mathcal{C}^\infty(x_k, x_{k+1})$, where $x_0 = x$ and $x_{m+1} = z$. Statement (2) of Proposition 11.5.6 shows that, after changing the sequences $(s_n^k)_n$ by adding constants, if necessary, the limits ℓ^k are solutions of Floer equations corresponding to one of the pairs (H^a, J^a), (H', J'), (H^b, J^b), (H'', J''), (H^c, J^c). The loops x_k are therefore critical points of $\mathcal{A}_{H^a}$, $\mathcal{A}_{H^b}$ or $\mathcal{A}_{H^c}$.

On the other hand, if there exists a limit ℓ_k, a solution that is not constant in s of the Floer equation associated with (H^a, J^a), (H^b, J^b) or (H^c, J^c), then we can deduce that $\mu(x_k) - \mu(x_{k+1}) \ge 1$ (as in Corollary 11.1.11) and therefore that $\mu(x) - \mu(z) \ge 1$, contrary to the assumption we made ($\mu(x) = \mu(z)$).

Remark 11.5.7. Note that we cannot exclude solutions of the Floer equation that are constant with respect to s, because we cannot exclude the case where one of the homotopies Γ', Γ'' or Γ_ρ is trivial.

It might also happen that some of the pairs (H^a, J^a), (H^b, J^b), (H^c, J^c) are equal (without the homotopy connecting the pairs necessarily being trivial). We therefore need to consider the case where x, y and z are not all distinct.

Let us return to our proof. Assume that among the limits $\ell^1, \ldots, \ell^m$, there is one, say ℓ^k, that is not constant in s. Following the proof of point (2) of Proposition 11.5.6, we may, and do, assume (after adding a constant to the sequence $(s_n^k)_n$, if necessary) that ℓ^k is a solution of the Floer equation associated with Γ' or Γ'', and that $s_n^k = -\rho_n$ or $s_n^k = \rho_n$. On the other hand, the proof of Theorem 9.1.7 gives sequences s_n^k with the property

$$\lim_{n \to +\infty} s_n^{k+1} - s_n^k = +\infty.$$

There are therefore at most two limits ℓ^k as above, one for $s_n^k = -\rho_n$, and one for $s_n^k = \rho_n$: indeed, such sequences would differ (by statement (2) of Proposition 11.5.6) from $-\rho_n$ or from ρ_n by bounded sequences (recall that there does not exist an ℓ^k that is not constant in s and is a Floer solution associated with (H^a, J^a), (H^b, J^b) or (H^c, J^c)).

Hence the broken trajectory toward which the sequence ℓ_n converges consists of solutions of the Floer equation that are constant in s, at most one trajectory associated with Γ' (for the sequence $s_n = -\rho_n$) and at most one associated with Γ'' (for $s_n = \rho_n$). Again by Proposition 11.5.6, if

$$u = \lim_{s \to +\infty} \ell_n(s - \rho_n, t) \quad \text{and} \quad v = \lim_{n \to +\infty} \ell_n(s + \rho_n, t),$$

then

$$u \in \mathcal{M}^{\Gamma'}(x', y') \quad \text{and} \quad v \in \mathcal{M}^{\Gamma''}(y'', z'')$$

for

$$x \in \operatorname{Crit} \mathcal{A}_{H^a}, \quad y', y'' \in \operatorname{Crit} \mathcal{A}_{H^b}, \quad z'' \in \operatorname{Crit} \mathcal{A}_{H^c}.$$

We want to show that $x' = x$, $y' = y''$ and $z'' = z$.

If in the broken trajectory that is the limit of ℓ_n there are two trajectories $\ell' \in \mathcal{C}^\infty_\downarrow(x, y)$ and $\ell'' \in \mathcal{C}^\infty_\downarrow(y, z)$ that are not constant in s, then by the above, $\ell' = u$ and $\ell'' = v$, hence

$$u \in \mathcal{M}^{\Gamma'}(x, y) \quad \text{and} \quad v \in \mathcal{M}^{\Gamma''}(y, z),$$

which concludes the proof. Indeed, there cannot be more than two trajectories that are constant in s because the arrival point of ℓ' coincides with the starting point of ℓ''.

Let us now assume that there is only one nonconstant Floer trajectory $\ell \in \mathcal{C}^\infty(x, z)$ in the limit of ℓ_n. This trajectory ℓ is therefore equal to either u or v. We may, and do, assume, without loss of generality, that $\ell = u$. Then

$$\lim_{n \to +\infty} \ell_n(s - \rho_n, t) = u \in \mathcal{M}^{\Gamma'}(x, z).$$

With the notation of the proof of Theorem 9.1.7 on broken trajectories, there exists an $s^\star \in \mathbf{R}$ such that the loop $u(s, \cdot) \in B(z, \varepsilon)$ for $s > s^\star$ and consequently the loop $\ell_n(s^\star - \rho_n, \cdot)$ is also in the ball $B(z, \varepsilon)$ for n sufficiently large.

The proof of Theorem 9.1.7 then implies that $\ell_n(s, \cdot) \in B(z, \varepsilon)$ for every $s > s^\star - \rho_n$. Otherwise there would be another nonconstant trajectory in the limit (constructed as in this proof). This implies that for $v(s, t) = \lim_{n \to +\infty} \ell_n(s + \rho_n, t)$, $v \in \mathcal{M}^{\Gamma''}(z, z)$ (in fact, this trajectory is constant and equal to z if we choose ε sufficiently small). This concludes the proof of Proposition 11.5.5 in this case as well.

Remark 11.5.8. The difficulty here comes from the fact that, the only definition we have of the convergence of a broken trajectory, as given in Theorem 9.1.7, does not guarantee a unique limit.[2] We must therefore call upon the proof of this theorem to construct the limit $(\ell^1, \ldots, \ell^m)$ considered here.

Finally, if all trajectories in the limit of ℓ_n are constant, in $\mathcal{C}^\infty(x, z)$ (in particular, we then have $x = z$), then the proof of Theorem 9.1.7 says that $\ell_n(s) \in B(x, \varepsilon)$ for every s. In particular,

$$u(s, t) = \lim_{n \to +\infty} \ell_n(s - \rho_n, t) \in \mathcal{M}^{\Gamma'}(x, z)$$

and
$$v(s, t) = \lim_{n \to +\infty} \ell_n(s + \rho_n, t) \in \mathcal{M}^{\Gamma''}(x, z).$$

We could also show that u is constant and equal to x, as is v, by choosing ε sufficiently small to have all trajectories of $\mathcal{M}^{\Gamma'}(x, x)$ and $\mathcal{M}^{\Gamma''}(x, x)$ that are nonconstant in s exit $B(x, \varepsilon)$.

This concludes the proof of Proposition 11.5.5.   □

We now have a sequence $\ell_n \notin \mathrm{Im}(\chi_{\rho_n})$ such that

$$\lim_{n \to +\infty} \ell_n(s - \rho_n, t) = u(s, t) \in \mathcal{M}^{\Gamma'}(x, y)$$

and
$$\lim_{n \to +\infty} \ell_n(s + \rho_n, t) = v(s, t) \in \mathcal{M}^{\Gamma''}(y, z).$$

To obtain the desired contradiction, we show the following result.

Proposition 11.5.9. *For n sufficiently large, $\ell_n = \chi_{\rho_n}(u, v)$.*

The proof follows the main lines of that of the uniqueness of the gluing (in Theorem 11.1.16). We show an analogue of Proposition 11.2.3.

Proposition 11.5.10. *For n sufficiently large, there exists a $Y_n \in w_{\rho_n}^\star TW$ such that*
$$\ell_n = \exp_{w_{\rho_n}} Y_n \quad and \quad \lim_{n \to +\infty} \|Y_n\|_\infty = 0.$$

After that, we will show an analogue of Proposition 11.2.4.

Proposition 11.5.11. *The vector field Y_n is in $W^{1,p}(w_{\rho_n}^\star TW)$. Moreover, $\lim_{n \to +\infty} \|Y_n\|_{W^{1,p}} = 0$.*

---

[2] Contrary to the case treated in Theorem 9.1.7.

Finally, we will conclude the proof by using the uniqueness given by the Newton–Picard method (Lemma 9.4.4).

Proof of Proposition 11.5.10. We begin with a lemma.

Lemma 11.5.12. *The sequence* $(\ell_n(s,t))_n$ *converges to* $y(t)$ *for the* $\mathcal{C}^\infty_{\mathrm{loc}}$ *topology.*

Proof. Note that for $s \in [-\rho_n + R, \rho_n - R]$, we have

$$(H_{\rho_n}, J_{\rho_n}) = (H^b, J^b).$$

Hence the restriction of ℓ_n to $[-\rho_n + R, \rho_n - R] \times S^1$ is a solution of the Floer equation associated with (H^b, J^b). In particular, the function

$$s \longmapsto \mathcal{A}_{H^b}(\ell_n(s))$$

is decreasing on this interval.

Let a denote the limit of (a convergent subsequence of) ℓ_n, whose existence follows from assertion (1) of Proposition 11.5.6. The proof of assertion (2) of this same proposition implies that

$$a \in \mathcal{M}^{(H^b, J^b)}(y', y'') \quad \text{for } y', y'' \in \mathrm{Crit}\, \mathcal{A}_{H^b}.$$

We fix an $s > R$ and a $\sigma < -R$. For n sufficiently large, we have $\sigma + \rho_n > s$. It follows that

$$
\begin{aligned}
\mathcal{A}_{H^b}(a(s)) &= \lim_{n \to +\infty} \mathcal{A}_{H^b}(\ell_n(s)) \\
&\geq \lim_{n \to +\infty} \mathcal{A}_{H^b}(\ell_n(\sigma + \rho_n)) \\
&= \mathcal{A}_{H^b}(v(\sigma)).
\end{aligned}
$$

By letting s tend to $+\infty$ and σ tend to $-\infty$, we find

$$\mathcal{A}_{H^b}(y'') \geq \mathcal{A}_{H^b}(y).$$

Likewise,

$$
\begin{aligned}
\mathcal{A}_{H^b}(a(\sigma)) &= \lim_{n \to +\infty} \mathcal{A}_{H^b}(\ell_n(\sigma)) \\
&\leq \lim_{n \to +\infty} \mathcal{A}_{H^b}(\ell_n(s - \rho_n)) \\
&= \mathcal{A}_{H^b}(u(s)).
\end{aligned}
$$

We again let s tend to $+\infty$ and σ tend to $-\infty$ and we find

$$\mathcal{A}_{H^b}(y') \leq \mathcal{A}_{H^b}(y).$$

But $\mathcal{A}_{H^b}(y') \geq \mathcal{A}_{H^b}(y'')$, so that

$$\mathcal{A}_{H^b}(y') = \mathcal{A}_{H^b}(y'') = \mathcal{A}_{H^b}(y),$$

hence a is constant in s (more precisely, $a(s) = y$) because the critical values of $\mathcal{A}_{H^b}$ are assumed to be distinct.   □

Assume that the solutions u and v are not constant in s. We choose balls $B(x, \delta)$, $B(y, \delta)$ and $B(z, \delta)$ in the loop space $\mathcal{L}W$ that satisfy the properties of Lemma 9.6.11. After decreasing δ, if necessary, we may, and do, also assume that the loops $u(0)$ and $v(0)$ are not contained in any of these balls. They do not contain any other loops of $\mathrm{Crit}\,\mathcal{A}_{H^a}$, $\mathrm{Crit}\,\mathcal{A}_{H^b}$ and $\mathrm{Crit}\,\mathcal{A}_{H^c}$ than x, y and z, respectively.

By the lemma that we just proved, we know that $\ell(0) \in B(y, \delta)$ for n sufficiently large. As in the proof of Proposition 9.6.3, let

$$\sigma_n = \sup\{s > 0 \mid \ell_n([-s, 0]) \subset B(y, \delta)\}$$
$$\tau_n = \sup\{s > 0 \mid \ell_n([0, s]) \subset B(y, \delta)\}$$
$$\sigma'_n = \inf\{s > 0 \mid \ell_n(]-\infty, -s]) \subset B(x, \delta)\}$$
$$\tau'_n = \inf\{s > 0 \mid \ell_n([s, +\infty[) \subset B(z, \delta)\}.$$

Since $\lim \ell_n(-\rho_n) = u(0)$ and $\lim \ell_n(\rho_n) = v(0)$, we have

$$-\sigma'_n < -\rho_n < -\sigma_n \quad \text{and} \quad \tau_n < \rho_n < \tau'_n.$$

The construction of these sequences also implies that

$$\ell_n(\sigma_n), \ell_n(\tau_n) \in \partial B(y, \delta), \quad \ell_n(\sigma'_n) \in \partial B(x, \delta), \quad \ell_n(\tau'_n) \in \partial B(z, \delta).$$

Consequently, we have the following result.

Lemma 11.5.13. *The sequences* $(\rho_n - \sigma_n)$, $(\rho_n - \sigma'_n)$, $(\rho_n - \tau_n)$ *and* $(\rho_n - \tau'_n)$ *are bounded.*

Proof. Suppose that $(\sigma'_n - \rho_n)$ tends to $+\infty$. Then by Proposition 11.5.6, the sequence $\ell_n(s - \sigma'_n)$ converges to ℓ, a solution of the Floer equation associated with (H^a, J^a) (see the proof of point (2) of Proposition 11.5.6, if necessary). Moreover, the definition of σ'_n implies that $\ell(s) \in B(x, \delta)$ for all negative s, so that consequently

$$\ell \in \mathcal{M}^{(H^a, J^a)}(x, y') \quad \text{for a } y' \in \mathrm{Crit}\,\mathcal{A}_{H^a}.$$

Since $\ell(0) \in \partial B(x, \delta)$, we know that $y' \neq x$. But this is not possible, because we have proved (when we proved Proposition 11.5.5) that the broken trajectory toward which ℓ_n tends cannot contain nonconstant trajectories of the Floer equation associated with (H^a, J^a).

Next, suppose that $\sigma_n - \rho_n$ tends to $-\infty$. Still by Proposition 11.5.6, the sequence $(\ell_n(s - \sigma_n))$ converges to a limit ℓ that is a solution of the Floer equation associated with (H^b, J^b). We have

$$\ell(0) = \lim_{n \to +\infty} \ell_n(\sigma_n) \in \partial B(y, \delta).$$

Moreover, σ_n tends to $+\infty$ (otherwise, if σ_n is bounded, then since ℓ_n converges to y in $\mathcal{C}^\infty_{loc}$, $\ell_n(\sigma_n)$ cannot be contained in $\partial B(y, \delta)$).

Let $s > 0$. For n sufficiently large, we have $s - \sigma_n \in\ ]-\sigma_n, 0]$, hence $\ell_n(s - \sigma_n) \in B(y, \delta)$, and therefore $\ell(s) \in B(y, \delta)$. It follows that ℓ is a nonconstant solution of the Floer equation associated with (H^b, J^b). It occurs in the broken trajectory that is the limit of ℓ_n (this trajectory would start with u, ℓ). This is impossible, as before.

We proceed in the same manner to prove the assertions concerning τ_n and τ'_n. $\qquad\square$

Let $A > 0$ be such that all sequences in the previous statement take on their values in $[-A, A]$ and such that

$$u(s) \in B(x, \delta) \text{ for } s < -A, \quad u(s) \in B(y, \delta) \text{ for } s > A,$$

$$v(s) \in B(y, \delta) \text{ for } s < -A \quad \text{and} \quad v(s) \in B(z, \delta) \text{ for } s > A.$$

As in the proof of Proposition 9.6.3, we cut $\mathbf{R}$ up into several intervals and define $Y_n(s)$ for s in each of these intervals:

(1) If $s < -\rho_n - A < -\sigma'_n$, then $\ell_n(s) \in B(x, \delta)$,

$$w_{\rho_n}(s) = u(s + \rho_n) \in B(x, \delta)$$

and we use Lemma 9.6.11.

(2) If $-\rho_n - A < s < -\rho_n + A$, then we use the fact that $\ell_n(s - \rho_n)$ tends to $u(s)$ uniformly for $s \in [-A, A]$.

(3) If $-\rho_n + A < s < \rho_n - A$, then $-\sigma_n < s < \tau_n$, hence $\ell_n(s) \in B(y, \delta)$. Next,

$$u(s + \rho_n) \quad \text{and} \quad v(s - \rho_n) \in B(y, \delta),$$

hence $w_{\rho_n}(s) \in B(y, \delta)$ (still by Lemma 9.6.11). We use this lemma to define Y_n.

(4) If $\rho_n - A < s < \rho_n + A$, then we use the fact that $\ell_n(s + \rho_n)$ tends to $v(s)$, uniformly for $s \in [-A, A]$.

(5) If $s > \rho_n + A > \tau'_n$, then we have $\ell_n(s) \in B(z, \delta)$ and $w_{\rho_n}(s) = v(s - \rho_n) \in B(z, \delta)$, which allows us to define Y_n using Lemma 9.6.11, as before.

This concludes the proof when u and v are not constant in s. If one of the two solutions (or both) is (are) constant, then the proof is simpler. Suppose, for example, that v is constant in s (in particular, we then have $y = z$). The proof of Theorem 9.1.7, which constructs the broken limit trajectory of ℓ_n, then implies that $\ell_n(s) \in B(z, \delta)$ for every $s > s^* - \rho_n$ (for some constant s^*). The pre-gluing $w_{\rho_n}(s)$ obviously has the same property since for $s \geq -\rho_n + A$,

$$u(s + \rho_n) \in B(y, \delta) = B(z, \delta) \quad \text{and} \quad v(s - \rho_n) = y = z \in B(z, \delta).$$

It will therefore suffice to define Y_n for the intervals described in (1) and (2), which can be done in an analogous manner.   □

The proof of Proposition 11.5.11 is exactly the same as that of Proposition 11.2.4 and its analogue Proposition 9.6.4 (in Subsection 9.6.c). The fact that

$$Y_n \in W^{1,p}(w_\rho^* TW)$$

follows from (the analogue of) Lemma 9.6.13 (proved in the same manner).

To show that $\lim \|Y_n\|_{W^{1,p}} = 0$, we make an estimate, as in the proof of Proposition 11.2.4, using (the analogue of) Lemma 13.7.1. Note that Lemma 9.6.14 is useful here (because $\mu(x) = \mu(y) = \mu(z)$, hence $W_n = 0$); it makes it easier to obtain the estimate of the $W^{1,p}$ norm of Y_n.   □

End of the Proof of Proposition 11.5.9. We want to show that for n sufficiently large,

$$\ell_n = \chi_{\rho_n}(u, v),$$

in other words,

$$\exp_{w_{\rho_n}} Y_n = \exp_{w_{\rho_n}} \gamma_{\rho_n},$$

that is, $Y_n = \gamma_{\rho_n}$. We know that

$$\mathcal{F}_{\rho_n}(Y_n) = \mathcal{F}_{\rho_n}(\gamma_{\rho_n}) = 0$$

and that $L_{\rho_n} = (d\mathcal{F}_{\rho_n})_0$ is bijective, as we saw in Section 11.5.a. But we cannot apply the local inversion theorem directly because the size of the neighborhood on which $\mathcal{F}_{\rho_n}$ is bijective could decrease when n increases and Y_n is not necessarily contained in this neighborhood. We use the uniqueness lemma 9.6.16 that states that the solution γ_{ρ_n} of $\mathcal{F}_{\rho_n}(Y) = 0$ obtained through the Newton–Picard method is the only one in the ball $B(0, \varepsilon_0)$, where the constant ε_0 does not depend on n.

Consequently, since the $W^{1,p}$ norm of Y_n tends to 0, we have $Y_n = \gamma_{\rho_n}$, concluding the proof of Proposition 11.5.9.   □

We therefore obtain the surjectivity of χ_ρ for ρ sufficiently large, which we needed to conclude the proof of Proposition 11.5.3.   □

This trivially implies Proposition 11.5.2: Lemma 11.5.1 asserts that Γ_ρ is regular for arbitrarily large values of ρ and Proposition 11.5.3 implies that, from a certain value of ρ,

$$\Phi^{\Gamma_\rho} = \Phi^{\Gamma'} \circ \Phi^{\Gamma''}$$

if the left-hand side is defined.

Finally, Proposition 11.5.2 obviously implies Proposition 11.2.9, which was the object of this section. Propositions 11.2.8 and 11.2.9 imply the invariance of the Floer homology with respect to the choice of a regular pair (H, J).

11.6 Conclusion

We have achieved the aims of the plan announced in Section 6.2 (p. 154) and proved the Arnold conjecture.

We must point out that Floer homology and its different relatives have many other applications to symplectic geometry and contact geometry than this conjecture. In fact, the second part of this book would be the starting point for readers interested in modern aspects of symplectic topology. Here are some directions and references for those who would like to go further.

First of all, there is the study of the Lagrangian submanifolds of symplectic manifolds,[3] already undertaken by Floer in [29]; see also the works of Oh [59, 60, 61], Seidel and Fukaya [34, 69, 70], and, closer to us, those of Damian [22] and Gadbled [36].

Next, there is the generalization of our construction in the case of symplectic manifolds with *contact-type* boundaries. In this case, the Floer homology is no longer isomorphic to the Morse homology as it was here, but takes into account the closed characteristics of the boundary. This leads to the symplectic homology developed by Viterbo [77] (see also the article by Oancea [58], and that by Cieliebak and Frauenfelder [20]).

Another branch goes toward the study of contact manifolds. A variant of the Floer construction for the symplectizations of contact manifolds gives a "contact homology" generated by the periodic trajectories of the Reeb fields of the manifold. This theory is due to Eliashberg, Givental and Hofer [27]. See also the works of Bourgeois [15].

But this could fill another book.

---

[3] We would like to update this list of references, adding especially the recent books and papers of some of the leading experts in the field [35, 71, 33, 10, 11], as well as the new results obtained by one of the authors [23, 24].

Chapter 12
The Elliptic Regularity of the Floer Operator

12.1 Elliptic Regularity: Why and How?

We have invoked several times, under the name "elliptic regularity", the regularity of the solutions of the Floer equation

$$\frac{\partial u}{\partial s} + J(u)\frac{\partial u}{\partial t} + \operatorname{grad} H_t(u) = 0.$$

The first time, in Chapter 6, we needed it to show the compactness of the space $\mathcal{M}$ of finite energy solutions (more precisely, Proposition 6.5.3). The statement we used is the following.

Lemma 12.1.1 (Elliptic Regularity). *Let U be an open subset of $\mathbf{C}$. Every sequence (u_n) of solutions of class $\mathcal{C}^\infty$ of the Floer equation*

$$\frac{\partial u}{\partial s} + J(u)\frac{\partial u}{\partial t} + \operatorname{grad} H_t(u) = 0$$

defined on U and satisfying

$$\sup_{n\in\mathbf{N}} \|\operatorname{grad} u_n\|_{L^\infty(U)} \le M$$

(for some real M) has a subsequence that converges uniformly on every compact subset of U, as do all its derivatives, to a limit that is therefore of class $\mathcal{C}^\infty$.

Next, in the proof of the transversality theorem 8.1.2 on p. 254, we also called on elliptic regularity to justify the fact that the solutions of the Floer equation in the Sobolev-type space $\mathcal{P}^{1,p}(x, y)$ are of class $\mathcal{C}^\infty$ and that the topology induced by that of $\mathcal{P}^{1,p}$ on this space of solutions is the same as that of $\mathcal{M}$, that is, the $\mathcal{C}^\infty_{\text{loc}}$ topology ($\mathcal{P}^{1,p}(x, y)$ is defined in Definition 8.2.2).

M. Audin, M. Damian, *Morse Theory and Floer Homology*,
Universitext, DOI 10.1007/978-1-4471-5496-9_12,
© Springer-Verlag London 2014

After that, the elliptic regularity argument appeared in similar situations: in Chapter 9, to prove that the $\mathcal{P}^{1,p}$ solutions produced by gluing are "true" solutions and converge to a broken trajectory in the right topology (Lemma 9.4.17), and then in Chapter 11, where compactness, transversality and gluing results are proved in a more general setting, where the almost complex structure J and the Hamiltonian H depend on s and sometimes on another parameter λ.

We therefore see that elliptic regularity plays a role in all steps of the construction of the Floer homology. This is why we will now give rigorous statements and detailed proofs of these properties. We have mainly used [51].

12.1.a (Linear) Elliptic Regularity Results

The elliptic regularity results that have been referred to in this text are related to the following theorem.

Theorem 12.1.2. *Let $p > 1$ and let $U \subset \mathbf{C}$ be an open subset. Let $f \in W_{\mathrm{loc}}^{k,p}(U)$ and let $u \in L_{\mathrm{loc}}^p(U)$ be a weak solution of $\overline\partial u = f$. Then*

$$u \in W_{\mathrm{loc}}^{k+1,p}(U).$$

Moreover, for every relatively compact open set V with $\overline V \subset U$, there exists a constant $C = C(k, p, K, U)$ such that

$$\|u\|_{W^{k+1,p}(V)} \leq C \left(\|f\|_{W^{k,p}(U)} + \|u\|_{L^p(U)} \right).$$

We will prove this theorem in Section 12.3. One of its first consequences is the following estimate, used in Chapter 8. This is the analogue of Theorem 12.1.2 for the operator L.

Theorem (Lemma 8.7.2). *Let $p > 1$, let $S : \mathbf{R} \times S^1 \to \mathrm{End}(\mathbf{R}^{2n})$ be a continuous map with $\lim_{s \to \pm\infty} S(s,t) = S^\pm(t)$ and finally, let*

$$L : W^{1,p}(\mathbf{R} \times S^1; \mathbf{R}^{2n}) \longrightarrow L^p(\mathbf{R} \times S^1; \mathbf{R}^{2n})$$

be the perturbed Cauchy–Riemann operator

$$LY = \frac{\partial Y}{\partial s} + J_0 \frac{\partial Y}{\partial t} + S \cdot Y.$$

There exists a constant $C > 0$ such that

$$\forall Y \in W^{1,p}(\mathbf{R} \times S^1; \mathbf{R}^{2n}), \quad \|Y\|_{W^{1,p}} \leq C \left(\|LY\|_{L^p} + \|Y\|_{L^p} \right).$$

More generally, if Y and LY are in L^p, then $Y \in W^{1,p}$ and the equality holds.

We will prove this in Section 12.2. We also use Theorem 12.1.2 to obtain a regularity result for the linearization of the Floer operator (which we used in the proofs of Lemma 8.5.1 and Proposition 8.7.1).

Theorem 12.1.3 (Elliptic Regularity, Linear Version). *Let L be the operator*

$$L = \frac{\partial}{\partial s} + J_0 \frac{\partial}{\partial t} + S, \quad \text{with } S \in \mathcal{C}^\infty\left(\mathbf{R} \times S^1; \mathrm{End}(\mathbf{R}^{2n})\right).$$

We suppose that

$$\lim_{s \to \pm\infty} S(s,t) = S^\pm(t) \quad \text{and} \quad \lim_{s \to \pm\infty} \frac{\partial S}{\partial s}(s,t) = 0.$$

If $Y \in L^p(\mathbf{R} \times S^1; \mathbf{R}^{2n})$ is such that $LY = 0$ in the sense of distributions, then Y is of class $\mathcal{C}^\infty$ and $Y \in W^{1,p}(\mathbf{R} \times S^1; \mathbf{R}^{2n})$. If $p > 2$, then we also have $Y \in W^{1,q}(\mathbf{R} \times S^1; \mathbf{R}^{2n})$ for every $q > 1$.

Proof. Since Y is in L^p,

$$\overline{\partial} Y = -SY \in L^p(\mathbf{R} \times S^1; \mathbf{R}^{2n}).$$

Using Theorem 12.1.2, we therefore find that $Y \in W^{1,p}_{\mathrm{loc}}$, hence $SY \in W^{1,p}_{\mathrm{loc}}$. By the same theorem, we have $Y \in W^{2,p}_{\mathrm{loc}}$ and, by induction, $Y \in W^{k,p}_{\mathrm{loc}}$ for every $k \in \mathbf{N}$ (this is an elliptic *bootstrapping*). Using Theorem C.4.9, we deduce that Y is of class $\mathcal{C}^\infty$. The previous theorem (also known as Lemma 8.7.2) tells us that it is in $W^{1,p}$.

Next, suppose that $p > 2$. By proceeding as above, to prove that $Y \in W^{1,q}(\mathbf{R} \times S^1)$ for every $q > 1$, it suffices to prove that $Y \in L^q(\mathbf{R} \times S^1)$ for every $q > 1$. Since Y is of class $\mathcal{C}^\infty$, an exponential decay property

$$\|Y(s,t)\| \le e^{-\delta|s|} \quad \forall\, s, t \text{ for a constant } \delta > 0$$

suffices. Now Theorem 8.9.1 guarantees this property provided that the function

$$s \longmapsto \int_0^1 \|Y(s,t)\|^2 \, dt$$

does not tend to infinity for $s \to \pm\infty$. Let us therefore verify that our Y satisfies this property. Hölder's inequality gives

$$\int_0^1 \|Y(s,t)\|^2 \, dt \le \left(\int_0^1 \|Y(s,t)\|^p \, dt \right)^{2/p}.$$

Hence, if $\int_0^1 \|Y(s,t)\|^2 \, dt$ tends to infinity, then the same holds for $\int_0^1 \|Y(s,t)\|^p \, dt$, which is impossible because

$$\int_{-\infty}^{+\infty} \int_0^1 \|Y(s,t)\|^p \, dt \, ds = \|Y\|_{L^p}^p < +\infty,$$

proving the theorem.   □

12.1.b (Nonlinear) Elliptic Regularity Results

"Nonlinear" elliptic regularity properties are included in the following statement.

Proposition 12.1.4. *For $p > 2$, a solution $u \in W_{\mathrm{loc}}^{1,p}(\mathbf{R} \times S^1; W)$ of the Floer equation is of class $\mathcal{C}^\infty$. On the space of solutions $W_{\mathrm{loc}}^{1,p}(\mathbf{R} \times S^1; W)$, the $W_{\mathrm{loc}}^{1,p}$ and $\mathcal{C}_{\mathrm{loc}}^\infty$ topologies coincide.*

The notation $W_{\mathrm{loc}}^{1,p}(\mathbf{R} \times S^1; W)$ is new in this book; we will clarify its meaning later. Also note that, contrary to the earlier statements, nonlinear elliptic regularity needs the assumption that $p > 2$. Here are some explanations.

Why Assume That $p > 2$?

In all regularity statements, the aim is to prove that a weak solution (solution in the sense of distributions) is a true solution of class $\mathcal{C}^\infty$. In our case, by assumption, the solution is in the Sobolev space $W^{1,p}(\mathbf{R} \times S^1)$. As we explained in Section 8.2, assuming that $p > 2$ guarantees, *via* Rellich's theorem (Theorem C.4.6), that this solution is *continuous*. At the same time, this allows us to work with local coordinates.

The regularity of a solution $u : \mathbf{R} \times S^1 \to W$ can be read in charts of W. But other properties that are involved here, for example L^p integrability (even on compact sets), are not invariant under transition maps. On the other hand, if u is in $W^{1,p}(\mathbf{R} \times S^1; \mathbf{R}^{2n})$ and if $\varphi : \mathbf{R}^{2n} \to \mathbf{R}^{2n}$ is continuous, then for $p > 2$, $\varphi \circ u \in W_{\mathrm{loc}}^{1,p}(\mathbf{R} \times S^1; \mathbf{R}^{2n})$. Indeed, $\varphi \circ u$ is in $L_{\mathrm{loc}}^p(\mathbf{R} \times S^1; \mathbf{R}^{2n})$ by the continuity of u, and

$$\frac{\partial(\varphi \circ u)}{\partial s} = (d\varphi)_u\left(\frac{\partial u}{\partial s}\right) \in L_{\mathrm{loc}}^p(\mathbf{R} \times S^1; \mathbf{R}^{2n})$$

(and likewise for the derivative with respect to t) because it is a product of a continuous function and an L_{loc}^p function. Consequently, we can define the space $W^{1,p}(\mathbf{R} \times S^1; W)$ as the subspace of continuous functions that, in coordinates, are represented by $W^{1,p}(\mathbf{R} \times S^1; \mathbf{R}^{2n})$ functions. An equivalent alternative is to embed W in $\mathbf{R}^m$ and to consider the $W_{\mathrm{loc}}^{1,p}(\mathbf{R} \times S^1; \mathbf{R}^m)$

functions that take on their values in W (the definition will not depend on the chosen embedding).

This is not the only reason to assume that $p > 2$. The main ingredient of the proof of all these regularity statements is an "elliptic bootstrapping" argument that asserts that if a solution is in $W_{loc}^{k,p}(\mathbf{R} \times S^1; \mathbf{R}^{2n})$, then it is also in $W_{loc}^{k+1,p}(\mathbf{R} \times S^1; \mathbf{R}^{2n})$. The regularity of the solution is then a consequence of Theorem C.4.9. We applied this argument in the proof of linear elliptic regularity (Theorem 12.1.3). In the *nonlinear* case, the condition $p > 2$ turns out to be crucial. See the proof of Theorem 12.1.5 in Section 12.4.c.

The proof of Lemma 12.1.1 relies on Proposition 12.1.4, but it is not an immediate consequence of it. This is because applying the Arzelà–Ascoli theorem gives a limit for the sequence (u_n) that is only continuous. To prove that this limit is in $W_{loc}^{1,p}$ in order to apply Proposition 12.1.4, we must also use the fact that the sequence of the $\|\operatorname{grad} u_n\|$ is uniformly bounded. The latter will be proved in Section 12.4.

Proposition 12.1.4 gives the regularity argument needed in the proof of Theorem 8.1.2 on p. 254, because by definition, the space $\mathcal{P}^{1,p}(x,y)$ is contained in $W_{loc}^{1,p}(\mathbf{R} \times S^1; W)$ (see the definition of $\mathcal{P}^{1,p}$ (Definition 8.2.2), where the charts are given explicitly). It therefore suffices to prove this proposition.

The proof that we will give relies on a statement similar to that of Theorem 12.1.2. We begin by taking a finite number of charts whose open sets cover W, to reduce to the case where $W = \mathbf{R}^{2n}$. The map $u \in W^{1,p}(\mathbf{R} \times S^1; \mathbf{R}^{2n})$ is therefore a solution of

$$\frac{\partial u}{\partial s} + J(u)\frac{\partial u}{\partial t} + \operatorname{grad} H_t(u) = 0.$$

Here J and H are of class $\mathcal{C}^\infty$ and may depend on s (as in Chapter 11), without this influencing the proof. Let

$$\widetilde{J}(s,t) = J(u(s,t)) \quad \text{and} \quad h(s,t) = \operatorname{grad} H_t(u(s,t)).$$

Using the continuity of u, we can easily see that

$$\widetilde{J} \in W_{loc}^{1,p}(\mathbf{R} \times S^1; \operatorname{End}(\mathbf{R}^{2n})) \quad \text{and} \quad h \in W_{loc}^{1,p}(\mathbf{R} \times S^1; \mathbf{R}^{2n}).$$

More generally, and without additional difficulties, we can prove that $\widetilde{J}$ and h have the same regularity as u: if $u \in W_{loc}^{k,p}(\mathbf{R} \times S^1; \mathbf{R}^{2n})$, then

$$\widetilde{J} \in W_{loc}^{k,p}(\mathbf{R} \times S^1; \operatorname{End}(\mathbf{R}^{2n})) \quad \text{and} \quad h \in W_{loc}^{k,p}(\mathbf{R} \times S^1; \mathbf{R}^{2n}).$$

Here is the statement we will need to prove.

Theorem 12.1.5. *Let $k \geq 0$, let $p > 2$, let*

$$\widetilde{J} \in W_{\mathrm{loc}}^{\min(k,1),p}(\mathbf{R} \times S^1; \mathrm{End}(\mathbf{R}^{2n})) \ \ \textit{with} \ \ \widetilde{J}^2 = -\mathrm{Id}$$

and let $h \in W_{\mathrm{loc}}^{k,p}(\mathbf{R} \times S^1; \mathbf{R}^{2n})$. If $u \in L_{\mathrm{loc}}^p(\mathbf{R} \times S^1; \mathbf{R}^{2n})$ is a solution of

$$\frac{\partial u}{\partial s} + \widetilde{J}\frac{\partial u}{\partial t} + h = 0$$

(in the sense of distributions), then $u \in W_{\mathrm{loc}}^{k+1,p}(\mathbf{R} \times S^1; \mathbf{R}^{2n})$.

Let $V \subset U \subset \mathbf{R} \times S^1$ be two relatively compact subsets and let $c_0 > 0$ satisfy

$$\|\widetilde{J}\|_{W^{\min(k,1),p}(U)} \leq c_0.$$

Then there exists a constant C (that depends on U, V, c_0, p and k) such that for every $\ell \in \{0, \ldots, \max(k-1,0)\}$, we have

$$\|u\|_{W^{\ell+1,p}(V)} \leq C \left(\|h\|_{W^{\ell,p}(U)} + \|u\|_{W^{\ell,p}(U)} \right).$$

12.1.c Ariadne's Thread

The six previous statements make up a new maze. To help the readers find their way, we present a new diagram

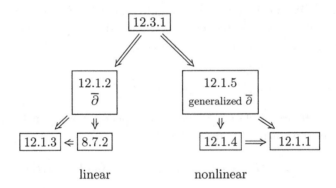

- We have proved that 12.1.2 and 8.7.2 $\Rightarrow$ 12.1.3.
- In Section 12.2, we will prove that 12.1.2 $\Rightarrow$ 8.7.2.
- In Section 12.3, we will prove that C.5.8 $\Rightarrow$ 12.3.1 $\Rightarrow$ 12.1.2.
- In Section 12.4, we will prove that 12.3.1 $\Rightarrow$ 12.1.5 $\Rightarrow$ 12.1.4 and that 12.1.5 and 12.1.4 $\Rightarrow$ 12.1.1.

12.2 Proof of Lemma 8.7.2

Let $K \subset \mathbf{R} \times S^1$ be compact and let $U \supset K$ be open. Then by Theorem 12.1.2, there exists a constant $C_1(K, U)$ such that

$$\|Y\|_{W^{1,p}(K)} \leq C_1 \left(\|\bar{\partial} Y\|_{L^p(U)} + \|Y\|_{L^p(U)} \right).$$

Since

$$\|\bar{\partial} Y\|_{L^p(U)} \leq \|LY\|_{L^p(U)} + \|SY\|_{L^p(U)},$$

it follows that

$$\|Y\|_{W^{1,p}(K)} \leq C_2 \left(\|LY\|_{L^p(U)} + \|Y\|_{L^p(U)} \right).$$

Next, let us suppose that $S(s, t) = S(t)$ and show the inequality in this case. By the above, we have

$$\|Y\|_{W^{1,p}([0,1] \times S^1)} \leq C_3 \left(\|LY\|_{L^p([-1,2] \times S^1)} + \|Y\|_{L^p([-1,2] \times S^1)} \right)$$

for some constant $C_3 > 0$. Since S does not depend on s, the operator L is invariant under translations in s, in the sense that

$$L(Y(s + s_0, t)) = (LY)(s + s_0, t).$$

It follows that for every $k \in \mathbf{Z}$,

$$\|Y\|_{W^{1,p}([k,k+1] \times S^1)} \leq C_3 \left(\|LY\|_{L^p([k-1,k+2] \times S^1)} + \|Y\|_{L^p([k-1,k+2] \times S^1)} \right).$$

By applying the inequality $(a + b)^p \leq 2^p (a^p + b^p)$ as in the proof of Proposition 8.7.3 (p. 277) we obtain

$$\|Y\|^p_{W^{1,p}([k,k+1] \times S^1)} \leq 2^p C_3^p \left(\|LY\|^p_{L^p([k-1,k+2] \times S^1)} + \|Y\|^p_{L^p([k-1,k+2] \times S^1)} \right).$$

We then take the sum over all integers k and find

$$\|Y\|^p_{W^{1,p}(\mathbf{R} \times S^1)} \leq C_4 \left(\|LY\|^p_{L^p(\mathbf{R} \times S^1)} + \|Y\|^p_{L^p \times S^1} \right)$$

$$\leq C_4 \left(\|LY\|_{L^p(\mathbf{R} \times S^1)} + \|Y\|_{L^p \times S^1} \right)^p$$

and therefore the desired equality when S does not depend on s. Let us return to the general case. Let $D^{\pm}$ be the perturbed Cauchy–Riemann operators associated with $S^{\pm}(t)$, respectively. Let $\varepsilon > 0$. If $M > 0$ is sufficiently large, then

$$\|S(s,t) - S^+(t)\| < \varepsilon \quad \text{for } s > M \text{ and } t \in S^1$$

and $\quad \|S(s,t) - S^-(t)\| < \varepsilon \quad \text{for } s < -M \text{ and } t \in S^1.$

Consequently, on $W^{1,p}([M + \infty[\times S^1; \mathbf{R}^{2n})$, we have $\|L - D^+\|^{\mathrm{op}} < \varepsilon$.

Let $Y \in W^{1,p}(\mathbf{R} \times S^1)$ be with support in $\{s > M\}$. We have (by what we just did for S independent of s)

$$
\begin{aligned}
\|Y\|_{W^{1,p}} &\leq C_5 \left(\left\|D^+Y\right\|_{L^p} + \|Y\|_{L^p} \right) \\
&= C_5 \left(\left\|D^+Y\right\|_{L^p([M,+\infty[\times S^1)} + \|Y\|_{L^p(\mathbf{R}\times S^1)} \right) \\
&\leq C_5 \left(\|LY\|_{L^p([M,+\infty[\times S^1)} + \varepsilon \|Y\|_{W^{1,p}([M,+\infty[\times S^1)} + \|Y\|_{L^p(\mathbf{R}\times S^1)} \right) \\
&= C_5 \left(\|LY\|_{L^p} + \varepsilon \|Y\|_{W^{1,p}} + \|Y\|_{L^p} \right).
\end{aligned}
$$

For ε sufficiently small ($\varepsilon \leq 1/2C_5$), the inequality of the lemma is satisfied by Y. Analogously, the same holds if the support of Y is in $\{s < -M\}$.

We now assume that Y has support in $\{|s| > M\}$. We decompose it into a sum $Y = Y^+ + Y^-$ where the term Y^+ has support in $\{s > M\}$ and Y^- has support in $\{s < -M\}$. Of course,

$$\left\|Y^{\pm}\right\|_{L^p} \leq \|Y\|_{L^p} \quad \text{and} \quad \left\|LY^{\pm}\right\|_{L^p} \leq \|LY\|_{L^p},$$

so that we have

$$
\begin{aligned}
\|Y\|_{W^{1,p}} &\leq \left\|Y^+\right\|_{W^{1,p}} + \left\|Y^-\right\|_{W^{1,p}} \\
&\leq C_6 \left(\left\|LY^+\right\|_{L^p} + \left\|LY^-\right\|_{L^p} + \left\|Y^+\right\|_{L^p} + \left\|Y^-\right\|_{L^p} \right) \\
&\leq 2C_6 \left(\|LY\|_{L^p} + \|Y\|_{L^p} \right).
\end{aligned}
$$

Next, we consider the case of a Y with support in $\{-M - 1 \leq s \leq M + 1\}$. The argument used at the beginning of the proof gives a constant C (that depends on M) such that

$$
\begin{aligned}
\|Y\|_{W^{1,p}} &= \|Y\|_{W^{1,p}([-M-1,M+1]\times S^1)} \\
&\leq C_7 \left(\|LY\|_{L^p} + \|Y\|_{L^p} \right).
\end{aligned}
$$

To conclude we use a plateau function $\beta : \mathbf{R} \to [0,1]$ that is zero for $|s| \leq M + 1$ and is 1 for $|s| \leq M$. We write $Y = \beta Y + (1 - \beta)Y$, so that the two pieces βY and $(1 - \beta)Y$ satisfy the inequality of the lemma. Note that

$$\|L(\beta Y)\|_{L^p} = \|\beta(s)LY + \beta'(s)Y\|_{L^p}$$
$$\leq \|LY\|_{L^p} + K\,\|Y\|_{L^p}$$

and likewise for $L((1 - \beta)Y)$, with $K = \sup_{s \in \mathbf{R}} |\beta'(s)|$. But then

$$\|Y\|_{W^{1,p}} \leq \|\beta Y\|_{W^{1,p}} + \|(1 - \beta)Y\|_{W^{1,p}}$$
$$\leq 2C_7\,(\|LY\|_{L^p} + K\,\|Y\|_{L^p})$$
$$\leq C\,(\|LY\|_{L^p} + \|Y\|_{L^p})$$

which concludes the proof of the lemma. $\qquad\qquad\qquad\qquad\qquad\qquad$ $\square$

12.3 Proof of Theorem 12.1.2

We will prove the theorem by induction on k. For $k = 0$, we have

$$\overline{\partial} u = f, \quad \text{with } u, f \in L^p_{\mathrm{loc}}.$$

Applying the operator ∂, we obtain

$$\Delta u = \partial f$$

(up to a factor 4). This allows us to reduce the problem to the case where u is a function with real values and is a solution of

$$\Delta u = \frac{\partial}{\partial s} g + \frac{\partial}{\partial t} h,$$

with g and h in $L^p_{\mathrm{loc}}(U)$ (and the derivatives are taken in the sense of distributions). We will show the following more general result.

Proposition 12.3.1. *If $u \in L^p_{\mathrm{loc}}(U)$ is a function with real values and satisfies*

$$\Delta u = f + \frac{\partial}{\partial s} g + \frac{\partial}{\partial t} h$$

in the sense of distributions, for f, g and $h \in L^p_{\mathrm{loc}}(U)$, then $u \in W^{1,p}_{\mathrm{loc}}(U)$ and for every relatively compact open set V with $\overline{V} \subset U$, there exists a constant $C = C(p, V, U) > 0$ such that

$$\|u\|_{W^{1,p}(V)} \leq C\big(\|f\|_{L^p(U)} + \|g\|_{L^p(U)} + \|h\|_{L^p(U)} + \|u\|_{L^p(U)}\big).$$

Proof. Let us first consider the case of the equation $\Delta u = 0$. Then u is harmonic and satisfies the mean value property (Proposition C.5.2). In particular, it is of class $\mathcal{C}^\infty$ (Lemma C.5.3) and is therefore in $W^{1,p}_{\mathrm{loc}}(U)$. Let V be an open set as in the proposition. Using the notation of the proof of Lemma C.5.3, we have $u = \psi \star u$, where

$$\psi = \chi_r \star \chi_r \star \chi_r$$

is of class $\mathcal{C}^1_0$ and the equality holds in U_{3r}, which we assume to contain $\overline{V}$ (it suffices that r be sufficiently small). It follows that

$$\left\| \frac{\partial}{\partial s} u \right\|_{L^p(V)} = \left\| \frac{\partial}{\partial s} \psi \star u \right\|_{L^p(V)}$$
$$\leq \sup_{z \in U} \left\| \frac{\partial}{\partial s} \psi(z) \right\| \cdot \|u\|_{L^p(V)}$$
$$= C \, \|u\|_{L^p(V)}$$

and an analogous estimate for $\partial u / \partial t$. We therefore obtain

$$\|u\|_{W^{1,p}(V)} \leq C(V,U) \, \|u\|_{L^p(V)} \leq C(V,U) \, \|u\|_{L^p(U)} \, .$$

Let us now turn to the general case. In order to define the convolutions, we use a function $\beta \in \mathcal{C}^\infty_0(U)$ with value 1 on V. Let

$$v = K \star \beta f + K_1 \star \beta g + K_2 \star \beta h,$$

where K is the fundamental solution of the Laplacian (see Section C.5) and K_1, K_2 are its partial derivatives:

$$K(z) = \frac{1}{2\pi} \log |z|, \quad K_1(s,t) = \frac{s}{2\pi(s^2 + t^2)}, \quad K_2(s,t) = \frac{t}{2\pi(s^2 + t^2)}.$$

Let (g_i) be a sequence of functions in $\mathcal{C}^\infty_0(U)$ that tends to βg in $L^p(U)$. Using the Calderón–Zygmund inequality (Theorem C.5.8), we find that the sequence of the $\nabla(K_1 \star g_i) = \nabla K_1 \star g_i$ is a Cauchy sequence in L^p, and therefore that $(\nabla(K_1 \star g_i))$ converges to $(\nabla K_1 \star (\beta g))$, which is in $L^p(U)$. Moreover,

$$\|\nabla(K_1 \star (\beta g))\|_{L^p(U)} \leq C_1 \, \|\beta g\|_{L^p(U)}$$
$$\leq C_2 \, \|g\|_{L^p(\mathrm{Supp}\,\beta)} \, .$$

Analogously,

$$\|\nabla(K_2 \star (\beta h))\|_{L^p(U)} \leq C_3 \|h\|_{L^p(\mathrm{Supp}\,\beta)}$$

and finally

$$\|\nabla(K \star (\beta f))\|_{L^p(V)} = \|\nabla K \star (\beta f)\|_{L^p(V)}$$
$$\leq \|K_1 \star (\beta f)\|_{L^p(V)} + \|K_2 \star (\beta f)\|_{L^p(V)}.$$

Using Young's inequality (note on p. 280), we deduce that

$$\|\nabla(K \star (\beta f))\|_{L^p(V)} \leq \|K_1\|_{L^1(V-\mathrm{Supp}\,\beta)} \|\beta f\|_{L^p(\mathrm{Supp}\,\beta)}$$
$$+ \|K_2\|_{L^1(V-\mathrm{Supp}\,\beta)} \|\beta f\|_{L^p(\mathrm{Supp}\,\beta)}$$
$$\leq C_4 \|f\|_{L^p(\mathrm{Supp}\,\beta)}.$$

Here, of course, $V - \mathrm{Supp}\,\beta = \{x - y \mid x \in V$ and $y \in \mathrm{Supp}\,\beta\}$. Combining these inequalities, we obtain

$$\|\nabla v\|_{L^p(V)} \leq C_5 \big(\|f\|_{L^p(U)} + \|g\|_{L^p(U)} + \|h\|_{L^p(U)}\big),$$

and then, using the Poincaré inequality (Lemma C.4.3),

$$\|v\|_{W^{1,p}(V)} \leq C_6 \big(\|f\|_{L^p(U)} + \|g\|_{L^p(U)} + \|h\|_{L^p(U)}\big).$$

We then have the following inequalities as distributions:

$$\Delta v = \Delta K \star (\beta f) + \Delta K_1 \star (\beta g) + \Delta K_2 \star (\beta h)$$
$$= \delta \star (\beta f) + \frac{\partial}{\partial s}\delta \star (\beta g) + \frac{\partial}{\partial t}\delta \star (\beta h)$$
$$= \beta f + \frac{\partial(\beta g)}{\partial s} + \frac{\partial(\beta g)}{\partial t}$$

(here δ is the Dirac distribution; see Subsection C.3.d). In particular, we have $\Delta(u - v) = 0$ in V. Using the upper bound obtained for the $W^{1,p}$ norm of u (applied to $u - v$) and that for the norm of v, we find

$$\|u\|_{W^{1,p}(V)} \leq \|u - v\|_{W^{1,p}(V)} + \|v\|_{W^{1,p}(V)}$$
$$\leq C\big(\|f\|_{L^p(U)} + \|g\|_{L^p(U)} + \|h\|_{L^p(U)} + \|u\|_{L^p(U)}\big),$$

which we wanted to prove. □

Consequently we now know that every $u \in L^p_{\text{loc}}(U)$ that is a solution of $\overline{\partial} u = f$ (for $f \in L^p_{\text{loc}}(U)$) is in $W^{1,p}_{\text{loc}}(U)$. More precisely, there exists a constant C (that depends only on U, p and the relatively compact open set V with $\overline{V} \subset U$) such that

$$\|u\|_{W^{1,p}(V)} \leq C\big(\|f\|_{L^p(U)} + \|u\|_{L^p(U)}\big).$$

We can now continue the proof of Theorem 12.1.2 (by induction on k). We assume that it holds for k and will now prove it for $k+1$.

If u, $f \in W^{k,p}_{\text{loc}}(U)$, then for a multi-index α of length k, we have

$$\overline{\partial}\partial^\alpha u = \partial^\alpha \overline{\partial} u = \partial^\alpha f, \quad \text{with } \partial^\alpha u \text{ and } \partial^\alpha f \in L^p_{\text{loc}}(U).$$

It follows that $\partial^\alpha u \in W^{1,p}_{\text{loc}}(U)$, that is, $u \in W^{k+1,p}_{\text{loc}}(U)$. If V is a relatively compact open set with $\overline{V} \subset U$, then

$$\|u\|_{W^{k+1,p}(V)} = \|u\|_{L^p(V)} + \left\|\frac{\partial u}{\partial s}\right\|_{W^{k,p}(V)} + \left\|\frac{\partial u}{\partial t}\right\|_{W^{k,p}(V)}.$$

Using the equalities

$$\overline{\partial}\frac{\partial u}{\partial s} = \frac{\partial f}{\partial s} \quad \text{and} \quad \overline{\partial}\frac{\partial u}{\partial t} = \frac{\partial f}{\partial t}$$

and the induction hypothesis, we have

$$\left\|\frac{\partial u}{\partial s}\right\|_{W^{k,p}(V)} \leq C'_1\left(\left\|\frac{\partial f}{\partial s}\right\|_{W^{k-1,p}(U')} + \left\|\frac{\partial u}{\partial s}\right\|_{L^p(U')}\right)$$

$$\text{by the induction hypothesis}$$

$$\leq C'_1\left(\|f\|_{W^{k,p}(U')} + \|u\|_{W^{1,p}(U')}\right)$$

$$\leq C_1\left(\|f\|_{W^{k,p}(U)} + \|u\|_{L^p(U)}\right),$$

where $V \subset U' \subset U$ are compact inclusions. Analogously,

$$\left\|\frac{\partial u}{\partial t}\right\|_{W^{k,p}(V)} \leq C_2\left(\|f\|_{W^{k,p}(U)} + \|u\|_{L^p(U)}\right).$$

This concludes the proof of Theorem 12.1.2. $\square$

12.4 (Nonlinear) Elliptic Regularity of the Floer Operator, Proofs

12.4.a How to Deduce Proposition 12.1.4...

from Theorem 12.1.5. We assume that the theorem has been proved. If

$$u \in W_{loc}^{k,p}(\mathbf{R} \times S^1; \mathbf{R}^{2n}) \text{ for a } k \geq 1,$$

then the theorem implies that

$$u \in W_{loc}^{k+1,p}(\mathbf{R} \times S^1; \mathbf{R}^{2n})$$

because $\tilde{J}$ and h have the same regularity as u. Then

$$u \in W_{loc}^{k,p}(\mathbf{R} \times S^1; \mathbf{R}^{2n}) \text{ for every } k,$$

and u is of class $\mathcal{C}^\infty$, using the fact that

$$\bigcap W_{loc}^{k,p} \subset \mathcal{C}^\infty,$$

which follows from Rellich's theorem (Theorem C.4.9).

To prove the second assertion of Proposition 12.1.4, we first show the following result.

Corollary 12.4.1. *Let $u \in \mathcal{C}^\infty(\mathbf{R} \times S^1; \mathbf{R}^{2n})$ be a solution of the Floer equation*

$$\frac{\partial u}{\partial s} + \tilde{J}\frac{\partial u}{\partial t} + h = 0$$

(with $\tilde{J} \in \mathcal{C}^\infty(\mathbf{R} \times S^1; \operatorname{End}(\mathbf{R}^{2n}))$, $\tilde{J}^2 = -\operatorname{Id}$ and $h \in \mathcal{C}^\infty(\mathbf{R} \times S^1; \mathbf{R}^{2n})$). Let $V \subset U \subset \mathbf{R} \times S^1$ be two relatively compact open subsets, let $p > 2$, $k \geq 1$ and $c_0 > 0$ be such that

$$\|\tilde{J}\|_{W^{k,p}(U)} \leq c_0.$$

Then there exists a constant c (depending on V, U, c_0, k and p) such that

$$\|u\|_{W^{k+1,p}(V)} \leq c\big(\|h\|_{W^{k,p}(U)} + \|u\|_{W^{k,p}(U)}\big).$$

This is the inequality of Theorem 12.1.5, for every $k \in \mathbf{N}$.

Proof of Corollary 12.4.1. Since the conditions of Theorem 12.1.5 are satisfied for every k, we have the desired inequality.   □

We first assume that (u_n) is a sequence that converges to u in $W_{loc}^{1,p}(\mathbf{R} \times S^1; \mathbf{R}^{2n})$, where each of the u_n, as well as u, is a class $\mathcal{C}^\infty$ solution of the Floer equation by the above. Let $\tilde{J}_n(s,t) = J(u_n(s,t))$ and let $h_n(s,t) = \operatorname{grad} H_t(u_n(s,t))$, so that (by the definitions of $\tilde{J}$ and h) the sequence $(\tilde{J}_n)$ converges to $\tilde{J}$ and (h_n) converges to h, both in $\mathcal{C}^0_{\text{loc}}$ and therefore also in L^p_{loc}.

We now assume that it has been proved that the sequence (u_n) converges to u in $W^{k,p}_{\text{loc}}(\mathbf{R} \times S^1; \mathbf{R}^{2n})$. Then $(\tilde{J}_n)$ converges to $\tilde{J}$ and (h_n) converges to h in $W^{k,p}_{\text{loc}}(\mathbf{R} \times S^1; \mathbf{R}^{2n})$. This is an immediate consequence of the fact that $W^{1,p}_{\text{loc}}$ convergence implies $\mathcal{C}^0_{\text{loc}}$ convergence for $p > 2$.

We want to show that (u_n) also converges to u in $W^{k+1,p}_{\text{loc}}(\mathbf{R} \times S^1; \mathbf{R}^{2n})$. Let $V \subset U \subset \mathbf{R} \times S^1$ be relatively compact open subsets. From the equations

$$\frac{\partial u}{\partial s} + \tilde{J}\frac{\partial u}{\partial t} + h = 0 \quad \text{and} \quad \frac{\partial u_n}{\partial s} + \tilde{J}_n\frac{\partial u_n}{\partial t} + h_n = 0$$

we deduce that

$$\frac{\partial(u_n - u)}{\partial s} + \tilde{J}_n\frac{\partial(u_n - u)}{\partial t} + h_n - h + (\tilde{J} - \tilde{J}_n)\frac{\partial u}{\partial t} = 0.$$

Since $\tilde{J}_n$ tends to $\tilde{J}$ in $W^{k,p}_{\text{loc}}(\mathbf{R} \times S^1; \mathbf{R}^{2n})$, there exists a $c_0 > 0$ such that

$$\|\tilde{J}_n\|_{W^{k,p}(U)} \le c_0 \quad \text{for every } n \in \mathbf{N}.$$

By Corollary 12.4.1, there exists a constant $c > 0$ that is independent of n, such that

$$\|u_n - u\|_{W^{k+1,p}(V)}$$
$$\le c\Big(\|h_n - h\|_{W^{k,p}(U)} + \|u_n - u\|_{W^{k,p}(U)} + \Big\|(\tilde{J}_n - \tilde{J})\frac{\partial u}{\partial t}\Big\|_{W^{k,p}(U)}\Big).$$

Since $\tilde{J}_n$ tends to $\tilde{J}$ and h_n tends to h in $W^{k,p}(\overline{U})$ and u is of class $\mathcal{C}^\infty$, we deduce that u_n tends to u in $W^{k+1,p}(V)$. By induction, u_n therefore tends to u in $W^{k,p}_{\text{loc}}$ for every k, hence also in $\mathcal{C}^\infty_{\text{loc}}$ (still by Rellich's theorem (Theorem C.4.9)).

12.4.b How to Deduce Lemma 12.1.1 from Theorem 12.1.5 and Proposition 12.1.4

Taking into account Proposition 12.1.4, it suffices to show that (a subsequence of) (u_n) admits a limit in the $W^{1,p}_{\text{loc}}$ topology. By the Arzelà–Ascoli theorem, there exists a subsequence, which we also denote by (u_n), that converges to a limit u in $\mathcal{C}^0_{\text{loc}}$. It now suffices to prove the following.

Lemma 12.4.2. *For every relatively compact open subset V of U, the sequence (u_n) is a Cauchy sequence for the $W^{1,p}_{\mathrm{loc}}(V)$ topology.*

Proof. We want to apply the equality of Theorem 12.1.5 to $u_n - u_m$ for $\ell = 0$. Since this is a local statement, we may, and do, assume that each of the u_m (is defined on V and) has values in the Euclidean space $\mathbf{R}^{2n}$. Let us show that the conditions of Theorem 12.1.5 are satisfied. For $m, n \in \mathbf{N}$, we have

$$\frac{\partial(u_n - u_m)}{\partial s} + J(u_n)\frac{\partial(u_n - u_m)}{\partial t}$$

$$= (J(u_m) - J(u_n))\frac{\partial u_m}{\partial t} + \operatorname{grad} H_t(u_m) - \operatorname{grad} H_t(u_n).$$

Let $\widetilde{J} = J(u_n)$ and

$$h = (J(u_m) - J(u_n))\frac{\partial u_m}{\partial t} + \operatorname{grad} H_t(u_m) - \operatorname{grad} H_t(u_n).$$

We first verify the conditions of Theorem 12.1.5 for $k = 0$. First of all, u_n and J are of class $\mathcal{C}^1$, hence $\widetilde{J} \in W^{1,p}(V)$. Next,

$$\left\|\frac{\partial J(u_n)}{\partial s}\right\|_{L^p(V)} = \left\|dJ(u_n) \cdot \frac{\partial u_n}{\partial s}\right\|_{L^p(V)}$$

$$\leq \sup_{w \in W} \|(dJ)_w\| \cdot \left\|\frac{\partial u_n}{\partial s}\right\|_{L^p(V)}$$

$$\leq \sup_{w \in W} \|(dJ)_w\| \cdot M \cdot (\operatorname{area}(V))^{1/p},$$

an upper bound that does not depend on n. The same upper bound holds for $\|\partial J(u_n)/\partial t\|_{L^p(V)}$ and

$$\|J(u_n)\|_{L^p(V)} \leq \sup_{w \in W} \|J_w\| \cdot (\operatorname{area}(V))^{1/p}.$$

We therefore find that $\|\widetilde{J}\|_{W^{1,p}(V)} \leq c_0$. Now h is continuous, hence is an element of $L^p(V)$. We may therefore apply Theorem 12.1.5 for $k = 1$ and $\ell = 0$: let $V' \supset V$ be a relatively compact open subset of U. The inequality of Theorem 12.1.5 can be written as

$$\|u_n - u_m\|_{W^{1,p}(V)} \leq C\left(\|u_n - u_m\|_{L^p(V')} + \|h\|_{L^p(V')}\right).$$

We can bound the second term on the right from above:

$$\|h\|_{L^p(V')} \leq \left\|(J(u_n) - J(u_m))\frac{\partial u_m}{\partial t}\right\|_{L^p(V')}$$

$$+ \|\operatorname{grad} H_t(u_m) - \operatorname{grad} H_t(u_n)\|_{L^p(V')}$$

$$\leq \sup_{w \in W} \|(dJ)_w\| \cdot \|u_n - u_m\|_{L^p(V')} \cdot M$$

$$+ \sup_{W \times S^1} \|d(\operatorname{grad} H)\| \cdot \|u_n - u_m\|_{L^p(V')}$$

$$\leq K \cdot \|u_n - u_m\|_{L^p(V')}.$$

Now, the sequence is convergent in $\mathcal{C}^0_{\text{loc}}$, hence convergent in $L^p(V')$ and consequently is a Cauchy sequence in the latter. This implies that it is also a Cauchy sequence in $W^{1,p}$, concluding the proof of the lemma.   □

We have now proved the regularity lemma 12.1.1, modulo Theorem 12.1.5 (*via* Proposition 12.1.4). We still need to prove the theorem, which we will now do.

12.4.c Proof of Theorem 12.1.5

When $\tilde{J}$ is (constant and equal to) the standard complex structure J_0, we recognize the statement of Theorem 12.1.2. In the general case, the proof is more complicated and the condition $p > 2$ is essential (note that $p > 1$ suffices to prove Theorem 12.1.2).

Step 1, the case $k = 0$.

We first prove the theorem for $k = 0$ (and $\ell = 0$). Following the strategy of the proof of Theorem 12.1.2, we quickly encounter a difficulty: when applying the operator $\partial/\partial s - \tilde{J}\,\partial/\partial t$ to the equation

$$\frac{\partial u}{\partial s} + \tilde{J}\frac{\partial u}{\partial t} + h = 0,$$

we find

$$\Delta u + \frac{\partial \tilde{J}}{\partial s}u - \tilde{J}\frac{\partial \tilde{J}}{\partial t}u + \frac{\partial h}{\partial s} - \tilde{J}\frac{\partial h}{\partial t} = 0.$$

We cannot apply Proposition 12.3.1 because, as a product of L^p_{loc} functions,

$$\frac{\partial}{\partial s}\tilde{J} \cdot u \in L^{p/2}_{\text{loc}}$$

(only!) by Hölder's inequality. In order to apply the same method, we begin by modifying the statement of Theorem 12.1.5, as follows.

Lemma 12.4.3. *Let U and V be two relatively compact open subsets of $\mathbf{R} \times S^1$ with $\overline{V} \subset U$ and let p, q, $r \in \mathbf{R}^+$ satisfy*

$$p > 2, \quad r > 1 \quad and \quad \frac{1}{p} + \frac{1}{q} = \frac{1}{r}.$$

Suppose that u is a solution (in the sense of distributions) of the equation

$$\frac{\partial u}{\partial s} + J \frac{\partial u}{\partial t} = f$$

(with J an almost complex structure in $W^{1,p}(U; \mathrm{End}(\mathbf{R}^{2n}))$ such that $\|J\|_{W^{1,p}(U)} \leq c_0$, $f \in L^r_{\mathrm{loc}}(U; \mathbf{R}^{2n}))$. Then we have:

(1) *If $u \in L^q_{\mathrm{loc}}(U; \mathbf{R}^{2n})$, then $u \in W^{1,r}_{\mathrm{loc}}(U; \mathbf{R}^{2n})$.*
(2) *There exists a constant $c > 0$ that depends on c_0, U and V, such that*

$$\|u\|_{W^{1,r}(V)} \leq c\big(\|f\|_{L^r(U)} + \|u\|_{L^q(U)}\big).$$

Remarks 12.4.4.

(1) If $r < 2$, then the relation between p, q and r implies that $q < 2r/(2-r)$. In this case, Theorem C.4.10 says that $W^{1,r}_{\mathrm{loc}} \subset L^q_{\mathrm{loc}}$.
(2) In the statement of Lemma 12.4.3, p and q can take on the value $+\infty$:

 - If $p = +\infty$, then $r = q < +\infty$.
 - If $q = +\infty$, then $r = p < +\infty$.

Proof of Lemma 12.4.3. By applying $\partial/\partial s - J\partial/\partial t$ to the equation of the lemma, we obtain

$$
\begin{aligned}
\Delta u &= -\frac{\partial J}{\partial s}\frac{\partial u}{\partial t} + J\frac{\partial J}{\partial t}\frac{\partial u}{\partial t} + \frac{\partial f}{\partial s} - J\frac{\partial f}{\partial t} \\
&= -\frac{\partial J}{\partial s}\frac{\partial u}{\partial t} - \frac{\partial J}{\partial t}J\frac{\partial u}{\partial t} + \frac{\partial f}{\partial s} - J\frac{\partial f}{\partial t} \\
&= -\frac{\partial J}{\partial s}\frac{\partial u}{\partial t} - \frac{\partial J}{\partial t}\left(f - \frac{\partial u}{\partial s}\right) + \frac{\partial f}{\partial s} - J\frac{\partial f}{\partial t}
\end{aligned}
$$

(using the facts that $J^2 = -\mathrm{Id}$ and that u is a solution). This leads to

$$
\begin{aligned}
\Delta u &= -\frac{\partial J}{\partial s}\frac{\partial u}{\partial t} + \frac{\partial J}{\partial t}\frac{\partial u}{\partial s} + \frac{\partial f}{\partial s} - \frac{\partial}{\partial t}(Jf) \\
&= -\frac{\partial}{\partial t}\left(\frac{\partial J}{\partial s} \cdot u\right) + \frac{\partial^2 J}{\partial t \partial s} \cdot u + \frac{\partial}{\partial s}\left(\frac{\partial J}{\partial t}u\right) - \frac{\partial^2 J}{\partial s \partial t} \cdot u + \frac{\partial f}{\partial s} - \frac{\partial}{\partial t}(Jf) \\
&= \frac{\partial}{\partial s}\left(\frac{\partial J}{\partial t} \cdot u + f\right) + \frac{\partial}{\partial t}\left(-\frac{\partial J}{\partial s} \cdot u - Jf\right).
\end{aligned}
$$

Using Hölder's inequality and the continuity of J, we obtain that

$$\frac{\partial J}{\partial t} \cdot u + f \quad \text{and} \quad -\frac{\partial J}{\partial s} \cdot u - Jf \in L^r_{\text{loc}}(U)$$

(this also applies to the cases where p or q is infinite). The conditions of Proposition 12.3.1 are therefore satisfied, which allows us to apply its conclusions, giving a constant $c_1 > 0$ such that

$$\|u\|_{W^{1,r}(V)} \le c_1 \left(\left\| \frac{\partial J}{\partial t} \cdot u \right\|_{L^r(U)} + \|f\|_{L^r(U)} + \left\| \frac{\partial J}{\partial s} \cdot u \right\|_{L^r(U)} + \|Jf\|_{L^r(U)} \right)$$

$$\le \left(\|J\|_{W^{1,p}(U)} \|u\|_{L^q(U)} + \|f\|_{L^r(U)} \right.$$

$$\left. + \|J\|_{W^{1,p}(U)} \|u\|_{L^q(U)} + \|J\|_{L^\infty(U)} \|f\|_{L^r(U)} \right)$$

$$\le c_1 \left(2c_0 \|u\|_{L^q(U)} + (1 + kc_0) \|f\|_{L^r(U)} \right)$$

(where we have used the continuity of the inclusion $W^{1,p}(U) \subset L^\infty(U)$). From this we deduce the existence of a constant c (independent of u and J) such that

$$\|u\|_{W^{1,r}(V)} \le c \left(\|f\|_{L^r(U)} + \|u\|_{L^q(U)} \right),$$

concluding the proof of the lemma. $\square$

Let us therefore return to the proof of the case $k = 0$ of Theorem 12.1.5.

We first show that $u \in W^{1,p}_{\text{loc}}(\mathbf{R} \times S^1)$. A direct application of Lemma 12.4.3 only gives $u \in W^{1,p/2}(\mathbf{R} \times S^1)$. To obtain the expected regularity, we would need to apply this lemma to the case where $q = \infty$, that is, with the condition $u \in L^\infty_{\text{loc}}(\mathbf{R} \times S^1)$, which is true if $u \in W^{1,r}_{\text{loc}}(\mathbf{R} \times S^1)$ for some $r > 2$. The number $r = p/2$ does not verify this inequality, but a bootstrapping argument allows us to increase the regularity of u and the value of r.

We assume that $u \in W^{1,r}_{\text{loc}}(\mathbf{R} \times S^1)$ for some $r \in {]}1, 2{[}$ is proved. Using the Sobolev injection of Theorem C.4.10, we can deduce that $u \in L^q_{\text{loc}}(\mathbf{R} \times S^1)$ for $q = 2r/(2 - r)$. Next, by Lemma 12.4.3, we have $u \in W^{1,r'}_{\text{loc}}(\mathbf{R} \times S^1)$ for

$$\frac{1}{r'} = \frac{1}{p} + \frac{1}{q}, \quad \text{that is, } r' = \frac{pq}{p+q} = \frac{2pr}{2p + 2r - pr}$$

(h is in L^p_{loc} and in particular in $L^{r'}_{\text{loc}}$ for $1 < r' \le p$). We see that if $p > 2$, then $r' > r$. *The condition $p > 2$ is therefore essential for improving the regularity of u.* We therefore consider the sequence (r_m) with

$$r_0 \in {]}1, 2{[}, \quad r_0 \le \frac{p}{2} \quad \text{and} \quad r_{m+1} = \frac{2pr_m}{2p + 2r_m - pr_m},$$

so that if $r_m < 2$, then $r_{m+1} > r_m$ and $u \in W^{1,r_{m+1}}(\mathbf{R} \times S^1)$. If $r_m \in]1,2[$ for every m, then the increasing sequence r_m converges to a limit $\ell \in]1,2]$... which is not allowed by the recursion relation because $p > 2$. We consequently have $r_m < 2 \leq r_{m+1}$ for some m, and therefore $u \in W^{1,r}_{\text{loc}}(\mathbf{R} \times S^1)$ for every r with $1 < r \leq 2$. On the other hand,

$$r' - 2 = \frac{2pr}{2p + 2r - pr} - 2 = \frac{4[(p-1)(r-1) - 1]}{2p + 2r - pr}$$

is positive when $r \in]1,2]$ is sufficiently close to 2. It follows that

$$u \in W^{1,r'}_{\text{loc}}(\mathbf{R} \times S^1) \subset L^\infty_{\text{loc}}(\mathbf{R} \times S^1) \quad \text{and therefore that } u \in W^{1,p}_{\text{loc}}(\mathbf{R} \times S^1),$$

by Lemma 12.4.3.

We will now show the inequality

$$\|u\|_{W^{1,p}(V)} \leq c\big(\|h\|_{L^p(U)} + \|u\|_{L^p(U)}\big).$$

To show that $u \in W^{1,p}_{\text{loc}}(\mathbf{R} \times S^1)$, we successively apply Lemma 12.4.3 for triples

$$(p, q_0, r_0), (p, q_1, r_1), \ldots, (p, q_m, r_m), (p, q_{m+1}, r_{m+1}), (p, +\infty, p)$$

satisfying the following properties:

- The r_m increase and, more precisely,

$$1 < r_0 < r_1 < \cdots < r_m < 2 < r_{m+1} < p.$$

- Moreover, $q_0 = p$ and $q_i = 2r_{i-1}/(2 - r_{i-1})$ for every $i \geq 1$.

Each application of Lemma 12.4.3 gives an inequality between the $W^{1,r}$, L^r and L^q norms. To write down these inequalities, we choose relatively compact open sets $(V_i)_{i=0,\ldots,m}$ such that

$$V \subset V_{m+1} \subset V_m \subset \cdots \subset V_0 \subset U.$$

The last application of Lemma 12.4.3, for the triple $(p, +\infty, p)$, gives

$$\|u\|_{W^{1,p}(V)} \leq k_1\big(\|h\|_{L^p(V_{m+1})} + \|u\|_{L^\infty(V_{m+1})}\big)$$
$$\leq k_2\big(\|h\|_{L^p(U)} + \|u\|_{W^{1,r_{m+1}}(V_{m+1})}\big)$$

with the continuous inclusion

$$W^{1,r_{m+1}}(V_{m+1}) \hookrightarrow L^\infty(V_{m+1}), \quad \text{because } r_{m+1} > 2.$$

Next, for $i \in \{1, \ldots, m+1\}$, we have

$$\|u\|_{W^{1,r_i}(V_i)} \le c_i \big(\|h\|_{L^{r_i}(V_{i-1})} + \|u\|_{L^{q_i}(V_{i-1})}\big)$$
$$\le C_i \big(\|h\|_{L^p(V_{i-1})} + \|u\|_{W^{1,r_{i-1}}(V_{i-1})}\big)$$

with the continuous inclusions

$$L^p(V_{i-1}) \subset L^{r_i}(V_{i-1}) \quad \text{for } r_i < p \text{ and } \overline{V}_{i-1} \text{ compact}$$

and $\quad W^{1,r_{i-1}}(V_{i-1}) \subset L^{q_i}(V_{i-1}) \quad \text{for } q_i = \dfrac{2r_{i-1}}{2 - r_{i-1}} \text{ and } \overline{V}_{i-1} \text{ compact.}$

Consequently, for every $i = 1, \ldots, m+1$, we have

$$\|u\|_{W^{1,r_i}(V_i)} \le C_i \big(\|h\|_{L^p(U)} + \|u\|_{W^{1,r_{i-1}}(V_{i-1})}\big).$$

Combining all these inequalities, we find

$$\|u\|_{W^{1,r_{m+1}}(V_{m+1})} \le k_3 \big(\|h\|_{L^p(U)} + \|u\|_{W^{1,r_0}(V_0)}\big),$$

which together with the inequality

$$\|u\|_{W^{1,p}(V)} \le k_2 \big(\|h\|_{L^p(U)} + \|u\|_{W^{1,r_{m+1}}(V_{m+1})}\big)$$

obtained earlier gives

$$\|u\|_{W^{1,p}(V)} \le k_4 \big(\|h\|_{L^p(U)} + \|u\|_{W^{1,r_0}(V_0)}\big).$$

Finally, the first application of Lemma 12.4.3, for $(p, q_0, r_0) = (p, p, r_0)$, gives

$$\|u\|_{W^{1,r_0}(V_0)} \le c_0 \big(\|h\|_{L^p(U)} + \|u\|_{L^p(U)}\big),$$

which, using the previous inequality, implies that

$$\|u\|_{W^{1,p}(U)} \le c \big(\|h\|_{L^p(U)} + \|u\|_{L^p(U)}\big),$$

the inequality we wanted to prove.

Step 2, the Case $k = 1$.

Let us show that $u \in W^{2,p}_{\text{loc}}(\mathbf{R} \times S^1)$. For the sake of simplicity, we will write $v = \partial u / \partial s$ (and $w = \partial u / \partial t$). Then v is a solution of the equation

$$\frac{\partial v}{\partial s} + \tilde{J} \frac{\partial v}{\partial t} + g = 0,$$

where we have set

$$g(s,t) = \frac{\partial h}{\partial s}(s,t) + \frac{\partial \tilde{J}}{\partial s}(s,t) \frac{\partial u}{\partial t}(s,t).$$

The situation is different from that considered on p. 470 because the g that occurs here is only in $L_{\text{loc}}^{p/2}(\mathbf{R} \times S^1)$ (again by Hölder) and no longer in $L_{\text{loc}}^p(\mathbf{R} \times S^1)$. We can apply Lemma 12.4.3 to the triple (p, q_0, r_0) with $q_0 = p$ and $r_0 \in \left]1, 2\right[$, $r_0 = p/2$ as in the previous proof and conclude that $v \in W_{\text{loc}}^{1,r_0}(\mathbf{R} \times S^1)$. In an analogous manner, we can prove that

$$w \in W_{\text{loc}}^{1,r_0}(\mathbf{R} \times S^1).$$

Continuing as above, we obtain

$$v, w \in L_{\text{loc}}^{q_1}(\mathbf{R} \times S^1) \quad \text{for } q_1 = \frac{2r_0}{2 - r_0}$$

(this is the Sobolev injection). Therefore, by Hölder,

$$\frac{\partial \tilde{J}}{\partial s} \cdot \frac{\partial u}{\partial t} \quad \text{and} \quad \frac{\partial \tilde{J}}{\partial t} \cdot \frac{\partial u}{\partial t} \in L_{\text{loc}}^{r_1}(\mathbf{R} \times S^1), \quad \text{where } \frac{1}{p} + \frac{1}{q_1} = \frac{1}{r_1}.$$

Consequently, $g \in L_{\text{loc}}^{r_1}$. We can then apply Lemma 12.4.3 again, to the triple (p, q_1, r_1), and find that v and w are in $W^{1,r_1}(\mathbf{R} \times S^1)$.

We can therefore apply Lemma 12.4.3 successively as before, because each application improves the integrability of g (the r for which $g \in L^r$). Finally, we obtain

$$v = \frac{\partial u}{\partial s} \quad \text{and} \quad w = \frac{\partial u}{\partial t} \in W_{\text{loc}}^{1,p}(\mathbf{R} \times S^1),$$

in other words, $u \in W^{2,p}(\mathbf{R} \times S^1)$, which we wanted to prove. This concludes the second step, the case where $k = 1$.

Step 3, the Induction on k.

Let us now suppose that Theorem 12.1.5 has been proved for k and prove it for $k + 1$. Let

$$\tilde{J} \in W_{\text{loc}}^{k+1,p}(\mathbf{R} \times S^1; \text{End}(\mathbf{R}^{2n})) \quad \text{with } \tilde{J}^2 = -\text{Id}, \quad \tilde{h} \in W_{\text{loc}}^{1,k+1}(\mathbf{R} \times S^1; \mathbf{R}^{2n}).$$

Let $u \in L_{\text{loc}}^p(\mathbf{R} \times S^1; \mathbf{R}^{2n})$ be a weak solution of

$$\frac{\partial u}{\partial s} + \tilde{J} \frac{\partial u}{\partial t} + h = 0.$$

By the induction hypothesis, $u \in W_{\text{loc}}^{k+1,p}(\mathbf{R} \times S^1; \mathbf{R}^{2n})$. We want to prove that $u \in W^{k+2,p}(\mathbf{R} \times S^1; \mathbf{R}^{2n})$. We denote its derivatives as above:

$$v = \frac{\partial u}{\partial s} \quad \text{and} \quad w = \frac{\partial u}{\partial t}.$$

We have seen that v satisfies

$$\frac{\partial v}{\partial s} + \tilde{J}\frac{\partial v}{\partial t} + \frac{\partial \tilde{J}}{\partial s}\cdot\frac{\partial u}{\partial t} + \frac{\partial h}{\partial s} = 0.$$

In order to apply the induction hypothesis to it, we need to know that

$$\frac{\partial \tilde{J}}{\partial s}\cdot\frac{\partial u}{\partial t} \in W^{k,p}_{\text{loc}}(\mathbf{R}\times S^1).$$

We will obtain this from the following more general result.

Lemma 12.4.5. *Let $p > 2$ and let $k \geq 1$. If f and $g \in W^{k,p}_{\text{loc}}(\mathbf{R}\times S^1; \mathbf{R})$, then $fg \in W^{k,p}_{\text{loc}}(\mathbf{R}\times S^1; \mathbf{R})$ and for every relatively compact open subset V, there exists a constant $K > 0$ such that*

$$\|fg\|_{W^{k,p}(V)} \leq K\|f\|_{W^{k,p}(V)}\|g\|_{W^{k,p}(V)}.$$

Proof. This is basically a consequence of the Leibniz rule. Let V be a relatively compact open set. We proceed by induction. To begin, let $k = 1$. We use the continuous injection $W^{1,p}(V) \subset L^\infty(V)$. We have

$$\begin{aligned}
\|fg\|_{L^p(V)} &\leq \|f\|_{L^p(V)}\|g\|_{L^\infty(V)} \\
&\leq K_1\|f\|_{L^p(V)}\|g\|_{W^{1,p}(V)} \\
&\leq K_1\|f\|_{W^{1,p}(V)}\|g\|_{W^{1,p}(V)},
\end{aligned}$$

$$\begin{aligned}
\left\|\frac{\partial(fg)}{\partial s}\right\|_{L^p(V)} &\leq \left\|\frac{\partial f}{\partial s}g\right\|_{L^p(V)} + \left\|f\frac{\partial g}{\partial s}\right\|_{L^p(V)} \\
&\leq \left\|\frac{\partial f}{\partial s}\right\|_{L^p(V)}\|g\|_{L^\infty(V)} + \left\|\frac{\partial g}{\partial s}\right\|_{L^p(V)}\|f\|_{L^\infty(V)} \\
&\leq K_2\|f\|_{W^{1,p}(V)}\|g\|_{W^{1,p}(V)},
\end{aligned}$$

and an analogous inequality holds for the derivative of fg with respect to t. The case $k = 1$ is thus proved. Let us assume that the statement is true for k. We have

$$\begin{aligned}
\left\|\frac{\partial(fg)}{\partial s}\right\|_{W^{k,p}(V)} &\leq \left\|\frac{\partial f}{\partial s}g\right\|_{W^{k,p}(V)} + \left\|f\frac{\partial g}{\partial s}\right\|_{W^{k,p}(V)} \\
&\leq K_3\left\|\frac{\partial f}{\partial s}\right\|_{W^{k,p}(V)}\|g\|_{W^{k,p}(V)} + K_4\|f\|_{W^{k,p}(V)}\left\|\frac{\partial g}{\partial s}\right\|_{W^{k,p}(V)} \\
&\leq K\|f\|_{W^{k+1,p}(V)}\|g\|_{W^{k+1,p}(V)}
\end{aligned}$$

using the induction hypothesis. The analogous inequality holds for the derivative with respect to t. Therefore

$$\|fg\|_{W^{k+1,p}(V)} \le K \|f\|_{W^{k+1,p}(V)} \|g\|_{W^{k+1,p}(V)}$$

and the lemma is proved. $\square$

By this lemma (Lemma 12.4.5), we can now apply the induction hypothesis and obtain

$$v = \frac{\partial u}{\partial s} \quad \text{and} \quad w = \frac{\partial u}{\partial t} \in W^{k+1,p}_{\text{loc}}(\mathbf{R} \times S^1; \mathbf{R}^{2n}),$$

and therefore $u \in W^{k+2,p}_{\text{loc}}(\mathbf{R} \times S^1; \mathbf{R}^{2n})$.

We still need to prove the inequality on the norms. Let U and V be relatively compact open sets with $\overline{V} \subset U$ and let $\ell \in \{0, \dots, k\}$. For $\ell = 0$, the desired inequality was proved above. For $\ell \ge 1$, we apply the induction hypothesis to v (and likewise to w) for $\ell - 1$, which gives

$$\|v\|_{W^{\ell,p}(V)} \le c \left(\left\| \frac{\partial h}{\partial s} \right\|_{W^{\ell-1,p}(U)} + \left\| \frac{\partial \widetilde{J}}{\partial s} \frac{\partial u}{\partial t} \right\|_{W^{\ell-1,p}(U)} + \|v\|_{W^{\ell-1,p}(U)} \right).$$

For $\ell \ge 2$, by Lemma 12.4.5, this inequality gives

$$\|v\|_{W^{\ell,p}(V)} \le c \left(\|h\|_{W^{\ell,p}(U)} + K \left\| \frac{\partial \widetilde{J}}{\partial s} \right\|_{W^{\ell-1,p}(U)} \left\| \frac{\partial u}{\partial t} \right\|_{W^{\ell-1,p}(U)} \right.$$
$$\left. + \|v\|_{W^{\ell-1,p}(U)} \right)$$
$$\le (\|h\|_{W^{\ell,p}(U)} + Kc_0 \|u\|_{W^{\ell,p}(U)} + \|u\|_{W^{\ell,p}(U)}).$$

For $\ell = 1$, we use that $\widetilde{J} \in W^{k+1,p}(V)$ with $k \ge \ell = 1$ to deduce that $\partial \widetilde{J}/\partial s \in W^{1,p}$ and therefore

$$\left\| \frac{\partial \widetilde{J}}{\partial s} \frac{\partial u}{\partial t} \right\|_{L^p(U)} \le \left\| \frac{\partial \widetilde{J}}{\partial s} \right\|_{L^\infty(U)} \left\| \frac{\partial u}{\partial t} \right\|_{L^p(U)}$$
$$\le K \left\| \frac{\partial \widetilde{J}}{\partial s} \right\|_{W^{1,p}(U)} \|u\|_{W^{1,p}(U)}$$
$$\le K \|\widetilde{J}\|_{W^{2,p}(U)} \|u\|_{W^{1,p}(U)}$$
$$\le Kc_0 \|u\|_{W^{1,p}(U)}$$

because $\|\widetilde{J}\|_{W^{k+1,p}(U)} \leq c_0$. Consequently, we also have

$$\|v\|_{W^{1,p}(V)} \leq c(\|h\|_{W^{1,p}(U)} + K c_0 \|u\|_{W^{1,p}(U)} + \|u\|_{W^{1,p}(U)}).$$

We have thus proved, for every $\ell = 0, \ldots, k$ (and for both w and v) the existence of an upper bound of the form

$$\|v\|_{W^{\ell,p}(V)} \leq c(\|h\|_{W^{\ell,p}(U)} + \|u\|_{W^{\ell,p}(U)}).$$

By writing

$$\|u\|_{W^{\ell+1,p}(V)} \leq \|u\|_{W^{\ell,p}(V)} + \|v\|_{W^{\ell,p}(V)} + \|w\|_{W^{\ell,p}(V)}$$

and using all these upper bounds, we can prove the desired inequality, thus concluding the proof of Theorem 12.1.5.

Chapter 13
The Lemmas on the Second Derivative of the Floer Operator and Other Technicalities

In this chapter we prove a number of technical results used in this book. All the particulars are given in detail, as they will not fail to elucidate certain complex, but essential, passages of the previous chapters.[1]

13.1 Versions of the Floer Operator

For this technical chapter, we will make a distinction in the notation between the operator

$$\mathcal{F}_\rho : T_{w_\rho} \mathcal{P}^{1,p}(x,z) \longrightarrow L^p(\mathbf{R} \times S^1; TW)$$

defined by

$$\mathcal{F}_\rho(X) = \mathcal{F}(\exp_{w_\rho}(X)) = \left(\frac{\partial}{\partial s} + J\frac{\partial}{\partial t} + \operatorname{grad} H \right)(\exp_{w_\rho}(X))$$

and the same operator, written in the trivializations, which we will denote by

$$F_\rho : W^{1,p}(\mathbf{R} \times S^1; \mathbf{R}^{2n}) \longrightarrow L^p(\mathbf{R} \times S^1; \mathbf{R}^{2n}).$$

We will also use the (nonlinear) operator

$$F : [\rho_0, +\infty[\times W^{1,p}(\mathbf{R} \times S^1; \mathbf{R}^{2n}) \longrightarrow L^p(\mathbf{R} \times S^1; \mathbf{R}^{2n})$$

defined in Section 9.4 for $\rho \geq \rho_0$ by $F(\rho, Y) = F_\rho(Y)$. Recall that F_ρ is the operator $\mathcal{F}_\rho$ after trivialization.

The source of $\mathcal{F}_\rho$ consists of the vector fields tangent to W along w_ρ that are in $W^{1,p}(\mathbf{R} \times S^1; \mathbf{R}^m)$, via the composition

$$\mathbf{R} \times S^1 \longrightarrow TW \hookrightarrow T_W \mathbf{R}^m \xrightarrow{\operatorname{pr}_2} \mathbf{R}^m.$$

---

[1] Adapted from [52, Chapter LXIII].

M. Audin, M. Damian, *Morse Theory and Floer Homology*,
Universitext, DOI 10.1007/978-1-4471-5496-9_13,
© Springer-Verlag London 2014

So $\mathcal{F}_\rho(X)$ is a vector field tangent to W along $\exp_{w_\rho}(X)$, which is in $L^p(\mathbf{R} \times S^1; \mathbf{R}^m)$ via the map above. To define F_ρ we use the trivializations described in Section 9.4 (and sketched in Figure 9.5). To verify that it is well defined, it suffices to apply Lemma 8.2.4 to see that:

- If $y \in W^{1,p}(\mathbf{R} \times S^1; \mathbf{R}^{2n})$, then $\sum y_i Z_i^\rho \in T_{w_\rho}\mathcal{P}^{1,p}(x,z)$.
- If $Y \in L^p(\mathbf{R} \times S^1; TW)$, then $(g(Y, Z_j^{\rho,x}))_j \in L^p(\mathbf{R} \times S^1; \mathbf{R}^{2n})$.

13.2 The Two Lemmas on dF

We want to prove the following lemmas.

Lemma (Lemma 9.4.8). *Let $r_0 > 0$. There exists a constant $K > 0$ such that for every $\rho \geq \rho_0$ and every $Z \in \overline{B}(0, r_0) \subset W^{1,p}(\mathbf{R} \times S^1; \mathbf{R}^{2n})$, we have*

$$\|(dF_\rho)_Z - (dF_\rho)_0\|^{\mathrm{op}} \leq K \|Z\|_{W^{1,p}}.$$

Lemma (Lemma 9.4.16). *Let $r_0 > 0$. There exists a constant $M > 0$ (that does not depend on ρ) such that for every $\rho \geq \rho_0$ and every $Z \in \overline{B}(0, r_0) \subset W^{1,p}(\mathbf{R} \times S^1; \mathbf{R}^{2n})$, we have*

$$\left\|\frac{\partial F}{\partial \rho}(\rho, Z) - \frac{\partial F}{\partial \rho}(\rho, 0)\right\|_{L^p} \leq M \|Z\|_{W^{1,p}}.$$

Remark 13.2.1. In the statement of Lemma 9.4.8, $\|\cdot\|^{\mathrm{op}}$ denotes the operator norm. An assertion that implies the two lemmas is that F is of class $\mathcal{C}^2$ and that the operator norm $\|d^2 F\|^{\mathrm{op}}$ is bounded on $[\rho_0, +\infty[\times \overline{B}(0, r_0)$.

We begin with a number of elementary results that we will use in the proofs. We first have Lemma 8.2.4 (which asserts that the product of a $W^{1,p}$ function and a bounded $\mathcal{C}^\infty$ function is a $W^{1,p}$ function). The first of the following two lemmas is of the same type.

Lemma 13.2.2. *Let $p > 2$ and let f and g be two elements of $W^{1,p}(\mathbf{R} \times S^1; \mathbf{R})$. There exists a constant $K > 0$ such that*

$$\|fg\|_{L^p} \leq K \|f\|_{L^p} \|g\|_{W^{1,p}}.$$

Proof. The fact that p is greater than 2 allows us to use the continuous injection

$$W^{1,p}(\mathbf{R} \times S^1; \mathbf{R}) \longleftrightarrow L^\infty(\mathbf{R} \times S^1; \mathbf{R}),$$

which has the property that $\|h\|_\infty \le K \|h\|_{W^{1,p}}$ for some constant $K > 0$. It follows that

$$\left(\int_{\mathbf{R} \times S^1} |fg|^p \right)^{1/p} \le \left(\int_{\mathbf{R} \times S^1} |f|^p \|g\|_\infty^p \right)^{1/p}$$

$$\le \|g\|_\infty \|f\|_{L^p} \le K \|f\|_{L^p} \|g\|_{W^{1,p}}. \qquad \square$$

Lemma 13.2.3. *Let W be a compact manifold and let*

$$A : W \times \mathbf{R}^m \times \mathbf{R}^m \longrightarrow \mathbf{R}^m, \qquad B : W \times \mathbf{R}^m \times \mathbf{R}^m \times \mathbf{R}^m \longrightarrow \mathbf{R}^m$$

be two $\mathcal{C}^\infty$ maps. We suppose that for every $p \in W$ and every $X \in \mathbf{R}^m$, $A(p, X, \cdot)$ is linear and $B(p, X, \cdot, \cdot)$ is bilinear. For every $r_1 > 0$, there exists a constant $C > 0$ such that for every $p \in W$ and every $X \in \overline{B}(0, r_1) \subset \mathbf{R}^m$, we have:

(1) *For every $v \in \mathbf{R}^m$, $\|A(p, X, v)\| \le C \|v\|$.*
(2) *For all $v_1, v_2 \in \mathbf{R}^m$,*

$$\|A(p, X, v_2) - A(p, 0, v_1)\| \le C \left(\|X\| \|v_1\| + \|v_2 - v_1\| \right).$$

(3) *For all $v, Y \in \mathbf{R}^m$, $\|B(p, X, v, Y)\| \le C \|v\| \|Y\|$.*
(4) *For all $v, Y_1, Y_2 \in \mathbf{R}^m$,*

$$\|B(p, X, v, Y_2) - B(p, 0, v, Y_1)\| \le C \left(\|X\| \|v\| \|Y_1\| + \|v\| \|Y_2 - Y_1\| \right).$$

Proof. The proof is direct and elementary:

(1) We view A as a map

$$A : W \times \mathbf{R}^m \longrightarrow \mathcal{L}(\mathbf{R}^m; \mathbf{R}^m).$$

Since it is continuous, the image of the compact set $W \times \overline{B}(0, r_1)$ is compact, hence bounded for the operator norm, which proves the first inequality.
(2) Since A is of class $\mathcal{C}^1$, we have

$$\|A(p, X) - A(p, 0)\|^{\mathrm{op}} \le \sup_{t \in [0,1]} \|(dA)_{p, tX}\| \|X\| \le C \|X\|.$$

It follows that

$$\begin{aligned}
\|A(p, X, v_2) - A(p, 0, v_1)\| &\le \|A(p, X, v_2 - v_1)\| + \|A(p, X, v_1) - A(p, 0, v_1)\| \\
&\le C \|v_2 - v_1\| + \|A(p, X) - A(p, 0)\|^{\mathrm{op}} \|v_1\| \\
&\quad \text{using point (1)} \\
&\le C \|v_2 - v_1\| + C \|X\| \|v_1\|.
\end{aligned}$$

(3) We view B as a map from $W \times \mathbf{R}^m$ to the bilinear maps on $\mathbf{R}^m$ and proceed as in (1).

(4) We write

$$\|B(p, X, v, Y_2) - B(p, 0, v, Y_1)\|$$
$$\leq \|B(p, X, v, Y_2 - Y_1)\| + \|B(p, X, v, Y_1) - B(p, 0, v, Y_1)\|$$

and proceed as in (2). $\square$

13.3 The Operator $\widetilde{\mathfrak{F}}_\rho$

We want to construct a commutative diagram

$$
\begin{array}{ccc}
W^{1,p}(\mathbf{R} \times S^1; \mathbf{R}^{2n}) & \xrightarrow{\ \widetilde{F}_\rho\ } & L^p(\mathbf{R} \times S^1; \mathbf{R}^{2n}) \\
{\scriptstyle i_\rho}\Big\downarrow & & \Big\uparrow{\scriptstyle p_\rho} \\
W^{1,p}(\mathbf{R} \times S^1; \mathbf{R}^m) & \xrightarrow[(\mathrm{Id}, \widetilde{\mathfrak{F}}_\rho)]{} & W^{1,p}(\mathbf{R} \times S^1; \mathbf{R}^m) \times L^p(\mathbf{R} \times S^1; \mathbf{R}^m),
\end{array}
$$

that is, to write

$$F_\rho(y) = p_\rho(i_\rho(y), \widetilde{\mathfrak{F}}_\rho(i_\rho(y)))$$

for certain maps i_ρ, p_ρ, $\widetilde{\mathfrak{F}}_\rho$ that will be defined later. Our aim is to simplify certain computations.

We begin by defining i_ρ by setting

$$i_\rho(y) = \sum_{i=1}^{2n} y_i Z_i^\rho.$$

This is a linear operator, whose norm we can easily evaluate:

$$
\begin{aligned}
\|i_\rho(y)\|_{W^{1,p}} &= \left\| \sum y_i Z_i^\rho \right\|_{W^{1,p}} \leq \sum \|y_i Z_i^\rho\|_{W^{1,p}} \\
&\leq \sum \|y_i\|_{W^{1,p}} \|Z_i^\rho\|_{\mathcal{C}^1} \quad \text{(we have applied Lemma 8.2.4)} \\
&\leq \sup_i \|Z_i^\rho\|_{\mathcal{C}^1} \sum \|y_i\|_{W^{1,p}} \leq 2n \sup_i \|Z_i^\rho\|_{\mathcal{C}^1} \|y\|_{W^{1,p}} \\
&= M \|y\|_{W^{1,p}}
\end{aligned}
$$

because, indeed, the choice of Z_i^ρ ensures that $\sup_i \|Z_i^\rho\| < \infty$:

- On $[-1, 1] \times S^1$, by compactness

- On $\{|s| \geq 1\} \times S^1$, the $\mathcal{C}^1$ norm of Z_i^ρ is bounded from above by the greater of the two norms $\|Z_i^u\|_{\mathcal{C}^1}$ and $\|Z_i^v\|_{\mathcal{C}^1}$.

Note that this last upper bound (for $|s| \geq 1$) does not depend on ρ. For $s \in [-1, 1]$ we can also use an upper bound that does not depend on ρ because Z_i^ρ is defined and smooth on the compact set $[\rho_0, +\infty] \times [-1, 1] \times S^1$.

We have now defined an operator i_ρ that is linear and continuous and whose operator norm is bounded by a constant C_1 *that does not depend on ρ*.

Next we define $\widetilde{\mathcal{F}}_\rho$. By considering TW as a subbundle of $T_W \mathbf{R}^m$, we can view $T_{w_\rho} \mathcal{P}^{1,p}(x, z)$ as a subspace of $W^{1,p}(\mathbf{R} \times S^1; \mathbf{R}^m)$. We will define the operator $\widetilde{\mathcal{F}}_\rho$ as an extension of $\mathcal{F}_\rho$ to the space $W^{1,p}(\mathbf{R} \times S^1; \mathbf{R}^m)$. Recall that we are using the notation listed at the beginning of Chapter 8. The symplectic manifold W is as usual endowed with an almost complex structure J that is compatible with the symplectic form ω and with the metric g defined by these two structures. As always, W is embedded in a space $\mathbf{R}^m$ (for m sufficiently large) and $T_W \mathbf{R}^m$ is the restriction of $T\mathbf{R}^m$ to W, and is isomorphic to the trivial vector bundle $W \times \mathbf{R}^m$. We have extended the inner product defined on TW by the metric g to an inner product $\widetilde{g}$ on $T_W \mathbf{R}^m$. The exponential map is a $\mathcal{C}^\infty$ map

$$\exp : TW \longrightarrow W$$

that satisfies

$$\begin{cases} \exp(p, 0) = \exp_p(0) = p \\ (d\exp_p)_0 : T_0(T_pW) \cong T_pW \to W \text{ is the identity} \end{cases}$$

(see Appendix A.5, if necessary). Let

$$\pi_p : \mathbf{R}^m = T_p\mathbf{R}^m \longrightarrow T_pW$$

be the orthogonal projection. We define the map

$$\widetilde{\exp} : W \times \mathbf{R}^m \longrightarrow W$$
$$(p, X) \longmapsto \exp_p(\pi_p(X)).$$

This is a $\mathcal{C}^\infty$ map that extends the exponential (defined on TW) to the fiber bundle $T_W \mathbf{R}^m$. We also extend the almost complex structure $J : TW \to TW$ to $\widetilde{J} : T_W \mathbf{R}^m \to T_W \mathbf{R}^m$ by setting

$$\widetilde{J}_p(X) = J_p(\pi_p(X)).$$

We can finally define $\widetilde{\mathcal{F}}_\rho$:

$$\widetilde{\mathcal{F}}_\rho(X) = \left(\frac{\partial}{\partial s} + \widetilde{J}\frac{\partial}{\partial t} + \operatorname{grad} H_t\right)\widetilde{\exp}(w_\rho, X) = \widetilde{\mathcal{F}} \circ \widetilde{\exp}(w_\rho, X).$$

It is clear that $\widetilde{\mathcal{F}}_\rho$ is an extension of $\mathcal{F}_\rho$. It is also true, though somewhat less clear, that $\widetilde{\mathcal{F}}_\rho(X) \in L^p(\mathbf{R} \times S^1; \mathbf{R}^m)$, and therefore that

$$\mathcal{F}_\rho(X) \in L^p(\mathbf{R} \times S^1; TW).$$

This is what the following lemma asserts.

Lemma 13.3.1. *If* $X \in W^{1,p}(\mathbf{R} \times S^1; \mathbf{R}^m)$, *then* $\widetilde{\mathcal{F}}_\rho(X) \in L^p(\mathbf{R} \times S^1; \mathbf{R}^m)$.

Proof. We have

$$\widetilde{\mathcal{F}}_\rho(0) = \mathcal{F}_\rho(0) = \mathcal{F}(w_\rho) \in L^p(\mathbf{R} \times S^1; \mathbf{R}^m)$$

because $\mathcal{F}(w_\rho)(s,t)$ is identically zero for $|s| \geq 1$ (w_ρ is of class $\mathcal{C}^\infty$ and coincides with u or v, which are solutions of the Floer equation). It therefore suffices to show that

$$\widetilde{\mathcal{F}}_\rho(X) - \widetilde{\mathcal{F}}_\rho(0) \in L^p(\mathbf{R} \times S^1; \mathbf{R}^m).$$

We have

$$\begin{aligned}
\widetilde{\mathcal{F}}_\rho(X) &= \frac{\partial}{\partial s}\widetilde{\exp}(w_\rho, X) + \widetilde{J}_{\widetilde{\exp}(w_\rho,X)}\frac{\partial}{\partial t}\widetilde{\exp}(w_\rho, X) + \operatorname{grad} H_t(\widetilde{\exp}(w_\rho, X)) \\
&= D_1\widetilde{\exp}_{(w_\rho,X)}\Big(\frac{\partial w_\rho}{\partial s}\Big) + D_2\widetilde{\exp}_{(w_\rho,X)}\Big(\frac{\partial X}{\partial s}\Big) \\
&\quad + \widetilde{J}_{\widetilde{\exp}(w_\rho,X)} \cdot \Big(D_1\widetilde{\exp}_{(w_\rho,X)}\Big(\frac{\partial w_\rho}{\partial t}\Big) + D_2\widetilde{\exp}_{(w_\rho,X)}\Big(\frac{\partial X}{\partial t}\Big)\Big) \\
&\quad + \operatorname{grad} H_t(\widetilde{\exp}(w_\rho, X)).
\end{aligned}$$

Since $X \in W^{1,p}(\mathbf{R} \times S^1; \mathbf{R}^m)$, we also have

$$X \in L^\infty(\mathbf{R} \times S^1; \mathbf{R}^m),$$

hence, since X has been taken continuous, there exists an $r_1 > 0$ such that $\|X(s,t)\| \leq r_1$ for every $(s,t) \in \mathbf{R} \times S^1$. We fix a pair (s,t) and repeatedly apply Lemma 13.2.3 (more precisely, its point (3)), for $A(p,X)(\cdot)$ equal to:

- First $D_1\widetilde{\exp}_{(p,X)}(\cdot)$
- Then $D_2\widetilde{\exp}_{(p,X)}(\cdot)$
- Then $\widetilde{J}_{\widetilde{\exp}(p,X)}D_1\widetilde{\exp}_{(p,X)}(\cdot)$
- And finally $\widetilde{J}_{\widetilde{\exp}(p,X)}D_2\widetilde{\exp}_{(p,X)}(\cdot)$ (with $p = w_\rho(s,t)$ and $X = X(s,t)$).

Still by Lemma 13.2.3, we also have

$$\begin{aligned}
\|\operatorname{grad} H_t(\widetilde{\exp}(p,X)) &- \operatorname{grad} H_t(\widetilde{\exp}(p,0))\| \\
&\leq \sup_{r \in [0,1]} \|d_{rX} \operatorname{grad} H_t \circ \widetilde{\exp}\| \, \|X\| \leq C \, \|X\| .
\end{aligned}$$

Finally, by computing at a fixed (s, t), we obtain

$$\|\widetilde{\mathcal{F}}_\rho(X) - \widetilde{\mathcal{F}}_\rho(0)\| \leq C\left(\|X\|\left\|\frac{\partial w_\rho}{\partial s}\right\| + \left\|\frac{\partial X}{\partial s}\right\|\right.$$
$$\left. + \|X\|\left\|\frac{\partial w_\rho}{\partial t}\right\| + \left\|\frac{\partial X}{\partial t}\right\| + \|X\|\right)$$
$$\leq k\left(\|X(s, t)\| + \left\|\frac{\partial X}{\partial s}(s, t)\right\| + \left\|\frac{\partial X}{\partial t}(s, t)\right\|\right)$$

because the norms of $\partial w_\rho / \partial s$ and $\partial w_\rho / \partial t$ are uniformly bounded (owing to the exponential decay of u and v). We therefore have

$$\|\widetilde{\mathcal{F}}_\rho(X) - \widetilde{\mathcal{F}}_\rho(0)\|_{L^p} \leq 3k\,\|X\|_{W^{1,p}} < +\infty \quad \text{and} \quad \widetilde{\mathcal{F}}_\rho(X) \in L^p(\mathbf{R} \times S^1; \mathbf{R}^m). \qquad \square$$

Remark 13.3.2. The fact that $\mathcal{F}(\exp_w X)$ is in L^p, as we announced in Section 8.2.d, is thus verified. Note that in the context of Chapter 8, w does not come from the gluing of two solutions, hence the proof of the inclusion $\mathcal{F}(\exp_w(0)) \in L^p(\mathbf{R} \times S^1; \mathbf{R}^m)$ set out above is not valid. The inclusion follows from the fact that $w \in \mathcal{C}_\chi^\infty(x, y)$ (see Section 8.2.c), in other words, from the exponential decay of

$$\frac{\partial w}{\partial s} \quad \text{and} \quad \frac{\partial w}{\partial t} - X_H(w),$$

which immediately implies that $\mathcal{F}(\exp_w(0)) = \mathcal{F}(w) \in L^p$.

To finish the construction of the commutative diagram we announced, we still need to define the map p_ρ. Recall that the jth component of $F_\rho(y)$ is defined, using parallel transport, as

$$(F_\rho(y))_j = g(\mathcal{F}_\rho(Y), Z_j^{\rho, Y}),$$

where $Y = \sum_{i=1}^{2n} y_i Z_i^\rho$ and $Z_j^{\rho, Y}$ is the result of the parallel transport of Z_j^ρ along the geodesic path $r \mapsto \exp_{w_\rho}(rY)$. We can view this parallel transport as a map

$$\mathcal{J} : TW \oplus TW \longrightarrow TW$$

that sends $p \in W$ and $Y, Z \in T_pW$ to $\mathcal{J}_p(Y, Z)$, the parallel transport of Z along $r \mapsto \exp_p(rY)$. As we did earlier for the metric g, we extend $\mathcal{J}$ to

$$\widetilde{\mathcal{J}} : W \times \mathbf{R}^m \times \mathbf{R}^m \longrightarrow \mathbf{R}^m$$
$$(p, Y, Z) \longmapsto \mathcal{J}_p(\pi_p(Y), \pi_p(Z)).$$

From this we deduce a map

$$P : W \times \mathbf{R}^m \times \mathbf{R}^m \times \mathbf{R}^m \longrightarrow \mathbf{R}$$
$$(p, X, Y, Z) \longmapsto \widetilde{g}_p(\widetilde{\mathcal{J}}(X, Z), Y),$$

which is linear in Y and Z and simply equals

$$P(p, 0, Z, Y) = \tilde{g}_p(Z, Y)$$

when $X = 0$. We can finally define

$$p_\rho : W^{1,p}(\mathbf{R} \times S^1; \mathbf{R}^m) \times L^p(\mathbf{R} \times S^1; \mathbf{R}^m) \longrightarrow L^p(\mathbf{R} \times S^1; \mathbf{R}^{2n})$$

by setting (for $j = 1, \ldots, 2n$)

$$(p_\rho(X, Y))_j = P(w_\rho, X, Z_j^\rho, Y) = \tilde{g}_{w_\rho}(\tilde{\mathfrak{J}}(X, Z_j^\rho), Y).$$

By the construction of the Z_j^ρ, we have

$$\sup_{s,t} \left\| Z_j^\rho(s,t) \right\| < +\infty.$$

Since X is in $W^{1,p}$, we have $\sup_{s,t} \|X(s,t)\| < +\infty$. Finally, since $\tilde{\mathfrak{J}}$ is of class $\mathcal{C}^\infty$, applying Lemmas 8.2.4 and 13.2.3, gives

$$\|p_\rho(X, Y)\| \le C \|Z\| \cdot \|Y\|_{L^p}$$

and therefore
$$p_\rho(X, Y) \in L^p(\mathbf{R} \times S^1; \mathbf{R}^{2n}).$$

To conclude, we clearly have $F_\rho(y) = p_\rho(i_\rho(y), \tilde{\mathfrak{F}}_\rho(i_\rho(y)))$, as desired.

13.4 Proof of the Two Lemmas: The First One

Let us finally prove the two lemmas.

Proof of Lemma 9.4.8. To apply the formula for F_ρ established in Section 13.3, we need a result that asserts that the property announced in Lemma 9.4.8 is stable under the composition of operators. This is taken care of by the following lemma, where φ and ψ denote maps between Banach spaces that are not necessarily linear but are differentiable (we will often denote this type of object by the word "operator").

Lemma 13.4.1. *Let G, H and K be Banach spaces and let $\varphi : G \to H$ and $\psi : H \to K$ be differentiable maps. We suppose there that exist an $r_0 > 0$ and $k_i > 0$ (for $i = 1, \ldots, 4$) such that:*

(1) For every $Z \in \overline{B}(0, r_0) \subset G$, $\|(d\varphi)_Z - (d\varphi)_0\|^{\mathrm{op}} \le k_1 \|Z\|$.
(2) $\|(d\varphi)_0\|^{\mathrm{op}} \le k_2$.

(3) *For every* $Z \in \overline{B}(0, r_0) \subset G$,

$$\left\| (d\psi)_{\varphi(Z)} - (d\psi)_{\varphi(0)} \right\|^{\mathrm{op}} \leq k_3 \left\| \varphi(Z) - \varphi(0) \right\|.$$

(4) $\left\| (d\psi)_{\varphi(0)} \right\|^{\mathrm{op}} \leq k_4$.

Then there exists a $k > 0$ *that depends only on the* k_i *and on* r_0, *such that for every* $Z \in \overline{B}(0, r_0)$, *we have*

$$\left\| (d\psi)_Z \circ \varphi - (d\psi)_0 \circ \varphi \right\|^{\mathrm{op}} \leq k \left\| Z \right\|.$$

We will apply this lemma to operators φ and ψ that depend on the parameter ρ. This is why we included the conditions on the norms of the differentials of these operators in the assumptions: we would like to obtain a constant k that does not depend on ρ.

Proof of Lemma 13.4.1. Let $v \in G$. We have

$$\left\| (d(\psi\varphi))_Z(v) - (d(\psi\varphi))_0(v) \right\| = \left\| (d\psi)_{\varphi(Z)}((d\varphi)_Z(v)) - (d\psi)_{\varphi(0)}((d\varphi)_0(v)) \right\|$$
$$\leq \left\| (d\psi)_{\varphi(Z)}((d\varphi)_Z(v)) - (d\psi)_{\varphi(0)}((d\varphi)_Z(v)) \right\|$$
$$+ \left\| (d\psi)_{\varphi(0)}((d\varphi)_Z(v)) - (d\varphi)_0(v) \right\|$$
$$\leq k_3 \left\| \varphi(Z) - \varphi(0) \right\| \left\| (d\varphi)_Z(v) \right\| + \left\| (d\psi)_{\varphi(0)} \right\| \left\| (d\varphi)_Z(v) - (d\varphi)_0(v) \right\|$$
$$\leq k_3 \sup_{r \in [0,1]} \left\| (d\varphi)_{rZ} \right\| \left\| Z \right\| \left\| (d\varphi)_Z \right\| \left\| v \right\| + k_4 k_1 \left\| Z \right\| \left\| v \right\|.$$

For every $r \in [0, 1]$,

$$\left\| (d\varphi)_{rZ} \right\| \leq \left\| (d\varphi)_{rZ} - (d\varphi)_0 \right\| + \left\| (d\varphi)_0 \right\|$$
$$\leq k_1 r \left\| Z \right\| + k_2 \leq k_1 \left\| Z \right\| + k_2.$$

It follows that

$$\left\| (d\psi \circ \varphi)_Z(v) - (d\psi \circ \varphi)_0(v) \right\| \leq k_3 (k_1 \left\| Z \right\| + k_2)^2 \left\| Z \right\| \left\| v \right\| + k_4 k_1 \left\| Z \right\| \left\| v \right\|$$
$$\leq \left(k_3 (k_1 r_0 + k_2)^2 + k_4 k_1 \right) \left\| Z \right\| \left\| v \right\|,$$

which we wanted to prove. □

To conclude the proof of Lemma 9.4.8, it suffices to apply this lemma:

- First to $\varphi = i_\rho$, $\psi = \mathrm{Id} \times \widetilde{\mathcal{F}}_\rho$
- And then to $\varphi = (\mathrm{Id} \times \widetilde{\mathcal{F}}_\rho) i_\rho$, $\psi = p_\rho \ldots$

provided that we first verify that these operators φ, ψ satisfy the necessary conditions (for constants independent of ρ). Let us show that this is indeed the case.

- For $\varphi = i_\rho$. This map is linear, hence equal to its derivative, $(di_\rho)_Z = i_\rho$, and therefore also $(di_\rho)_Z - (di_\rho)_0 = 0$, so that assumption (1) is satisfied. We have also seen that $\|i_\rho\|^{\mathrm{op}} \le C_1$ for a constant C_1 that does not depend on ρ, hence (2) holds.

- For $\psi = \mathrm{Id} \times \widetilde{\mathcal{F}}_\rho$. Since $\varphi(0) = i_\rho(0) = 0$, it will suffice to verify that for every $X \in i_\rho(\overline{B}(0, r_0)) \subset B(0, C_1 r_0)$, we have

$$\|(d\psi)_X - (d\psi)_0\|^{\mathrm{op}} \le k_3 \|X\| \quad \text{and} \quad \|(d\psi)_X\|^{\mathrm{op}} \le k_4$$

(for constants k_3 and k_4 that do not depend on ρ). We also have

$$\|(d(\mathrm{Id} \times \widetilde{\mathcal{F}}_\rho))_X - (d(\mathrm{Id} \times \widetilde{\mathcal{F}}_\rho))_0\|^{\mathrm{op}} = \|(d\widetilde{\mathcal{F}}_\rho)_X - (d\widetilde{\mathcal{F}}_\rho)_0\|$$

and

$$\|(d(\mathrm{Id} \times \widetilde{\mathcal{F}}_\rho))_0\|^{\mathrm{op}} \le 1 + \|(d\widetilde{\mathcal{F}}_\rho)_0\|^{\mathrm{op}}.$$

It therefore suffices to verify that conditions (3) and (4) are satisfied for $\psi = \widetilde{\mathcal{F}}_\rho$. Recall that

$$\widetilde{\mathcal{F}}_\rho(X) = \Big(\frac{\partial}{\partial s} + \tilde{J}\frac{\partial}{\partial t} + \mathrm{grad}\, H_t\Big)\widetilde{\exp}(w_\rho, X) = \widetilde{\mathcal{F}}(\widetilde{\exp}(w_\rho, X))$$

and therefore

$$(d\widetilde{\mathcal{F}}_\rho)_X(v) = (d\widetilde{\mathcal{F}})_{\widetilde{\exp}(w_\rho, X)}(D_2\widetilde{\exp}_{(w_\rho, X)}(v)).$$

The computation of $(d\widetilde{\mathcal{F}})_u$ (for $u = \widetilde{\exp}(w_\rho, X)$) is identical to that carried out in Section 8.4 and gives

$$(d\widetilde{\mathcal{F}})_u(Y) = \frac{\partial Y}{\partial s} + D_1\tilde{J}_{(u, \partial u/\partial t)}(Y) + \tilde{J}\Big(u, \frac{\partial Y}{\partial t}\Big) + (d\,\mathrm{grad}\, H)_u(Y)$$

(recall that $\tilde{J}$ is the extension of J to $W \times \mathbf{R}^m$ defined earlier, and therefore is linear with respect to the second variable). The derivative $(d\widetilde{\mathcal{F}}_\rho)_X(v)$ is therefore the sum of four terms:

$$(d\widetilde{\mathcal{F}}_\rho)_X(v) = \frac{\partial}{\partial s}\big(D_2\widetilde{\exp}_{(w_\rho, X)}(v)\big) \qquad\qquad \text{term}_1$$

$$+ D_1\tilde{J}_{(\widetilde{\exp}(w_\rho, X),\, \frac{\partial}{\partial t}\widetilde{\exp}(w_\rho, X))}(D_2\widetilde{\exp}_{(w_\rho, X)}(v)) \qquad \text{term}_2$$

$$+ \tilde{J}\Big(\widetilde{\exp}(w_\rho, X),\, \frac{\partial}{\partial t}(D_2\widetilde{\exp}_{(w_\rho, X)}(v))\Big) \qquad\qquad \text{term}_3$$

$$+ (d\,\mathrm{grad}\, H_t)_{(\widetilde{\exp}(w_\rho, X))}(D_2\widetilde{\exp}_{(w_\rho, X)}(v)). \qquad\qquad \text{term}_4$$

Let us rewrite each of these four terms by expanding those containing $\partial/\partial s$ and $\partial/\partial t$. To clarify the notation, we write $\tilde{J}_p(\cdot)$ for $\tilde{J}(p, \cdot)$ and $D_1\tilde{J}_p(\cdot, \cdot)$

for $D_1 \widetilde{J}_{(p,\cdot)}(\cdot)$ (the maps are linear in each of their arguments). The four terms are then

$$\text{term}_1 = D_1 D_2 \widetilde{\exp}_{(w_\rho,X)}\left(\frac{\partial w_\rho}{\partial s}, v\right) + D_2 D_2 \widetilde{\exp}_{(w_\rho,X)}\left(\frac{\partial X}{\partial s}, v\right)$$
$$+ D_2 \widetilde{\exp}_{(w_\rho,X)}\left(\frac{\partial v}{\partial s}\right),$$

$$\text{term}_2 = D_1 \widetilde{J}_{\widetilde{\exp}(w_\rho,X)}\left(D_2 \widetilde{\exp}_{(w_\rho,X)}(v), D_1 \widetilde{\exp}_{(w_\rho,X)}\left(\frac{\partial w_\rho}{\partial t}\right)\right)$$
$$+ D_1 \widetilde{J}_{\widetilde{\exp}(w_\rho,X)}\left(D_2 \widetilde{\exp}_{(w_\rho,X)}(v), D_2 \widetilde{\exp}_{(w_\rho,X)}\left(\frac{\partial X}{\partial t}\right)\right),$$

$$\text{term}_3 = \widetilde{J}_{\widetilde{\exp}(w_\rho,X)}\left(D_1 D_2 \widetilde{\exp}_{(w_\rho,X)}\left(\frac{\partial w_\rho}{\partial t}, v\right)\right.$$
$$\left. + D_2 D_2 \widetilde{\exp}_{(w_\rho,X)}\left(\frac{\partial X}{\partial t}, v\right)\right) + \widetilde{J}_{\widetilde{\exp}(w_\rho,X)}\left(D_2 \widetilde{\exp}_{(w_\rho,X)}\left(\frac{\partial v}{\partial t}\right)\right),$$

$$\text{term}_4 = (d \operatorname{grad} H_t)_{\widetilde{\exp}(w_\rho,X)}(D_2 \widetilde{\exp}_{(w_\rho,X)}(v)).$$

Despite the length of this formula, conditions (3) and (4) can be verified rather easily. We fix a pair $(s,t) \in \mathbf{R} \times S^1$ and apply Lemma 13.2.3 to certain linear maps $A(p, X, \cdot)$ or bilinear maps $B(p, X, \cdot, \cdot)$ for $p = w_\rho(s, t)$ and $X = X(s, t)$. The maps A and B are those that occur in the terms above, namely:

- The linear maps:
  - First $D_2 \widetilde{\exp}_{(p,X)}(\cdot)$
  - Then $\widetilde{J}_{\widetilde{\exp}(p,X)}(D_2 \widetilde{\exp}_{(p,X)}(\cdot))$
  - And finally $(d \operatorname{grad} H_t)_{\widetilde{\exp}(p,X)}(D_2 \widetilde{\exp}_{(p,X)}(\cdot))$
- the bilinear maps:
  - $D_i D_2 \widetilde{\exp}_{(p,X)}(\cdot, \cdot)$
  - As well as $D_1 \widetilde{J}_{\widetilde{\exp}(p,X)}(D_2 \widetilde{\exp}_{(p,X)}(\cdot), D_i \widetilde{\exp}_{(p,X)}(\cdot))$
  - And $\widetilde{J}_{\widetilde{\exp}(p,X)}(D_i D_2 \widetilde{\exp}_{(p,X)}(\cdot, \cdot))$ (for $i = 1, 2$).

We apply Lemma 13.2.3 to them in order to evaluate the Euclidean norm $\|((d\widetilde{\mathcal{F}}_\rho)_X(v) - (d\widetilde{\mathcal{F}}_\rho)_0(v))(s, t)\|$ (for fixed (s, t)). Since

$$X \in B(0, C_1 r_0) \subset W^{1,p}(\mathbf{R} \times S^1; \mathbf{R}^m),$$

we have, for every pair $(s, t) \in \mathbf{R} \times S^1$,

$$\|X(s, t)\| \leq \|X\|_{L^\infty} \leq k \|X\|_{W^{1,p}} \leq k C_1 r_0 = r_1,$$

which means that we can use Lemma 13.2.3 and that *the constants obtained through this lemma will not depend on (s, t)* (which allows us to leave the (s, t) out of the notation from now on). We used the continuous inclusion

$W^{1,p} \subset L^\infty$ given by Theorem C.4.9. We therefore obtain

$$\|(d\widetilde{\mathcal{F}}_\rho)_X(v) - (d\widetilde{\mathcal{F}}_\rho)_0(v)\|$$

$$\leq C\Big(\|X\|\Big\|\frac{\partial w_\rho}{\partial s}\Big\|\,\|v\| + \Big\|\frac{\partial X}{\partial s}\Big\|\,\|v\| + \|X\|\Big\|\frac{\partial v}{\partial s}\Big\|\Big) \qquad \text{term}_1$$

$$+ C\Big(\|X\|\,\|v\|\Big\|\frac{\partial w_\rho}{\partial t}\Big\| + \|v\|\Big\|\frac{\partial X}{\partial t}\Big\|\Big) \qquad\qquad \text{term}_2$$

$$+ C\Big(\|X\|\Big\|\frac{\partial w_\rho}{\partial t}\Big\|\,\|v\| + \Big\|\frac{\partial X}{\partial t}\Big\|\,\|v\| + \|X\|\Big\|\frac{\partial v}{\partial t}\Big\|\Big) \qquad \text{term}_3$$

$$+ C\,\|X\|\,\|v\|. \qquad\qquad\qquad\qquad\qquad\qquad\qquad\qquad \text{term}_4$$

But the norms of the partial derivatives of w_ρ with respect to s and t are uniformly bounded with respect to (s,t) and with respect to ρ, as we have already noted. There therefore exists a constant (that we will still call C) such that for every $(s,t) \in \mathbf{R} \times S^1$ and $\rho \geq \rho_0$, we have

$$\|(d\widetilde{\mathcal{F}}_\rho)_X(v) - (d\widetilde{\mathcal{F}}_\rho)_0(v)\| \leq C\Big(\|X\|\Big\|\frac{\partial v}{\partial s}\Big\| + \|X\|\Big\|\frac{\partial v}{\partial t}\Big\|\Big)$$

$$+ C\Big(\|X\|\,\|v\| + \Big\|\frac{\partial X}{\partial s}\Big\|\,\|v\| + \Big\|\frac{\partial X}{\partial t}\Big\|\,\|v\|\Big).$$

We now let (s,t) vary and study the L^p norms. By Lemma 13.2.2, we have

$$\Big\|(d\widetilde{\mathcal{F}}_\rho)_X(v) - (d\widetilde{\mathcal{F}}_\rho)_0(v)\Big\|_{L^p} \leq C\Big(\Big\|\|X\|\Big\|\frac{\partial v}{\partial s}\Big\| + \|X\|\Big\|\frac{\partial v}{\partial t}\Big\|\Big\|_{L^p}\Big)$$

$$+ C\Big(\Big\|\|X\|\,\|v\| + \Big\|\frac{\partial X}{\partial s}\Big\|\,\|v\| + \Big\|\frac{\partial X}{\partial t}\Big\|\,\|v\|\Big\|_{L^p}\Big)$$

$$\leq Ck\,\|v\|_{W^{1,p}}\Big(\|X\|_{L^p} + \Big\|\frac{\partial X}{\partial s}\Big\|_{L^p} + \Big\|\frac{\partial X}{\partial t}\Big\|_{L^p}\Big)$$

$$+ Ck\Big(\Big(\Big\|\frac{\partial v}{\partial s}\Big\|_{L^p} + \Big\|\frac{\partial v}{\partial t}\Big\|_{L^p}\Big)\|X\|_{W^{1,p}}\Big)$$

$$\leq 5Ck\,\|X\|_{W^{1,p}}\,\|v\|_{W^{1,p}}.$$

It follows that for every $X \in \overline{B}(0, C_1 r_0) \subset W^{1,p}(\mathbf{R} \times S^1; \mathbf{R}^m)$,

$$\big\|(d\widetilde{\mathcal{F}}_\rho)_X - (d\widetilde{\mathcal{F}}_\rho)_0\big\|^{\mathrm{op}} \leq 5Ck\,\|X\|_{W^{1,p}},$$

that is, finally, condition (3) of Lemma 13.4.1. But we still need to verify that condition (4) of the same lemma is satisfied, namely that $\|(d\widetilde{\mathcal{F}}_\rho)_0\|^{\mathrm{op}} \leq k_4$ for some $k_4 > 0$ that does not depend on ρ. Substituting $X = 0$ in the formula with four terms from before, we obtain (for fixed (s,t))

$$
\begin{aligned}
\left\|(d\widetilde{\mathcal{F}}_\rho)_0(v)\right\| &= \left\|(d\widetilde{\mathcal{F}})_{w_\rho}(v)\right\| \\
&= \left\|\frac{\partial v}{\partial s} + D_1\widetilde{J}_{w_\rho}\left(\frac{\partial w_\rho}{\partial t}, v\right) + \widetilde{J}_{w_\rho}\left(\frac{\partial v}{\partial t}\right) + (d\operatorname{grad} H_t)_{w_\rho}(v)\right\| \\
&\leq \left\|\frac{\partial v}{\partial s}\right\| + C\left\|\frac{\partial w_\rho}{\partial t}\right\| \|v\| + C\left\|\frac{\partial v}{\partial t}\right\| + C\|v\|
\end{aligned}
$$

for a constant $C > 0$ that does not depend on ρ. Still using the fact that the partial derivatives of w_ρ are uniformly bounded in (s,t) and in ρ, we obtain another constant (still denoted by) C such that

$$
\left\|(d\widetilde{\mathcal{F}}_\rho)_0(v)\right\| \leq C\left(\|v\| + \left\|\frac{\partial v}{\partial s}\right\| + \left\|\frac{\partial v}{\partial t}\right\|\right).
$$

By taking the L^p norms of the two sides, this implies that

$$
\left\|(d\widetilde{\mathcal{F}}_\rho)_0(v)\right\|_{L^p} \leq 3C\,\|v\|_{W^{1,p}}
$$

and therefore that

$$
\left\|(d\widetilde{\mathcal{F}}_\rho)_0\right\|^{\mathrm{op}} \leq 3C,
$$

which is condition (4) of Lemma 13.4.1. After these long verifications, we can now apply this lemma to $\varphi = i_\rho$ and $\psi = \operatorname{Id}\widetilde{\mathcal{F}}_\rho$.

- We can also apply it to $\varphi = (\operatorname{Id} \times \widetilde{\mathcal{F}}_\rho) \circ i_\rho$: condition (1) is the result of the application of the same lemma 13.4.1 to $\varphi = i_\rho$ and $\psi = (\operatorname{Id} \times \widetilde{\mathcal{F}}_\rho)$. We finally arrive at

$$
\left\|(d\varphi)_0\right\|^{\mathrm{op}} \leq \left\|(d(\operatorname{Id} \times \widetilde{\mathcal{F}}_\rho))_0\right\|^{\mathrm{op}} \left\|(di_\rho)_0\right\|^{\mathrm{op}} \leq k_2,
$$

taking into account the verifications we just carried out.

- We still need to verify that the conditions are also satisfied for $\psi = p_\rho$, the map

$$
W^{1,p}(\mathbf{R} \times S^1; \mathbf{R}^m) \times L^p(\mathbf{R} \times S^1; \mathbf{R}^m) \longrightarrow L^p(\mathbf{R} \times S^1; \mathbf{R}^m)
$$

defined by

$$
(p_\rho(X, Y))_i = P(w_\rho, X, Z_i^\rho, Y) \quad \text{for } i = 1, \dots, n
$$

(P is the bilinear map in the last two components that was defined earlier). To verify condition (3), it suffices to prove the following result.

Lemma 13.4.2. *For every* $X \in \overline{B}(0, C_1 r_0) \subset W^{1,p}(\mathbf{R} \times S^1; \mathbf{R}^m)$ *and every* $Y \in L^p(\mathbf{R} \times S^1; \mathbf{R}^m)$, *we have*

$$\left\| (dp_\rho)_{(X,Y)} - (dp_\rho)_0 \right\|^{\mathrm{op}} \leq k_3 \left\| (X,Y) - \varphi(0) \right\|$$

for a constant $k_3 > 0$ *that does not depend on* ρ.

Proof. It will, of course, suffice to establish this estimate for each of the components p_ρ^i of p_ρ. Recall that $\varphi(0) = (0, \widetilde{\mathcal{F}}_\rho(0)) = (0, \mathcal{F}(w_\rho))$ and let

$$Y_0^\rho = \mathcal{F}(w_\rho) \in L^p(\mathbf{R} \times S^1; \mathbf{R}^m) \cap \mathcal{C}_0^\infty(\mathbf{R} \times S^1; \mathbf{R}^m).$$

For $(v, w) \in W^{1,p}(\mathbf{R} \times S^1; \mathbf{R}^m) \times L^p(\mathbf{R} \times S^1; \mathbf{R}^m)$, we have

$$(dp_\rho^i)_{(X,Y)}(v, w) = (D_2 P)_{(w_\rho, X, Z_\rho^i, Y)} v + P(w_\rho, X, Z_\rho^i, w).$$

We fix a pair $(s, t) \in \mathbf{R} \times S^1$. At this point, we have

$$\left\| (dp_\rho^i)_{(X,Y)}(v, w) - (dp_\rho^i)_{(0,Y_0^\rho)}(v, w) \right\|$$
$$\leq \left\| (D_2 P)_{(w_\rho, X, Z_\rho^i, Y)} v - (D_2 P)_{(w_\rho, 0, Z_\rho^i, Y_0^\rho)} v \right\|$$
$$+ \left\| P(w_\rho, X, Z_\rho^i, w) - P(w_\rho, 0, Z_\rho^i, w) \right\|.$$

We apply Lemma 13.2.3 to the bilinear map $P_{(p,X)}(\cdot, \cdot)$ and the analogue of this lemma (which we did not have the courage to write down) to the trilinear map $(D_2 P)_{(p, X, \cdot, \cdot)}(\cdot)$ (with $p = w_\rho(s, t)$ and $X = X(s, t)$). As above, we have

$$\|X(s, t)\| \leq r_1 \quad \text{for every } (s, t) \in \mathbf{R} \times S^1,$$

hence Lemma 13.2.3 can be applied and gives a constant $C > 0$ that does not depend on (s, t). We find that

$$\left\| (dp_\rho^i)_{(X,Y)}(v, w) - (dp_\rho^i)_{(0,Y_0^\rho)}(v, w) \right\|$$
$$\leq C \left(\|Z_i^\rho\| \|Y - Y_0^\rho\| \|v\| + \|X\| \|Z_i^\rho\| \|Y_0^\rho\| \|v\| + \|X\| \|Z_i^\rho\| \|w\| \right).$$

By construction, $\|Z_i^\rho\|$ is uniformly bounded (with respect to ρ, s and t). The norm $\|Y_0^\rho\|$ is also uniformly bounded (because $Y_0^\rho(s, t) = 0$ for $|s| \geq 1$ and $\lim_{\rho \to +\infty} Y_0^\rho(s, t) = 0$ on $[-1, 1]$). We thus find a positive constant (still denoted by) C such that

$$\left\| (dp_\rho^i)_{(X,Y)}(v, w) - (dp_\rho^i)_{(0,Y_0^\rho)}(v, w) \right\|$$
$$\leq C \left(\|Y - Y_0^\rho\| \|v\| + \|X\| \|v\| + \|X\| \|w\| \right).$$

Letting (s,t) vary, we take the L^p norms of the two sides and bound the right-hand side from above using Lemma 13.2.2, which gives

$$\left\|(dp_\rho^i)_{(X,Y)}(v,w) - (dp_\rho^i)_{(0,Y_0^\rho)}(v,w)\right\|_{L^p}$$
$$\leq Ck\left(\|Y - Y_0^\rho\|_{L^p}\|v\|_{W^{1,p}} + \|X\|_{W^{1,p}}\|v\|_{L^p} + \|X\|_{W^{1,p}}\|w\|_{L^p}\right)$$
$$\leq Ck\left(\|X\|_{W^{1,p}} + \|Y - Y_0^\rho\|_{L^p}\right)\left(\|v\|_{W^{1,p}} + \|w\|_{L^p}\right)$$
$$= Ck\left\|(X,Y) - (0,Y_0^\rho)\right\|_{W^{1,p}\times L^p}\left\|(v,w)\right\|_{W^{1,p}\times L^p}. \qquad \square$$

Condition (3) is therefore satisfied. Let us verify that the same holds for (4). For fixed (s,t), we have

$$\left\|(dp_\rho^i)_{(0,Y_0^\rho)}(v,w)\right\| = \left\|(D_2P)_{(w_\rho,0,Z_i^\rho,Y_0^\rho)}(v) + P(w_\rho,0,Z_i^\rho,w)\right\|$$
$$\leq C\left(\|Z_i^\rho\|\,\|Y_0^\rho\|\,\|v\| + \|Z_i^\rho\|\,\|w\|\right).$$

Since the norms of Z_i^ρ and of Y_0^ρ are uniformly bounded, this gives

$$\left\|(dp_\rho^i)_{(0,Y_0^\rho)}(v,w)\right\| \leq C\left(\|v\| + \|w\|\right),$$

an inequality to which we apply the L^p norm to obtain

$$\left\|(dp_\rho^i)_{(0,Y_0^\rho)}(v,w)\right\|_{L^p} \leq C\left(\|v\|_{L^p} + \|w\|_{L^p}\right) \leq C\left\|(v,w)\right\|_{W^{1,p}\times L^p}.$$

Condition (4) is therefore satisfied.

We can finally apply Lemma 13.4.1, which gives

$$\text{for } \|y\|_{W^{1,p}} \leq r_0, \text{ we have } \|(dF_\rho)_y - (dF_\rho)_0\|^{\mathrm{op}} \leq k\|y\|_{W^{1,p}}.$$

This concludes the proof of Lemma 9.4.8. $\qquad \square$

13.5 Proof of the Two Lemmas: The Second One

Proof of Lemma 9.4.16. The outline of this proof is the same as that of the proof of Lemma 9.4.8: we prove an abstract lemma that can be applied to the composition $F_\rho = p_\rho \circ (\mathrm{Id}, \widetilde{\mathcal{F}}_\rho) \circ i_\rho$. Here is the abstract lemma.

Lemma 13.5.1. *Let G, H and K be Banach spaces and let*

$$\varphi_\rho : G \longrightarrow H, \qquad \psi_\rho : H \longrightarrow K$$

be (nonlinear) operators of class $\mathcal{C}^1$ that are differentiable in $\rho \geq \rho_0$. We suppose that there exist an $r_0 > 0$ and constants $k_i > 0$ (for $i = 1, \ldots, 7$) that *do not depend on ρ, such that for every $z \in \overline{B}(0, r_0) \subset G$, we have:*

(1) *The conditions of Lemma 13.4.1 hold for φ and ψ (with the constants $k_1, \ldots, k_4$).*

(2) $\left\| \dfrac{\partial \varphi_\rho}{\partial \rho}(z) - \dfrac{\partial \varphi_\rho}{\partial \rho}(0) \right\| \leq k_5 \, \|z\|.$

(3) $\left\| \dfrac{\partial \psi_\rho}{\partial \rho}(\varphi_\rho(z)) - \dfrac{\psi_\rho}{\partial \rho}(\varphi_\rho(0)) \right\| \leq k_6 \, \|\varphi_\rho(z) - \varphi_\rho(0)\|.$

(4) $\left\| \dfrac{\varphi_\rho}{\partial \rho}(0) \right\| \leq k_7.$

Then there exists an $M > 0$ that does not depend on ρ, such that for every $z \in \overline{B}(0, r_0)$, we have

$$\left\| \frac{\partial}{\partial \rho}(\psi_\rho \circ \varphi_\rho)(z) - \frac{\partial}{\partial \rho}(\psi_\rho \circ \varphi_\rho)(0) \right\| \leq M \, \|z\|.$$

Proof. We have

$$\left\| \frac{\partial}{\partial \rho}(\psi_\rho \circ \varphi_\rho)(z) - \frac{\partial}{\partial \rho}(\psi_\rho \circ \varphi_\rho)(0) \right\|$$

$$\leq \left\| \frac{\partial \psi_\rho}{\partial \rho}(\varphi_\rho(z)) - \frac{\partial \psi_\rho}{\partial \rho}(\varphi_\rho(0)) \right\|$$

$$\quad + \left\| (d\psi_\rho)_{\varphi_\rho(z)}\left(\frac{\partial \varphi_\rho}{\partial \rho}(z) \right) - (d\psi_\rho)_{\varphi_\rho(0)}\left(\frac{\partial \varphi_\rho}{\partial \rho}(z) \right) \right\|$$

$$\leq k_6 \, \|\varphi_\rho(z) - \varphi_\rho(0)\|$$

$$\quad + \left\| (d\psi_\rho)_{\varphi_\rho(z)}\left(\frac{\partial \varphi_\rho}{\partial \rho}(z) \right) - (d\psi_\rho)_{\varphi_\rho(0)}\left(\frac{\partial \varphi_\rho}{\partial \rho}(z) \right) \right\|$$

$$\quad + \left\| (d\psi_\rho)_{\varphi_\rho(0)}\left(\frac{\partial \varphi_\rho}{\partial \rho}(z) - \frac{\partial \varphi_\rho}{\partial \rho}(0) \right) \right\|$$

$$\leq k_6 \, \|\varphi_\rho(z) - \varphi_\rho(0)\|$$

$$\quad + k_3 \, \|\varphi_\rho(z) - \varphi_\rho(0)\| \left\| \frac{\partial \varphi_\rho}{\partial \rho}(z) \right\| + k_4 \left\| \frac{\partial \varphi_\rho}{\partial \rho}(z) - \frac{\partial \varphi_\rho}{\partial \rho}(0) \right\|$$

$$\leq k_6 \, \|\varphi_\rho(z) - \varphi_\rho(0)\|$$

$$\quad + k_3 \, \|\varphi_\rho(z) - \varphi_\rho(0)\| \left(\left\| \frac{\partial \varphi_\rho}{\partial \rho}(z) - \frac{\partial \varphi_\rho}{\partial \rho}(0) \right\| + \left\| \frac{\partial \varphi_\rho}{\partial \rho}(0) \right\| \right) + k_4 k_5 \, \|z\|$$

$$\leq \|\varphi_\rho(z) - \varphi_\rho(0)\| \, (k_6 + k_3 k_5 \, \|z\| + k_7) + k_4 k_5 \, \|z\|.$$

Next,

$$\|\varphi_\rho(z) - \varphi_\rho(0)\| \leq \sup_{t \in [0,1]} \|(d\varphi_\rho)_{tz}\| \, \|z\|$$

$$\leq \sup_{t \in [0,1]} (\|(d\varphi_\rho)_{tz} - (d\varphi_\rho)_0\| + \|(d\varphi_\rho)_0\|) \, \|z\|$$

$$\leq (k_1 \|z\| + k_2) \, \|z\|$$

$$\leq (k_1 r_0 + k_2) \, \|z\| \,.$$

This concludes the proof of Lemma 13.5.1. □

We are going to apply this to:

- $\varphi = i_\rho$ and $\psi = \mathrm{Id} \times \widetilde{\mathcal{F}}_\rho$
- $\varphi = \mathrm{Id} \times \widetilde{\mathcal{F}}_\rho$ and $\psi = p_\rho$.

Let us verify that in both cases the operators satisfy the conditions of Lemma 13.5.1:

- Condition (1) has already been verified for Lemma 9.4.8.
- Let us verify conditions (2) and (4) for $\varphi_\rho = i_\rho$. We have $i_\rho(Y) = \sum y_i Z_i^\rho$, hence

$$\frac{\partial i_\rho}{\partial \rho}(Y) = \sum_{i=1}^{2n} y_i \frac{\partial Z_i^\rho}{\partial \rho}, \quad \text{in particular} \quad \frac{\partial i_\rho}{\partial \rho}(0) = 0.$$

This gives

$$\left\| \frac{\partial i_\rho}{\partial \rho}(Y) - \frac{\partial i_\rho}{\partial \rho}(0) \right\|_{W^{1,p}} = \left\| \sum_{i=1}^{2n} y_i \frac{\partial Z_i^\rho}{\partial \rho} \right\|_{W^{1,p}} \leq \sum_{i=1}^{2n} \left\| y_i \frac{\partial Z_i^\rho}{\partial \rho} \right\|_{W^{1,p}}$$

$$\leq \sum_{i=1}^{2n} \|y_i\|_{W^{1,p}} \left\| \frac{\partial Z_i^\rho}{\partial \rho} \right\|_{\mathcal{C}^1}$$

(again by Lemma 8.2.4). Now the choice of the $Z_i^\rho(s,t)$ (see p. 316) ensures that there exists a constant $C > 0$ that does not depend on ρ, such that for every $i = 1, \ldots, 2n$,

$$\left\| \frac{\partial Z_i}{\partial \rho} \right\|_{\mathcal{C}^1} \leq C.$$

It follows that

$$\left\| \frac{\partial i_\rho}{\partial \rho}(Y) - \frac{\partial i_\rho}{\partial \rho}(0) \right\|_{W^{1,p}} \leq C \sum_{i=1}^{2n} \|y_i\|_{W^{1,p}} \leq 2n \, C \, \|Y\|_{W^{1,p}} \,.$$

Condition (4) is therefore satisfied because $\partial i_\rho / \partial \rho(0) = 0$.

- Let us now verify condition (3) for $\psi_\rho = \mathrm{Id} \times \widetilde{\mathcal{F}}_\rho$. Note that for $\varphi_\rho = i_\rho$, we have $\varphi_\rho(0) = 0$ and

$$\|\varphi_\rho(z)\| \leq \|i_\rho\| \, \|z\| \leq C_1 r_0.$$

It therefore suffices to prove that for every $X \in B(0, C_1 r_0)$,

$$\left\| \frac{\partial(\mathrm{Id} \times \widetilde{\mathcal{F}}_\rho)}{\partial\rho}(X) - \frac{\partial(\mathrm{Id} \times \widetilde{\mathcal{F}}_\rho)}{\partial\rho}(0) \right\|_{L^p} \leq k_6 \, \|X\|_{W^{1,p}},$$

in other words, that

$$\left\| \frac{\partial\widetilde{\mathcal{F}}_\rho}{\partial\rho}(X) - \frac{\partial\widetilde{\mathcal{F}}_\rho}{\partial\rho}(0) \right\|_{L^p} \leq k_6 \, \|X\|_{W^{1,p}}.$$

Recall that

$$\begin{aligned}
\widetilde{\mathcal{F}}_\rho(X) &= \left(\frac{\partial}{\partial s} + \widetilde{J}\frac{\partial}{\partial t} + \mathrm{grad}\, H_t \right)\left(\widetilde{\exp}_{w_\rho}(X) \right) \\
&= D_1\widetilde{\exp}_{(w_\rho, X)}\left(\frac{\partial w_\rho}{\partial s} \right) + D_2\widetilde{\exp}_{(w_\rho, X)}\left(\frac{\partial X}{\partial s} \right) \\
&\quad + \widetilde{J}_{\widetilde{\exp}(w_\rho, X)}\left(D_1\widetilde{\exp}_{(w_\rho, X)}\left(\frac{\partial w_\rho}{\partial t} \right) + D_2\widetilde{\exp}_{(w_\rho, X)}\left(\frac{\partial X}{\partial t} \right) \right) \\
&\quad + \mathrm{grad}\, H_t(\widetilde{\exp}(w_\rho, X)).
\end{aligned}$$

It follows that

$$\begin{aligned}
\frac{\partial}{\partial\rho}\widetilde{\mathcal{F}}_\rho(X) &= D_1 D_1\widetilde{\exp}_{(w_\rho, X)}\left(\frac{\partial w_\rho}{\partial\rho}, \frac{\partial w_\rho}{\partial s} \right) + D_1\widetilde{\exp}_{(w_\rho, X)}\left(\frac{\partial^2 w_\rho}{\partial\rho\partial s} \right) \\
&\quad + D_1 D_2\widetilde{\exp}_{(w_\rho, X)}\left(\frac{\partial w_\rho}{\partial\rho}, \frac{\partial X}{\partial s} \right) \\
&\quad + D_1\widetilde{J}_{\widetilde{\exp}(w_\rho, X)}\left(\frac{\partial w_\rho}{\partial\rho}, D_1\widetilde{\exp}_{(w_\rho, X)}\left(\frac{\partial w_\rho}{\partial t} \right) \right) \\
&\quad + D_1\widetilde{J}_{\widetilde{\exp}(w_\rho, X)}\left(\frac{\partial w_\rho}{\partial\rho}, D_2\widetilde{\exp}_{(w_\rho, X)}\left(\frac{\partial X}{\partial t} \right) \right) \\
&\quad + \widetilde{J}_{\widetilde{\exp}(w_\rho, X)}\left[D_1 D_1\widetilde{\exp}_{(w_\rho, X)}\left(\frac{\partial w_\rho}{\partial\rho}, \frac{\partial w_\rho}{\partial t} \right) \right. \\
&\qquad\quad \left. + D_1\widetilde{\exp}_{(w_\rho, X)}\left(\frac{\partial^2 w_\rho}{\partial\rho\partial t} \right) + D_1 D_2\widetilde{\exp}_{(w_\rho, X)}\left(\frac{\partial w_\rho}{\partial\rho}, \frac{\partial X}{\partial t} \right) \right] \\
&\quad + (d\,\mathrm{grad}\, H_t)_{\widetilde{\exp}(w_\rho, X)}\left(D_1\widetilde{\exp}_{(w_\rho, X)}\left(\frac{\partial w_\rho}{\partial\rho} \right) \right).
\end{aligned}$$

We fix a pair $(s, t) \in \mathbf{R} \times S^1$ and apply Lemma 13.2.3 to all the linear maps $A_{(p,X)}(\cdot)$ and bilinear maps $B_{(p,X)}(\cdot, \cdot)$ that occur in this formula. Here $p = w_\rho(s, t)$ and $X = X(s, t)$ and we have $\|X(s, t)\|_{\mathcal{C}^0} \leq r_1$, which allows us to use Lemma 13.2.3. At the point (s,t) and for the Euclidean norm of $\mathbf{R}^m$, we obtain the estimate

$$\left\|\frac{\partial}{\partial\rho}\widetilde{\mathcal{F}}_\rho(X) - \frac{\partial}{\partial\rho}\widetilde{\mathcal{F}}_\rho(0)\right\|$$

$$\leq C\left(\|X\|\left\|\frac{\partial w_\rho}{\partial\rho}\right\|\left\|\frac{\partial w_\rho}{\partial s}\right\| + \|X\|\left\|\frac{\partial^2 w_\rho}{\partial\rho\partial s}\right\| + \left\|\frac{\partial w_\rho}{\partial\rho}\right\|\left\|\frac{\partial X}{\partial s}\right\|\right.$$

$$\left. + \|X\|\left\|\frac{\partial w_\rho}{\partial\rho}\right\|\left\|\frac{\partial w_\rho}{\partial t}\right\| + \left\|\frac{\partial w_\rho}{\partial\rho}\right\|\left\|\frac{\partial X}{\partial t}\right\| + \|X\|\left\|\frac{\partial^2 w_\rho}{\partial\rho\partial t}\right\| + \|X\|\left\|\frac{\partial w_\rho}{\partial\rho}\right\|\right).$$

Since all derivatives of w_ρ are uniformly bounded by a constant $k > 0$, this leads to

$$\left\|\frac{\partial}{\partial\rho}\widetilde{\mathcal{F}}_\rho(X) - \frac{\partial}{\partial\rho}\widetilde{\mathcal{F}}_\rho(0)\right\| \leq C\left(2k^2\|X\| + 3k\|X\| + k\left\|\frac{\partial X}{\partial s}\right\| + k\left\|\frac{\partial X}{\partial t}\right\|\right)$$

$$\leq C_1\left(\|X\| + \left\|\frac{\partial X}{\partial s}\right\| + \left\|\frac{\partial X}{\partial t}\right\|\right).$$

Letting (s,t) vary and taking the L^p norms, we obtain

$$\left\|\frac{\partial}{\partial\rho}\widetilde{\mathcal{F}}_\rho(X) - \frac{\partial}{\partial\rho}\widetilde{\mathcal{F}}_\rho(0)\right\|_{L^p} \leq C_1\left(\|X\|_{L^p} + \left\|\frac{\partial X}{\partial s}\right\|_{L^p} + \left\|\frac{\partial X}{\partial t}\right\|_{L^p}\right)$$

$$\leq 3C_1\|X\|_{W^{1,p}}.$$

- Let us verify the conditions for $\varphi_\rho = (\mathrm{Id}\times\widetilde{\mathcal{F}}_\rho)\circ i_\rho$. We can see that condition (2) is satisfied by applying Lemma 13.5.1 to the situation studied above. By condition (4), since we have

$$\varphi_\rho(Y) = (i_\rho(Y), \widetilde{\mathcal{F}}_\rho i_\rho(Y)),$$

the derivative is

$$\frac{\partial\varphi_\rho}{\partial\rho}(0) = \left(\frac{\partial i_\rho}{\partial\rho}(0), \frac{\partial\widetilde{\mathcal{F}}_\rho}{\partial\rho}(0) + (d\widetilde{\mathcal{F}}_\rho)_0\left(\frac{\partial i_\rho}{\partial\rho}(0)\right)\right) = \left(0, \frac{\partial\widetilde{\mathcal{F}}_\rho}{\partial\rho}(0)\right).$$

Next,

$$\left\|\frac{\partial\widetilde{\mathcal{F}}_\rho}{\partial\rho}(0)\right\|_{L^p} = \left\|\frac{\partial}{\partial\rho}\left(\frac{\partial w_\rho}{\partial s} + \widetilde{J}_{w_\rho}\frac{\partial w_\rho}{\partial t} + \mathrm{grad}\, H_t(w_\rho)\right)\right\|_{L^p}$$

$$= \left\|\frac{\partial^2 w_\rho}{\partial\rho\partial s} + D_1\widetilde{J}_{w_\rho}\left(\frac{\partial w_\rho}{\partial\rho}, \frac{\partial w_\rho}{\partial t}\right) + \widetilde{J}_{w_\rho}\frac{\partial^2 w_\rho}{\partial\rho\partial t} + (d\,\mathrm{grad}\, H_t)_{w_\rho}\left(\frac{\partial w_\rho}{\partial\rho}\right)\right\|_{L^p}$$

$$\leq C\left(\left\|\frac{\partial^2 w_\rho}{\partial\rho\partial s}\right\|_{L^p} + \left\|\left\|\frac{\partial w_\rho}{\partial\rho}\right\|\left\|\frac{\partial w_\rho}{\partial t}\right\|\right\|_{L^p} + \left\|\frac{\partial^2 w_\rho}{\partial\rho\partial t}\right\|_{L^p} + \left\|\frac{\partial w_\rho}{\partial\rho}\right\|_{L^p}\right).$$

Now all derivatives of w_ρ are uniformly bounded for the L^p norm. This holds on $[-1,1]\times S^1$ (because they are uniformly bounded in $\mathcal{C}^\infty$); for

$|s| \geq 1$ we use the fact that $w_\rho(s,t) = u(s + \rho, t)$ (or $v(s - \rho, t)$) and the exponential decay of u and v, which implies that their derivatives are L^p. We therefore have

$$\left\| \frac{\partial \varphi_\rho}{\partial \rho}(0) \right\| \leq k,$$

where $k > 0$ is independent of ρ.

- Let us verify condition (3) for $\psi_\rho = P_\rho$. We have

$$\varphi_\rho(0) = (0, \widetilde{\mathcal{F}}_\rho(0)).$$

Let $Y_0 = \widetilde{\mathcal{F}}_\rho(0)$ and let us compute the derivatives (with respect to ρ) of the $p_\rho^i(X, Y)$ for $i = 1, \ldots, 2n$. We have

$$\frac{\partial p_\rho^i(X, Y)}{\partial \rho} = \frac{\partial P}{\partial \rho}(w_\rho, X, Z_i^\rho, Y)$$

$$= (D_1 P)_{(w_\rho, X, Z_i^\rho, Y)} \left(\frac{\partial w_\rho}{\partial \rho} \right) + P \left(w_\rho, X, \frac{\partial Z_i^\rho}{\partial \rho}, Y \right).$$

We fix a pair $(s, t) \in \mathbf{R} \times S^1$ and apply Lemma 13.2.3 to the bilinear map $P_{(p,X)}(\cdot, \cdot)$ and to the trilinear map $D_1 P_{(p,X,\cdot,\cdot)}(\cdot)$ (for $p = w_\rho(s, t)$ and $X = X(s, t)$). This gives

$$\left\| \frac{\partial p_\rho^i}{\partial \rho}(X, Y) - \frac{\partial p_\rho^i}{\partial \rho}(0, Y_0) \right\|$$

$$\leq C \left(\|X\| \, \|Z_i^\rho\| \, \|Y_0\| \, \left\| \frac{\partial w_\rho}{\partial \rho} \right\| + \|Z_i^\rho\| \, \left\| \frac{\partial w_\rho}{\partial \rho} \right\| \, \|Y - Y_0\| \right.$$

$$\left. + \|X\| \, \left\| \frac{\partial Z_i^\rho}{\partial \rho} \right\| \, \|Y_0\| + \left\| \frac{\partial Z_i^\rho}{\partial \rho} \right\| \, \|Y - Y_0\| \right).$$

Since $\|Z_i^\rho\|$, $\|\partial Z_i^\rho / \partial \rho\|$, $\|\partial w_\rho / \partial \rho\|$ as well as $\|Y_0\| = \|\mathcal{F}_{w_\rho}\|$ are uniformly bounded by a constant k (that does not depend on ρ, s or t), it follows that

$$\left\| \frac{\partial p_\rho^i}{\partial \rho}(X, Y) - \frac{\partial p_\rho^i}{\partial \rho}(0, Y_0) \right\| \leq 2kC \left(\|X\| + \|Y - Y_0\| \right)$$

and, by taking the L^p norms,

$$\left\| \frac{\partial p_\rho^i}{\partial \rho}(X, Y) - \frac{\partial p_\rho^i}{\partial \rho}(0, Y_0) \right\| \leq 2kC \left(\|X\|_{L^p} + \|Y - Y_0\|_{L^p} \right)$$

$$\leq 2kC \left(\|X\|_{W^{1,p}} + \|Y - Y_0\|_{L^p} \right).$$

Each component p_ρ^i of p_ρ satisfies condition (3), hence so does p_ρ.

We have therefore verified all conditions, so that Lemma 13.5.1 can be applied to conclude the proof of Lemma 9.4.16. $\square$

13.6 Another Technical Lemma

We will now prove one of the technical lemmas[2] used earlier (to prove that $\widehat{\psi}$ is immersive).

Lemma (Lemma 9.5.1). *The sequence* (α_n) *is bounded and we have*

$$\lim_{n \to +\infty} \left\| \left(\frac{\partial w_\rho}{\partial \rho} - \alpha_n \frac{\partial w_\rho}{\partial s} \right)_{\rho_n} \right\|_{L^p} = 0.$$

Proof of Lemma 9.5.1. We first show that the sequence (α_n) is bounded. Let

$$A_n = \left\| \left(D_1 \widetilde{\exp}_{(w_\rho, \gamma(\rho))} \left(\frac{\partial w_\rho}{\partial \rho} \right) + D_2 \widetilde{\exp}_{(w_\rho, \gamma(\rho))} \left(\frac{\partial \gamma}{\partial \rho} \right) \right)_{\rho = \rho_n} \right\|_{L^p}$$

$$B_n = \left\| \left(D_1 \widetilde{\exp}_{(w_\rho, \gamma(\rho))} \left(\frac{\partial w_\rho}{\partial s} \right) + D_2 \widetilde{\exp}_{(w_\rho, \gamma(\rho))} \left(\frac{\partial \gamma}{\partial s} \right) \right)_{\rho = \rho_n} \right\|_{L^p},$$

so that, by definition, we have $|\alpha_n| = A_n/B_n$. Let us show that A_n is bounded from above and that B_n is bounded from below by a positive constant. We fix an $r_0 > 0$. We have

$$\lim_{\rho \to +\infty} \|\gamma\|_{W^{1,p}} = 0, \text{ hence } \|\gamma(\rho_n)\|_{W^{1,p}} \leq r_0$$

for n sufficiently large and therefore, once again using the continuous injection

$$W^{1,p}(\mathbf{R} \times S^1; \mathbf{R}^m) \hookrightarrow L^\infty(\mathbf{R} \times S^1; \mathbf{R}^m)$$

we have

$$\sup_{(s,t) \in \mathbf{R} \times S^1} \|\gamma(s,t)\| \leq K r_0.$$

For a fixed (s,t) and $\rho = \rho_n$ we can then apply Lemma 13.2.3 to the linear maps $D_i \widetilde{\exp}_{(p,X)}(\cdot)$ for $i = 1, 2$, $p = w_{\rho_n}(s,t)$ and $X = \gamma(\rho_n)(s,t)$. It follows that for the Euclidean norm, at (s,t) and for $\rho = \rho_n$, we have

$$\left\| D_1 \widetilde{\exp}_{(w_\rho, \gamma(\rho))} \left(\frac{\partial w_\rho}{\partial \rho} \right) \right\| \leq C \left\| \frac{\partial w_\rho}{\partial \rho} \right\|$$

and

$$\left\| D_2 \widetilde{\exp}_{(w_\rho, \gamma(\rho))} \left(\frac{\partial w_\rho}{\partial \rho} \right) \right\| \leq C \left\| \frac{\partial \gamma}{\partial \rho} \right\|.$$

Taking the L^p norms, we therefore have

$$A_n \leq C \left(\left\| \left(\frac{\partial w_\rho}{\partial \rho} \right)_{\rho = \rho_n} \right\|_{L^p} + \left\| \left(\frac{\partial \gamma}{\partial \rho} \right)_{\rho = \rho_n} \right\|_{L^p} \right).$$

---

[2] This one is more important than its predecessors.

Recall that

$$w_\rho(s,t) \begin{cases} = u(s+\rho,t) & \text{for } s \le -1 \\ \text{tends to } y(t) & \text{for } s \in [-1,1] \text{ and } \rho \to +\infty \\ = v(s-\rho,t) & \text{for } s \ge 1, \end{cases}$$

hence

$$\left\| \frac{\partial w_\rho}{\partial \rho} \right\|_{L^p} \le \left\| \frac{\partial u}{\partial s} \right\|_{L^p} + \left\| \frac{\partial v}{\partial s} \right\|_{L^p} + 1$$

for ρ sufficiently large. In particular, this norm is uniformly bounded with respect to ρ. We also have

$$\lim_{s \to +\infty} \left\| \frac{\partial \gamma}{\partial \rho} \right\| = 0$$

by Proposition 9.4.15. It follows that the sequence A_n is bounded. Let us now turn to B_n. For $\rho = \rho_n$, we have

$$B_n \ge \left\| D_1\widetilde{\exp}_{(w_\rho,\gamma(\rho))} \frac{\partial w_\rho}{\partial s} \right\|_{L^p} - \left\| D_2\widetilde{\exp}_{(w_\rho,\gamma(\rho))} \frac{\partial \gamma}{\partial s} \right\|_{L^p}$$

$$\ge \left\| D_1\widetilde{\exp}_{(w_\rho,0)} \frac{\partial w_\rho}{\partial s} \right\|_{L^p} - \left\| D_1\widetilde{\exp}_{(w_\rho,\gamma(\rho))} \frac{\partial w_\rho}{\partial s} - D_1\widetilde{\exp}_{(w_\rho,0)} \frac{\partial w_\rho}{\partial s} \right\|_{L^p}$$

$$- C \left\| \frac{\partial \gamma}{\partial s} \right\|_{L^p}$$

(by the analogue of the lower bound of $D_2\widetilde{\exp}$ given above for the third term). We fix a pair $(s,t) \in \mathbf{R} \times S^1$ and (once more) set $\rho = \rho_n$. By Lemma 13.2.3, we have

$$\left\| D_1\widetilde{\exp}_{(w_\rho,\gamma(\rho))} \frac{\partial w_\rho}{\partial s} - D_1\widetilde{\exp}_{(w_\rho,0)} \frac{\partial w_\rho}{\partial s} \right\| \le C \left\| \gamma(\rho) \right\| \left\| \frac{\partial w_\rho}{\partial s} \right\|$$

$$\le Ck \left\| \gamma(\rho) \right\| \quad \text{because} \quad \left\| \frac{\partial w_\rho}{\partial s} \right\|_{\mathcal{C}^0} \le k.$$

Using the equality $D_1\widetilde{\exp}_{(w_\rho,0)} = \text{Id}$, we find that

$$B_n \ge \left\| \frac{\partial w_\rho}{\partial s} \right\|_{L^p} - Ck \left\| \gamma(\rho) \right\|_{L^p} - C \left\| \frac{\partial \gamma}{\partial s} \right\|_{L^p}.$$

Since

$$\frac{\partial w_\rho}{\partial s}(s,t) = \frac{\partial u}{\partial s}(s+\rho,t) \quad \text{for } s \ge -1,$$

we have

$$\left\| \frac{\partial w_\rho}{\partial s} \right\|_{L^p} \ge \left\| \frac{\partial u}{\partial s} \right\|_{L^p(]-\infty,\rho-1] \times S^1)} \ge C_0 > 0$$

and (by Lemma 9.4.13)

$$\lim_{\rho\to+\infty}\|\gamma(\rho)\|_{L^p}=0,\quad \lim_{\rho\to+\infty}\left\|\frac{\partial\gamma}{\partial s}\right\|_{L^p}=\lim_{\rho\to+\infty}\|\gamma\|_{W^{1,p}}=0.$$

There therefore exists a constant C_1 such that $B_n\geq C_1$ for every n. Consequently, the sequence (α_n) is bounded.

Next, we have, by hypothesis,

$$\frac{\partial}{\partial\rho}\left(\exp_{w_\rho}\gamma_\rho(s,t)\right)_{\rho_n}=\alpha_n\frac{\partial}{\partial s}\left(\exp_{w_\rho}\gamma_\rho(s,t)\right)_{\rho_n},$$

or

$$\frac{\partial}{\partial\rho}\left(\widetilde{\exp}_{w_\rho}\gamma_\rho(s,t)\right)_{\rho_n}=\alpha_n\frac{\partial}{\partial s}\left(\widetilde{\exp}_{w_\rho}\gamma_\rho(s,t)\right)_{\rho_n},$$

that is,

$$\left(D_1\widetilde{\exp}_{(w_\rho,\gamma(\rho))}\frac{\partial w_\rho}{\partial\rho}+D_2\widetilde{\exp}_{(w_\rho,\gamma(\rho))}\frac{\partial\gamma}{\partial\rho}\right)_{\rho_n}$$
$$=\alpha_n\left(D_1\widetilde{\exp}_{(w_\rho,\gamma(\rho))}\frac{\partial w_\rho}{\partial s}+D_2\widetilde{\exp}_{(w_\rho,\gamma(\rho))}\frac{\partial\gamma}{\partial s}\right)_{\rho_n}.$$

The estimates used above show that

$$\lim_{n\to+\infty}\left\|D_2\left(\widetilde{\exp}_{(w_\rho,\gamma(\rho))}\frac{\partial\gamma}{\partial\rho}\right)_{\rho_n}\right\|_{L^p}=\lim_{n\to+\infty}\left\|D_2\left(\widetilde{\exp}_{(w_\rho,\gamma(\rho))}\frac{\partial\gamma}{\partial s}\right)_{\rho_n}\right\|_{L^p}=0.$$

Since the sequence α_n is bounded, we have

$$\lim_{n\to+\infty}\left\|\left(D_1\widetilde{\exp}_{(w_\rho,\gamma(\rho))}\left(\frac{\partial w_\rho}{\partial\rho}-\alpha_n\frac{\partial w_\rho}{\partial\rho}\right)\right)_{\rho_n}\right\|_{L^p}=0.$$

We once more fix a pair $(s,t)\in\mathbf{R}\times S^1$. By Lemma 13.2.3, for the Euclidean norm, at (s,t) and for $\rho=\rho_n$, we have

$$\left\|D_1\widetilde{\exp}_{(w_\rho,\gamma(\rho))}\left(\frac{\partial w_\rho}{\partial\rho}-\alpha_n\frac{\partial w_\rho}{\partial\rho}\right)-D_1\widetilde{\exp}_{(w_\rho,0)}\left(\frac{\partial w_\rho}{\partial\rho}-\alpha_n\frac{\partial w_\rho}{\partial\rho}\right)\right\|$$
$$\leq C\|\gamma(\rho)\|\left\|\frac{\partial w_\rho}{\partial\rho}-\alpha_n\frac{\partial w_\rho}{\partial\rho}\right\|$$
$$\leq Ck\|\gamma(\rho)\|$$

because

$$\left\|\frac{\partial w_\rho}{\partial\rho}\right\|_{\mathfrak{C}^0},\ \left\|\frac{\partial w_\rho}{\partial s}\right\|_{\mathfrak{C}^0}\quad\text{and }\alpha_n\text{ are bounded.}$$

Taking the L^p norms and using the fact that $\lim_{\rho\to+\infty}\|\gamma\|_{L^p}=0$, we deduce that the L^p norm (for $\rho=\rho_n$) of

$$D_1\widetilde{\exp}_{(w_\rho,\gamma(\rho))}\left(\frac{\partial w_\rho}{\partial\rho}-\alpha_n\frac{\partial w_\rho}{\partial\rho}\right)-D_1\widetilde{\exp}_{(w_\rho,0)}\left(\frac{\partial w_\rho}{\partial\rho}-\alpha_n\frac{\partial w_\rho}{\partial\rho}\right)$$

tends to 0 when n tends to infinity. Therefore, since we saw that the norm of the first term tends to 0,

$$\lim_{n \to +\infty} \left\| D_1 \widetilde{\exp}_{(w_\rho, 0)} \left(\frac{\partial w_\rho}{\partial \rho} - \alpha_n \frac{\partial w_\rho}{\partial \rho} \right) \right\|_{L^p} = 0,$$

that is,

$$\lim_{n \to +\infty} \left\| \left(\frac{\partial w_\rho}{\partial \rho} - \alpha_n \frac{\partial w_\rho}{\partial s} \right)_{\rho_n} \right\|_{L^p} = 0,$$

which we wanted to prove.   □

13.7 Two Other Technical Lemmas

We will now prove two lemmas[3] used in the proof of the uniqueness of the gluing. Here is the first one.

Lemma (Lemma 9.6.14).

$$\lim_{n \to +\infty} \| \chi_n \|_{W^{1,p}} = 0.$$

Proof. We have

$$\int_{\mathbf{R} \times S^1} \| \chi_n \|^2 \, ds \, dt = \int_{\mathbf{R} \times S^1} \langle \chi_n, \chi_n \rangle \, ds \, dt = \int_{\mathbf{R} \times S^1} \langle \zeta_n, \chi_n \rangle \, ds \, dt.$$

By applying, for example, Lemma 8.2.4, we find a constant $M > 0$ such that

$$\int_{\mathbf{R} \times S^1} \langle \zeta_n, \chi_n \rangle \, ds \, dt \leq M \| \zeta_n \|_{L^\infty} \int_{\mathbf{R} \times S^1} \| \chi_n \| \, ds \, dt.$$

Since $Y_n = i(\zeta_n)$, $(\zeta_n)_j = \langle Y_n, Z_j \rangle$ and by Proposition 9.6.3, we have $\lim_{n \to +\infty} \| \zeta_n \|_{L^\infty} = 0$. Let $\varepsilon > 0$. We deduce from the above that there exists an N_ε such that for every $n \geq N_\varepsilon$,

$$\int_{\mathbf{R} \times S^1} \| \chi_n \|^2 \, ds \, dt \leq M \varepsilon \int_{\mathbf{R} \times S^1} \| \chi_n \| \, ds \, dt.$$

Let us write χ_n in the "canonical" basis of W_n:

$$\chi_n = \alpha_n \left(\frac{\partial u}{\partial s} \#_{w_n} 0 \right) + \beta_n \left(0 \#_{w_n} \frac{\partial v}{\partial s} \right) \quad \text{with } \alpha_n, \beta_n \in \mathbf{R}.$$

---

[3] Also important, though technical.

It follows that

$$
\int_{\mathbf{R}\times S^1} \|\chi_n\|\, ds\, dt = \int_{]-\infty,-1]\times S^1} \|\chi_n\|\, ds\, dt
$$
$$
+ \int_{[-1,1]\times S^1} \|\chi_n\|\, ds\, dt + \int_{[1,+\infty[\times S^1} \|\chi_n\|\, ds\, dt
$$
$$
= \int_{]-\infty,-1]\times S^1} |\alpha_n| \left\|\frac{\partial u}{\partial s}(s+\rho_n,t)\right\|\, ds\, dt
$$
$$
+ \int_{[-1,1]\times S^1} \|\chi_n\|\, ds\, dt + \int_{[1,+\infty[\times S^1} |\beta_n| \left\|\frac{\partial v}{\partial s}(s-\nu(\rho_n),t)\right\|\, ds\, dt.
$$

We are going to give an upper bound for each of these three terms. To simplify the notation and shorten the formulas, we set

$$
M_n = \sqrt{\int\!\!\int_{]-\infty,-1]\times S^1} |\alpha_n|^2 \left\|\frac{\partial u}{\partial s}(s+\rho_n,t)\right\|^2\, ds\, dt}.
$$

We obviously have

$$
M_n \leq \|\chi_n\|_{L^2}.
$$

Consequently,

$$
\int_{]-\infty,-1]\times S^1} |\alpha_n| \left\|\frac{\partial u}{\partial s}(s+\rho_n,t)\right\|\, ds\, dt
$$
$$
= M_n \frac{\displaystyle\int_{]-\infty,-1]\times S^1} \left\|\frac{\partial u}{\partial s}(s+\rho_n,t)\right\|\, ds\, dt}{\displaystyle\sqrt{\int\!\!\int_{]-\infty,-1]\times S^1} \left\|\frac{\partial u}{\partial s}(s+\rho_n,t)\right\|^2\, ds\, dt}}
$$
$$
= M_n \frac{\displaystyle\int_{]-\infty,-1+\rho_n]\times S^1} \left\|\frac{\partial u}{\partial s}(s,t)\right\|\, ds\, dt}{\displaystyle\sqrt{\int\!\!\int_{]-\infty,-1+\rho_n]\times S^1} \left\|\frac{\partial u}{\partial s}(s,t)\right\|^2\, ds\, dt}}.
$$

The numerator of the last fraction can be bounded from above by

$$
\int_{]-\infty,-1+\rho_n]\times S^1} \left\|\frac{\partial u}{\partial s}(s,t)\right\|\, ds\, dt \leq \left\|\frac{\partial u}{\partial s}\right\|_{L^1(\mathbf{R}\times S^1;\mathbf{R}^{2n})}
$$

and its denominator can be bounded from below by

$$
\sqrt{\int\!\!\int_{]-\infty,-1+\rho_n]\times S^1} \left\|\frac{\partial u}{\partial s}(s,t)\right\|^2\, ds\, dt} \geq \left\|\frac{\partial u}{\partial s}\right\|_{L^2(]-\infty,0]\times S^1;\mathbf{R}^{2n})}.
$$

Let

$$K_1 = \frac{\left\|\dfrac{\partial u}{\partial s}\right\|_{L^1(\mathbf{R} \times S^1; \mathbf{R}^{2n})}}{\left\|\dfrac{\partial u}{\partial s}\right\|_{L^2(]-\infty,0] \times S^1; \mathbf{R}^{2n})}},$$

so that we have

$$\int_{]-\infty,-1] \times S^1} |\alpha_n| \left\|\frac{\partial u}{\partial s}(s + \rho_n, t)\right\| ds\, dt \le K_1 \left\|\chi_n\right\|_{L^2}.$$

Like K_1, all constants $K_i > 0$ below are independent of n. In the same manner, we have

$$\int_{[1,+\infty[\times S^1} |\beta_n| \left\|\frac{\partial v}{\partial s}(s - \nu(\rho_n), t)\right\| ds\, dt \le K_2 \left\|\chi_n\right\|_{L^2(\mathbf{R} \times S^1; \mathbf{R}^{2n})}$$

for the third term. The middle term can be bounded from above by simply using the Cauchy–Schwarz inequality:

$$\int_{[-1,1] \times S^1} \left\|\chi_n\right\| ds\, dt \le K_3 \left\|\chi_n\right\|_{L^2([-1,1] \times S^1; \mathbf{R}^{2n})} \le K_3 \left\|\chi_n\right\|_{L^2(\mathbf{R} \times S^1; \mathbf{R}^{2n})}.$$

We thus obtain

$$\left\|\chi_n\right\|_{L^1} \le K_4 \left\|\chi_n\right\|_{L^2},$$

so that for $n \ge N_\varepsilon$, we have

$$\left\|\chi_n\right\|_{L^2}^2 \le M K_4 \varepsilon \left\|\chi_n\right\|_{L^2}, \quad \text{hence } \left\|\chi_n\right\|_{L^2} \le M K_4 \varepsilon,$$

and therefore

$$\lim_{n \to +\infty} \left\|\chi_n\right\|_{L^2} = 0 \text{ and finally } \lim_{n \to +\infty} \left\|\chi_n\right\|_{L^1} = 0.$$

Returning to the decomposition of χ_n, it follows that

$$\lim_{n \to +\infty} \int_{]-\infty,1] \times S^1} |\alpha_n| \left\|\frac{\partial u}{\partial s}(s + \rho_n, t)\right\| = 0,$$

hence $\lim_{n \to +\infty} \alpha_n = 0$ and likewise $\lim_{n \to +\infty} \beta_n = 0$. Consequently,

$$\left\|\chi_n\right\|_{W^{1,p}} \le |\alpha_n| \left\|\frac{\partial u}{\partial s} \#_{w_n} 0\right\|_{W^{1,p}} + |\beta_n| \left\|0 \#_{w_n} \frac{\partial v}{\partial s}\right\|_{W^{1,p}}$$

tends to 0 because the $W^{1,p}$ norms of the two vectors of the basis of W_n we use are obviously bounded (uniformly with respect to n). This concludes the proof of Lemma 9.6.14.   □

The second lemma (used in the proof of the uniqueness of the gluing) that we want to prove here is the following.

Lemma (Lemma 9.6.15). *There exist positive constants K_1 and K_2 such that for every $n \in \mathbf{N}$,*

$$\|Y_n\|_{W^{1,p}} \le K_1 \frac{\|\chi_n\|_{W^{1,p}} + \|Y_n\|_{L^\infty} + \|\widetilde{\mathcal{F}}(0)\|_{L^p}}{1 - K_2 \|Y_n\|_{L^\infty}}.$$

We of course use the notation defined near Lemma 9.6.15. Recall that $\zeta_n \in W^{1,p}(\mathbf{R} \times S^1; \mathbf{R}^{2n})$ can be decomposed into $\chi_n + \omega_n$, where χ_n is of the form $\alpha \#_{\omega_n} \beta$ ($\alpha \in \operatorname{Ker} L^u$, $\beta \in \operatorname{Ker} L^v$) and ω_n is orthogonal to the vectors of this form (see p. 352).

Proof. The constants C_i below are independent of n. We have

$$\|Y_n\|_{W^{1,p}} = \|i(\zeta_n)\|_{W^{1,p}} \le C_1 \|\zeta_n\|_{W^{1,p}} = C_1 \|\chi_n + \omega_n\|_{W^{1,p}}$$
$$\le C_1 \left(\|\chi_n\|_{W^{1,p}} + \|\omega_n\|_{W^{1,p}} \right),$$

where we have used the fact that $\|i\|$ is bounded (independently of n), which we proved on p. 480. We apply Proposition 9.4.7 to $\omega_n \in W_n^\perp$ and find

$$\|Y_n\|_{W^{1,p}} \le C_1 \left(\|\chi_n\|_{W^{1,p}} + \|\omega_n\|_{W^{1,p}} \right)$$
$$\le C_1 \|\chi_n\|_{W^{1,p}} + C_2 \|L(\omega_n)\|_{L^p}$$
$$= C_1 \|\chi_n\|_{W^{1,p}} + C_2 \|L(\zeta_n - \chi_n)\|_{L^p}$$
$$\le C_1 \|\chi_n\|_{W^{1,p}} + C_2 \|L(\zeta_n)\|_{L^p} + C_2 \|L(\chi_n)\|_{L^p}.$$

The norm of the linear operator L is bounded from above by a constant that does not depend on n. Indeed, $L = (dF)_0$ for $F = p \circ (\operatorname{Id} \times \widetilde{\mathcal{F}}) \circ i$. For the operators that occur in this composition, we have verified conditions (2) and (4) of Lemma 13.5.1, exactly what we need to conclude that the norm $\|(dF)_0\|$ of the differential of the composition is uniformly bounded. We must however stress that these results were obtained for the pre-gluing w_ρ and not for a pre-gluing of the form $w_{\nu,\rho}$. The readers can verify that in the more general case, the arguments are similar in all details.

Let us return to the estimate we just obtained for the norm of Y_n. From the above, we deduce that

$$\|Y_n\|_{W^{1,p}} \le C_1 \|\chi_n\|_{W^{1,p}} + C_2 \|L(\zeta_n)\|_{L^p} + C_3 \|\chi_n\|_{W^{1,p}}$$
$$= (C_1 + C_3) \|\chi_n\|_{W^{1,p}} + C_2 \|L(\zeta_n)\|_{L^p}.$$

By Lemma 9.6.14, we know that the first term tends to 0. We still need to bound the L^p norm of $L(\zeta_n)$. We have

$$
\begin{aligned}
L(\zeta_n) = (dF)_0(\zeta_n) &= (d(p \circ (\mathrm{Id} \times \widetilde{\mathcal{F}}) \circ i))_0(\zeta_n) \\
&= (d(p \circ (\mathrm{Id} \times \widetilde{\mathcal{F}})))_0 i(\zeta_n) \\
&= (d(p \circ (\mathrm{Id} \times \widetilde{\mathcal{F}})))_0(Y_n) \\
&= (D_1 p)_{(0, \widetilde{\mathcal{F}}(0))}(Y_n) + (D_2 p)_{(0, \widetilde{\mathcal{F}}(0))}(d\widetilde{\mathcal{F}})_0(Y_n).
\end{aligned}
$$

The map $p = p_\rho$ (which now depends on n),

$$
p : W^{1,p}(\mathbf{R} \times S^1 ; \mathbf{R}^m) \times L^p(\mathbf{R} \times S^1 ; \mathbf{R}^m) \longrightarrow L^p(\mathbf{R} \times S^1 ; \mathbf{R}^{2n}),
$$

is defined by the formula

$$
p((X, Y))_i(s, t) = P(w_n(s, t), X(s, t), Z_i(s, t), Y(s, t)),
$$

where the map

$$
P : W \times \mathbf{R}^m \times \mathbf{R}^m \times \mathbf{R}^m \longrightarrow \mathbf{R}^{2n}
$$

is linear in the last variable. We have proved (in the proof of Lemma 9.4.16) that for all $v, w \in W^{1,p}(\mathbf{R} \times S^1 ; \mathbf{R}^m)$, we have

$$
\left\| (D_1 p)_{(0, \widetilde{\mathcal{F}}(0))}(v) \right\|_{L^p} \leq C_4 \left\| v \right\|_{L^p} \quad \text{and} \quad \left\| (D_2 p)_{(0, \widetilde{\mathcal{F}}(0))}(w) \right\|_{L^p} \leq C_5 \left\| w \right\|_{L^p}.
$$

We can improve the first estimate slightly by noting that $\widetilde{\mathcal{F}}(0) = \mathcal{F}(w_n)$ is zero for s outside of $[-1, 1]$ (since w_n is then a Floer trajectory). Since p is linear in its second variable, it follows that for every $v \in W^{1,p}(\mathbf{R} \times S^1 ; \mathbf{R}^m)$, we have

$$
\forall (s, t) \in (\mathbf{R} - [-1, 1]) \times S^1, \quad (D_1 p)_{(0, \widetilde{\mathcal{F}}(0))} v(s, t) = 0.
$$

The argument used in the proof of Lemma 9.4.16 then gives

$$
\left\| (D_1 p)_{(0, \widetilde{\mathcal{F}}(0))} v \right\|_{L^p} \leq C_4 \left\| v \right\|_{L^p([-1,1] \times S^1 ; \mathbf{R}^m)}.
$$

Using these remarks, we give a bound for $\| L(\zeta_n) \|_{L^p}$:

$$
\begin{aligned}
\| L(\zeta_n) \|_{L^p} &\leq \left\| (D_1 p)_{(0, \widetilde{\mathcal{F}}(0))}(Y_n) \right\|_{L^p} + \left\| (D_2 p)_{(0, \widetilde{\mathcal{F}}(0))}(d\widetilde{\mathcal{F}})_0(Y_n) \right\|_{L^p} \\
&\leq C_4 \| Y_n \|_{L^p([-1,1] \times S^1 ; \mathbf{R}^m)} + C_5 \left\| (d\widetilde{\mathcal{F}})_0(Y_n) \right\|_{L^p(\mathbf{R} \times S^1 ; \mathbf{R}^m)} \\
&\leq C_6 \| Y_n \|_{L^\infty([-1,1] \times S^1 ; \mathbf{R}^m)} + C_5 \left\| (d\widetilde{\mathcal{F}})_0(Y_n) \right\|_{L^p(\mathbf{R} \times S^1 ; \mathbf{R}^m)} \\
&\leq C_6 \| Y_n \|_{L^\infty(\mathbf{R} \times S^1 ; \mathbf{R}^m)} + C_5 \left\| (d\widetilde{\mathcal{F}})_0(Y_n) \right\|_{L^p(\mathbf{R} \times S^1 ; \mathbf{R}^m)}.
\end{aligned}
$$

The first term tends to 0 by Proposition 9.6.3. For the second term, recall that $\widetilde{\ell}_n = \exp_{w_n} Y_n$, so that $\widetilde{\mathcal{F}}(Y_n) = \mathcal{F}(\ell_n) = 0$ because ℓ_n is a Floer trajectory. Let us write a Taylor-type formula for $\widetilde{\mathcal{F}}$, similar to the one we wrote for F in order to apply the Newton–Picard method (Lemma 9.4.4) to it. We have

$$\widetilde{\mathcal{F}}(Y) = \widetilde{\mathcal{F}}(0) + (d\widetilde{\mathcal{F}})_0(Y) + \mathcal{N}(Y),$$

where $\mathcal{N} : W^{1,p}(\mathbf{R} \times S^1; \mathbf{R}^m) \to L^p(\mathbf{R} \times S^1; \mathbf{R}^m)$ satisfies

$$\mathcal{N}(0) = 0 \quad \text{and} \quad (d\mathcal{N})_Z = (d\widetilde{\mathcal{F}})_Z - (d\widetilde{\mathcal{F}})_0.$$

Applied to $Y = Y_n$, this gives

$$0 = \widetilde{\mathcal{F}}(0) + (d\widetilde{\mathcal{F}})_0(Y_n) + \mathcal{N}(Y_n).$$

This is what we use to give an upper bound for the second term in the inequality above. Here is another lemma.

Lemma 13.7.1. *There exist constants $C_7 > 0$ and $r_1 > 0$ such that for every $Y \in W^{1,p}(\mathbf{R} \times S^1; \mathbf{R}^{2n})$, if $\|Y\|_{L^\infty} \leq r_1$, then*

$$\|\mathcal{N}(Y)\|_{L^p} \leq C_7 \|Y\|_{L^\infty} \|Y\|_{W^{1,p}}.$$

Let us admit this lemma for the moment. We then have

$$\left\|(d\widetilde{\mathcal{F}})_0(Y_n)\right\|_{L^p} = \left\|\widetilde{\mathcal{F}}(0) + \mathcal{N}(Y_n)\right\|_{L^p} \leq \left\|\widetilde{\mathcal{F}}(0)\right\|_{L^p} + \|\mathcal{N}(Y_n)\|_{L^p}.$$

Since $\|Y_n\|_{L^\infty}$ tends to 0, we can apply the lemma for n sufficiently large. This gives

$$\left\|(d\widetilde{\mathcal{F}})_0(Y_n)\right\|_{L^p} \leq \left\|\widetilde{\mathcal{F}}(0)\right\|_{L^p} + C_7 \|Y_n\|_{L^\infty} \|Y_n\|_{W^{1,p}}.$$

Combining the upper bounds for the $W^{1,p}$ norm of Y_n, for the L^p norm of $L(\zeta_n)$ and the one we just obtained, we find that for n sufficiently large,

$$\begin{aligned}
\|Y_n\|_{W^{1,p}} &\leq (C_1 + C_3) \|\chi_n\|_{W^{1,p}} + C_2 \|L(\zeta_n)\|_{L^p} \\
&\leq (C_1 + C_3) \|\chi_n\|_{W^{1,p}} + C_8 \|Y_n\|_{L^\infty} + C_9 \left\|(d\widetilde{\mathcal{F}})_0(Y_n)\right\|_{L^p} \\
&\leq (C_1 + C_3) \|\chi_n\|_{W^{1,p}} + C_8 \|Y_n\|_{L^\infty} \\
&\qquad + C_9 \left\|\widetilde{\mathcal{F}}(0)\right\|_{L^p} + C_{10} \|Y_n\|_{L^\infty} \|Y_n\|_{W^{1,p}},
\end{aligned}$$

which implies that

$$\|Y_n\|_{W^{1,p}} \leq \frac{(C_1 + C_3) \|\chi_n\|_{W^{1,p}} + C_8 \|Y_n\|_{L^\infty} + C_9 \left\|\widetilde{\mathcal{F}}(0)\right\|_{L^p}}{1 - C_{10} \|Y_n\|_{L^\infty}}. \qquad \square$$

We still need to prove Lemma 13.7.1.

Proof of Lemma 13.7.1. We have

$$
\|\mathcal{N}(Y)\|_{L^p} = \|\mathcal{N}(Y) - \mathcal{N}(0)\|_{L^p} = \left\|\int_0^1 \frac{\partial}{\partial \sigma}\mathcal{N}(\sigma Y)\, d\sigma\right\|_{L^p}
$$

$$
= \left\|\int_0^1 (d\mathcal{N})_{\sigma Y}(Y)\, d\sigma\right\|_{L^p}
$$

$$
\le \left\|\int_0^1 \|(d\mathcal{N})_{\sigma Y}(Y)\|\, d\sigma\right\|_{L^p}
$$

$$
= \left\|\int_0^1 \|((d\widetilde{\mathcal{F}})_{\sigma Y} - (d\widetilde{\mathcal{F}})_0)Y\|\, d\sigma\right\|_{L^p}.
$$

We fix a pair $(s,t) \in \mathbf{R} \times S^1$. When we verified condition (3) of Lemma 13.5.1 (p. 496), we obtained estimates for the Euclidean norm $\|((d\widetilde{\mathcal{F}})_X - (d\widetilde{\mathcal{F}})_0)(v)(s,t)\|$. These estimates hold for $\|X(s,t)\| \le r_1$ for some $r_1 > 0$. We take up these estimates again, after first noting that they hold for $w_n = w_{\nu,\rho_n}$ even if they were obtained for $w_\rho = w_{\mathrm{Id},\rho}$. We must therefore prove that for $\|X(s,t)\| < r_1$, there exists a $K > 0$ such that

$$
\|((d\widetilde{\mathcal{F}})_X - (d\widetilde{\mathcal{F}})_0)v(s,t)\| \le K\,\|X(s,t)\|\,\|v(s,t)\|
$$

$$
+ \left\|\frac{\partial X}{\partial s}(s,t)\right\|\,\|v(s,t)\| + \left\|\frac{\partial X}{\partial t}(s,t)\right\|\,\|v(s,t)\|
$$

$$
+ \|X(s,t)\|\,\left\|\frac{\partial v}{\partial s}(s,t)\right\| + \|X(s,t)\|\,\left\|\frac{\partial v}{\partial t}(s,t)\right\|.
$$

We replace X by σY and v by Y to find that for a constant C_7 that does not depend on n and for $\|Y\|_{L^\infty} < r_1$, we have

$$
\|\mathcal{N}(Y)\|_{L^p} \le \left\|\int_0^1 C_7\sigma\Big(\|Y(s,t)\|^2\right.
$$

$$
+ \|Y(s,t)\|\left\|\frac{\partial Y}{\partial s}(s,t)\right\| + \|Y(s,t)\|\left\|\frac{\partial Y}{\partial t}(s,t)\right\|\Big)\, d\sigma\bigg\|_{L^p}
$$

$$
\le C_7\Big\|\|Y(s,t)\|\Big(\|Y(s,t)\| + \left\|\frac{\partial Y}{\partial s}(s,t)\right\| + \left\|\frac{\partial Y}{\partial t}(s,t)\right\|\Big)\Big\|_{L^p}
$$

$$
\le C_7\,\|Y\|_{L^\infty}\Big\|\Big(\|Y\| + \left\|\frac{\partial Y}{\partial s}\right\| + \left\|\frac{\partial Y}{\partial t}\right\|\Big)\Big\|_{L^p}
$$

$$
\le C_7\,\|Y\|_{L^\infty}\,\|Y\|_{W^{1,p}},
$$

proving Lemma 13.7.1. $\square$

13.8 Variants with Parameter(s) of the Lemmas on the Second Derivative

In this section we give different versions with parameter(s) of the lemmas on the second derivative of the Floer operator used earlier.

For the proof of Theorem 11.2.2, we needed a variant of Lemma 9.4.16 on the second derivative of the Floer operator: we needed to take into account that H and J depend on the parameter ρ used for the gluing. That is what we will now do.

To verify the conditions of Lemma 13.5.1, we proved that there exists a constant C_1 such that for all s, t with $\|X(s,t)\| \leq r_1$ and every ρ,

$$\left\| \frac{\partial \widetilde{\mathcal{F}}_\rho}{\partial \rho}(X) - \frac{\partial \widetilde{\mathcal{F}}_\rho}{\partial \rho}(0) \right\| \leq C_1 \left(\|X\| + \left\| \frac{\partial X}{\partial s} \right\| + \left\| \frac{\partial X}{\partial t} \right\| \right).$$

The formula computing the derivative $\partial \widetilde{\mathcal{F}}_\rho(X)$ contains two new terms due to the dependence of J and H on ρ; these are

$$P(X) = \frac{\partial J}{\partial \rho}(s + \rho) \left(D_1 \widetilde{\exp}_{(w_\rho, X)} \left(\frac{\partial w_\rho}{\partial t} \right) + D_2 \widetilde{\exp}_{(w_\rho, X)} \left(\frac{\partial X}{\partial t} \right) \right)$$

and $\quad Q(X) = \operatorname{grad} \dfrac{\partial H_{s+\rho,t}}{\partial \rho} \left(\widetilde{\exp}(w_\rho, X) \right).$

Lemma 13.2.3 gives

$$\|P(X) - P(0)\| \leq C \left(\|X\| + \left\| \frac{\partial X}{\partial t} \right\| \right).$$

Next, for every pair (s,t),

$$(w_\rho(s,t), \sigma X(s,t)) \in W \times \overline{B}(0,r) \ \text{(a compact set)}$$

and

$$\frac{\partial H_{s+\rho}}{\partial \rho} = 0 \quad \text{for } |s + \rho| \geq R.$$

Consequently,

$$\left\| \left(d \operatorname{grad} \frac{\partial H_{s+\rho,t}}{\partial \rho} \right)_{\widetilde{\exp}(p,X)} \right\|$$

is bounded on the compact set $[-R, R] \times S^1 \times W \times \overline{B}(0,r)$, so that finally

$$\|Q(X) - Q(0)\| \leq \sup_{\sigma \in [0,1]} \left\| \left(d \operatorname{grad} \frac{\partial H_{s+\rho,t}}{\partial \rho} \right)_{\widetilde{\exp}(w_\rho, \sigma X)} \cdot D_2 \widetilde{\exp}_{(w_\rho, \sigma X)} \right\|$$

$$\leq C \|X\|,$$

which allows us to find the desired estimate and to conclude the proof.

We will also prove the variant of Lemma 9.4.8 that we needed in Section 11.4.b, which is as follows.

Lemma (Lemma 11.4.5). *Let $r_0 > 0$. There exists a constant $K > 0$ such that for every $\rho \geq \rho_0$ and every $(\lambda, Z) \in \mathbf{R} \times W^{1,p}(\mathbf{R} \times S^1; \mathbf{R}^{2n})$ (with $\|Z\| \leq r_0$), we have*

$$\left\|(d\overline{F}_\rho)_{(\lambda, Z)} - (d\overline{F}_\rho)_{(0,0)}\right\|^{\mathrm{op}} \leq K(\|Z\|_{W^{1,p}} + |\lambda|).$$

Proof. We have

$$\left\|(d\overline{F}_\rho)_{(\lambda, Z)} - (d\overline{F}_\rho)_{(0,0)}\right\|^{\mathrm{op}} \leq \left\|(d\overline{F}_\rho)_{(\lambda, Z)} - (d\overline{F}_\rho)_{(\lambda, 0)}\right\|^{\mathrm{op}}$$
$$+ \left\|(d\overline{F}_\rho)_{(\lambda, 0)} - (d\overline{F}_\rho)_{(0,0)}\right\|^{\mathrm{op}}.$$

Let us analyze the two terms on the right-hand side separately. We begin with the first one. Let $(a, Y) \in \mathbf{R} \times W^{1,p}(\mathbf{R} \times S^1; \mathbf{R}^{2n})$. We have

$$(d\overline{F}_\rho)_{(\lambda, Z)}(a, Y) = (d\overline{F}_\rho)_{(\lambda, Z)}(0, Y) + (d\overline{F}_\rho)_{(\lambda, Z)}(a, 0)$$
$$= (dF_\rho^{\Gamma_{\lambda + \lambda_\star}})_Z(Y) + \frac{\partial}{\partial\sigma}\Big|_{\sigma = \lambda}\left(\mathcal{F}_\rho^{\Gamma_{\lambda + \lambda_\star + a\sigma}}(\exp_{w_\rho}(Z))\right)_{(Z_i^{\rho, Z})}$$
$$= (dF_\rho^{\Gamma_{\lambda + \lambda_\star}})_Z(Y) + a\left(\frac{\partial J}{\partial\lambda}(\lambda + \lambda_\star, s + \rho)\frac{\partial(\exp_{w_\rho} Z)}{\partial t}\right.$$
$$\left. + \mathrm{grad}_{\exp_{w_\rho}(Z)}\frac{\partial H}{\partial\lambda}(\lambda + \lambda_\star, s + \rho, t)\right)_{(Z_i^{\rho, Z})}$$

(expressions in which $(Z_i^{\rho, Z})$ denotes the orthonormal frame at the point $\exp_{w_\rho(s,t)} Z(s, t)$, obtained by parallel transport of the frame $(Z_i^\rho(s, t))$ along the curve $r \mapsto \exp_{w_\rho(s,t)}(rZ(s, t))$).

We use the notation

$$d\overline{F}_\rho(\lambda, Z)(a, 0) = a\left(V_\rho(\lambda + \lambda_\star, Z)\right)_{(Z_i^{\rho, Z})}$$

and note that $V_\rho(\lambda_\star, 0)$ is the vector field V_ρ that occurs in the formula computing $L_\rho^\Gamma(a, 0)$.

To bound $\|(d\overline{F}_\rho)_{(\lambda, Z)} - (d\overline{F}_\rho)_{(\lambda, 0)}\|^{\mathrm{op}}$ from above, we write

$$\left\|(d\overline{F}_\rho)_{(\lambda, Z)}(a, Y) - (d\overline{F}_\rho)_{(\lambda, 0)}(a, Y)\right\|_{L^p}$$
$$\leq \left\|(dF_\rho^{\Gamma_{\lambda + \lambda_\star}})_Z(Y) - (dF_\rho^{\Gamma_{\lambda + \lambda_\star}})_0(Y)\right\|_{L^p}$$
$$+ |a|\left\|(V_\rho(\lambda + \lambda_\star, Z))_{(Z_i^{\rho, Z})} - (V_\rho(\lambda + \lambda_\star, 0))_{(Z_i^{\rho, Z})}\right\|_{L^p}.$$

To bound the first term of this sum, we use Lemma 9.4.8, or more precisely its analogue for the pair (H, J) defined by the homotopy $\Gamma_{\lambda + \lambda_\star}$. We have already evoked the possibility of this analogy in the proof of Theorem 11.2.2. We have

$$\left\| (dF_\rho^{\Gamma_{\lambda+\lambda_\star}})_Z(Y) - (dF_\rho^{\Gamma_{\lambda+\lambda_\star}})_0(Y) \right\|_{L^p} \le k_1 \|Z\|_{W^{1,p}} \|Y\|_{W^{1,p}}$$

for a constant $k_1 > 0$ that does not depend on ρ. To bound the remaining term, we view $V_\rho(\lambda + \lambda_\star, \bullet)$ as a map

$$W^{1,p}(\mathbf{R} \times S^1; \mathbf{R}^m) \longrightarrow L^p(\mathbf{R} \times S^1; \mathbf{R}^m),$$

and write (with the notation of Chapter 11)

$$\widetilde{V}_\rho(\lambda + \lambda_\star, Z) = \frac{\partial \widetilde{J}}{\partial \lambda}(\lambda + \lambda_\star, s + \rho) \frac{\partial(\exp_{w_\rho} Z)}{\partial t}$$

$$+ \operatorname{grad}_{\widetilde{\exp}_{w_\rho}(Z)}\left(\frac{\partial H}{\partial \lambda}(\lambda + \lambda_\star, s + \rho, t) \right)$$

$$= \frac{\partial \widetilde{J}}{\partial \lambda}(\lambda + \lambda_\star, s + \rho)\left(D_1 \widetilde{\exp}_{(w_\rho, Z)}\left(\frac{\partial w_\rho}{\partial t} \right) + D_2 \widetilde{\exp}_{(w_\rho, Z)}\left(\frac{\partial Z}{\partial t} \right) \right)$$

$$+ \operatorname{grad}_{\widetilde{\exp}(w_\rho, Z)} \frac{\partial H}{\partial \lambda}(\lambda + \lambda_\star, s + \rho, t).$$

We use the following result.

Lemma 13.8.1. *Let $r_0 > 0$. There exists a constant $K > 0$ such that for every $\rho \ge \rho_0$ and every $Z \in \overline{B}(0, r_0) \subset W^{1,p}(\mathbf{R} \times S^1; \mathbf{R}^m)$, we have*

$$\left\| \widetilde{V}_\rho(\lambda + \lambda_\star, Z) - \widetilde{V}_\rho(\lambda + \lambda_\star, 0) \right\|_{L^p} \le K \|Z\|_{W^{1,p}}.$$

Proof. Let us write

$$\left\| \widetilde{V}_\rho(\lambda + \lambda_\star, Z) - \widetilde{V}_\rho(\lambda + \lambda_\star, 0) \right\|_{L^p} \le$$

$$\le \left\| \frac{\partial \widetilde{J}}{\partial \lambda}(\lambda + \lambda_\star, s + \rho)\left[D_1 \widetilde{\exp}_{(w_\rho, Z)}\left(\frac{\partial w_\rho}{\partial t} \right) + D_2 \widetilde{\exp}_{(w_\rho, Z)}\left(\frac{\partial Z}{\partial t} \right) \right.\right.$$

$$\left.\left. - D_1 \widetilde{\exp}_{(w_\rho, 0)}\left(\frac{\partial w_\rho}{\partial t} \right) \right] \right\|_{L^p}$$

$$+ \left\| \operatorname{grad}_{\widetilde{\exp}(w_\rho, Z)} \frac{\partial H}{\partial \lambda}(\lambda + \lambda_\star, s + \rho, t) - \operatorname{grad}_{\widetilde{\exp}(w_\rho, 0)} \frac{\partial H}{\partial \lambda}(\lambda + \lambda_\star, s + \rho, t) \right\|_{L^p}.$$

The map

$$\frac{\partial \widetilde{J}}{\partial \lambda} : [0, 1] \times \mathbf{R} \longrightarrow \operatorname{End}(TW)$$

has compact support. There therefore exists a constant $C > 0$ such that

$$\left\| \frac{\partial \widetilde{J}}{\partial \lambda}(\lambda, s) \right\|^{\mathrm{op}} \le C \quad \text{for every } (\lambda, s) \in [0, 1] \times \mathbf{R}.$$

The first term on the right-hand side of our inequality can therefore be bounded from above by

$$C\left\|D_1\widetilde{\exp}_{(w_\rho,Z)}\left(\frac{\partial w_\rho}{\partial t}\right) + D_2\widetilde{\exp}_{(w_\rho,Z)}\left(\frac{\partial Z}{\partial t}\right) - D_1\widetilde{\exp}_{(w_\rho,0)}\left(\frac{\partial w_\rho}{\partial t}\right)\right\|_{L^p}.$$

We apply Lemmas 13.2.3 and 13.2.2 to

$$A(p,X,V) = D_1\widetilde{\exp}_{(p,X)}V \quad \text{and} \quad A(p,X,V) = D_2\widetilde{\exp}_{(p,X)}V,$$

to bound this expression from above (using the same reasoning as in Section 13.5) by $K\|Z\|_{W^{1,p}}$.

To bound the second term (the one with the gradients), note that the $W^{1,p}$ upper bound for Z, $\|Z\|_{W^{1,p}} \leq r_0$, implies that Z is bounded, $\|Z\|_{L^\infty} \leq r_1$ (for some $r_1 > 0$). Consider the map

$$\varphi : [0,1] \times \mathbf{R} \times S^1 \times W \times \overline{B}(0,r_1) \longrightarrow \mathbf{R}^m$$
$$(\lambda,s,t,p,X) \longmapsto \operatorname{grad}_{\widetilde{\exp}_{(p,X)}}\frac{\partial H}{\partial\lambda}(\lambda,s,t).$$

It is of class $\mathcal{C}^1$ and has compact support. There therefore exists a constant $C > 0$ such that $\|d\varphi\|^{\mathrm{op}} \leq C$. It follows that for the Euclidean norm,

$$\|\varphi(\lambda+\lambda_\star,s+\rho,t,w_\rho(s,t),Z) - \varphi(\lambda+\lambda_\star,s+\rho,t,w_\rho(s,t),0)\| \leq C\|Z\|.$$

Taking the L^p norm, we deduce that the second term on the right-hand side of our inequality is bounded from above as we wished:

$$\left\|\operatorname{grad}_{\widetilde{\exp}_{(w_\rho,Z)}}\frac{\partial H}{\partial\lambda}(\lambda+\lambda_\star,s+\rho,t) - \operatorname{grad}_{\widetilde{\exp}_{(w_\rho,0)}}\frac{\partial H}{\partial\lambda}(\lambda+\lambda_\star,s+\rho,t)\right\|_{L^p}$$
$$\leq C\|Z\|_{L^p} \leq C\|Z\|_{W^{1,p}}.$$

This concludes the proof of Lemma 13.8.1.   □

But the proof of Lemma 11.4.5 is not finished yet. As in Chapter 13, we use a commutative diagram.

$$
\begin{array}{ccc}
W^{1,p}(\mathbf{R}\times S^1;\mathbf{R}^{2n}) & \xrightarrow{\ z\mapsto V_\rho(\lambda+\lambda_\star,Z)\ } & L^p(\mathbf{R}\times S^1;\mathbf{R}^{2n}) \\
\Big\downarrow{i_\rho} & & \Big\uparrow{p_\rho} \\
W^{1,p}(\mathbf{R}\times S^1;\mathbf{R}^m) & \xrightarrow[\ (\mathrm{Id},\widetilde{V}_\rho)\ ]{} & W^{1,p}(\mathbf{R}\times S^1;\mathbf{R}^m)\times L^p(\mathbf{R}\times S^1;\mathbf{R}^m)
\end{array}
$$

Let $\varphi = i_\rho$, $\psi = (\mathrm{Id},\widetilde{V}_\rho)$ and $\chi = p_\rho$. To finish establishing the desired upper bound, we need the following lemma.

Lemma 13.8.2. *There exists a constant $k_2 > 0$ (that does not depend on ρ) such that for $\|Z\|_{W^{1,p}} \leq r_0$, we have*

$$\|\chi\psi\varphi(Z) - \chi\psi\varphi(0)\|_{L^p} \leq k_2 \|Z\|_{W^{1,p}}.$$

Proof. The map φ is linear, its norm is uniformly bounded with respect to ρ, hence

$$\|\varphi(Z)\|_{W^{1,p}} \leq C r_0.$$

By Lemma 13.8.1, there exists a $K > 0$ such that

$$\|\psi\varphi(Z) - \psi\varphi(0)\|_{W^{1,p} \times L^p} = \|\varphi(Z) - \varphi(0)\|_{W^{1,p}} + \left\|\widetilde{V}_\rho(Z) - \widetilde{V}_\rho(0)\right\|_{L^p}$$
$$\leq C \|Z\|_{W^{1,p}} + K \|Z\|_{W^{1,p}}.$$

Next, we set $a = \psi(\varphi(Z))$ and $b = \psi(\varphi(0))$. We then have

$$\|\chi(a) - \chi(b)\|_{L^p} \leq \sup_{r \in [0,1]} \left\|(d\chi)_{ra+(1-r)b}\right\|^{\mathrm{op}} \|a - b\|_{L^p}$$
$$\leq \sup_{r \in [0,1]} \left\|(d\chi)_{ra+(1-r)b}\right\|^{\mathrm{op}} (C + K) \|Z\|_{W^{1,p}}.$$

Here $b = \psi(\varphi(0)) = \psi(0) = (0, \widetilde{V}_\rho(0))$ and we know that

$$\widetilde{V}_\rho(s,t) = \frac{\partial \widetilde{J}}{\partial \lambda}(\lambda + \lambda_*, s + \rho) \cdot D_1\widetilde{\exp}_{(w_\rho, Z)} \frac{\partial w_\rho}{\partial t}.$$

For a fixed triple (λ, s, t), the Euclidean norm of this vector is uniformly bounded by a constant that does not depend on ρ, which, explicitly, equals

$$\sup_{(\lambda,s) \in [0,1] \times \mathbf{R}} \left\|\frac{\partial \widetilde{J}}{\partial \lambda}\right\| \sup_{\substack{p \in W \\ \|Z\| \leq r_0}} \left\|D_1\widetilde{\exp}_{(p,Z)}\right\| \sup_{(s,t) \in S^1 \times \mathbf{R}} \left\|\frac{\partial w_\rho}{\partial t}\right\|.$$

We continue as in the proof of Lemma 13.4.1, with $\widetilde{V}_\rho$ playing the role of Y_0^ρ, and obtain

$$\left\|(d\chi)_{ra+(1-r)b} - (d\chi)_b\right\|^{\mathrm{op}} \leq k_3 r \|ra + (1-r)b - b\|_{L^p}$$
$$= k_3 r \|a - b\|_{L^p}$$
$$\leq k_3(C + K) \|Z\|_{W^{1,p}}$$
$$\leq k_3(C + K)r_0.$$

With our estimate of $\|\psi\varphi(Z) - \psi\varphi(0)\|$, we deduce from this that

$$\|\chi\psi\varphi(Z) - \chi\psi\varphi(0)\|_{L^p} \leq k_3(C + K)^2 r_0 \|Z\|_{W^{1,p}},$$

proving Lemma 13.8.2. $\qquad\square$

We now continue proving the estimate of Lemma 11.4.5. By the previous lemma (13.8.2), we have

$$\left\|(d\overline{F}_\rho)_{(\lambda,Z)}(a,Y) - (d\overline{F}_\rho)_{(\lambda,0)}(a,Y)\right\|_{L^p}$$
$$\leq k_1 \|Z\|_{W^{1,p}} \|Y\|_{W^{1,p}} + |a|\, k_2 \|Z\|_{W^{1,p}}$$
$$= (k_1 + k_2)(|a| + \|Y\|_{W^{1,p}}) \|Z\|_{W^{1,p}},$$

hence

$$\left\|(d\overline{F}_\rho)_{(\lambda,Z)} - (d\overline{F}_\rho)_{(\lambda,0)}\right\|^{\mathrm{op}} \leq (k_1 + k_2) \|Z\|_{W^{1,p}}.$$

We have thus bounded the first term on the right of the inequality:

$$\left\|(d\overline{F}_\rho)_{(\lambda,Z)} - (d\overline{F}_\rho)_{(0,0)}\right\|^{\mathrm{op}} \leq \left\|(d\overline{F}_\rho)_{(\lambda,Z)} - (d\overline{F}_\rho)_{(\lambda,0)}\right\|^{\mathrm{op}}$$
$$+ \left\|(d\overline{F}_\rho)_{(\lambda,0)} - (d\overline{F}_\rho)_{(0,0)}\right\|^{\mathrm{op}},$$

and we still need to bound the second term.

For $(a,Y) \in \mathbf{R} \times W^{1,p}(\mathbf{R} \times S^1; \mathbf{R}^{2n})$, we write

$$(d\overline{F}_\rho)_{(\lambda,0)}(a,Y) = (dF_\rho^{\Gamma_{\lambda+\lambda_\star}})_0(Y) + a(V_\rho(\lambda + \lambda_\star, 0))_{(Z_i^\rho)},$$

where

$$V_\rho(\lambda + \lambda_\star, 0) = \frac{\partial J}{\partial \lambda}(\lambda + \lambda_\star, s + \rho)\frac{\partial w_\rho}{\partial t} + \mathrm{grad}_{w_\rho}\frac{\partial H}{\partial \lambda}(\lambda + \lambda_\star, s + \rho, t).$$

We therefore have

$$\left\|(d\overline{F}_\rho)_{(\lambda,0)}(a,Y) - (d\overline{F}_\rho)_{(0,0)}(a,Y)\right\|_{L^p}$$
$$\leq \left\|(dF_\rho^{\Gamma_{\lambda+\lambda_\star}})_0(Y) - (dF_\rho^{\Gamma_{\lambda_\star}})_0(Y)\right\|_{L^p}$$
$$+ |a| \left\|(V_\rho(\lambda + \lambda_\star, 0))_{Z_i^\rho} - (V_\rho(\lambda_\star, 0))_{Z_i^\rho}\right\|_{L^p}.$$

As in Section 11.2.b (and following the example of Proposition 8.4.4),

$$(dF_\rho^{\Gamma_{\lambda+\lambda_\star}})_0(Y) = L_\rho^{\Gamma_\lambda}(Y) = \frac{\partial Y}{\partial s} + J_0\frac{\partial Y}{\partial t} + S(\lambda)Y,$$

where

$$S : [0,1] \times \mathbf{R} \times S^1 \longrightarrow M_{2n}(\mathbf{R})$$

is a map of class $\mathcal{C}^\infty$. Consequently,

$$\left\|(dF_\rho^{\Gamma_{\lambda+\lambda_\star}})_0(Y) - (dF_\rho^{\Gamma_{\lambda_\star}})_0(Y)\right\|_{L^p} = \|S(\lambda)(Y) - S(0)(Y)\|_{L^p}$$
$$\leq k_4 |\lambda| \|Y\|_{L^p}$$
$$\leq k_4 |\lambda| \|Y\|_{W^{1,p}}$$

with $k_4 = \sup_{\lambda \in [0,1]} \partial S / \partial \lambda$. Next,

$$\left\| \left(V_\rho(\lambda + \lambda_\star), 0 - V_\rho(\lambda_\star, 0) \right)_{Z_i^\rho} \right\|_{L^p}$$

$$\leq \left\| \left(\frac{\partial J}{\partial \lambda}(\lambda + \lambda_\star, s + \rho) - \frac{\partial J}{\partial \lambda}(\lambda_\star, s + \rho) \right) \left(\frac{\partial w_\rho}{\partial t} \right)_{Z_i^\rho} \right\|_{L^p}$$

$$+ \left\| \left(\operatorname{grad}_{w_\rho} \left(\frac{\partial H}{\partial \lambda}(\lambda + \lambda_\star, s + \rho, t) - \frac{\partial H}{\partial \lambda}(\lambda_\star, s + \rho, t) \right) \right)_{Z_i^\rho} \right\|_{L^p}$$

$$\leq \left(\sup_{\substack{\lambda \in [0,1] \\ s \in \mathbf{R}}} \frac{\partial^2 J}{\partial \lambda^2}(\lambda, s) \right) |\lambda| \left\| \left(\frac{\partial w_\rho}{\partial t} \right)_{Z_i^\rho} \right\|_{L^p}$$

$$+ |\lambda| \sup_{\substack{\lambda \in [0,1] \\ (s,t) \in \mathbf{R} \times S^1}} \left\| \left(\operatorname{grad}_{w_\rho} \frac{\partial^2 H}{\partial \lambda^2}(\lambda, s, t) \right)_{Z_i^\rho} \right\|_{L^p} \leq k_5 |\lambda|.$$

This leads to

$$\left\| (d\overline{F}_\rho)_{(\lambda,0)}(a, Y) - (d\overline{F}_\rho)_{(0,0)}(a, Y) \right\|_{L^p} \leq k_4 |\lambda| \, \|Y\|_{W^{1,p}} + k_5 |a| \, |\lambda| \,,$$

which shows that

$$\left\| (d\overline{F}_\rho)_{(\lambda,0)} - (d\overline{F}_\rho)_{(0,0)} \right\|^{\mathrm{op}} \leq k_6 |\lambda| \,.$$

Combining this inequality with

$$\left\| (d\overline{F}_\rho)_{(\lambda,Z)} - (d\overline{F}_\rho)_{(\lambda,0)} \right\|^{\mathrm{op}} \leq (k_1 + k_2) \, \|Z\|_{W^{1,p}} \,,$$

which we obtained earlier, we finally find

$$\left\| (d\overline{F}_\rho)_{(\lambda,Z)} - (d\overline{F}_\rho)_{(0,0)} \right\|^{\mathrm{op}} \leq (k_1 + k_2) \, \|Z\|_{W^{1,p}} + k_6 |\lambda|$$

$$\leq k(\|Z\|_{W^{1,p}} + |\lambda|),$$

which is what we needed to conclude the proof of Lemma 11.4.5. $\qquad \square$

In Section 11.2.c, to establish the desired properties of ψ, we used the following statement, which it is now time to prove.

Lemma (Lemma 11.4.7). *There exists a constant $C > 0$ that does not depend on ρ, such that for $\rho \geq \rho_0$, we have*

$$\left\| \frac{\partial \overline{F}_\rho}{\partial \rho}(\overline{\lambda}_\rho, \gamma_\rho) - \frac{\partial \overline{F}_\rho}{\partial \rho}(0, 0) \right\|_{L^p} \leq C \, \|(\overline{\lambda}_\rho, \gamma_\rho)\|_{\mathbf{R} \times W^{1,p}} \,.$$

Proof. We apply Lemma 9.4.16 to the operators F^{Γ_λ} for $\lambda \in [0,1]$ (see the proof of Theorem 11.2.2). Consequently, for $Z \in \overline{B}(0,r_0)$, we have

$$\left\|\frac{\partial F^{\Gamma_\lambda}}{\partial \rho}(\rho, Z) - \frac{\partial F^{\Gamma_\lambda}}{\partial \rho}(\rho, 0)\right\|_{L^p} \leq M \|Z\|_{W^{1,p}}$$

for a constant $M > 0$ that does not depend on ρ (nor on λ because $\lambda \in [0,1]$). In particular, since $\overline{F}_\rho(\lambda, Z) = F_\rho^{\Gamma_{\lambda+\lambda_*}}(Z)$, we have

$$\left\|\frac{\partial \overline{F}_\rho}{\partial \rho}(\overline{\lambda}_\rho, \gamma_\rho) - \frac{\partial \overline{F}_\rho}{\partial \rho}(\overline{\lambda}_\rho, 0)\right\|_{L^p} \leq M \|\gamma_\rho\|_{W^{1,p}}.$$

To conclude the proof of the lemma, it suffices to show the existence of a constant $C \geq 0$ that does not depend on ρ such that

$$\left\|\frac{\partial \overline{F}_\rho}{\partial \rho}(\overline{\lambda}_\rho, 0) - \frac{\partial \overline{F}_\rho}{\partial \rho}(0, 0)\right\|_{L^p} \leq C \left|\overline{\lambda}_\rho\right|.$$

For arbitrary $\lambda \in \mathbf{R}$, we have

$$\overline{F}_\rho(\lambda, 0) = \left(\mathcal{F}_\rho^{\Gamma_{\lambda+\lambda_*}}(w_\rho)\right)_{Z_i^\rho}$$
$$= \left(\frac{\partial w_\rho}{\partial s} + J_{s+\rho}^{\lambda+\lambda_*}(w_\rho)\frac{\partial w_\rho}{\partial t} + \operatorname{grad} H_{s+\rho,t}^{\lambda+\lambda_*}(w_\rho)\right)_{Z_i^\rho}.$$

Let $\chi(\rho, \lambda) = \overline{F}_\rho(\lambda, 0) \in L^p(\mathbf{R}\times S^1; \mathbf{R}^{2n})$. The function (of (s,t)) $\partial\chi/\partial\lambda(\rho, \lambda)$ has compact support. Indeed, the derivatives of $J_{s+\rho}^{\lambda+\lambda_*}$ and $\operatorname{grad} H_{s+\rho,t}^{\lambda+\lambda_*}$ with respect to λ are zero when $|s + \rho| \geq R$ because the isotopies Γ_λ are constant for $|s| \geq R$. Hence $\partial^2\chi/\partial\rho\partial\lambda$ also has compact support as a function of (s,t). It follows that

$$\left\|\frac{\partial\chi}{\partial\rho}(\rho, \lambda) - \frac{\partial\chi}{\partial\rho}(\rho, 0)\right\|_{L^p} \leq |\lambda| \cdot \left\|\sup_\lambda \frac{\partial^2\chi}{\partial\rho\partial\lambda}\right\|_{L^p}$$
$$= |\lambda| \cdot \left\|\sup_\lambda \frac{\partial^2\chi}{\partial\rho\partial\lambda}\right\|_{L^p([-R-\rho, R-\rho]\times S^1; \mathbf{R}^{2n})}$$
$$\leq K |\lambda| \cdot \sup_{\substack{\lambda\in\mathbf{R} \\ \rho\geq\rho_0 \\ (s,t)\in[-R-\rho, R-\rho]\times S^1}} \left\|\frac{\partial^2\chi}{\partial\rho\partial\lambda}(s,t)\right\|$$

(the norm in the last term is the Euclidean norm of $\mathbf{R}^{2n}$). Like the norm of $\partial w_\rho/\partial t$, the norms of the Z_i^ρ and their derivatives with respect to ρ are bounded by constants that do not depend on ρ. The same holds for the derivatives of $J_{s+\rho}^{\lambda+\lambda_*}$ and $\operatorname{grad} H_{s+\rho}^{\lambda+\lambda_*}$ with respect to ρ and λ. It follows that $\partial^2\chi/\partial\rho\,\partial\lambda$ is bounded (for the Euclidean norm) for $(\lambda, \rho, s, t) \in \mathbf{R} \times [\rho_0, +\infty[\times \mathbf{R} \times S^1$, concluding the proof of Lemma 11.4.7. $\square$

Chapter 14
Exercises for the Second Part

As its title may suggest, this chapter contains exercises on the second part (of this book).

14.1 Exercises on Chapter 5

Exercise 1. Let E be a symplectic vector space of dimension $2n$. If F is a subset of E, then we let F° denote the orthogonal vector subspace for the symplectic form, which consists of all vectors x such that $\omega(x, y) = 0$ for every $y \in F$.

For a subspace F of E, show that

$$\dim F + \dim F^\circ = \dim E.$$

We call F *isotropic* if the form ω is zero on F, that is, if $F \subset F^\circ$. What can we say about the dimension of F? We call F *Lagrangian* if F is isotropic and $\dim F = n$.

Let F be a "co-isotropic" subspace (that is, one whose orthogonal is isotropic). Show that ω induces a symplectic form on the quotient vector space F/F°. Let L be a Lagrangian subspace of E such that $L + F = E$. Show that the composition

$$L \cap F \subset F \longrightarrow F/F^\circ$$

is the injection of a Lagrangian subspace.

Exercise 2. Let V be a manifold and let η be a 1-form on V. We can view η as a section

$$\eta : V \longrightarrow T^\star V$$

M. Audin, M. Damian, *Morse Theory and Floer Homology*,
Universitext, DOI 10.1007/978-1-4471-5496-9_14,
© Springer-Verlag London 2014

of the cotangent bundle. If λ denotes the Liouville form on T^*V, then what is the form $\eta^*\lambda$ on V?

Exercise 3 (Lagrangian submanifolds). If (W, ω) is a symplectic manifold of dimension $2n$, then we call a submanifold $j : L \subset W$ *Lagrangian* if $\dim L = n$ and $j^*\omega = 0$.

(1) Prove that in a symplectic surface, all curves are Lagrangian.
(2) Prove that if L_1 is Lagrangian in W_1 and L_2 is Lagrangian in W_2, then $L_1 \times L_2$ is Lagrangian in $W_1 \times W_2$. Construct a Lagrangian torus T^n in $\mathbf{R}^{2n}$. Prove that every symplectic manifold contains Lagrangian tori.
(3) Let η be a 1-form on a manifold V. We view η as a section of T^*V (as in Exercise 2 on p. 515). Prove that the image of η is a Lagrangian submanifold if and only if the form η is closed.
(4) Let f be a $\mathcal{C}^\infty$ function on a compact manifold V. By the above, the 1-form df defines a Lagrangian submanifold of T^*V. Prove that it meets the zero section.
(5) Consider the product manifold $W \times W$ endowed with the symplectic form $\omega \oplus (-\omega)$. Prove that the diagonal is a Lagrangian submanifold. Let φ be a diffeomorphism from W into itself. Under what condition on φ is the graph of φ a Lagrangian submanifold of $W \times W$?

Exercise 4. Let w be a $\mathcal{C}^\infty$ map from the sphere S^2 to the cotangent space T^*V of a manifold V. Show that

$$\int_{S^2} w^*\omega = 0.$$

Exercise 5. Let ω be a symplectic form on a compact surface Σ. Prove that Σ is oriented, and then that

$$\int_{\Sigma} \omega \neq 0.$$

Consider the inclusion $\mathbf{P}^1(\mathbf{C}) \subset \mathbf{P}^n(\mathbf{C})$ induced by the inclusion $\mathbf{C}^2 \subset \mathbf{C}^{n+1}$. Prove that it is a symplectic submanifold. Deduce that there exists a $\mathcal{C}^\infty$ map

$$w : S^2 \longrightarrow \mathbf{P}^n(\mathbf{C})$$

such that if ω now denotes the symplectic form of $\mathbf{P}^n(\mathbf{C})$, then

$$\int_{S^2} w^*\omega \neq 0.$$

Exercise 6. Let φ^1 be a Hamiltonian diffeomorphism of W. Show that the graph of φ^1 is transversal to the diagonal of $W \times W$ at (x, x) if and only if the trajectory of x is nondegenerate.

Exercise 7 (The Group of Hamiltonian Diffeomorphisms). In this exercise we consider a compact manifold W endowed with a symplectic form ω. Let $\operatorname{Ham}(W)$ denote the set of diffeomorphisms of W that are Hamiltonian flows at time 1.

(1) Suppose that the Hamiltonian H_t generates the isotopy φ_t and that the Hamiltonian K_t generates ψ_t. Let

$$G_t = H_t + K_t \circ \varphi_t^{-1}.$$

Show that

$$X_{G_t}(x) = X_{H_t}(x) + (T_{\varphi_t^{-1}(x)}\varphi_t)(X_{K_t} \circ \varphi_t^{-1}(x)).$$

Deduce from this that $\varphi_t \circ \psi_t$ is the Hamiltonian isotopy generated by the Hamiltonian[1] $H_t + K_t \circ \varphi_t^{-1}$.

(2) Describe the Hamiltonian isotopy generated by $-H_t \circ \varphi_t$.

(3) Show that the set $\operatorname{Ham}(W)$ is a subgroup of the group of symplectic diffeomorphisms of W.

(4) Let Φ be a symplectic diffeomorphism of W. Describe the Hamiltonian isotopy generated by the Hamiltonian $H_t \circ \Phi$. Prove that the subgroup $\operatorname{Ham}(W)$ is a normal subgroup of the group of all symplectic diffeomorphisms of W.

Exercise 8. Let x be a nondegenerate critical point of an autonomous Hamiltonian H on $\mathbf{R}^{2n}$. We let φ^t denote the flow of X_H. Express X_H in the coordinates (p_i, q_i). Show that the Jacobian matrix of φ^t satisfies

$$\frac{d}{dt}\left(\operatorname{Jac}_x \varphi^t\right) = (J_0 \operatorname{Hess}_x(H)) \cdot \operatorname{Jac}_x \varphi^t$$

and that consequently

$$\operatorname{Jac}_x \varphi^t = e^{t J_0 \operatorname{Hess}_x(H)}.$$

Let x be a critical point of an autonomous Hamiltonian H on a symplectic manifold W. Prove that if x is nondegenerate as a periodic trajectory, then it is nondegenerate as a critical point of H.

---

[1] Even if H and K are autonomous, the composed Hamiltonian isotopy does not (in general) come from an autonomous Hamiltonian. Bonus question: When is it the case?

Exercise 9 (Harmonic Oscillator). On the symplectic manifold $\mathbf{R}^{2n}$, we consider the Hamiltonian

$$H(q,p) = \frac{1}{2} \sum \alpha_i (p_i^2 + q_i^2),$$

where the α_i are positive real numbers, say $0 < \alpha_1 \le \alpha_2 \le \cdots \le \alpha_n$.

(1) Write down the corresponding Hamiltonian system and solve it.
(2) We suppose that all α_i/α_j are irrational. Show that the system has exactly n families of periodic solutions, each contained in a plane. We fix a solution contained in the plane with equation $(q_j = p_j = 0)_{j \ne i}$. What are the Floquet multipliers of this solution? Is it nondegenerate?
(3) We suppose that all α_i are equal. What can you say about the periodic solutions?

Exercise 10. Let E be a vector space endowed with a symplectic form ω and an almost complex structure J calibrated by ω; we let $\perp$ denote orthogonality for the inner product $\omega(\cdot, J\cdot)$. Show that a subspace L is Lagrangian if and only if $L^\perp = JL$.

Exercise 11. Let (W, ω) be a symplectic manifold and let J be an almost complex structure calibrated by ω. Let $V \subset W$ be a complex submanifold, that is, one that is stable under J:

$$\forall x \in V, \quad J_x(T_x V) \subset T_x V.$$

Verify that ω defines a nondegenerate form on V.

Exercise 12 (Complex, but not Symplectic). Consider the map

$$f : \mathbf{C}^2 \longrightarrow \mathbf{C}^2$$
$$(z_1, z_2) \longmapsto (2z_1, 2z_2)$$

and the quotient $\mathcal{H}$ ("Hopf surface") of $\mathbf{C}^2 - \{0\}$ for the action of $\mathbf{Z}$ given by

$$n \cdot (z_1, z_2) = f^n(z_1, z_2).$$

Show that the quotient is a complex manifold (that is, with complex analytic transition maps) that is diffeomorphic to $S^3 \times S^1$. Consequently, its second de Rham cohomology group is zero. Deduce that $\mathcal{H}$ does not have any symplectic structure.[2]

---

[2] In [18], you can find examples of manifolds that are symplectic but not complex.

Exercise 13 (Cayley Numbers and Almost Complex Structures).
Recall that the algebra of *Cayley numbers* or *octaves* is a real vector space $\mathbf{O}$
of dimension 8, endowed with a basis that we denote by

$$(1, i, j, k, \ell, \ell i, \ell j, \ell k)$$

and with multiplication (that is right and left distributive over addition)
defined by

$$i^2 = j^2 = k^2 = \ell^2 = ijk = jki = kij = -1, \quad i\ell = -\ell i, \text{ etc.}$$

Recall that this multiplication is neither commutative nor associative (because $(ij)\ell = -i(j\ell)$), but that it does satisfy $(ab)b = a(bb)$ for all a and b.

Consider the Euclidean space $\mathbf{R}^7$ of imaginary octaves, that is, the sub-
space generated by $(i, j, k, \ell i, \ell j, \ell k)$. Let $V \subset \mathbf{R}^7$ be an oriented submanifold
of dimension 6. For any point x of V, we let $n(x)$ denote the unitary normal
vector (defined by the orientations of V and $\mathbf{R}^7$) and we define

$$J_x : T_x V \longrightarrow \mathbf{R}^7$$

by setting $J_x(u) = n(x) \cdot u$ (multiplication in the sense of octaves). Show
that J_x has values in $T_x V$ and that the endomorphisms J_x define an almost
complex structure J on V. In this way, all hypersurfaces of $\mathbf{R}^7$ are almost
complex.[3]

Exercise 14. We write the matrices with $2n$ lines and $2n$ columns as block
matrices

$$A = \begin{pmatrix} X & Y \\ Z & T \end{pmatrix}, \quad X, Y, Z, T \in M_n(\mathbf{R}).$$

Under which conditions on the matrices X, Y, Z and T is the matrix A an
element of the group $\mathrm{Sp}(2n; \mathbf{R})$?

Exercise 15. Let S be a real symmetric matrix. Show that

$$\exp(J_0 S) \in \mathrm{Sp}(2n; \mathbf{R}).$$

Conversely, suppose that the matrix S is such that

$$\forall t, \quad \exp(t J_0 S) \in \mathrm{Sp}(2n; \mathbf{R});$$

what can you say about S?

---

[3] Replacing $\mathbf{O}$ by $\mathbf{H}$ and 7 by 3 would be an analogous (but more complicated) way in
which to show that every oriented surface embedded in $\mathbf{R}^3$ admits an almost complex
structure.

Exercise 16. Use Corollary 5.6.7 to prove that the determinant of a symplectic matrix is 1.

Exercise 17 (Symplectization of a Contact Manifold). Let V be a manifold endowed with a 1-form α that is nonsingular (that is, such that $\alpha_x \neq 0$ for every $x \in V$) and such that

$$\forall x \in V, \quad (d\alpha)_x|_{\text{Ker }\alpha_x} \text{ is a nondegenerate bilinear form.}$$

We call α a *contact form* on V. The dimension of V must be odd; we write it as $2n + 1$.

(1) Show that $\alpha \wedge (d\alpha)^{\wedge n}$ is a volume form on V.
(2) Show that there exists a unique vector field X on V such that

$$i_X \alpha \equiv 1 \quad \text{and} \quad i_X(d\alpha) = 0$$

(we call X the *Reeb vector field* of α).
(3) Consider $W = V \times \mathbf{R}$ endowed with the 2-form ω defined by

$$\omega_{(x,\sigma)} = d(e^\sigma \alpha).$$

Show that (W, ω) is a symplectic manifold (called the *symplectization* of the contact manifold (V, α)).
(4) Determine the Hamiltonian vector field of the function $H(x, \sigma) = \sigma$.

Example.

Let $V = S^{2n+1} \subset \mathbf{C}^{n+1}$ be the unit sphere ($\mathbf{C}^{n+1}$ is endowed with coordinates $(q_1 + ip_1, \ldots, q_{n+1} + ip_{n+1})$) and consider the 1-form

$$\alpha = \frac{1}{2} \sum (p_i dq_i - q_i dp_i).$$

Prove that α is a contact form. Determine $\text{Ker }\alpha$ and the Reeb vector field X of α. Prove that the symplectization of (S^{2n+1}, α) is symplectomorphic to $\mathbf{C}^{n+1} - \{0\}$ endowed with its standard symplectic form.

Exercise 18. We call a function H on a symplectic manifold a *periodic Hamiltonian*[4] if there exists a circle action

$$S^1 \times W \longrightarrow W$$

---

[4] For this notion, basic results, and more, see for example [5].

such that

$$\frac{d}{dt}\left(\exp(2i\pi t)\cdot x\right)\big|_{t=0} = X_H(x)$$

for every $x \in W$.

(1) Show that the fixed points of the circle action are the critical points of H.

(2) Show that all (periodic) orbits of H are degenerate.

Exercise 19. We let the circle $\mathbf{S}^1$ act on the complex projective space $\mathbf{P}^n(\mathbf{C})$ by

$$u \cdot [z_0, \ldots, z_n] = [u^{m_0} z_0, \ldots, u^{m_n} z_n], \quad m_i \in \mathbf{Z}.$$

Show that the function

$$H([z_0, \ldots, z_n]) = \frac{1}{2} \frac{\sum m_i \left|z_i^2\right|}{\sum |z_i|^2}$$

is a periodic Hamiltonian associated with this action.

Under what condition (on the m_i) is this Hamiltonian a Morse function? What are then the indices of its critical points?

Exercise 20. We return to the quadric Q of Exercise 8 on p. 19. Consider the functions g and h that are restrictions to Q of the functions on $\mathbf{P}^3(\mathbf{C})$ defined by

$$g([z]) = \frac{\text{Im}(z_1 \bar{z}_0)}{\sum |z_i|^2} \quad \text{and} \quad h([z]) = \frac{\text{Im}(z_3 \bar{z}_2)}{\sum |z_i|^2}.$$

Show that g and h are periodic Hamiltonians on Q.

As in Exercise 8, we fix real numbers λ and μ such that $0 < \lambda < \mu$ and we consider the function f that is the restriction to Q of

$$f([z]) = \frac{\lambda \text{Im}(z_1 \bar{z}_0) + \mu \text{Im}(z_3 \bar{z}_2)}{\sum |z_i|^2}.$$

Express the Hamiltonian vector field X_f of f using those of g and h. Deduce the critical points of f. What are their indices (this question can be answered without any computations by using Exercises 18 and 21)?

Exercise 21 (Difficult). Consider a periodic Hamiltonian H on a compact symplectic manifold W. Let x be a critical point of H.

(1) Using an equivariant version of Darboux's theorem, show that there exist an almost complex structure and local coordinates in the neighborhood of x such that:

- The linearization of the action of S^1 on the complex vector space $T_x W$ is of the form

$$t \cdot (z_1, \ldots, z_n) = (t^{\alpha_1} z_1, \ldots, t^{\alpha_n} z_n).$$

- The Hamiltonian can be written as

$$H(x_1, \ldots, x_n, y_1, \ldots, y_n) = \frac{1}{2} \sum_i \alpha_i (x_i^2 + y_i^2).$$

(2) Suppose that the critical point x is *isolated*. Show that it is nondegenerate and of even index.

(3) Show that a connected symplectic manifold endowed with a periodic Hamiltonian whose critical points are isolated is simply connected.

(4) Show that a periodic Hamiltonian on a compact connected symplectic manifold whose critical points are all isolated has a local minimum and a local maximum.

14.2 Exercises on Chapter 6

Exercise 22. Verify that the quotient of the map

$$\mathbf{R}^2 \longrightarrow \mathbf{R}^2$$
$$(p, q) \longmapsto (p, q + 1/2)$$

on the torus $T^2 = \mathbf{R}^2/\mathbf{Z}^2$ is a diffeomorphism φ that preserves the symplectic form ($\varphi^\star \omega = \omega$) but does not have any fixed points. Show that there exists a vector field X on T^2 such that

$$\varphi = \varphi_X^1$$

but that X is not a Hamiltonian vector field.

Exercise 23. Let W be a symplectic manifold endowed with a circle action that preserves the symplectic form. Suppose that W is simply connected. Prove that the action is associated with a periodic Hamiltonian $H : W \to \mathbf{R}$ (in the sense of Exercise 18 on p. 520). Let $\zeta \in S^1$ and let φ be the diffeomorphism defined by $\varphi(x) = \zeta \cdot x$. Prove that φ is a Hamiltonian diffeomorphism and that it has at least $\sum \dim HM_i(W; \mathbf{Z}/2)$ fixed points.

Exercise 24. Let $x \in \mathcal{L}W$, and let u be a curve in $\mathcal{L}W$ that passes through x, that is, a map
$$u : \mathbf{R} \times S^1 \longrightarrow W$$
with $u(0, t) = x(t)$. Let Y be the vector tangent to $\mathcal{L}W$ defined by u. For a function $f : \mathcal{L}W \to \mathbf{R}$, we set
$$Y(x) \cdot f = \frac{\partial}{\partial s} f \circ u(s, t)|_{s=0}.$$
Show that this formula defines something and that this something is a derivation on the functions.

Exercise 25. On the torus $\mathbf{T}^2 = \mathbf{R}/\mathbf{Z} \times \mathbf{R}/\mathbf{Z}$, we consider the symplectic form $\omega = dy \wedge dx$. Let H and K be the functions from $\mathbf{R}^2$ to $\mathbf{R}$ defined by
$$H(x, y) = \frac{1}{2\pi} \cos(2\pi x), \quad K(x, y) = \frac{1}{2\pi} \sin(2\pi y).$$
Show that H and K define (autonomous) Hamiltonians on $\mathbf{T}^2$ and determine the associated Hamiltonian vector fields X_H and H_K.

Determine the flows φ_t of X_H and ψ_t of X_K as well as the periodic orbits of period 1 of X_H and X_K. Are the Hamiltonians H and K nondegenerate?

Compute the composition $\sigma_t = \psi_t \circ \varphi_t$. Determine the Hamiltonian F_t that generates the Hamiltonian isotopy σ_t (see Exercise 7 on p. 517). Determine the periodic orbits of period 1 of X_{F_t} and indicate which are contractible. Show that F_t is nondegenerate.

Exercise 26. On the space $\mathcal{L}W$, consider the action form
$$(\alpha_H)_x(Y) = \int_0^1 \omega(\dot{x}(t) - X_t(x(t)), Y(t)) \, dt.$$
Let $x_0 \in \mathcal{L}W$ be a fixed loop. We fix an extension u_0 of x_0 to the disk D^2. Show that x_0 has a neighborhood U in $\mathcal{L}W$ such that every loop $x \in U$ admits an extension u_x to the disk D^2, so that
$$\mathcal{A}_H(x) = -\int_D u_x^{\star}\omega + \int_0^1 H_t(x(t)) \, dt$$
defines a $\mathcal{C}^\infty$ function on U. Deduce that the form α_H is closed.

Exercise 27. Let α be a closed form on a manifold V and let X be a pseudo-gradient field adapted to α. We define the *energy* of a trajectory γ of the vector field X to be
$$E(\gamma) = \int_{-\infty}^{+\infty} -\alpha(\dot{\gamma}(s)) \, ds.$$
Show that if the energy of γ is finite, then γ connects two zeros of α.

Exercise 28 (Naturality of the Floer Equation). Let $u : \mathbf{R} \times S^1$ be a solution of the Floer equation

$$\frac{\partial u}{\partial s} + J(u)\frac{\partial u}{\partial t} + \operatorname{grad} H_t(u) = 0.$$

We are given a time-dependent Hamiltonian K_t with $K_{t+1} = K_t$ and the flow of symplectic diffeomorphisms ψ^t that it generates. Prove that the map $\widetilde{u}$ defined by

$$\widetilde{u}(s,t) = (\psi^t)^{-1}(u(s,t))$$

satisfies

$$\frac{\partial \widetilde{u}}{\partial s} + \widetilde{J}(\widetilde{u})\frac{\partial \widetilde{u}}{\partial t} + \operatorname{grad} \widetilde{H}_t(\widetilde{u}) = 0$$

for almost complex structures $\widetilde{J}$, and a Hamiltonian $\widetilde{H}_t$ that needs to be determined.

Exercise 29. Let V be a compact manifold endowed with a Riemannian metric and let f be a Morse function on V. Consider the functional

$$\gamma \longmapsto E(\gamma) = \frac{1}{2}\int_{\mathbf{R}}\left(\left\|\frac{d\gamma}{ds}\right\|^2 + \left\|\operatorname{grad}_{\gamma(s)} f\right\|^2\right) ds.$$

Let a and b be two critical points of f and let $\gamma : \mathbf{R} \to V$ be such that

$$\lim_{s \to -\infty} \gamma(s) = a, \qquad \lim_{s \to +\infty} \gamma(s) = b.$$

Show that

$$E(\gamma) = \frac{1}{2}\int_{\mathbf{R}}\left\|\frac{d\gamma}{ds} + \operatorname{grad}_{\gamma(s)} f\right\|^2 ds + f(a) - f(b).$$

Determine the extrema of E on the curves γ connecting a to b.

Exercise 30. Prove that the set of critical points of $\mathcal{A}_H$ (without a nondegeneracy assumption) is compact (this is a consequence of the Arzelà–Ascoli theorem).

Exercise 31 ("Removable" Singularities—difficult). Let (W, ω) be a compact symplectic manifold and let J be an almost complex structure calibrated by ω. Let $u : \mathbf{C} \to W$ be a J-holomorphic curve, that is, in coordinates $s + it \in \mathbf{C}$, a curve such that

$$\frac{\partial u}{\partial s} + J(u)\frac{\partial u}{\partial t} = 0.$$

Show that if u has finite energy, then it extends to a J-holomorphic map

$$\mathbf{P}^1(\mathbf{C}) = \mathbf{C} \cup \{\infty\} \longrightarrow W.$$

Exercise 32. Consider the map $z \mapsto z^n$ from $\mathbf{C}$ to $\mathbf{C}$. Let $A(r)$ be the area of the image of the disk of center 0 with radius r and let $\ell(r)$ be its circumference. Compute $A(r)$ and $\ell(r)$. Can the inequality

$$\ell(r)^2 \le 2\pi r A'(r)$$

obtained in the proof of Proposition 6.6.2 be improved?

Exercise 33. Consider the complex curve C_1 with equation

$$y^2 = 4x^3 - x - 1$$

and the map

$$u_\alpha : C_1 \longrightarrow \mathbf{C}^2$$

defined by $(x, y) \mapsto (\alpha^2 x, \alpha^3 y)$. We complete the curve C_1 to obtain a curve in $\mathbf{P}^2(\mathbf{C})$ and extend u_α to a map

$$u_\alpha : C_1 \longrightarrow \mathbf{P}^2(\mathbf{C}).$$

Study the limit of u_α when α tends to 0 (Figure 14.1).

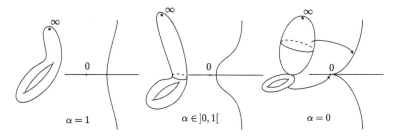

Fig. 14.1

Exercise 34 (Forms with Integral Periods). Let α be a closed 1-form on a manifold V. Suppose that α has "integral periods",[5] that is, with the notation of Section 6.7.a, that the image of φ_α is contained in $\mathbf{Z} \subset \mathbf{R}$. Show that the formula

$$f(x) = \int_{x_0}^x \alpha$$

defines a map $f : V \to \mathbf{R}/\mathbf{Z}$ and that

$$f^\star \, d\theta = 2\pi\alpha.$$

---

[5] This means that the de Rham cohomology class of α is contained in the image of $H^1(V; \mathbf{Z}) \to H^1(V; \mathbf{R})$.

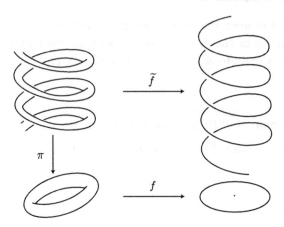

Fig. 14.2

Show that the integration cover $\pi : \widetilde{V} \to V$ is the pullback of the cover in the diagram

$$\begin{array}{ccc} \widetilde{V} & \xrightarrow{\ \widetilde{f}\ } & \mathbf{R} \\ {\scriptstyle \pi}\downarrow & & \downarrow{\scriptstyle \exp} \\ V & \xrightarrow[\ f\ ]{} & \mathbf{R}/\mathbf{Z} \end{array}$$

or in Figure 14.2 and that it is cyclic. Next consider the action form α_H (as in Section 6.7.b) on the projective space $\mathbf{P}^n(\mathbf{C})$. Verify that we still have

$$\int_{S^2} w^\star \omega \in \mathbf{Z}.$$

Deduce that there exists an infinite cyclic cover of $\mathcal{L}\mathbf{P}^n(\mathbf{C})$ on which α_H has a primitive $\widetilde{f}_H$.

14.3 Exercises on Chapter 7

Exercise 35. What does the relation ${}^t A J A = J$ imply for the determinant of a symplectic matrix A?

To prove that this determinant is $+1$, we can proceed as in Section 5.6.d. Another method consists in showing that the symplectic group is generated by the maps

$$x \longmapsto x + \lambda \omega(x, a) a$$

(symplectic transvections). This is what we ask you to do in this exercise.

Exercise 36. Let T be a symplectic transvection (Exercise 35). Compute $\rho(T)$. Does the map ρ satisfy

$$\rho(AB) = \rho(A)\rho(B)?$$

Exercise 37 (Fundamental Group of U(n)). The group $SU(n)$ acts on the unit sphere $S^{2n-1} \subset \mathbf{C}^n$ in such a way that the stabilizer the last vector of the canonical basis can be identified with $SU(n-1)$. Deduce that $SU(n)$ is simply connected.

Show that the map

$$U(n) \xrightarrow{\ \det\ } S^1$$

induces an isomorphism of the fundamental groups.

Exercise 38. Consider the matrix

$$A(t) = \begin{pmatrix} 1 + 4\pi^2 t^2 & 2\pi t \\ 2\pi t & 1 \end{pmatrix} \quad \text{for } t \in [0,1].$$

Verify that the path $t \mapsto A(t)$ is in S (defined in Section 7.1.a) and compute its Maslov index.

Do the same (this is more delicate) for the matrix

$$A(t) = \begin{pmatrix} 1 - 4\pi^2 t^2 & -2\pi t \\ 2\pi t & 1 \end{pmatrix} \quad \text{for } t \in [0,1].$$

Exercise 39. In $\mathbf{R}^4$ endowed with the coordinates (q_1, q_2, p_1, p_2), the symplectic form $\omega = dp_1 \wedge dq_1 + dp_2 \wedge dq_2$ and the complex structure $J = \left(\begin{smallmatrix} 0 & \mathrm{Id} \\ -\mathrm{Id} & 0 \end{smallmatrix} \right)$, consider the quadratic form

$$H = \frac{1}{2}(p_1^2 + p_2^2) + (q_2 p_1 - q_1 p_2)$$

and the associated symmetric matrix

$$S = \begin{pmatrix} 0 & 0 & 0 & -1 \\ 0 & 0 & 1 & 0 \\ 0 & 1 & 1 & 0 \\ -1 & 0 & 0 & 1 \end{pmatrix} = \begin{pmatrix} 0 & -\alpha \\ -\alpha & \mathrm{Id} \end{pmatrix} \quad \text{with } \alpha = \begin{pmatrix} 0 & 1 \\ -1 & 0 \end{pmatrix}.$$

Show that

$$A = \exp(tJS) = \begin{pmatrix} \exp(t\alpha) & t\exp(t\alpha) \\ 0 & \exp(t\alpha) \end{pmatrix} = \begin{pmatrix} \cos t & -\sin t & t\cos t & -t\sin t \\ \sin t & \cos t & t\sin t & t\cos t \\ & & \cos t & -\sin t \\ & 0 & \sin t & \cos t \end{pmatrix},$$

that this is a symplectic matrix with (double) eigenvalues $e^{\pm it}$, that it is not diagonalizable (for $t \neq 0$) and that it is in $\mathrm{Sp}(2n)^+$ (for $t \neq 0$).

Next, compute $\rho(A)$ (for $t \in]0, \pi[$):

(1) Show that $m_0 = 0$ and that $\rho(A) = (e^{it})^\sigma$, where σ is the signature of Q on the characteristic space E corresponding to the eigenvalue e^{it}.
(2) Show that $X = (1, -i, 0, 0) \in E$ and that $\mathrm{Im}\,\omega(\overline{X}, X) = 0$. Deduce that $\sigma = 0$ and that $\rho(A) = 1$.

Exercise 40 (Grassmannian of the Lagrangians). Consider the space Λ_n of Lagrangian vector subspaces of $\mathbf{R}^{2n} = \mathbf{C}^n$. Prove that the group $\mathrm{U}(n)$ acts transitively on Λ_n and that the stabilizer of

$$\mathbf{R}^n = \{X \in \mathbf{C}^n \mid \mathrm{Im}(X) = 0\}$$

is isomorphic to the orthogonal group $\mathrm{O}(n)$. Deduce that Λ_n is a connected compact manifold of dimension $n(n+1)/2$.

Show that the map

$$\det^2 : \mathrm{U}(n) \longrightarrow S^1$$

defines a continuous map from Λ_n to S^1 and that it induces an isomorphism of the fundamental groups.

Exercise 41 (Maslov Class of a Lagrangian Immersion). Let $f : L \to \mathbf{R}^n$ be an immersion of a manifold of dimension n in $\mathbf{R}^{2n}$. Suppose that f is *Lagrangian*, that is, that $f^\star\omega = 0$ or equivalently that for every x in L, $T_x f(T_x L)$ is a Lagrangian subspace of $\mathbf{R}^{2n}$.

So, sending each point to the tangent space at that point defines a "Gauss" map $\gamma(f) : L \to \Lambda_n$. The composition

$$\gamma(f)_\star : \pi_1(L) \longrightarrow \pi_1(\Lambda_n) = \mathbf{Z}$$

therefore sends each loop in L to an integer: its Maslov class. Determine the Maslov classes of the (Lagrangian) immersions of S^1 in $\mathbf{R}^2$ defined by the drawings in Figure 14.3. Show that the Maslov class of an embedded circle is ± 2 (use the "turning tangents" theorem; see [8]).

Fig. 14.3

Exercise 42 (Relative Maslov Index). Let W be a manifold endowed with a symplectic form ω and let

$$j : L \hookrightarrow W$$

be a Lagrangian embedding (see Exercise 41). With each disk

$$u : D^2 \longrightarrow W$$

with boundary in L, that is, with $u(\partial D^2) \subset j(L)$, we can associate an integer $\mu_L(u)$ as follows: trivialize $u^\star TW$ using a symplectic trivialization

$$\Phi : u^\star TW \longrightarrow D^2 \times \mathbf{R}^{2n};$$

the class of the loop

$$S^1 \longrightarrow \Lambda_n$$
$$z \longmapsto \Phi(T_{u(z)}L)$$

in $\pi_1(\Lambda_n) \equiv \mathbf{Z}$ is then the integer $\mu_L(u)$ in question. Verify that this integer does not depend on the choice of the trivialization Φ.

Let v be another disk in W with boundary in L. Suppose that u and v are homotopic relative to L, that is, that there exists a homotopy

$$h : D^2 \times [0,1] \longrightarrow W$$

such that

$$\begin{cases} h(\cdot, 0) = u \\ h(\cdot, 1) = v \\ h(z, t) \in L \quad \text{if } z \in S^1. \end{cases}$$

Prove that $\mu_L(u) = \mu_L(v)$. So μ_L defines a map from the group $\pi_2(W, L)$ of relative homotopy classes to $\mathbf{Z}$. Prove that this map is a group homomorphism.

From now on, suppose that $\pi_2(W) = 0$. Prove that in this case, $\mu_L(u)$ depends only on the restriction of u to the boundary and therefore defines a group homomorphism $\pi_1(L) \to \mathbf{Z}$.

Exercise 43. Let P be a polynomial with complex coefficients and let $\alpha \in \mathbf{C}$ be a root of P of multiplicity m. We begin by recalling a proof of Rouché's theorem.

(1) Let γ be the circle $\gamma(t) = \alpha + \varepsilon e^{2i\pi t}$ ($t \in [0,1]$). Show that if ε is sufficiently small so that α is the unique root of P in the closed disk B_ε with

boundary γ, then

$$m = \frac{1}{2i\pi} \int_\gamma \frac{P'(z)}{P(z)} \, dz.$$

(2) Let $\delta = \sup_{z \in \mathrm{Im}\,\gamma} |P(z)|$. Let Q be a polynomial with

$$\sup_{z \in B_\varepsilon} |P(z) - Q(z)| < \delta.$$

Verify that Q does not have any roots in the circle γ. Prove that the image of γ under h is contained in the open disk of center 1 with radius 1. Deduce that

$$\int_\gamma \frac{h'(z)}{h(z)} \, dz = 0.$$

(3) Prove that Q has exactly m roots (counted with multiplicities) in the disk B_ε. This is Rouché's theorem.

Deduce a proof of Proposition 7.3.6.

14.4 Exercises on Chapter 8

Exercise 44. Show that the kernel of the operator Γ considered in Proposition 8.1.4 is not finite-dimensional.

Exercise 45 (Another Proof of Theorem 8.6.11). Let $\Sigma : \mathbf{R} \to \mathrm{End}(\mathbf{R}^{2n})$ be a continuous map such that

$$\Sigma(s) = \pi \, \mathrm{Id} \quad \text{for } s < -s_0 \quad \text{and} \quad \Sigma(s) = 3\pi \, \mathrm{Id} \quad \text{for } s > s_0.$$

Show that the operator F defined by

$$F(Y) = \frac{\partial Y}{\partial s} + J_0 \frac{\partial Y}{\partial t} + \sigma \cdot Y$$

is a Fredholm operator from $W^{1,p}(\mathbf{R} \times S^1; \mathbf{R}^{2n})$ to $L^p(\mathbf{R} \times S^1; \mathbf{R}^{2n})$. Show that

$$\dim \mathrm{Ker}\, F = 2n \# \{\ell \in \mathbf{Z}^\star \mid 1 < 2\ell < 3\} = 2n,$$

and then that $\dim \mathrm{Ker}\, F^\star = 0$ and that F is surjective.

14.5 Exercises on Chapter 10

Exercise 46. Consider the operator

$$L_0 : W^{1,2}(\mathbf{R}; \mathbf{R}^N) \longrightarrow L^2(\mathbf{R}; \mathbf{R}^N)$$
$$Y \longmapsto \frac{dY}{ds} + A_0(s),$$

where $A_0(s)$ is a diagonal matrix (for every s) that is constant for $|s|$ sufficiently large, and is of the form

$$A = \begin{pmatrix} \mathrm{Id}_{m^+} & 0 \\ 0 & -\mathrm{Id}_{n^+} \end{pmatrix} \text{ for } s \geq M \quad \text{and} \quad \begin{pmatrix} \mathrm{Id}_{m^-} & 0 \\ 0 & -\mathrm{Id}_{n^-} \end{pmatrix} \text{ for } s \leq -M.$$

(1) Verify that L_0 is a Fredholm operator. Determine its index as a function of $m^\pm$ and $n^\pm$.
(2) Taking inspiration from the methods of Section 8.8, deduce another proof of Proposition 10.2.8.

14.6 Exercises on Chapter 11

Exercise 47. We use the notation and results of Exercise 25 on p. 523, where we determined the contractible and periodic solutions of period 1 of a Hamiltonian F_t on the torus $\mathbf{T}^2$. Compute the indices of these trajectories (a computation essentially asked in Exercise 38) and determine the Floer complex for this Hamiltonian (which we assume to be regular).

Appendices: What You Need to Know to Read This Book

Appendix A
A Bit of Differential Geometry

In this chapter, we list, more or less succinctly depending on the case, the different objects and tools from differential geometry used in this book.

A.1 Manifolds and Submanifolds

See [45], [48], [47], [74] and [63] for the basic notions set out in this section.

A.1.a Manifolds

A manifold is a space that, locally, greatly resembles $\mathbf{R}^n$. Let us be more precise. A topological manifold of dimension n is a separated topological space such that every point is contained in an open subset homeomorphic to an open subset of $\mathbf{R}^n$. A pair (U, φ), where U is such an open space and φ is a homeomorphism, is a local coordinate system or chart. The manifolds we consider will be at least paracompact, and in particular separable.

We also require that V be a countable union of compact sets and a countable union of open sets of charts. In this book, we will mostly use compact manifolds, for which these properties automatically hold.

The set of charts of a manifold is called an atlas. Two charts (U, φ) and (U', φ') are called compatible if the composition

$$\varphi(U \cap U') \xrightarrow{\varphi^{-1}} U \cap U' \xrightarrow{\varphi'} \varphi'(U \cap U'),$$

which maps one open subset of $\mathbf{R}^n$ to another, is a diffeomorphism (of class $\mathcal{C}^\infty$). If the manifold V has an atlas whose charts are mutually compatible, then we call V a differential manifold (or a smooth or $\mathcal{C}^\infty$ manifold).

M. Audin, M. Damian, *Morse Theory and Floer Homology*,
Universitext, DOI 10.1007/978-1-4471-5496-9,
© Springer-Verlag London 2014

Examples. The sphere S^n, the projective spaces $\mathbf{P}^n(\mathbf{R})$ and $\mathbf{P}^n(\mathbf{C})$ and the torus $\mathbf{R}^n/\mathbf{Z}^n$ are (smooth) manifolds.

Using this definition, a zero-dimensional manifold is a discrete countable set.

Using charts and the *ad hoc* notion on the open subsets of $\mathbf{R}^n$, we define the notion of $\mathcal{C}^\infty$ map from one manifold to another: if U and V are contained in open subsets of charts on manifolds M and N, respectively, then the function $f : U \to V$ is of class $\mathcal{C}^k$ (for $0 \le k \le \infty$) if the composition

$$\varphi(U) \xrightarrow{\varphi^{-1}} U \xrightarrow{f} V \xrightarrow{\psi} \psi(V)$$

is of class $\mathcal{C}^k$. The class $\mathcal{C}^k$ property is local and is well defined by this condition.

A.1.b Characterization of Submanifolds

Among the manifolds, there are submanifolds of $\mathbf{R}^n$. A submanifold of $\mathbf{R}^n$ is a subspace V that, locally, greatly resembles a linear subspace in the sense that each of its points has an open neighborhood U in $\mathbf{R}^n$ that is diffeomorphic to a neighborhood of 0 in $\mathbf{R}^n$ by a diffeomorphism φ such that $\varphi(U \cap V) = \varphi(U) \cap \mathbf{R}^d$. The integer d is the dimension of the submanifold V.

Theorem A.1.1. *Let $V \subset \mathbf{R}^n$. The following properties are equivalent:*

(1) *V is a submanifold of dimension d of $\mathbf{R}^n$.*
(2) *Every point x of V has an open neighborhood U in $\mathbf{R}^n$ such that there exists a submersion $g : U \to \mathbf{R}^{n-d}$ with $U \cap V = g^{-1}(0)$.*
(3) *Every point x of V has an open neighborhood U in $\mathbf{R}^n$ such that there exist a neighborhood Ω of 0 in $\mathbf{R}^d$ and an immersion $h : \Omega \to \mathbf{R}^n$ that is a homeomorphism from Ω onto $U \cap V$.*

In other words, a submanifold can be described locally by equations (where the number of equations is the codimension) or by parametrization (where the number of parameters is the dimension). All these properties are consequences of the implicit function theorem and/or of the local inversion theorem.

An excellent and indispensable exercise is to decide, given in $\mathbf{R}^n$ or in another manifold a subset suspected of being a submanifold, which of these criteria is best sequenced for proving its guilt.

The definition of a submanifold of a manifold is analogous.

Of course, submanifolds are manifolds (this is included in the definition). For example, a "level set" of a function with real values, that is, the inverse image of a real number α, falls under property (2). It is a submanifold when f is a submersion along $f^{-1}(\alpha)$.

The converse also holds: manifolds can be considered as submanifolds, as we will now recall.

A.1.c Partitions of Unity, Embedding Theorems

Partitions of Unity.

This is an essential tool, which allows us to prove many results by concentrating on their local aspects. Let V be a compact manifold[1] of dimension n and let $(U_i, \varphi_i)_{1 \leq i \leq N}$ be a finite atlas of V. We can show that there exist a cover of V by open sets Ω_i such that $\overline{\Omega}_i \subset U_i$ and functions h_i with support in U_i and value 1 on Ω_i.

Setting

$$p_i = \frac{h_i}{\sum h_i},$$

we deduce that for every cover of V by finitely many open sets $\Omega_1, \ldots, \Omega_N$, there exists a family $(p_i)_{1 \leq i \leq N}$ of functions

$$p_i : V \longrightarrow [0, +\infty[$$

such that

$$\text{Supp}(p_i) \subset \Omega_i \quad \text{and} \quad \sum_{i=1}^{N} p_i \equiv 1.$$

Embedding of a Compact Manifold in a Euclidean Space.

Let V be a compact manifold of dimension n and let $(U_i, \varphi_i)_{1 \leq i \leq N}$ be a finite atlas of V. We use the functions h_i introduced above to construct a map F defined by

$$F = (h_1 \varphi_1, \ldots, h_N \varphi_N, h_1, \ldots, h_N) : V \longrightarrow (\mathbf{R}^n)^N \times \mathbf{R}^N = \mathbf{R}^{(n+1)N}.$$

We can verify that F is an injective immersion, and therefore an embedding; see the following theorem.

Theorem A.1.2 (Whitney embedding theorem). *Let V be a compact manifold; then there exists an embedding of V as a submanifold in a Euclidean space $\mathbf{R}^N$.* $\qquad\square$

Using a general position argument similar to the one we will recall later, we can prove that the dimension of the Euclidean space can be reduced to $2 \dim V + 1$.

---

[1] Paracompact suffices...

Remark. This result belongs to real differential geometry; it does not have an analogue in complex analytic geometry: by Liouville's theorem, no compact analytical manifold is an analytic submanifold of $\mathbf{C}^N$.

A.1.d Boundaries

A manifold with boundary is a topological space V such that every point has a neighborhood homeomorphic to an open subset of the half-space $(x_n \leq 0)$ in $\mathbf{R}^n$. The points that do not have a neighborhood homeomorphic to an open subset of $\mathbf{R}^n$ are the boundary points. The boundary, denoted by ∂V, is a submanifold of dimension $n - 1$. We can prove (see Section A.4) that the boundary has a neighborhood of the form $\partial V \times [0, \varepsilon[$.

A.1.e Tangent Vectors, Tangent Maps

Let us recall that we can define a vector tangent to the manifold V at x as an equivalence class of curves on V passing through x, namely

$$c : \,]-\varepsilon, \varepsilon[\, \longrightarrow V \quad \text{such that } c(0) = x,$$

for the equivalence relation that identifies c_1 and c_2 if for a chart φ centered at x, we have

$$(\varphi \circ c_1)'(0) = (\varphi \circ c_2)'(0).$$

The set of vectors tangent at x is a vector space that we denote by $T_x V$. This allows us to define the tangent map

$$T_x f : T_x V \longrightarrow T_{f(x)} W$$

associated with a map $f : V \to W$, simply by sending the class of the curve c to that of the curve $f \circ c$.

It also allows us to consider a tangent vector as a derivation on the functions, that is, as a linear map X defined on the set of $\mathcal{C}^\infty$ functions in the neighborhood of x and satisfying

$$X(fg) = f(x)X(g) + g(x)X(f).$$

For every x, given a vector $X \in T_x V$ and a function $f : V \to \mathbf{R}$, we let $X(f)(x) = T_x f(X) \in \mathbf{R}$; this defines the function $X(f)$.

Remark A.1.3. This function is often denoted by $(df)_x$ instead of $T_x f$, in particular when f is a function with real values. We will do so here.

Describing the tangent space of a submanifold using each of the characterizations is quite instructive (in particular, we find that $T_x(f^{-1}(0)) = \operatorname{Ker} T_x f$ when f is submersive).

A.1.f Vector Fields

We also define the *tangent bundle*[2] by putting the topology and *ad hoc* structure of manifold on the disjoint union of the tangent spaces at the points of the manifold.

The vector fields are $\mathcal{C}^\infty$ sections[3] of the tangent bundle. In other words, a vector field consists of, for every point, a tangent vector that depends in a $\mathcal{C}^\infty$ manner on the point in question. In general, we will use Roman capitals such as X to denote vector fields, while X_x will denote the value of the field X at the point x.

If X is a vector field and f is a function, then we denote by $X \cdot f$ the derivative of f along X defined by

$$(X \cdot f)(x) = X_x \cdot f = T_x f(X_x).$$

All derivations arise from vector fields.

Lie Bracket.

The composition of two derivations is not a derivation; however,

$$f \longmapsto X \cdot (Y \cdot f) - Y \cdot (X \cdot f)$$

is one. We denote the corresponding vector field by $[X, Y]$.

A vector field can also be considered as a differential equation on the manifold. See Section A.4.

A.1.g Differential Forms

A differential form of degree p on a manifold V (also called a p-form) is a section of the bundle $\Lambda^p T^\star V$. In less pretentious terms, it consists of, for every $x \in V$, an exterior derivative of degree p on the tangent space $T_x V$ that depends in a $\mathcal{C}^\infty$ manner on x. In local coordinates $(x_1, \ldots, x_n)$ on V, this can be written as

$$\alpha = \sum \alpha_{i_1, \ldots, i_p} dx_{i_1} \wedge \cdots \wedge dx_{i_p},$$

where the $\alpha_{i_1, \ldots, i_p}$ are functions and the $dx_1, \ldots, dx_n$ denote the canonical basis of $(\mathbf{R}^n)^\star$.

---

[2] And, likewise, the cotangent bundle, by using the duals of the tangent spaces.

[3] A section of a vector bundle $\pi : E \to V$ is a map $s : V \to E$ such that $\pi \circ s = \mathrm{Id}_V$.

A map $f : V \to W$ sends differential forms on W to differential forms on V through

$$(f^\star\alpha)_x(X_1,\ldots,X_p) = \alpha_{f(x)}(T_xf(X_1),\ldots,T_xf(X_p)).$$

The most important operation on differential forms is exterior differentiation. It transforms a p-form into a $(p+1)$-form; in coordinates, we have

$$d\alpha = \sum d\alpha_{i_1,\ldots,i_p} \wedge dx_{i_1} \wedge \cdots \wedge dx_{i_p}$$

(where $d\alpha_{i_1,\ldots,i_p}$ is the differential of the function $\alpha_{i_1,\ldots,i_p}$).

It satisfies $d \circ d = 0$. There are closed forms ($d\alpha = 0$) and exact forms ($\alpha = d\beta$). The exact forms are closed, but the converse does not hold in general, giving rise to de Rham cohomology.

We will in particular need 1-forms and 2-forms, the exterior derivative, closed forms, exact forms, the notion of volume form and Stokes's theorem. See [45, Chapter V] and [74, Chapter VII].

A.1.h Matters of Orientation

We call a manifold orientable if it has an oriented atlas (such that all of its transition maps preserve the orientation). A manifold with a volume form is orientable (the proof is immediate). The converse is also true, we can construct a volume form using a partition of unity (see [45, Chapter V] if the manifold is compact and [37, p. 46] in the general case).

The boundary of an oriented manifold has a natural orientation.

Example. If $f : \mathbf{R}^n \to \mathbf{R}$ is a submersion, then the submanifold $f^{-1}(0)$ is orientable. To show this, we can use the gradient of the function, which is a vector field that is normal to the submanifold.

A.2 Critical Points, Critical Values and Sard's Theorem

See for example [39] for this section.

A.2.a Critical Points

A point x of the manifold M is called *critical* for the map

$$f : M \longrightarrow N$$

with values in the manifold N if the linear map T_xf does not have maximal rank:

- Either $\dim M \le \dim N$ and f is not an immersion at x
- Or $\dim M \ge \dim N$ and f is not a submersion at x.

Let m and n be the dimensions of M and N, respectively and alphabetically. When $m \leq n$, the condition is $\dim \operatorname{Ker} T_x f > 0$; when $m \geq n$, it is $\operatorname{rk} T_x f < n$. We can summarize this by saying that x is critical if the corank of f at x is positive, using the *ad hoc* definition of corank, that is, $\inf(m, n) - \operatorname{rk} T_x f$.

Example (Basic example). When $N = \mathbf{R}$, we have $n = 1$ and a point x is critical if and only if $T_x f \equiv 0$.

A.2.b Sard's Theorem

A critical value of the map f is a point of the target manifold N that is the image of a critical point. The other points of N are *regular values*. We should note, in particular, that a regular value is not necessarily a value, that is, is not necessarily contained in the image of f. Moreover, there can be noncritical points whose images are critical values.

Sard's theorem states that under certain conditions, almost all values of a differentiable map are regular (note that the notion of negligible set and therefore that of "almost everywhere" are well defined on a manifold). More precisely, we have the following result.

Theorem A.2.1 (Sard's theorem). *Let $f : M \to N$ be a $\mathcal{C}^\infty$ map; then the set of critical values of f has measure zero in N.*

Remark A.2.2. When the dimension m of M is less than n, the dimension of N, then $f(M)$ itself has measure zero in N. This is a not entirely trivial consequence of the fact that the subspace $\mathbf{R}^m$ has measure zero in $\mathbf{R}^n$. For example, in this case, a differentiable map from M to N is never surjective. The theorem is therefore above all interesting (and more difficult to prove) when $m \geq n$.

See for example [39, p. 34ff.] for a proof.

A.2.c Regular Level Sets of a Function, Sublevel Sets

If $f : V \to \mathbf{R}$ is a function and if α is a regular value of f, then by the regular value theorem (that is, characterization (2) of Theorem A.1.1), the *level set* $f^{-1}(\alpha)$ is a submanifold of codimension 1 of V. The *sublevel set* $V^\alpha = f^{-1}(]-\infty, \alpha])$ is, in turn, a manifold with boundary $f^{-1}(\alpha)$.

Let $f : (V, \partial V) \to W$ be a $\mathcal{C}^\infty$ map from a manifold with boundary to a manifold W. We suppose that the point w of W is a regular value for both f and $f|_{\partial V}$; then $f^{-1}(w)$ is a submanifold of V, with boundary

$$\partial f^{-1}(w) = (f|_{\partial V})^{-1}(w).$$

A.3 Transversality

This notion, due to Thom at the beginning of the 1950s, is essential in geometry. It concerns the relative position of two submanifolds.

A.3.a First Notion of Transversality

The story begins with (yet) another application of the implicit function theorem.

Theorem A.3.1. *Let M and N be two submanifolds of a manifold P. Let u be a point of $M \cap N$ such that*

$$T_u M + T_u N = T_u P.$$

Then in the neighborhood of u, the intersection $M \cap N$ is a submanifold of P. Its codimension is the sum of the codimensions of M and of N, and its tangent space at u is

$$T_u(M \cap N) = T_u M \cap T_u N.$$

We have assumed that everything is of class $\mathcal{C}^\infty$, but class $\mathcal{C}^1$ suffices.

Proof. The statement is local in the neighborhood of u. Let us therefore suppose that $P = \mathbf{R}^p$. Let m be the codimension of M and let n be that of N, so that, always in the neighborhood of u, we may also assume that $M = f^{-1}(0)$ and $N = g^{-1}(0)$ for submersions f and g. The condition of general position on the tangent spaces can then be written as

$$\dim(\operatorname{Ker} T_u f + \operatorname{Ker} T_u g) = p.$$

Let us therefore consider the map $F = (f,g) : \mathbf{R}^p \to \mathbf{R}^m \times \mathbf{R}^n$. It satisfies $F^{-1}(0) = M \cap N$ and the kernel of its differential in u is

$$\operatorname{Ker} T_u F = \operatorname{Ker} T_u f \cap \operatorname{Ker} T_u g,$$

a subspace whose dimension is therefore

$$\dim \operatorname{Ker} T_u F = \dim \operatorname{Ker} T_u f + \dim \operatorname{Ker} T_u g - \dim(\operatorname{Ker} T_u f + \operatorname{Ker} T_u g)$$
$$= p - m + p - n - p = p - (m + n).$$

Consequently, $T_u F$ is surjective and F is a submersion in the neighborhood of u, so that $M \cap N$ is a submanifold. The proof also gives its tangent space, namely the kernel of $T_u F$, that is, the intersection of the tangent spaces, and its codimension, which is the sum of the codimensions. $\qquad\square$

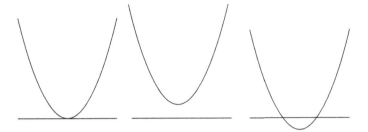

Fig. A.1

Example A.3.2. The example of a surface M and a plane N in $P = \mathbf{R}^3$ is already quite instructive. The two submanifolds are of codimension 1, so the "general position" condition is simply that they are not tangent. A submanifold of $\mathbf{R}^n$ and its (affine) tangent space are never transverse.

We say that two submanifolds M and N of P are *transverse* at the point $u \in P$ if

$$\begin{cases} \text{either } u \notin M \cap N, \\ \text{or } u \in M \cap N \qquad \text{and } T_u M + T_u N = T_u P. \end{cases}$$

We call them *transverse*, denoted by $M \pitchfork N$, if they are transverse at every point.

Figure A.1 shows two submanifolds of $\mathbf{R}^2$ that are not transverse... and the fact that they become so after a tiny deformation.

Remark A.3.3. This property is completely general: transversality is a *generic* notion, it can always be attained through a small deformation. It is also a *stable* notion: a small deformation of two transverse submanifolds preserves their transversality. To prove the first assertion, we can use Sard's theorem. Namely, since M and N are described by submersions f and g as in the proof above, almost all values are regular for F, so that $f^{-1}(\varepsilon)$ and $g^{-1}(\eta)$ are transverse for almost all (ε, η) near $(0,0)$.

Remark A.3.4. For two submanifolds whose dimensions add up to less than the dimension of the surrounding manifold (for example two curves in $\mathbf{R}^3$), transversality means the absence of any intersection.

More generally, if $f : M \to N$ is a differentiable map and if $P \subset N$ is a submanifold, then we say that f is *transverse* to P (at u) if

$$\begin{cases} \text{either } u \notin f(M) \cap P, \\ \text{or } u = f(x) \in f(M) \cap P \quad \text{and } T_x f(T_x M) + T_u P = T_u N. \end{cases}$$

As before, we denote this by $f \pitchfork P$.

Proposition A.3.5. *If f is transverse to P (at every point) and if $f^{-1}(P)$ is nonempty, then $f^{-1}(P)$ is a submanifold of M.*   □

Remark A.3.6. If $N \subset P$ is a (co-orientable) orientable submanifold of the orientable manifold P and if $f : M \to P$ is transverse to N, then $f^{-1}(N)$ is (co-orientable) orientable in the orientable manifold M. The case treated in Section A.1.h is that where the submanifold N is the point 0 and $P = \mathbf{R}$.

A direct application of Sard's theorem is the following first result on transversality.

Theorem A.3.7. *Let M, N, and S be three manifolds and let P be a submanifold of N. Let*

$$F : M \times S \longrightarrow N$$

be a map transverse to P. Then for almost all $s \in S$, the map $F_s : M \to N$ is transverse to P.

We in fact see the manifold S as a parameter space.

Proof of Theorem A.3.7. By applying Proposition A.3.5, we see that $F^{-1}(P)$ is a submanifold Q of $M \times S$. The projection

$$\pi : Q \subset M \times S \longrightarrow S$$

is a differentiable map for which, by Sard's theorem, almost all $s \in S$ are regular values. We can easily verify that the regular values of π are exactly those s for which the map F_s is transverse to P.   □

Remark A.3.8. The greater the parameter space S, the higher the probability that a map $M \times S \to N$ is transverse to the submanifold P. This explains the great usefulness of this result.

A.3.b $\mathcal{C}^k$ Topology

The transversality theorems say that sufficiently close to a given map, there exists a map transverse to a given submanifold, or, that we can "perturb" ("slightly" being implied) a map to make it transverse to a submanifold. To state the theorems, we need to define a notion of proximity, that is, a topology, or rather several, on the space of maps from manifold M to manifold N.

Let us begin with the case where the two manifolds are open subsets of Euclidean spaces. The $\mathcal{C}^\infty$ (resp. $\mathcal{C}^k$) topology is that of the uniform convergence of the function and all of its derivatives (resp. those of order at most k) on compact subsets.

Remark A.3.9. This topology is metrizable: we use the pseudo distances

$$d^r_K(f, g) = \sup_{x \in K} \left| f^{(r)}(x) - g^{(r)}(x) \right|$$

and we let K run through a countable family of compact sets covering the source space.

In the general case of two manifolds M and N, we define the $\mathcal{C}^k$ topology (where k may be infinite) by giving a fundamental system of open neighborhoods for it. For a function f, these neighborhoods are indexed by the (K, V, ε) such that:

- $\varepsilon > 0$.
- K is a compact subset of the open set of a chart of M.
- V is the open set of a chart of N.
- And we have $f(K) \subset V$.

We set

$$\mathcal{U}^k_{K,V,\varepsilon}(f) = \left\{ g \in \mathcal{C}^k(M, N) \mid g(K) \subset V \text{ and } d^r_K < \varepsilon \text{ for } |r| \leq k \right\}.$$

This topology is metrizable since M is assumed to be separable, like all manifolds in this book. We will let d_∞ denote a distance defining the $\mathcal{C}^\infty$ topology.

A.3.c Transversality Theorems

Theorem A.3.10 (Local transversality). *Let M and N be two manifolds and let P be a proper submanifold of N. Let $f : M \to N$ be a differentiable map and let a be a point of M. Then there exist a compact neighborhood K of a in M and an open neighborhood $\mathcal{U}$ of f in $\mathcal{C}^\infty(M, N)$ such that*

$$\{g \in \mathcal{U} \mid g \pitchfork P \text{ at every point of } K\}$$

is a dense open subset of $\mathcal{U}$.

Theorem A.3.11 (Transversality). *Let K be a compact subset of M. The set of maps from M to N transverse to the submanifold P of N along K is a dense open subset of $\mathcal{C}^\infty(M, N)$.*

Corollary A.3.12. *The set of maps $f : M \to N$ transverse to the submanifold P of N is dense in $\mathcal{C}^\infty(M, N)$; moreover, it is open if M is compact.*

Outline of a Proof of Theorem A.3.10. If $f(a) \notin P$, then let K be a compact neighborhood of a such that $f(K) \cap P = \varnothing$ and let $\mathcal{U}$ be the open set

$$\mathcal{U} = \{g \in \mathcal{C}^\infty(M, N) \mid g(K) \cap P = \varnothing\}.$$

Owing to the properness of P, these sets have the required property.

If $f(a) \in P$, then let us consider the open set of a chart V of submanifold $P \subset N$ in the neighborhood of $f(a)$. We may, and do, assume that $V = \mathbf{R}^n$ and $V \cap P = \mathbf{R}^p \times \{0\} \subset \mathbf{R}^p \times \mathbf{R}^q = \mathbf{R}^n$, with $f(a) = 0$. Let U be a neighborhood of a in M such that $f(\overline{U}) \subset V$ and let K be a compact neighborhood of a contained in U. Finally, let us set

$$\mathcal{U} = \{g \in \mathcal{C}^\infty(M, N) \mid g(\overline{U}) \subset V\}$$

and let us show that K and $\mathcal{U}$ are suitable.

Let α be a function with values in $[0, 1]$ and support in U that is identically 1 on K. We define a map $G : M \times (\{0\} \times \mathbf{R}^q) \to N$ by setting

$$G(x, v) = \begin{cases} g(x) & \text{if } x \notin U \\ g(x) + \alpha(v)v & \text{if } x \in U. \end{cases}$$

Clearly, G is transverse to $\mathbf{R}^p \times \{0\}$, which by Theorem A.3.7 gives the desired density.

The openness of the set of maps transverse to P along K follows from the openness of the set of matrices with maximal rank in the space of matrices. $\qquad \square$

Proof of Theorem A.3.11. Let $f \in \mathcal{C}^\infty(M, N)$. For every $a \in K$, let K_a and $\mathcal{U}_a$ be a compact set and an open set, respectively, such as those whose existence is ensured by Theorem A.3.10, so that

$$\mathcal{U}_a' = \{g \in \mathcal{U}_a \mid f \pitchfork P \text{ along } K_a\}$$

is a dense open subset of $\mathcal{U}_a$. Since K is compact, we can cover it by a finite number N of K_{a_i}; we then set

$$\mathcal{U}' = \bigcap_{i=1}^N \mathcal{U}_{a_i}'.$$

As a finite intersection of dense open subsets, this is a dense open subset of $\mathcal{U}_a$. If $g \in \mathcal{U}'$, then f is transverse to P along the union of the K_{a_i}, hence along K. $\qquad \square$

It occasionally happens (and will occasionally happen) that we need a somewhat different transversality property: we do not want to consider all the functions from M to N, but only those with a property specific to the problem under consideration, which may not be an open property. In other words, we want to consider only the functions satisfying some constraint.

Following [47], let us say that a subset $\mathcal{F} \subset \mathcal{C}^\infty(M, N)$ is *locally transverse* to P if, for every function $f \in \mathcal{F}$ and every $a \in M$, there exist a neighborhood K of a in M and a neighborhood $\mathcal{V}$ of f in $\mathcal{F}$ such that, for every $g \in \mathcal{V}$, there exist a neighborhood U of 0 in a space $\mathbf{R}^q$ and a family

$$G : M \times U \longrightarrow N$$

such that

- $G_0 = g$.
- For all $t \in U$, $G_t \in \mathcal{F}$.
- G is transverse to P on $K \times U$.

This definition adapts itself to most constraints, which in general do not define open sets. It is used, for example, to prove the immersion theorem and Whitney's embedding theorem. Another advantage is that the proof of the transversality theorem gives "transversality with constraints" without needing any modification.

Theorem A.3.13. *If $\mathcal{F} \subset \mathcal{C}^\infty(M, N)$ is locally transverse to the submanifold $P \subset N$, then for every compact $K \subset M$, the set of elements of $\mathcal{F}$ that are transverse to P along K is a dense open subset of $\mathcal{F}$.* $\square$

A.4 Vector Fields as Differential Equations

A.4.a Flows

A vector field can be seen as a differential equation

$$c'(t) = X_{c(t)}$$

whose solution through x at $t = 0$ we denote by φ_X^t. As a rule, it is only defined for t near 0. In that case, however, we have

$$\varphi_X^t(\varphi_X^{t'}(x)) = \varphi_X^{t+t'}(x)$$

whence we easily deduce that φ_X^t is a diffeomorphism equal to the identity for $t = 0$.

A very important result that we will use continually is the fact that on a compact manifold, the flow is defined for all t.

Theorem A.4.1. *The flow of a vector field on a compact manifold V is well defined on $\mathbf{R} \times V$.*

The same of course holds for a vector field with compact support on an arbitrary manifold. See for example [54, p. 10] for a proof.

Collar Neighborhoods of the Boundary.

The boundary ∂V of a manifold V admits a "collar"[4] neighborhood, that is, a neighborhood of the form $\partial V \times [0, \varepsilon[$, which we can obtain by integrating a vector field. Namely, we choose a vector field defined in the neighborhood of the boundary and not tangent to it (this is easy to obtain using a partition of unity) and integrate it.

A.4.b Lie Derivative, Cartans' Formula

The Lie derivative $\mathcal{L}_X$ extends the derivation of functions (0-forms). It is defined by

$$\mathcal{L}_X \alpha = \left(\frac{d}{dt} (\varphi^t)^* \alpha \right)_{t=0}$$

(and therefore transforms a p-form into another p-form).

Cartans' formula links the Lie derivative and the exterior derivative. It also involves the interior product of a form by a vector field:

$$(i_X \alpha)_x (Y_1, \ldots, Y_p) = \alpha_x (X, Y_1, \ldots, Y_p)$$

(an operation that sends a p-form to a $(p-1)$-form). The identity states that

$$\mathcal{L}_X = d i_X + i_X d.$$

Again, see [45, Chapter V].

A.4.c Linearization along a Solution

Let us consider a vector field X on a manifold V, that is, the differential equation

$$\dot{x} = X(x),$$

where we use the notation $\dot{x} = dx/dt$.

Traditionally, we think of the linearized equation as that describing the solutions "infinitesimally close" to a given solution. If $x(t)$ and $y(t)$ are close solutions, then in a chart we write

$$y(t) = x(t) + Y(t),$$

giving

$$\frac{dY}{dt} = \frac{dy}{dt} - \frac{dx}{dt} = X(y(t)) - X(x(t)) = (dX)_{x(t)} (Y(t))$$

---

[4] We used this in Section 4.7.

at order 1. This *linear* differential equation in Y is the linearized equation. Let us describe it in a more intrinsic way.

Let us consider a solution $x(t)$ of our differential equation and a vector field tangent to V along x. For example, $X = d/dt$ is such a solution.

Lemma A.4.2. *The Lie derivative $\mathcal{L}_X$ defines an operator D on the local sections of x^*TV such that for every function f defined along x, we have*

$$D(fY) = \dot{f}Y + fDY.$$

Proof. We define DY by:

- Extending Y to $\widetilde{Y}$ in a neighborhood of x (or of a point of x, everything is local)
- Computing $\mathcal{L}_X \widetilde{Y}$ $(= [\widetilde{Y}, X])$
- Restricting this vector field to x.

Let us verify that the result is independent of the choice of the extension $\widetilde{Y}$ of Y by noting that if Z is a field whose restriction to the solution x is identically zero, then the restriction of $\mathcal{L}_X Z$ to x is zero. This is what Lemma A.4.3 below states.

The "linearity" with respect to the functions is an immediate consequence of the identity

$$\mathcal{L}_X(fY) = (X \cdot f)Y + f\mathcal{L}_X Y. \qquad \square$$

Lemma A.4.3. *If Z is a vector field on V defined in the neighborhood of x and identically zero on x, then $\mathcal{L}_X Z$ is zero at every point of x.*

Proof. The definition of $\mathcal{L}_X Z$ uses the flow φ^t of X:

$$\mathcal{L}_X Z = \frac{d}{dt}\left((\varphi^{-t})_* Z\right)|_{t=0}.$$

At every point of x, the vector $Z(x(t))$ is zero; hence $(\varphi^t)_* Z(x)$ is also zero, identically. Consequently, $\mathcal{L}_X Z$ is zero at every point of the trajectory x. $\square$

We call the linear equation $DY = 0$ the *linearized equation*. Note that X itself is obviously a solution of the variational equation. We have the following result.

Lemma A.4.4. *The solutions Y of the equation linearized along x are vector fields $Y(t)$ defined along x such that*

$$Y(t) = (T_{x(0)}\varphi^t)(Y(0)).$$

Indeed, if $Y(t)$ is defined by this formula, then

$$Y(0) = (T_{x(0)}\varphi^t)^{-1}Y(t) = (T_{x(t)}\varphi^{-t})Y(t)$$

does not depend on t, so that the formula indeed defines a solution of the linear equation. It has value $Y(0)$ for $t = 0$ and is the only solution to do so.   □

In Coordinates.

In order to use coordinates, let us write down the matrix form of this equation. If $(e_1(t), \ldots, e_m(t))$ is a basis of local sections of the vector bundle TV along x, then a vector field Y along x can be written as $Y(t) = \sum y_i(t)e_i(t)$ and

$$DY = \sum_{i=1}^m (\dot{y}_i e_i + y_i D e_i)$$

$$= \sum_{i=1}^m \left(\dot{y}_i e_i + y_i \sum_{j=1}^m a_{ij} e_j \right) = \sum_{i=1}^m \left(\dot{y}_i + \sum_{k=1}^m a_{k,i} y_k \right) e_i.$$

Writing y for the column vector with elements y_i and letting $A(t)$ denote the matrix with elements $A(t)_{ij} = a_{ji}(t)$, this gives

$$\dot{y} + A(t)y = 0.$$

Even more locally, let us assume that V is an open subset of $\mathbf{R}^m$, so that the vector field X may be seen as a map

$$V \longrightarrow \mathbf{R}^m$$

$$x \longmapsto X(x).$$

For the basis $(e_1(t), \ldots, e_m(t))$, let us use the canonical base $(\partial/\partial x_1, \ldots, \partial/\partial x_m)$ of $\mathbf{C}^m$ restricted to the trajectory; then

$$\left[X, \frac{\partial}{\partial x_i} \right] = -\frac{\partial X}{\partial x_i} \quad \text{so that } A(t) = -(dX)_{x(t)}.$$

The variational equation is the *linearization* $\dot{y} = (dX)_{x(t)}y$ of the original differential equation. We again find the "Poincaré" linearization mentioned above.

A.4.d The Case of a Time Dependent Vector Field

In this book, we will need to consider "time dependent" vector fields, that is, differential systems

$$\dot{x} = X_t(x(t)),$$

where $(t, x) \mapsto X_t(x)$ is a vector field that depends on the additional parameter t (time). The situation seems to be somewhat different from what we have been considering up to now, but can be reduced to it by considering the vector field

$$\widetilde{X}(u, x) = \frac{d}{du} + X_u(x) \in T_{(u,x)}(\mathbf{R} \times V)$$

on $\mathbf{R} \times V$. The trajectories of $\widetilde{X}$ are the solutions $\widetilde{x}(t) = (u(t), x(t)) \in \mathbf{R} \times V$ of

$$\dot{u}(t) = 1, \quad \dot{x}(t) = X_{u(t)}(x(t)).$$

These include the $t \mapsto (t, x(t))$, where x is a solution of $\dot{x} = X_t(x)$, our original equation. The flow of $\widetilde{X}$ is

$$\widetilde{\varphi}^t(u, x) = (u + t, \varphi^t(x)),$$

where φ^t denotes the flow of X_t, a solution of

$$\varphi^0 = \mathrm{Id} \quad \text{and} \quad \frac{d}{dt}\varphi^t = X_t \circ \varphi^t.$$

The linearization of the differential equation along such a solution can be applied to sections of $\widetilde{x}^* T(\mathbf{R} \times V)$, that is, to vectors

$$t \longmapsto (y(t), Y(t))$$

satisfying

$$\frac{d}{dt}\begin{pmatrix} y \\ Y \end{pmatrix} = \begin{pmatrix} 0 & 0 \\ \partial X_t/\partial t & (dX_t)_{x(t)} \end{pmatrix} \begin{pmatrix} y \\ Y \end{pmatrix}.$$

The solutions are therefore of the form (y, Y), where y is constant and Y satisfies

$$\frac{dY}{dt} = y\frac{\partial X_t}{\partial t} + (dX_t)_{x(t)}Y.$$

In particular, for $y = 0$, this is

$$\frac{dY}{dt} = (dX_t)_{x(t)}Y,$$

where we recognize the form above. The results therefore hold, in particular Lemma A.4.4, which gives

$$(y(t), Y(t)) = T_{\widetilde{x}(0)}\widetilde{\varphi}^t(y(0), Y(0)) = (y(0), T_{x(t)}\varphi^t(Y(0))).$$

For $y(0) = 0$, we see that Y is a solution of

$$\frac{dY}{dt} = (dX_t)_{x(t)}Y \text{ if and only if } Y(t) = T_{x(t)}\varphi^t(Y(0)).$$

A.5 Riemannian Metrics, Exponential Map

A *Riemannian metric* on a manifold is a section of the vector bundle of bilinear forms on the tangent space to this manifold that at each point is an inner product on the tangent space at that point.

For example, if V is a submanifold of $\mathbf{R}^n$, then the Euclidean metric on $\mathbf{R}^n$ induces an inner product on the vector spaces $T_x V$ and a Riemannian metric on V.

When a manifold has a partition of unity, we can use it to endow the manifold with a *Riemannian metric*; in particular, this applies to every compact manifold.

A Riemannian metric g defines a derivative of vector fields along a vector field, the *covariant derivative* called the *Levi-Cività connection*, the unique $(X, Y) \mapsto D_X Y$ such that

$$D_{fX}Y = f D_X Y \quad \text{and} \quad D_X(fY) = (x \cdot f)Y + f D_X Y$$
$$D_X Y - D_Y X = [X, Y]$$
$$X \cdot g(Y, Z) = g(D_X Y, Z) + g(Y, D_X Z).$$

See [37, §II B].

On a Riemannian manifold, we therefore have the notion of a geodesic. A geodesic is a solution $t \mapsto \gamma(t)$ of the differential equation

$$D_{\dot\gamma}\gamma = 0.$$

Given a point $x \in V$ and a vector $Y \in T_x V$, there exists a unique geodesic through x with tangent vector Y at x; that is,

$$\gamma_Y(t) \quad \text{with } \gamma_Y(0) = x \text{ and } \dot\gamma_Y(0) = Y.$$

The geodesics are solutions of a differential equation of order 2. We assume that V is (geodesically) complete, namely that $\gamma_Y(t)$ is well defined for every $t \in \mathbf{R}$. We then define

$$\exp_x : T_x V \longrightarrow V$$
$$Y \longmapsto \gamma_Y(1).$$

We can show that $\exp_x$ is a local diffeomorphism and that

$$T_0 \exp_x : T_x V \longrightarrow T_x V$$

is none other than the identity. See [37, §II C].

Since V is endowed with a Riemannian metric, we can consider, for every R, the subspace

$$\{(x, Y) \in TV \mid \|Y\| < R\} \subset TV.$$

We call this type of space a "disk bundle": the fiber at $x \in V$ is the disk of radius R in the Euclidean space $T_x V$.

When the manifold V is compact, there exists a nonnegative real number r such that the exponential defines a diffeomorphism

$$(x, Y) \longmapsto (x, \exp_x Y)$$

from the disk bundle of radius r

$$\{(x, Y) \in TV \mid \|Y\| < r\}$$

onto its image in $V \times V$. The supremum of the set of such r is called an injectivity radius.

With a Riemannian metric and its Levi-Cività connection is associated a notion of "parallel transport". Given a vector X tangent to V at x, we define its parallel transport along a curve $t \mapsto \gamma(t)$ with origin $x = \gamma(0)$ as follows: $X(t) \in T_{\gamma(t)}V$ is the unique "parallel" section, that is, section with zero covariant derivative, of $\gamma^* TV$ satisfying the initial condition $X(0) = X$.

Appendix B
A Bit of Algebraic Topology

In a book devoted to (Morse, Floer) homology, we inevitably use some algebraic homology (Künneth formula, long exact sequences). But we also need a minimum of algebraic topology (homotopy groups, first Chern class, ...). We take stock of all of this in the present chapter.

B.1 A Bit of Algebraic Homology

Let us recall (see for example [25]) that a *chain complex* is a sequence $C_\bullet$ of modules endowed with linear maps

$$\partial : C_k \longrightarrow C_{k-1}$$

such that $\partial \circ \partial = 0$.

B.1.a The Künneth Formula over Z/2

In this subsection, $C_\bullet$ and $D_\bullet$ are complexes of vector spaces[1] over $\mathbf{Z}/2$. Their tensor product is the complex defined by

$$(C \otimes D)_k = \bigoplus_{i+j=k} C_i \otimes D_j$$

with boundary operator

$$\partial_k^{C \otimes D}(c \otimes d) = ((\partial_i^C c) \otimes d, c \otimes (\partial_j^D d)) \in C_{i-1} \otimes D_j \oplus C_i \otimes D_{j-1} \subset (C \otimes D)_{k-1}$$

for $c \otimes d \in C_i \otimes D_j \subset (C \otimes D)_k$.

---

[1] The result is true over any field, but not over a ring. In particular, it is not true for integral homology. See Remark B.1.2 and [25].

M. Audin, M. Damian, *Morse Theory and Floer Homology*,
Universitext, DOI 10.1007/978-1-4471-5496-9,
© Springer-Verlag London 2014

We will show the following result.

Proposition B.1.1. *The homology of the tensor product complex is the tensor product of the homologies:*

$$H_\star(C_\bullet \otimes D_\bullet) = H_\star(C_\bullet) \otimes H_\star(D_\bullet).$$

Proof. Let us first note that:

- $C \otimes 0 = 0$.
- $H_\star(C_\bullet \oplus C'_\bullet) = H_\star(C_\bullet) \oplus H_\star(C'_\bullet)$.
- $(C \oplus C') \otimes D = C \otimes D \oplus C' \otimes D$.
- If the proposition is true for $C_\bullet$ and $D_\bullet$ and also for $C'_\bullet$ and $D_\bullet$, then it is true for $(C \oplus C')_\bullet$ and $D_\bullet$.

We therefore prove the proposition by induction on the length $\ell(D_\bullet)$ of the second chain complex, where, of course,

$$\ell(D_\bullet) = \# \{j \mid D_j \neq 0\}.$$

There is nothing to prove when $\ell(D_\bullet) = 1$. Let us consider a complex of length 2. If the two nonzero vector spaces in $D_\bullet$ do not have consecutive indices, then the property is clear by taking the direct sum. Let us therefore suppose that the chain complex $D_\bullet$ is

$$0 \longrightarrow D_{j-1} \overset{\partial}{\longrightarrow} D_{j-1} \longrightarrow 0.$$

If $\partial = 0$, then we also have the result by taking the direct sum.

Let us first suppose that ∂ is an isomorphism. In this case, the homology of the chain complex $D_\bullet$ is zero and we consequently wish to show that the homology of $(C \otimes D)_\bullet$ is also zero. Let us consider an element of the kernel of

$$\partial_{i+j} : C_i \otimes D_j \oplus C_{i+1} \otimes D_{j-1} \longrightarrow C_{i-1} \otimes D_j \oplus C_i \otimes D_{j-1}$$

(the exponents denote the degrees) and let us show that it is contained in the image of

$$\partial_{i+j+1} : C_{i+1} \otimes D_j \longrightarrow C_i \otimes D_j.$$

We therefore write

$$\partial\left(\sum_a x_a^i \otimes y_a^j, \sum_b z_b^{i+1} \otimes t_b^{j-1}\right) = 0,$$

that is,

$$\sum_a (\partial x_a^i) \otimes y_a^j = 0$$

and

$$\sum_a x_a^i \otimes \partial y_a^i + \sum_b \partial z_b^{i+1} \otimes t_b^{j-1} = 0.$$

Under our hypothesis, ∂^D is an isomorphism. Let us therefore apply $\mathrm{Id}\otimes\partial^{-1}$ to the second relation. We obtain

$$\sum_a x_a^i \otimes y_a^j = \sum_b \partial z_b^{i+1} \otimes \partial^{-1} t_b^{j-1}$$

(computed modulo 2). Finally, we have

$$\partial\left(\sum_b z_b^{i+1} \otimes \partial^{-1} t_b^{j-1}, 0\right) = \left(\sum_a x_a^i \otimes y_a^j, \sum_b z_b^{i+1} \otimes t_b^{j-1}\right),$$

so that our element of the kernel of ∂_{i+j} belongs to the image of ∂_{i+j+1}.

Let us now consider the general case of a chain complex $D_\bullet$ of length 2. We decompose D_j and D_{j-1} as direct sums

$$D_j = \mathrm{Ker}(\partial) \oplus D_j' \quad \text{and} \quad D_{j-1} = E_{j-1}' \oplus \mathrm{Im}(\partial);$$

then $D_\bullet$ is the direct sum of the two chain complexes

$$0 \longrightarrow \mathrm{Ker}(\partial) \xrightarrow{\ 0\ } E_{j-1} \longrightarrow 0 \quad \text{and} \quad 0 \longrightarrow D_j' \xrightarrow{\ \cong\ } \mathrm{Im}(\partial) \longrightarrow 0$$

and the result follows from previous ones.

Finally, let us assume that the proposition has been proved for chain complexes of length k and let $D_\bullet$ be a chain complex of length $k+1$, namely

$$0 \longrightarrow D_{k+1} \xrightarrow{\ \partial\ } D_k \longrightarrow \cdots \longrightarrow D_1 \longrightarrow 0.$$

We decompose as above:

$$D_{k+1} = \mathrm{Ker}(\partial) \oplus D_{k+1}' \quad \text{and} \quad D_k = \mathrm{Im}(\partial) \oplus E_k'.$$

The chain complex is then the direct sum of the three complexes

$$0 \longrightarrow \mathrm{Ker}(\partial) \longrightarrow 0,$$

and $\qquad 0 \longrightarrow E_k' \longrightarrow D_{k-1} \longrightarrow \cdots 0 \longrightarrow D_{k+1}' \xrightarrow{\ \cong\ } \mathrm{Im}(\partial) \longrightarrow 0,$

all of length less than $k+1$.   □

Remark B.1.2. It is when we decompose D_j or D_{k+1} as direct sums of the kernel of ∂ and a complement that we really use the fact that our chain complexes consist of vector spaces, and not simply of modules over a commutative ring.

B.1.b Exact Sequences of Complexes

Let us quickly recall that if $A_\bullet$, $B_\bullet$ and $C_\bullet$ are chain complexes, then an exact sequence of chain complexes and morphisms of chain complexes

$$0 \longrightarrow A_\bullet \xrightarrow{\ i\ } B_\bullet \xrightarrow{\ j\ } C_\bullet \longrightarrow 0$$

induces, for every k, an exact sequence

$$H_k(A) \xrightarrow{i_\star} H_k(B) \xrightarrow{j_\star} H_k(C)$$

(as can be verified directly), while the morphism induced by i or j is in general not injective or surjective, respectively. This lack of exactness is "measured" by a long exact sequence.

$$H_k(A) \longrightarrow H_k(B) \longrightarrow H_k(C)$$

$$H_{k-1}(A) \xrightarrow{\quad\quad} \cdots$$

Let us just indicate how the *connecting morphism* ∂ is defined (all remaining verifications are analogous and direct). Let $[c] \in H_k(C)$ be an element represented by a $c \in C_k$ with $\partial_C(c) = 0$. The diagram

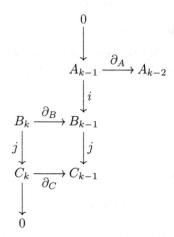

gives $c = j(b)$ with

$$j(\partial_B b) = \partial_C(j(b)) = \partial_C c = 0,$$

so that $\partial_B(b) \in \mathrm{Ker}(j)$, whence $\partial_B(b) = i(a)$ for some $a \in A_{k-1}$. Moreover, this element is a cycle: we have

$$i(\partial_A a) = \partial_B(i(a)) = \partial_B \partial_B(b) = 0$$

and i is injective.

B.2 Chern Classes

Second Cohomology Group.

We have mentioned the first Chern class of a complex vector bundle, even though we have not used it much. It lives in the cohomology group $H^2(W; \mathbf{Z})$ obtained, for example, using the Morse complex as in the first part of this book.

First Chern Class.

The most economical way to define it is by taking the maximal exterior power of this fiber bundle, thus obtaining a complex line bundle. The first Chern class is then the Euler class of the latter:

$$c_1(E) = c_1(\Lambda^n E) = e(\Lambda^n(E)) \in H^2(W; \mathbf{Z})$$

if E is a fiber bundle of rank n on a space W. We refer to [56] for these notions.

We have used the first Chern class $c_1(TW)$ of the tangent bundle TW of a symplectic manifold, seen as a complex vector bundle using an almost complex structure calibrated by the symplectic form. Let us note that this class is well defined, simply because the set of such almost complex structures is contractible (and in particular connected) and the Chern class c_1 lives in the discrete space $H^2(W; \mathbf{Z})$.

Appendix C
A Bit of Analysis

We first recall the statement of the Arzelà–Ascoli theorem. Then we set out the basis of Fredholm theory. Next, we will prove some lemmas on elliptic regularity, as well as the properties of $\overline{\partial}$ that we have used throughout this text.

C.1 The Arzelà–Ascoli Theorem

Let us recall this very useful theorem, which characterizes the relatively compact subsets of the space of continuous functions on a compact space, and which we use in several compactness statements. See [17] for this theorem and for references.

Theorem C.1.1 (Arzelà–Ascoli). *Let (E, d) be a compact metric space and let $\mathcal{F}$ be a bounded family of continuous functions $f : E \to \mathbf{R}$ that are uniformly equicontinuous on E, that is, that satisfy*

$$\forall\, \varepsilon > 0, \ \exists\, \delta > 0 \text{ such that } \forall\, f \in \mathcal{F}, \quad d(x, y) < \delta \Longrightarrow |f(x) - f(y)| < \varepsilon.$$

Then $\mathcal{F}$ is relatively compact in the space of continuous functions on E.

In other words, from every sequence of elements of $\mathcal{F}$ we can extract a sequence that converges uniformly on E (to a continuous function).

Remark C.1.2. In all the cases where we applied this theorem in this book, the family of functions was equicontinuous because it was "equi-Lipschitz".

M. Audin, M. Damian, *Morse Theory and Floer Homology*,
Universitext, DOI 10.1007/978-1-4471-5496-9,
© Springer-Verlag London 2014

C.2 Fredholm Theory

As is usually done and for the sake of simplicity, in this chapter we will call an *operator*[1] a *continuous* linear map from a normed vector space to another (this is sometimes also called a *bounded linear map*).

C.2.a Fredholm Operators

We say that an operator L from a Banach space E to a Banach space F is *Fredholm* if it has an index, namely if $\operatorname{Ker} L$ is a finite-dimensional subspace and $\operatorname{Im} L$ is a finite-codimensional subspace (or $\operatorname{Coker} L$ is a finite-dimensional space). The *index* of the operator is then

$$\operatorname{Ind}(L) = \dim \operatorname{Ker} L - \dim \operatorname{Coker} L.$$

Examples C.2.1.

(1) A bijective operator has an index, namely zero.
(2) If E is a finite-dimensional vector space, then every linear map $L : E \to E$ has index zero... since this assertion is equivalent to

$$\dim \operatorname{Ker} L + \dim \operatorname{Im} L = \dim E.$$

Remark C.2.2. If $L : E \to F$ is a Fredholm operator, then $\operatorname{Ind}(L)$ is the Euler characteristic of the chain complex

$$0 \longrightarrow E \overset{L}{\longrightarrow} F \longrightarrow 0$$

since in this simple case, the Euler characteristic is

$$\chi = \dim(\operatorname{Ker} L / \{0\}) - \dim(F / \operatorname{Im}(L)).$$

The theory of Fredholm operators is explained very well in the talk by Grisvard [41] that we have borrowed from shamelessly, hoping that we will be forgiven for this borrowing because of the publicity it will bring to this little-known article (we have no doubts about that). Here is a first list of properties that can all be verified directly.

Proposition C.2.3. *Let* $L_0 : E_0 \to F_0$, $L_1 : E_1 \to F_1$, $L : E \to F$ *and* $L' : F \to G$ *be Fredholm operators. Then we have:*

(1) $L_0 \oplus L_1$ *is a Fredholm operator and*

$$\operatorname{Ind}(L_0 \oplus L_1) = \operatorname{Ind}(L_0) + \operatorname{Ind}(L_1).$$

---

[1] In the remainder of this book, we have occasionally used the term "operators" for differentiable maps that are not necessarily linear and have also occasionally considered non-continuous operators. As a rule, we always specify what the term refers to.

(2) *If H is a vector space of finite dimension m, then $L \otimes \mathrm{Id}_H$ is a Fredholm operator, and index $\mathrm{Ind}(L \otimes \mathrm{Id}_H) = m \, \mathrm{Ind}(L)$.*

(3) *$L' \circ L$ is a Fredholm operator and $\mathrm{Ind}(L' \circ L) = \mathrm{Ind}(L') + \mathrm{Ind}(L)$.*

Proof. The first assertion is clear and the second one follows from the first by choosing a basis for H and writing

$$E \otimes H \cong E \oplus \cdots \oplus E \quad \text{and} \quad L \otimes \mathrm{Id}_H = L \oplus \cdots \oplus L.$$

By applying Remark C.2.2, we could also have considered the short exact sequence of chain complexes

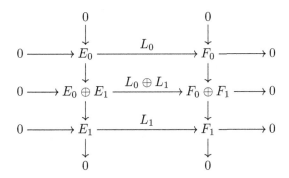

and applied the additivity of the Euler characteristic[2] to prove the first assertion. This introduces the elegant argument that Grisvard uses to prove the third assertion. That argument is as follows. We consider the commutative diagram

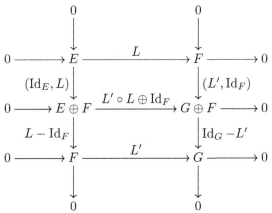

[2] This is a consequence of the existence of a long exact sequence associated with a short exact sequence of chain complexes; see Section B.1.b.

whose vertical arrows form short exact sequences of complexes. We deduce from it that

$$\text{Ind}(L)+\text{Ind}(L') = \text{Ind}(L'\circ L\oplus\text{Id}_F) = \text{Ind}(L'\circ L)+\text{Ind}(\text{Id}_F) = \text{Ind}(L'\circ L). \quad \square$$

The Fredholm operators defined this way are indeed those we defined in Chapter 8. We have the following result.

Proposition C.2.4. *Let $L : E \to F$ be an operator whose kernel has finite dimension and whose image has finite codimension; then its image is closed.*

Proof. Let H be a closed subspace[3] of E such that $\text{Ker}(L) \oplus H = E$ and G be a finite-dimensional subspace of F such that $\text{Im}(L) \oplus G = F$. Consider the linear map

$$\Gamma : H \oplus G \longrightarrow F$$
$$(x, y) \longmapsto L(x) + y.$$

Since G has finite dimension, this map is continuous. Moreover, it is easy to check that it is bijective. Using Banach's theorem, its inverse is also continuous and therefore its image $\Gamma(H \oplus 0)$ must be closed. But $\Gamma(H \oplus 0) = \text{Im}(L)$ and the proof is finished. $\square$

C.2.b Basic Properties

Proposition C.2.5. *Let $L : E \to F$ be an operator between two Banach spaces. For L to be Fredholm, it is necessary and sufficient that there exists an operator $L' : F \to E$ such that $L \circ L' - \text{Id}_F$ and $L' \circ L - \text{Id}_E$ have finite rank. When this is the case, L' is also a Fredholm operator and*

$$\text{Ind}(L') = -\text{Ind}(L).$$

Proof. To begin, let us assume that L is a Fredholm operator. We choose a complement E_0 of $\text{Ker}\, L$ in E, so that the restriction L_0 of L to E_0 is an isomorphism from E_0 onto $\text{Im}(L)$. We consider the inverse L_0^{-1} of L_0. We also choose a projection $p : F \to \text{Im}(L)$ that we take to be continuous, and we set

$$L' = L_0^{-1} \circ p;$$

then L' is continuous. We have

$$\text{Im}(L' \circ L - \text{Id}_E) = \text{Ker}(L) \quad \text{and} \quad \text{Im}(L \circ L' - \text{Id}_F) = \text{Ker}\, p,$$

---

[3] This is a simple consequence of the Hahn–Banach theorem.

which are both finite-dimensional. We also have

$$L \circ L' \circ L = L \quad \text{and} \quad L' \circ L \circ L' = L'.$$

Conversely, if L' has the two properties, then let us show that L and L' are Fredholm operators. Let $A = L \circ L' - \mathrm{Id}_F$ and let $B = L' \circ L - \mathrm{Id}_E$. We have

$$\mathrm{Ker}(L) \subset \mathrm{Ker}(L' \circ L) \subset \mathrm{Im}(B)$$

(the first kernel is therefore finite-dimensional) and

$$\mathrm{Im}(L) \supset \mathrm{Im}(L \circ L') = \mathrm{Im}(\mathrm{Id}_F + A).$$

If $G = \mathrm{Ker}(A)$, then F/G is isomorphic to $\mathrm{Im}(A)$, hence finite-dimensional. Therefore G has finite codimension. However, $\mathrm{Id}_F + A$ equals Id_F on $\mathrm{Ker}(A)$, hence $\mathrm{Im}(\mathrm{Id}_F + A) \supset G$, so that the image indeed has finite codimension.

So L has an index, as does L'. The formula for the index follows from the additivity formula of Proposition C.2.3 and from the following proposition, which will imply that the index of $\mathrm{Id}_F + A$ is zero. □

Proposition C.2.6. *If $u : E \to E$ is an operator of finite rank, then*

$$\mathrm{Ind}(\mathrm{Id}_E + u) = 0.$$

If $L : E \to F$ is a Fredholm operator and if $u : E \to F$ is an operator of finite rank, then $L + u$ is Fredholm and its index is

$$\mathrm{Ind}(L + u) = \mathrm{Ind}(L).$$

Proof. The first assertion is a computation of dimensions, which we can deal with using the Euler characteristic. We set $G = \mathrm{Im}(u)$. This is a finite-dimensional subspace of E and it is stable under $\mathrm{Id}_E + u$. The diagram of exact sequences of chain complexes is

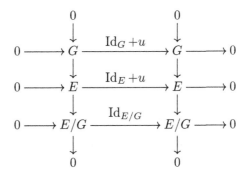

(the vertical arrows are inclusions and projections). The index is then the sum

$$\mathrm{Ind}(\mathrm{Id}_E + u) = \mathrm{Ind}(\mathrm{Id}_G + u) + \mathrm{Ind}(\mathrm{Id}_{E/G}),$$

where the first term on the right-hand side is zero because G is finite-dimensional, while the second is zero because the index of the identity is always zero.

Since we have now completed the proof of Proposition C.2.5, nothing prevents us from applying it to prove the second assertion. We therefore use an L' as in the proposition. Then $(L + u) \circ L' - \mathrm{Id}_F$ also has finite rank, so that

$$\mathrm{Ind}(L + u) + \mathrm{Ind}(L') = 0 \text{ and therefore } \mathrm{Ind}(L + u) = \mathrm{Ind}(L). \qquad \square$$

Proposition C.2.7. *If $K : E \to E$ is a compact operator on a Banach space, then $\mathrm{Id}_E + K$ is a Fredholm operator.*

Proof. We consider $L = \mathrm{Id}_E + K : E \to E$. First, $\mathrm{Id}_E|_{\mathrm{Ker}(L)} = -K|_{\mathrm{Ker}(L)}$, so $\mathrm{Id}_E|_{\mathrm{Ker}(L)}$ is a compact operator, which means that the unit ball of $\mathrm{Ker}(L)$ is compact, and therefore that $\mathrm{Ker}(L)$ is finite-dimensional.

Let us now show that the image of L is closed. We choose a complement E_0 of $\mathrm{Ker}(L)$ in E and show that there exists a constant $C > 0$ such that

$$\forall x \in E_0, \quad \|x\| \le C \|L(x)\|.$$

Indeed, if this were not the case, then we would be able to find a sequence (x_k) of elements of norm 1 in E_0 such that

$$\lim_{k \to +\infty} (x_k + K(x_k)) = 0.$$

Since K is compact, we would then be able to extract a sequence such that $(K(x_k))$ converges. But then (x_k) would also converge. The limit x would then have the following properties

$$\|x\| = 1, \quad x \in E_0 \cap \mathrm{Ker}(L),$$

which is absurd.

We therefore have the desired inequality, which implies that the image of L is closed: if (x_k) is a sequence in E such that

$$\lim_{k \to +\infty} L(x_k) = y,$$

then (x_k) is a Cauchy sequence and therefore converges to a vector of E whose image is y.

Finally, we consider the transposes $E' \to E'$ (here E' denotes the dual of E, endowed with the weak topology[4]). The operator ${}^tK$ is compact, hence we can use the same argument as for $\mathrm{Ker}(L)$ to show that the dimension of $\mathrm{Ker}({}^tL)$ is finite. Together with the fact that $\mathrm{Im}(L)$ is closed, this concludes the proof of the proposition.   □

From these propositions, we deduce three results that are essential for the theory of Fredholm operators.

Theorem C.2.8. *Let $L : E \to F$ be an operator between Banach spaces. For L to be a Fredholm operator, it is necessary and sufficient that there exists an $L' : F \to E$ such that*

$$L \circ L' - \mathrm{Id}_F \quad and \quad L' \circ L - \mathrm{Id}_E$$

are compact operators.

Proof. Operators of finite rank are compact, so Proposition C.2.5 gives the necessity of the condition. Next, we have

$$\mathrm{Ker}(L) \subset \mathrm{Ker}(L' \circ L) \quad and \quad \mathrm{Im}(L) \supset \mathrm{Im}(L \circ L')$$

so that the result follows from the previous proposition.   □

Theorem C.2.9 (Invariance of the index under small perturbations). *Let $L : E \to F$ be a Fredholm operator between two Banach spaces. There exists a constant $\varepsilon > 0$ such that, for every operator $u : E \to F$ of norm $\|u\| < \varepsilon$, the operator $L + u$ is Fredholm and*

$$\mathrm{Ind}(L + u) = \mathrm{Ind}(L).$$

Proof. We use an operator L' as given by Proposition C.2.5 and set

$$\varepsilon = \frac{1}{\|L'\|}.$$

Hence, for $\|u\| < \varepsilon$, the operators $\mathrm{Id}_F + u \circ L'$ and $\mathrm{Id}_E + L' \circ u$ are invertible. In particular, their indices are zero and we have

$$(L + u) \circ L' = L \circ L' + u \circ L' = \mathrm{Id}_F + A + u \circ L'$$

for an operator A of finite rank. Since $\mathrm{Id}_F + u \circ L'$ is invertible, the operator $\mathrm{Id}_F + A + u \circ L'$ has index zero (by Proposition C.2.6). Since

$$\mathrm{Im}((L + u) \circ L') \subset \mathrm{Im}(L + u),$$

---

[4] We always have that $\mathrm{Ker}\,{}^tL$ is the annihilator of $\mathrm{Im}(L)$; we do not always have that $\mathrm{Im}(L)$ is the annihilator of $\mathrm{Ker}\,{}^tL$, but the latter is true if $\mathrm{Im}(L)$ is closed.

this image has finite codimension. We can show in the same manner (using $L' \circ L = \mathrm{Id}_E + B$ with B of finite rank) that $\mathrm{Ker}(L + u)$ is finite-dimensional. Finally, we have on the one hand,

$$\mathrm{Ind}(L + u) + \mathrm{Ind}(L') = 0,$$

and on the other hand,

$$\mathrm{Ind}(L) + \mathrm{Ind}(L') = 0,$$

whence it follows that

$$\mathrm{Ind}(L + u) = \mathrm{Ind}(L). \qquad \qquad \square$$

Theorem C.2.10. *Let $L : E \to F$ be a Fredholm operator between two Banach spaces. For every compact operator $K : E \to F$, the operator $L + K$ is Fredholm and*

$$\mathrm{Ind}(L + K) = \mathrm{Ind}(L).$$

Proof. We still use the operator L' from Proposition C.2.5; the operators

$$(L + K) \circ L' - \mathrm{Id}_F \quad \text{and} \quad L' \circ (L + K) - \mathrm{Id}_E$$

are compact, so that $L + K$ is Fredholm (Theorem C.2.8). The same holds for $L + tK$ for every $t \in [0, 1]$, so that, by Theorem C.2.9, we have

$$\mathrm{Ind}(L + K) = \mathrm{Ind}(L). \qquad \qquad \square$$

Remark C.2.11. Theorem C.2.9 asserts that the index is a continuous map on the set of Fredholm operators, which is an open subset of the space of operators from E to F.

Remark C.2.12. The operator $\mathrm{Id}_E + K$, which by Proposition C.2.7 is Fredholm, therefore has index zero.

C.2.c Another Useful Result

To prove that the linearized operator L of the Floer equation is a Fredholm operator, we used Proposition 8.7.4, which we repeat here.

Proposition (8.7.4). *Let E, F and G be three Banach spaces. Let $L : E \to F$ be an operator and let $K : E \to G$ be a compact operator. We suppose that there exists a constant $C > 0$ such that*

$$\forall x \in E, \quad \|x\|_E \leq C \left(\|L(x)\|_F + \|K(x)\|_G \right).$$

Then the kernel of L is finite-dimensional and the image of L is closed.

Proof. The proof is inspired by that of Proposition C.2.7. Let us first show that Ker L is a finite-dimensional subspace of E. To do this, let us show that its unit ball is compact. Let (x_k) be a sequence of elements of this ball:

$$\|x_k\|_E \le 1 \quad \text{and} \quad L(x_k) = 0.$$

The hypothesis is that

$$\|x_k\|_E \le C \|K(x_k)\|.$$

The image of the unit ball under K is relatively compact, hence after extracting a subsequence, if necessary, we may, and do, assume that the sequence $(K(x_k))$ converges in G. This implies that (x_k) is a Cauchy sequence, whence, since E is complete, that it converges in E and therefore in the unit ball. This proves the compactness of the unit ball.

Let us now show that $\text{Im}(L)$ is a closed subspace of F. Let (x_k) be a sequence of elements of E such that the sequence $(L(x_k))$ converges to an element $y \in F$ and let us show that y belongs to the image of L:

- If the sequence (x_k) is bounded, then the inequality gives

$$\|x_k\|_E \le C\left(\|L(x_k)\|_F + \|K(x_k)\|_G\right),$$

  where $L(x_k) \to y$ in F and $K(x_k)$ remains in a compact subset of G. It follows that (x_k) admits a subsequence that is a Cauchy sequence and therefore converges. Its limit x satisfies $y = L(x)$.
- If the sequence (x_k) is not bounded, then let us show that we obtain a contradiction. In this case, the sequence admits a subsequence with

$$\lim_{k \to +\infty} \|x_k\| = +\infty.$$

Since Ker L is a finite dimensional subspace, we can find a complement E_0 and we may, and do, assume that $x_k \in E_0$ for every k. Let

$$u_k = \frac{x_k}{\|x_k\|_E} \in E_0.$$

Our inequality gives

$$\|u_k\|_E \le C\left(\|L(u_k)\|_F + \|K(u_k)\|_G\right).$$

Once more, the sequence $(K(u_k))$ admits a convergent subsequence. Here the sequence $(L(u_k))$ converges to 0, hence we may, and do, assume that (u_k) is a Cauchy sequence and therefore converges in E_0 to a limit

$$u \in \text{Ker } L \cap E_0 = \{0\}.$$

Consequently $u = 0$ though it should have norm 1, giving the expected contradiction.   □

C.2.d Fredholm Maps

We call a differentiable map

$$\mathcal{F} : E \longrightarrow F$$

from one Banach space to another a *Fredholm* map if at every point it has a (continuous) differential

$$T_x\mathcal{F} : E \longrightarrow F$$

that is moreover a Fredholm operator. Let us note that in this case the index of $T_x\mathcal{F}$ does not depend on x (by Theorem C.2.9 and Remark C.2.11). We therefore denote it by $\mathrm{Ind}(\mathcal{F})$.

The local inversion theorem in Banach spaces (see [19]) allows us to prove the following result, as in the finite-dimensional case.

Theorem C.2.13. *Let $\mathcal{F} : E \to F$ be a Fredholm map and let $y \in F$ be such that*

$$\forall\, x \in \mathcal{F}^{-1}(y), \quad T_x\mathcal{F} : E \longrightarrow F$$

is surjective. Then $\mathcal{F}^{-1}(y)$ is a manifold of dimension $\mathrm{Ind}(\mathcal{F})$ and its tangent space at x is $\mathrm{Ker}\, T_x\mathcal{F}$.

C.3 Distribution Spaces, Weak Solutions

C.3.a Distributions

We quickly recall the basic definitions of distribution theory. We refer the readers to their favorite book. As for us, we used [13].

For every open subset U of $\mathbf{R}^n$, we consider the space $\mathcal{C}_0^\infty(U)$ of functions of class $\mathcal{C}^\infty$ with compact support in U. The space $\mathcal{D}'(U)$ of distributions on U is a dual of $\mathcal{C}_0^\infty(U)$. More precisely, it is the space of linear functionals on $\mathcal{C}_0^\infty(U)$ that are continuous in the sense that for every compact subset $K \subset U$, there exist an integer p and a constant C such that

$$\text{for every } \varphi \in \mathcal{C}_0^\infty(U) \text{ with support in } K, \quad |\langle u, \varphi \rangle| \le C \sup_{\substack{x \in K \\ |\alpha| \le p}} \left| \frac{\partial^\alpha \varphi}{\partial x^\alpha}(x) \right|.$$

We say that a sequence u_n of distributions converges to a linear functional u if we have that

$$\text{for every } \varphi \in \mathcal{C}_0^\infty(U), \quad \lim_{n \to +\infty} \langle u_n, \varphi \rangle = \langle u, \varphi \rangle.$$

It is not entirely trivial, but the limit u is then also a distribution.

We define the support of a distribution in an obvious manner (as the complement of the greatest open set restricted to which the distribution is zero) and we let $\mathcal{E}'(U)$ denote the space of distributions with compact support in U.

Examples.

(1) Taking the value of functions at a given point of U defines a linear functional on $\mathcal{C}_0^\infty(U)$ that is a distribution, namely

$$\langle \delta_a, \varphi \rangle = \varphi(a),$$

the Dirac delta function at a (we write $\delta = \delta_0$).

(2) More generally, linear combinations of partial derivatives (such as $\overline{\partial}$, Δ) taken at a point a are also distributions.

(3) If f is a locally integrable function on U, then for every $\varphi \in \mathcal{C}_0^\infty(U)$, we can define the linear functional

$$\langle f, \varphi \rangle = \int f\varphi \, dx,$$

which is a distribution. If two locally integrable functions f and g are equal almost everywhere on U, then they define the same linear functional. Moreover, if the sequence (f_n) converges to f for the L^1 norm on the compact subsets of U, then it tends to f in the sense of distributions, so that L^1_{loc} is consequently a subspace of $\mathcal{D}'(U)$. The same holds for L^p_{loc} (with Hölder's inequality).

C.3.b Derivatives

We define the derivatives of a distribution u (by keeping in mind the formula for integration by parts and) by setting

$$\left\langle \frac{\partial u}{\partial x_i}, \varphi \right\rangle = -\left\langle u, \frac{\partial \varphi}{\partial x_i} \right\rangle.$$

We can easily verify that the resulting linear functional is indeed a distribution. We can therefore iterate the process.

For example, δ is the derivative of the Heaviside step function H (with value 0 for $x < 0$ and 1 for $x \geq 0$): H is locally integrable, hence a distribution, and computational rules give

$$\langle H', \varphi \rangle = -\int H(x)\varphi'(x) \, dx = -\int_0^\infty \varphi'(x) \, dx = \varphi(0).$$

C.3.c Convolution

By copying the definition of the convolution of two functions (let us take u integrable and φ of class $\mathcal{C}^\infty$),

$$(u \star \varphi)(x) = \int \varphi(x - y)u(y)\,dy = \langle u(y), \varphi(x - y)\rangle,$$

we can convolute a distribution with compact support and a $\mathcal{C}^\infty$ function with compact support by setting, for $u \in \mathcal{E}'(\mathbf{R}^n)$, for every $\varphi \in \mathbf{C}_0^\infty(\mathbf{R}^n)$ and at every point x,

$$(u \star \varphi)(x) = \langle u(y), \varphi(x - y)\rangle.$$

We refer, for example, to the course [13] for all properties of convolution and in particular for those that follow. The function $u\star\varphi$ thus defined belongs to $\mathcal{C}_0^\infty(\mathbf{R}^n)$, its support satisfies

$$\mathrm{Supp}(u \star \varphi) \subset \mathrm{Supp}\,u + \mathrm{Supp}\,\varphi,$$

and its derivatives satisfy

$$\frac{\partial^\alpha}{\partial x^\alpha}(u \star \varphi) = u \star \left(\frac{\partial^\alpha \varphi}{\partial x^\alpha}\right) = \left(\frac{\partial^\alpha u}{\partial x^\alpha}\right) \star \varphi.$$

If u is a distribution with compact support and φ and ψ are two $\mathcal{C}^\infty$ functions with compact support, then we have the following associativity property:

$$(u \star \varphi) \star \psi = u \star (\varphi \star \psi).$$

More generally, we can convolute distributions, for example two functions in L_{loc}^1 whose supports A and B are "convolutive", that is, such that

$$\forall R > 0, \exists \rho(R) > 0 \text{ such that}$$
$$(x \in A, y \in B, \|x + y\| \leq R) \Longrightarrow (\|x\| \leq \rho(R), \|y\| \leq \rho(R)).$$

This is a commutative (and associative) product.

In this way, we can define the convolution of a distribution in $\mathcal{E}'(U)$ and a $\mathcal{C}^\infty$ function, or of an arbitrary distribution and a $\mathcal{C}^\infty$ function with compact support. In both cases, the result is a $\mathcal{C}^\infty$ function.

Another useful remark is the fact that δ, the Dirac delta function at 0, is an identity for this "product":

$$\delta \star \varphi = \varphi$$

(this follows from the definition of convolution).

C.3.d Fundamental Solution, Weak Solutions

Let L be a differential operator. If f is a function in L^p_{loc} (or more generally a distribution), then we call *weak solution* of the equation $Lu = f$ a solution in the space of distributions. If L has constant coefficients, then the properties of convolution given above imply that $Lu = \delta \star Lu = L\delta \star u$, so that the equation can also be written as $L\delta \star u = f$. We call *fundamental solution* of the equation $Lu = 0$, or "fundamental solution of L", a distribution E that satisfies

$$L\delta \star E = L(E) = \delta,$$

where $L\delta$ is seen as a distribution.

For example, by Cauchy's formula, this is the case for the function $1/\pi z$ when L is the operator $\overline{\partial}$, as we will prove in Section C.5.

Formally, if E is a fundamental solution of L, then we may hope to have

$$L\delta \star (E \star f) = (L\delta \star E) \star f = \delta \star f = f$$

for every function f, and therefore to be able to express the solutions of $Lu = f$ through convolution with a fundamental solution. This is indeed the case. More precisely, we have the following result.

Theorem C.3.1 ([13, Theorem 8.1.2]). *If L is a differential operator with constant coefficients that admits a fundamental solution E and if f is a distribution with compact support, then the equation $Lu = f$ admits a unique weak solution with compact support, namely $u = E \star f$.*

Proof. The argument above shows that $u = E \star f$ is indeed a solution. The uniqueness of this solution comes from the fact that it has compact support: if u is a solution with compact support then the supports of u, $L\delta$ and E satisfy the "convolutivity" condition and the resulting associativity gives

$$u = \delta \star u = (E \star (L\delta)) \star u = E \star ((L\delta) \star u) = E \star f. \qquad \square$$

C.4 Sobolev Spaces on $\mathbf{R}^n$

Let us recall here the definition of Sobolev spaces. We let U denote an open subset of $\mathbf{R}^n$. We let $\mathcal{C}^\infty(\overline{U})$ denote the space of restrictions to $\overline{U}$ of the $\mathcal{C}^\infty$ functions on $\mathbf{R}^n$ and let $\mathcal{C}^\infty_c(U)$ denote the space of $\mathcal{C}^\infty$ functions with compact support on U.

The Sobolev space $W^{s,p}(U)$ is a completion of the space of $\mathcal{C}^\infty$ functions on U whose derivatives up to order s are all in $L^p(U)$. More precisely, we define the norm $\|\cdot\|_{s,p}$ of a $\mathcal{C}^\infty$ function on U by setting

$$\|u\|_{s,p} = \left(\int_U \sum_{|\alpha| \le s} |\partial^\alpha u(x)|^p \, dx \right)^{1/p}.$$

The Sobolev space $W^{s,p}(U)$ is the completion of $\mathcal{C}^\infty(\overline{U})$ for this norm and $W_0^{s,p}(U)$ is the closure of $\mathcal{C}_c^\infty(U)$.

In fact, these spaces are distribution spaces: the elements of $W^{s,p}(U)$ are the functions with "weak derivatives", as we show in the following proposition.

Proposition C.4.1. *Let U be an open subset of $\mathbf{R}^n$ whose boundary is a submanifold of class $\mathcal{C}^1$. Let $u \in L^p(U)$. Then u belongs to $W^{s,p}(U)$ if and only if for every α with $|\alpha| \le s$, there exists a function $u_\alpha \in L^p(U)$ such that for every function $\varphi \in \mathcal{C}_c^\infty(U)$, we have*

$$\int_U u(x)\partial^\alpha \varphi(x) \, dx = (-1)^{|\alpha|} \int_U u_\alpha(x)\varphi(x) \, dx.$$

Idea of the Proof of Proposition C.4.1. By a change of coordinates, we reduce the proof to the case where U is a half-space (take $x_1 > 0$ to illustrate the ideas). We leave it to the readers to verify that the elements $W^{s,p}$ are weak derivatives.

Let us suppose that u indeed has weak derivatives u_α and let us show that $u \in W^{s,p}(U)$. Let us fix a function β of class $\mathcal{C}^\infty$ on $\mathbf{R}^n$, with support in the unit ball and such that

$$\int_{\mathbf{R}^n} \beta(x) \, dx = 1,$$

and let us define β_δ by

$$\beta_\delta(x) = \delta^{-n}\beta(\delta^{-1}x).$$

Let us also fix a function γ of class $\mathcal{C}^\infty$ on $\mathbf{R}^n$ with value 1 on the unit ball and identically zero outside of the ball of radius 2. Then the function

$$u_\delta(x) = \gamma(\delta x)u(x_1 + \delta, x_2, \dots, x_n)$$

defined for $x_1 > -\delta$ has compact support and has weak derivatives up to order s that converge, for the L^p norm, to weak derivatives of u. Moreover, the convolution

$$\beta_\delta \star u_\delta(x) = \int_{\mathbf{R}^n} \beta_\delta(x - y)u_\delta(y) \, dy$$

is $\mathcal{C}^\infty$ with compact support and converges (for the $\|\cdot\|_{s,p}$ norm) to u. Therefore u is indeed an element of $W^{s,p}$. $\square$

These weak derivatives behave well. In fact, even if it is not yet obvious, we have desired result.

Proposition C.4.2. *Let U be a bounded open subset of $\mathbf{R}^n$ and let $u \in W^{1,p}(U)$ be an element with (weak) derivatives of order 1 all identically zero on U. Then u is locally constant. If we moreover suppose that $u \in W_0^{1,p}(U)$, then u is identically zero.*

Proof. We first suppose that U is a cube and that the mean value of u is zero. The function u is then the limit (for the norm on $W_0^{1,p}$) of a sequence (u_ν) of $\mathcal{C}^\infty$ functions with mean value zero. The (Poincaré) lemma below asserts that this sequence converges to 0 for the L^p norm. Hence u is zero. We have thus proved that u is constant on every cube where its (weak) derivatives (of order 1) are zero. The result follows. $\qquad\square$

The Poincaré lemma used in this proof is an inequality.

Lemma C.4.3 (Poincaré inequality). *For $p > 1$ and for a bounded open subset U of $\mathbf{R}^n$, there exists a constant C (depending only on p and U) such that, for every function $u \in W_0^{1,p}(U)$ (with compact support in U), we have*

$$\|u\|_{L^p(U)} \leq C \, \|\operatorname{grad} u\|_{L^p(U)} \, .$$

If $U = {]0,1[}^n$ is a cube, then for every $u \in W^{1,p}(U)$ with mean value zero, we have

$$\|u\|_{L^p(U)} \leq n \, \|\operatorname{grad} u\|_{L^p(U)} \, .$$

Proof. Using the density of $\mathcal{C}^\infty \cap W^{1,p}$ in $W^{1,p}$, we may, and do, assume that u is smooth and has compact support in U. After applying an affine transformation of $\mathbf{R}^n$, if necessary, we may, and do, also assume that the open set U is contained in the half-space $x_n > 0$ (and that $0 \in \partial U$). Since U is bounded, it has a finite diameter D and we have $0 \leq x_n \leq D$ on U. We can write

$$u(x) = \int_0^{x_n} \frac{\partial u}{\partial x_n}(x_1, \ldots, x_{n-1}, t)\, dt,$$

and then

$$|u(x)|^p \leq \left[\int_0^{x_n} \left| \frac{\partial u}{\partial x_n}(x_1, \ldots, x_{n-1}, t) \right| dt \right]^p$$

$$\leq D^{p/q} \int_0^{x_n} \left| \frac{\partial u}{\partial x_n}(x_1, \ldots, x_{n-1}, t) \right|^p dt$$

by applying Hölder's inequality ($1/p + 1/q = 1$, so that $p/q = p - 1$). We then integrate the two sides over U or, which amounts to the same, over $\mathbf{R}^{n-1} \times [0, D]$, giving

$$\int_{\mathbf{R}^n} |u(x)|^p \, dx \leq D^{1+p/q} \int_U \left| \frac{\partial u}{\partial x_n} \right|^p dx$$

and finally,

$$\|u\|_{L^p} \leq D \left\| \frac{\partial u}{\partial x_n} \right\|_{L^p},$$

whence the first assertion follows. For the second one, we use induction on n. We use the density of the $\mathcal{C}^\infty$ functions on $\overline{U}$ to assume that u is $\mathcal{C}^\infty$ on the closed cube. We initialize the induction by noting (as we have already done in Lemma 10.4.1) that a function with mean value zero on $[0,1]$ satisfies

$$\int_0^1 |u(t)|^p \, dt \leq \int_0^1 |u'(t)|^p \, dt.$$

Actually, for every t, t_1 in $[0,1]$, we have

$$u(t_1) - u(t) = \int_t^{t_1} \frac{du}{d\tau} \, d\tau,$$

a relation that we integrate with respect to t over $[0,1]$ to obtain

$$u(t_1) = \int_0^1 \int_t^{t_1} \frac{u(\tau)}{d\tau} \, d\tau \, dt,$$

from which we deduce that

$$\int_0^1 |u(t_1)|^p \, dt_1 \leq \int_0^1 \int_0^1 \int_t^{t_1} \left| \frac{u(\tau)}{d\tau} \right|^p \, d\tau \, dt \, dt_1$$

$$\leq \int_0^1 |u'(\tau)|^p \, d\tau.$$

We pass from n to $n+1$ by considering

$$v(t) = \int_{[0,1]^n} u(x_1, \ldots, x_n, t) \, dx_1 \cdots dx_n,$$

a function on $[0,1]$ with mean value zero, to which we apply the case $n = 1$ and Hölder's inequality:

$$\int_0^1 |v(t)|^p \, dt \leq \int_0^1 |v'(t)|^p \, dt \leq \int_{[0,1]^{n+1}} \left| \frac{\partial u}{\partial x_{n+1}} \right|^p \, dx.$$

For fixed t, we apply the induction hypothesis to the function $u(x,t) - v(t)$, giving

$$\int_{[0,1]^n} |u(x_1, \ldots, x_n, t) - v(t)|^p \, dx_1 \cdots dx_n$$

$$\leq n^p \int_{[0,1]^n} \left| \mathrm{grad}_{x_1, \ldots, x_n} u(x_1, \ldots, x_n, t) \right|^p \, dx_1 \cdots dx_n,$$

which we then integrate with respect to t to find

$$\|u - v\|_{L^p} \leq n \|\mathrm{grad}_{x_1,\dots,x_n} u\|_{L^p}$$

and finally

$$\|u\|_{L^p} \leq \|u - v\|_{L^p} + \|v\|_{L^p}$$
$$\leq n \|\mathrm{grad}_{x_1,\dots,x_n} u\|_{L^p} + \left\|\frac{\partial u}{\partial x_{n+1}}\right\|_{L^p}$$
$$\leq (n+1) \|\mathrm{grad}\, u\|_{L^p}.$$

This completes the proof. □

The $\mathcal{C}^\infty$ functions are dense, in the following precise sense.

Proposition C.4.4 (See [17, Section 9.3]). *Let U be an open subset of $\mathbf{R}^n$ whose boundary is a submanifold of class $\mathcal{C}^1$. Then the restrictions to U of the $\mathcal{C}^\infty$ functions with compact support on $\mathbf{R}^n$ form a dense subspace of $W^{1,p}(U)$.*

Relations Between Sobolev Spaces

Let us begin with an example.

Example C.4.5. Let us consider the function

$$u(x) = \frac{1}{\|x\|^\alpha}$$

on the unit ball $\|x\| < 1$ of $\mathbf{R}^n$. It is not continuous at 0 if $\alpha > 0$. We have

$$\frac{\partial u}{\partial x_i} = -\alpha \frac{x_i}{\|x\|^{\alpha+2}}, \quad \text{hence} \quad \left|\frac{\partial u}{\partial x_i}\right| \leq \alpha \|x\|^{-\alpha-1}.$$

The pth powers of these derivatives are integrable on the unit ball if and only if $(\alpha + 1)p < n$. Therefore, if α satisfies

$$0 < \alpha < \frac{n}{p} - 1,$$

then the function u belongs to $W^{1,p}$ without being continuous at 0. Such an α can only exist if $p < n$. This example is typical for the property expressed in the following theorem, which is a particular case of Rellich's theorem.

Theorem C.4.6 (Rellich, [17, Section 9.3]). *Let U be a bounded open subset of $\mathbf{R}^n$ and let $p > n$. Then $W^{1,p}(U; \mathbf{R}^m)$ is a subspace of $\mathcal{C}^0(U; \mathbf{R}^m)$ and the injection*

$$W^{1,p}(U; \mathbf{R}^m) \subset \mathcal{C}^0(U; \mathbf{R}^m)$$

is a compact operator.

Remark C.4.7. Let us note, in particular, that over $\mathbf{R}$, the elements of $W^{1,2}$ are continuous functions; see [17].

The case $p = n = 2$ (over $\mathbf{R}^2$), which is the one we are interested in, is more subtle, as shown by the following example.

Example C.4.8. For every $\delta \in \,]0,1[$, let us define a continuous function u_δ on $\mathbf{C}$ by setting

$$u_\delta(z) = \begin{cases} 1 & \text{if } |z| \leq \delta \\ \dfrac{\log|z|}{\log \delta} & \text{if } \delta \leq |z| \leq 1 \\ 0 & \text{if } |z| \geq 1. \end{cases}$$

For $\delta \leq |z| \leq 1$, we have

$$\|\operatorname{grad} u_\delta(z)\| \leq \frac{1}{|\log \delta|\,|z|},$$

so that

$$\int_{\mathbf{C}} \|\operatorname{grad} u_\delta(z)\|^2 \, dz \leq \int_{\delta \leq |z| \leq 1} \frac{dz}{|\log \delta|^2\,|z|^2} = \int_\delta^1 \frac{2\pi s^{-1}\,ds}{|\log \delta|^2} = \frac{2\pi}{|\log \delta|}.$$

Thus u_δ is both a continuous function with compact support and an element of $W^{1,p}(\mathbf{C})$ (we could also make it $\mathcal{C}^\infty$ through a convolution with a suitable function) and it satisfies $u_\delta(0) = 1$.

The sequence (v_n) defined by $v_n = u_{1/n}$ is therefore a sequence of continuous functions with compact support that are elements of $W^{1,2}(\mathbf{C})$. It tends to 0 for the $W^{1,2}$ norm but not for the L^∞ norm.

The following theorems bring together the Sobolev estimates and a compactness statement called Rellich's theorem.

Theorem C.4.9 (See [17, Section 9.3]). *Let U be a bounded open subset of $\mathbf{R}^n$ whose boundary is of class $\mathcal{C}^1$. Let $k \in \mathbf{N}$, $k \geq 1$, and let p satisfy $1 < p < +\infty$. Then we have:*

(1) *If $p < n/k$, then $W^{k,p}(U) \subset L^q(U)$ with $q = np/(n-kp)$.*
(2) *If $p = n/k$, then $W^{k,p}(U) \subset L^q(U)$ for every $q \geq p$.*
(3) *If $p > n/k$, then $W^{k,p}(U) \subset L^\infty(U)$.*

And the inclusions are all continuous. Moreover, for $u \in W^{k,p}(U)$, we have

$$|\alpha| \leq k \implies \left\| \frac{\partial^\alpha u}{\partial x^\alpha} \right\|_{L^\infty(U)} \leq C\,\|u\|_{W^{k,p}(U)}.$$

In particular, for $m = [k - n/p]$, we have a continuous injection

$$W^{k,p}(U) \subset \mathcal{C}^m(U).$$

The following statement concentrates on the case $k = 1$.

Theorem C.4.10 (Rellich–Kondrachov [17, Section 9.3]). *Let U be a bounded open subset of $\mathbf{R}^n$ and let $p < n$. Then there exists a constant $C = C(p, U) > 0$ such that, for every function u on U, we have*

$$\|u\|_{L^q} \le C \|u\|_{W^{1,p}} \quad \text{for every } q \le \frac{n}{n-p}.$$

Moreover, for $q < np/(n-p)$, the injection

$$W^{1,p}(U; \mathbf{R}^m) \subset L^q(U; \mathbf{R}^m)$$

is a compact operator.

C.5 The Cauchy–Riemann Equation

The operator $\overline{\partial}$ plays a great part in the theory of Floer homology, as we have seen. On $\mathbf{R}^2 = \mathbf{C}$, we consider the two operators

$$\overline{\partial} = \frac{1}{2}\left(\frac{\partial}{\partial x} + i\frac{\partial}{\partial y}\right) \quad \text{and} \quad \partial = \frac{1}{2}\left(\frac{\partial}{\partial x} - i\frac{\partial}{\partial y}\right).$$

A function u of class $\mathcal{C}^1$ on an open subset U of $\mathbf{C}$ is holomorphic if and only if it satisfies the Cauchy–Riemann equation

$$\overline{\partial} u = 0.$$

The function

$$N(z) = \frac{1}{\pi z}$$

(Cauchy kernel) is a fundamental solution of the Cauchy–Riemann equation in the sense given in Section C.3.d, as shown by the following lemma.

Lemma C.5.1. *Let u and f be continuous functions with compact support in $L^p(\mathbf{C})$. Then u is a weak solution of $\overline{\partial} u = f$ if and only if $u = N \star f$.*

In other words,

$$u(z) = \frac{1}{2i\pi}\int_{\mathbf{C}} \frac{f(w)}{w - z}\, dw \wedge d\overline{w}.$$

Remark. When u is $\mathcal{C}^1$, Cauchy's formula (a consequence, for example of Stokes's theorem, see [40, p. 3]) gives, for every disk $D \subset \mathbf{C}$ and for every z in D,

$$u(z) = \frac{1}{2i\pi}\int_{\partial D} \frac{u(w)\, dw}{w - z} + \frac{1}{2i\pi}\int_{D} \frac{\partial u}{\partial \overline{w}} \frac{dw \wedge d\overline{w}}{w - z}.$$

If u has compact support and D contains that support, then the first integral is zero.

Proof of Lemma C.5.1. Using Theorem C.3.1 it suffices to show that $\bar{\partial} N = \delta$. Let $\varphi \in \mathcal{C}_0^\infty(\mathbf{C})$. We have

$$
\begin{aligned}
\langle \bar{\partial} N, \varphi \rangle &= \int_{\mathbf{C}} -\bar{\partial}\varphi(z) N(z) \, dz \\
&= \int_{\mathbf{R}^2} -\frac{1}{2}\left(\frac{\partial\varphi}{\partial x} + i\frac{\partial\varphi}{\partial y}\right) \frac{x - iy}{\pi(x^2 + y^2)} \, dx \, dy \\
&= -\frac{1}{2\pi}\int_{\mathbf{R}^2} \frac{x\frac{\partial\varphi}{\partial x} + y\frac{\partial\varphi}{\partial y}}{x^2 + y^2} \, dx \, dy - \frac{i}{2\pi}\int_{\mathbf{R}^2} \frac{-y\frac{\partial\varphi}{\partial x} + x\frac{\partial\varphi}{\partial y}}{x^2 + y^2} \, dx \, dy \\
&= -\frac{1}{2\pi}\int_0^{+\infty}\int_0^{2\pi} \frac{\partial}{\partial\rho}\varphi(\rho\cos\theta, \rho\sin\theta) \, d\rho \, d\theta \\
&\qquad - \frac{i}{2\pi}\int_0^{+\infty}\int_0^{2\pi} \frac{1}{\rho}\frac{\partial}{\partial\theta}\varphi(\rho\cos\theta, \rho\sin\theta) \, d\rho \, d\theta \\
&= \varphi(0). \qquad\qquad\qquad\qquad\qquad\qquad\qquad\qquad\qquad\qquad\qquad \square
\end{aligned}
$$

C.5.a The Laplacian

On $\mathbf{R}^n$, the Laplacian is the operator

$$
\Delta = \sum_{i=1}^n \frac{\partial^2}{\partial x_i^2}.
$$

The $\mathcal{C}^2$ functions on an open set U that satisfy $\Delta u = 0$ are called *harmonic* functions. Let us recall that in the case $n = 2$, which is the one we are interested in, harmonic functions are the real parts of analytic functions. Harmonic functions satisfy the mean value property.

Proposition C.5.2 (Mean value property). *Let u be a harmonic function on $U \subset \mathbf{R}^2$. We have*

$$
u(x) = \frac{1}{\pi r^2}\int_{B(x,r)} u(z) \, dz \quad \text{for every ball } B(x, r) \subset U.
$$

An L_{loc}^1 function with this mean value property is necessarily $\mathcal{C}^\infty$. In fact, we have the following result.

Lemma C.5.3. *An L_{loc}^p function satisfying the mean value equality is of class $\mathcal{C}^\infty$.*

Proof. The idea is that the u on the left-hand side is more regular than the one in the integral (a *bootstrapping*). To prove this, let us note that the mean value equality is also equivalent to

$$u = \chi_r \star u, \quad \text{with } \chi_r = \frac{1}{\pi r^2} \chi_{B(0,r)},$$

which holds over $U_r = \{x \in U \mid B(x,r) \subset U\}$. This implies that

$$u = \underbrace{\chi_r \star \chi_r \star \cdots \star \chi_r}_{m \text{ times}} \star u \quad \text{on } U_{mr}.$$

The result immediately follows from the regularity of convolutions (above, Section C.3.c) if we know that

$$\underbrace{\chi_r \star \chi_r \star \cdots \star \chi_r}_{m \text{ times}} \in \mathcal{C}_0^{m-2}(\mathbf{R}^2),$$

which we will now show by induction. First,

$$\chi_r \star \chi_r(x) = \frac{1}{(\pi r^2)^2} \operatorname{Aire}(B_r(0,0) \cap B_r(x)),$$

which we can easily verify to be a continuous function with compact support; more precisely,

$$\chi_r \star \chi_r(x) = \frac{1}{(\pi r^2)^2} \left(2 \arccos \frac{\|x\|}{2r} - \frac{\|x\| \sqrt{4r^2 - \|x\|^2}}{2} \right)$$

(if $B_r(0) \cap B_r(x) \neq \varnothing$ and 0 otherwise).

Next, if $f \in \mathcal{C}_0^k(\mathbf{R}^2)$, then $\chi_r \star f \in \mathcal{C}_0^{k+1}(\mathbf{R}^2)$. In fact, this function clearly has compact support. Moreover, the convolution is of class $\mathcal{C}_0^k$ and, if $|\alpha| = k$, then

$$\frac{\partial^\alpha}{\partial x^\alpha}(\chi_r \star f) = \chi_r \star \frac{\partial^\alpha}{\partial x^\alpha} f,$$

so that $(\partial^\alpha / \partial x^\alpha) f$ is continuous. Let us call it g and let us show that it is of class $\mathcal{C}^1$. We have

$$\pi r^2 (\chi_r \star g)(s,t) = \int_{B_r} g(x,y) \, dx \, dy$$

$$= \int_{s-r}^{s+r} \left(\int_{t-\sqrt{r^2-(x-s)^2}}^{t+\sqrt{r^2-(x-s)^2}} g(x,y) \, dy \right) dx,$$

so that the function is differentiable in t and its derivative is continuous. The same holds for its derivative in s. $\qquad \square$

Being of class $\mathcal{C}^2$ is not an essential condition for the harmonicity, as expressed by the following lemma (often called "Weyl's lemma").

Lemma C.5.4. *Every weak solution* $u \in L_{\mathrm{loc}}^p(U)$ *(for* $p \geq 1$*) of* $\Delta u = 0$ *is harmonic.*

Proof. We use a family of functions β_δ of class $\mathcal{C}^\infty$ that approximate the Dirac delta function at 0 (as in the proof of Proposition C.4.1): we choose $\beta : \mathbf{R}^n \to \mathbf{R}$ nonnegative and of class $\mathcal{C}^\infty$, with support in the unit ball, and such that $\int_{\mathbf{R}^n} \beta(x)\,dx = 1$, and we set $\beta_\delta = \delta^{-n}\beta(\delta^{-1}x)$. The support of β_δ is contained in the ball of radius δ and its integral over $\mathbf{R}^n$ equals 1.

Let $u \in L_{\mathrm{loc}}^p(U)$. The function $u \star \beta_\delta$ is of class $\mathcal{C}^\infty$, its support is contained in $\{x \in U \mid B(x,\delta) \subset U\}$, and we have

$$\Delta(u \star \beta_\delta) = \beta_\delta \star \Delta u$$

(by definition of the weak derivatives), so that $u \star \beta_\delta$ is harmonic if u is a weak solution. In particular, for every δ, the convolution $u \star \beta_\delta$ satisfies the mean value equality.

However, $u \star \beta_\delta$ converges to u for the L^p norm and almost everywhere on the compact subsets of U when δ tends to 0. So the weak solution u also satisfies the mean value property, and therefore is of class $\mathcal{C}^\infty$ and consequently harmonic by Lemma C.5.3. $\square$

The real and imaginary parts of a weak solution of the Cauchy–Riemann equation are the weak solutions of the Laplace equations. We therefore have the following result.

Lemma C.5.5. *Every weak solution* u *of the Cauchy–Riemann equation that is locally integrable over an open set* U *is holomorphic.*

Proposition C.5.6 (Mean value inequality). *Let* u *be a function of class* $\mathcal{C}^2$ *on* $U \subset \mathbf{R}^2$ *that satisfies* $\Delta u \geq 0$*. We have*

$$u(x) \leq \frac{1}{\pi r^2} \int_{B(x,r)} u(z)\,dz \quad \text{for every ball } B(x,r) \subset U.$$

Let us give a proof of this inequality, (which transforms without effort into a proof of the equality and) which follows from Stokes's theorem.

Proof of the Mean Value Inequality (and Equality). Since $\Delta u \geq 0$, we have $\int_{B_\rho} \Delta u \geq 0$. However, by the "divergence theorem" (the *ad hoc* version of Stokes's theorem), we have

$$\int_{B_\rho} \Delta u = \int_{\partial B_\rho} \frac{\partial u}{\partial \nu} = \rho \int_0^{2\pi} \frac{\partial}{\partial \rho} u(\rho e^{i\theta})\,d\theta.$$

Next,

$$\int_0^{2\pi} \frac{\partial}{\partial \rho} u(\rho e^{i\theta})\, d\theta = \frac{d}{d\rho}\left(\frac{1}{\rho}\int_{B_\rho} u\right) \quad \text{whence} \quad \frac{d}{d\rho}\left(\frac{1}{\rho}\int_{B_\rho} u\right) \geq 0,$$

so that the function $\rho \mapsto \frac{1}{\rho}\int_{B_\rho} u$ is nondecreasing and so that for $r \geq \rho$, we have

$$\frac{1}{2\pi\rho}\int_{\partial B_\rho} u \leq \frac{1}{2\pi r}\int_{\partial B_r} u.$$

When ρ tends to 0, the left-hand side tends to $u(0)$, giving

$$2\pi r u(0) \leq \int_{\partial B_r} u.$$

We integrate this from 0 to r to obtain

$$\pi r^2 u(0) \leq \int_{B_r} u,$$

the desired inequality.   □

Still in the case $n = 2$, we consider the function (Poisson kernel)

$$K(z) = \frac{1}{2\pi} \log |z|.$$

We can easily verify[5] that K belongs to $L^1_{\text{loc}}(\mathbf{R}^2)$ and that $\Delta K = \delta$ (in the sense of distributions). Consequently, K is a fundamental solution of Δ (in the sense of Section C.3.d).

Let us note that

$$\Delta = 4\partial\bar{\partial},$$

and that, moreover, the Poisson and Cauchy kernels are linked by

$$N(z) = 4\partial K.$$

We have $\Delta K = 0$ but, beware, the second derivatives of K are not even integrable over the compact sets. We do still have the following consequence of Theorem C.3.1.

Proposition C.5.7. *Let u and f be two functions with compact support on $\mathbf{R}^2$. We suppose that u, $f \in L^1(\mathbf{R}^2)$. Then the function u is a weak solution of $\Delta u = f$ if and only if $u = K \star f$.*

---

[5] This is an exercise, write K in polar coordinates.

Let K_i $(i = 1, 2)$ be the partial derivatives with respect to x and y of the fundamental solution K:

$$K_1(z) = \frac{x}{2\pi \, |z|^2}, \quad K_2(z) = \frac{y}{2\pi \, |z|^2}.$$

These are also locally integrable functions. Moreover, in the sense of distributions, we have

$$\Delta K_1 = \frac{\partial}{\partial s} \Delta K = \frac{\partial}{\partial s} \delta \quad \text{and} \quad \Delta K_2 = \frac{\partial}{\partial t} \delta.$$

Theorem C.5.8 (Calderón–Zygmund inequality). *For every p with $1 < p < +\infty$, there exists a constant $C(p) > 0$ such that for every $\mathcal{C}^\infty$ function f with compact support on $\mathbf{R}^2$, we have*

$$\|\mathrm{grad}(K_j \star f)\|_{L^p} \leq C(p) \, \|\Delta f\|_{L^p}.$$

We refer to [51] for a proof.

References

1. Arnold, V.I.: Sur une propriété topologique des applications globalement canoniques de la mécanique classique. C. R. Acad. Sci. Paris **261**, 3719–3722 (1965)
2. Arnold, V.I.: First steps in symplectic topology. Russ. Math. Surv. **41**, 1–21 (1986)
3. Audin, M.: Symplectic and almost complex manifolds. In: [7], pp. 41–74
4. Audin, M.: Topologie: Revêtements et groupe fondamental. ULP, Strasbourg (2004). Cours de Magistère, 2e année, http://www-irma.u-strasbg.fr/~maudin/courstopalg.pdf
5. Audin, M.: Torus Actions on Symplectic Manifolds. Progress in Mathematics, vol. 93, Birkhäuser, Basel (2004). Revised and enlarged edition
6. Audin, M.: Vladimir Igorevich Arnold and the invention of symplectic topology. (2012, to appear)
7. Audin, M., Lafontaine, J. (eds.): Holomorphic Curves in Symplectic Geometry. Progress in Mathematics, vol. 117, Birkhäuser, Basel (1994)
8. Berger, M., Gostiaux, B.: Géométrie différentielle: variétés, courbes et surfaces. Presses Universitaires de France (1987)
9. Biran, P.: Lagrangian barriers and symplectic embeddings. Geom. Funct. Anal. **11**, 407–464 (2001)
10. Biran, P., Cornea, O.: A Lagrangian quantum homology. In: New Perspectives and Challenges in Symplectic Field Theory. CRM Proc. Lecture Notes, vol. 49, pp. 1–44. Am. Math. Soc., Providence (2009)
11. Biran, P., Cornea, O.: Rigidity and uniruling for Lagrangian submanifolds. Geom. Topol. **13**, 2881–2989 (2009)
12. Bismut, J.M., Zhang, W.: An extension of a theorem by Cheeger and Müller. Astérisque **205**, 235 (1992). With an appendix by François Laudenbach
13. Bony, J.M.: Cours d'analyse. École polytechnique, Palaiseau (1994)
14. Bott, R.: Lectures on Morse theory, old and new. Bull. Am. Math. Soc. **7**, 331–358 (1982)
15. Bourgeois, F.: A survey of contact homology. In: New Perspectives and Challenges in Symplectic Field Theory. CRM Proc. Lecture Notes, vol. 49, pp. 45–71. Am. Math. Soc., Providence (2009)
16. Bourgeois, F., Oancea, A.: Fredholm theory and transversality for the parametrized and for the S^1-invariant symplectic action. J. Eur. Math. Soc. **12**(5), 1181–1229 (2010)
17. Brezis, H.: Functional Analysis, Sobolev Spaces and Partial Differential Equations. Universitext. Springer, New York (2011)

18. Cannas da Silva, A.: Lectures on Symplectic Geometry. Lecture Notes in Math. Springer, Berlin (2001)

19. Cartan, H.: Calcul Différentiel. Méthodes. Hermann, Paris (1967)

20. Cieliebak, K., Frauenfelder, U.A.: A Floer homology for exact contact embeddings. Pac. J. Math. **239**, 251–316 (2009)

21. Conley, C., Zehnder, E.: Morse-type index theory for flows and periodic solutions of Hamiltonian equations. Commun. Pure Appl. Math. **37**, 207–253 (1984)

22. Damian, M.: Constraints on exact Lagrangians in cotangent bundles of manifolds fibered over the circle. Comment. Math. Helv. **84**, 705–746 (2009)

23. Damian, M.: Floer homology on the universal cover, Audin's conjecture and other constraints on Lagrangian submanifolds. Comment. Math. Helv. **87**, 433–462 (2012)

24. Damian, M.: On the topology of monotone Lagrangian submanifolds. Ann. Sci. Ec. Norm. Sup. (to appear)

25. Dold, A.: Lectures on Algebraic Topology. Classics in Mathematics. Springer, Berlin (1995). Reprint of the 1972 edition

26. Ekeland, I.: Convexity Methods in Hamiltonian Mechanics. Springer, Berlin (1990)

27. Eliashberg, Y., Givental, A., Hofer, H.: Introduction to symplectic field theory. Geom. Funct. Anal. (Special Volume, Part II), 560–673 (2000)

28. Floer, A.: A relative Morse index for the symplectic action. Commun. Pure Appl. Math. **41**, 393–407 (1988)

29. Floer, A.: Morse theory for Lagrangian intersections. J. Differ. Geom. **28**, 513–547 (1988)

30. Floer, A.: Symplectic fixed points and holomorphic spheres. Commun. Math. Phys. **120**, 575–611 (1989)

31. Floer, A.: Witten's complex and infinite dimensional Morse theory. J. Differ. Geom. **30**, 207–221 (1989)

32. Floer, A., Hofer, H., Salamon, D.: Transversality in elliptic Morse theory for the symplectic action. Duke Math. J. **80**, 251–292 (1995)

33. Fukaya, K., Oh, Y.G., Ohta, H., Ono, K.: Lagrangian Intersection Floer Theory—Anomaly and Obstruction. AMS/IP Studies in Advanced Mathematics. International Press, Somerville (2009)

34. Fukaya, K., Seidel, P.: Floer homology, A_∞-categories and topological field theory. In: Geometry and Physics, Aarhus, 1995. Lecture Notes in Pure and Appl. Math., vol. 184, pp. 9–32. Dekker, New York (1997)

35. Fukaya, K., Seidel, P., Smith, I.: Exact Lagrangian submanifolds in simply-connected cotangent bundles. Invent. Math. **172**, 1–27 (2008)

36. Gadbled, A.: Obstructions to the existence of monotone Lagrangian embeddings into cotangent bundles of manifolds fibered over the circle. Ann. Inst. Fourier (Grenoble) **59**, 1135–1175 (2009)

37. Gallot, S., Hulin, D., Lafontaine, J.: Riemannian Geometry. Universitext. Springer, Berlin (1987)

38. Gelfand, I.M., Lidskii, V.B.: On the structure of the regions of stability of linear canonical systems of differential equations with periodical coefficients. Usp. Mat. Nauk **10**, 3–40 (1955). Am. Math. Soc. Transl., Ser. 2 **8** (1958)

39. Golubitski, M., Guillemin, V.: Stable Mappings and Their Singularities. Graduate Texts in Math., vol. 14. Springer, Berlin (1973)

40. Griffiths, P.A., Harris, J.: Principles of Algebraic Geometry. Wiley, New York (1978)

41. Grisvard, P.: Opérateurs à indice—lemme de compacité. In: Théorème d'Atiyah-Singer sur l'indice d'un opérateur différentiel elliptique, Séminaire Henri Cartan. Secrétariat mathématique, 11 rue Pierre Curie, Paris 5e (1964)

42. Gromov, M.: Pseudo-holomorphic curves in symplectic manifolds. Invent. Math. **82**, 307–347 (1985)
43. Gutt, J.: The Conley–Zehnder index for a path of symplectic matrices (2012). arXiv:1201.3728
44. Jost, J.: Compact Riemann Surfaces. Universitext. Springer, Berlin (2006). An introduction to contemporary mathematics
45. Lafontaine, J.: Introduction aux Variétés Différentielles. Presses Universitaires de Grenoble, Grenoble (1996)
46. Latour, F.: Existence de 1-formes fermées non singulières dans une classe de cohomologie de Rham. Publ. Math. IHÉS **80**, 135–194 (1994)
47. Laudenbach, F.: Topologie différentielle (1992). Cours à l'École Polytechnique
48. Laudenbach, F.: Calcul différentiel et intégral. École Polytechnique (1997)
49. Laudenbach, F.: Symplectic geometry and Floer homology, pp. 1–50. Sociedade Brasileira de Matemática (2004)
50. McDuff, D., Salamon, D.: Introduction to Symplectic Topology. Oxford Science Publications. Clarendon, New York (1995)
51. McDuff, D., Salamon, D.: J-Holomorphic Curves and Symplectic Topology. American Mathematical Society Colloquium Publications, vol. 52. Am. Math. Soc., Providence (2004)
52. Melville, H.: Moby-Dick. Bibliothèque de la Pléiade. Gallimard, Paris (2006). Traduction de Philippe Jaworski
53. Milnor, J.: Lectures on the h-Cobordism Theorem. Princeton University Press, Princeton (1963). Notes by Siebenmann and Sondow
54. Milnor, J.: Morse Theory. Princeton University Press, Princeton (1963)
55. Milnor, J.: Topology from the Differentiable Viewpoint. University Press of Virginia, Charlottesville (1965)
56. Milnor, J., Stasheff, J.: Characteristic Classes. Princeton University Press, Princeton (1974)
57. Moser, J.: On the volume elements on a manifold. Trans. Am. Math. Soc. **120**, 286–294 (1965)
58. Oancea, A.: A survey of Floer homology for manifolds with contact type boundary or symplectic homology. In: Symplectic geometry and Floer homology. A survey of the Floer homology for manifolds with contact type boundary or symplectic homology, Ensaios matemáticos, vol. 7, pp. 51–91. Sociedade Brasileira de Matemática (2004)
59. Oh, Y.G.: Floer cohomology of Lagrangian intersections and pseudo-holomorphic disks. I. Commun. Pure Appl. Math. **46**, 949–993 (1993)
60. Oh, Y.G.: Floer cohomology, spectral sequences and the Maslov class of Lagrangian embeddings. Int. Math. Res. Not. **7**, 305–346 (1996)
61. Oh, Y.G.: Symplectic topology as the geometry of action functional. I. Relative Floer theory on the cotangent bundle. J. Differ. Geom. **46**, 499–577 (1997)
62. Pansu, P.: Compactness. In: [7], pp. 233–249
63. Rouvière, F.: Petit Guide de Calcul Différentiel à L'usage de la Licence et de L'agrégation. Cassini, Paris (2003). Deuxième édition revue et augmentée
64. Rudin, W.: Analyse Réelle et Complexe. Masson, Paris (1975)
65. Salamon, D.: Morse theory, the Conley index and Floer homology. Bull. Lond. Math. Soc. **32**, 113–140 (1990)
66. Salamon, D.: Lectures on Floer homology. In: Eliashberg, Y., Traynor, L. (eds.) Symplectic Topology. I.A.S./Park City Math. Series. Am. Math. Soc., Providence (1999)
67. Salamon, D., Zehnder, E.: Morse theory for periodic solutions of Hamiltonian systems and the Maslov index. Commun. Pure Appl. Math. **45**, 1003–1063 (1992)

68. Schwarz, M.: Morse Homology. Birkhäuser, Basel (1993)

69. Seidel, P.: Graded Lagrangian submanifolds. Bull. Soc. Math. Fr. **128**, 103–149 (2000)

70. Seidel, P.: A long exact sequence for symplectic Floer cohomology. Topology **42**, 1003–1063 (2003)

71. Seidel, P.: Fukaya Categories and Picard–Lefschetz Theory. ETH Lecture Notes Series. European Math. Soc., Zurich (2008)

72. Smale, S.: On gradient dynamical systems. Ann. Math. **74**, 199–206 (1961)

73. Smale, S.: An infinite dimensional version of Sard's theorem. Am. J. Math. **87**, 861–866 (1965)

74. Spivak, M.: Differential Geometry. Publish or Perish, Houston (1975)

75. Steenrod, N.: The Topology of Fibre Bundles. Princeton University Press, Princeton (1951)

76. Takens, F.: The minimal number of critical points of a function on a compact manifold and the Lusternik-Schnirelman category. Invent. Math. **6**, 197–244 (1968)

77. Viterbo, C.: Functors and computations in Floer homology with applications. I. Geom. Funct. Anal. **9**, 985–1033 (1999)

Index of Notation

M. Audin, M. Damian, *Morse Theory and Floer Homology*,
Universitext, DOI 10.1007/978-1-4471-5496-9,
© Springer-Verlag London 2014

Index

A

action
  form, 185
  functional, 158
additivity
  of the Maslov index, 198
almost complex
  manifold, 141
  structure, 140
Ariadne's thread, 224, 458
Arnold (Vladimir), vii, ix, 151
Arnold conjecture, ix, 127, 151, 451
Arzelà (Cesare), 561
Arzelà–Ascoli theorem, 561
Ascoli (Giulio), 561
asphericity
  symplectic, 156

B

Banach (Stefan), 186
Banach manifold, 186
basis
  symplectic, 129
Betti (Enrico), 86
Betti numbers, 86
bootstrapping, 170, 364, 581
  elliptic, 455, 457
Borsuk (Karol), 106
Borsuk–Ulam theorem, 106
bottle, 63, 119
Bourgeois (Frédéric), 451
bracket, 539
broken trajectories
  for Floer, 308

for Morse, 57
form a manifold with boundary, 61
Brouwer (Luitzen Egbertus Jan), 50
Brouwer's theorem, 50, 103
bubble, 176, 179, 180, 182, 525
bundle
  cotangent, 18, 131
    as a symplectic manifold, 131
  disk, 553
  tangent, 539
Burgunder (Emily), viii

C

calibrated
  almost complex manifold, 141
  almost complex structure, 143
canonical form, 131
Carleman (Torsten), 263
Carneiro (André), ix
Cartan (Élie), 548
Cartan (Henri), 548
Cartans' formula, 548
Cauchy
  kernel, 579
  problem, 167
Cauchy (Augustin Louis), 61, 164, 169
Cauchy–Lipschitz theorem, 61
Cauchy–Riemann
  equation, 164
  operator, 236
Cauchy–Schwarz inequality, 169
Cayley numbers, 519
cellular homology, 110
chain complex, 555

M. Audin, M. Damian, *Morse Theory and Floer Homology*,
Universitext, DOI 10.1007/978-1-4471-5496-9,
© Springer-Verlag London 2014